Survey of Numerical Analysis

The Authors

Henry A. Antosiewicz, Professor of Mathematics, University of Southern California, Los Angeles, California

Hans F. Bückner, Mathematics Research Center, United States Army, Professor of Mathematics, University of Wisconsin, Madison, Wisconsin

Harvey Cohn, Professor of Mathematics and Head of Mathematics Department, University of Arizona, Tucson, Arizona

Philip J. Davis, Chief, Numerical Analysis Section, National Bureau of Standards, Washington, D.C.

Walter Gautschi, Mathematics Panel, Oak Ridge National Laboratory, Oak Ridge, Tennessee

Marshall Hall, Jr., Professor of Mathematics, California Institute of Technology, Pasadena, California

Urs Hochstrasser, Scientific Counselor, Embassy of Switzerland, Washington, D.C.

Marvin Marcus, Associate Professor of Mathematics, University of British Columbia, Vancouver, B.C.

Morris Newman, Mathematician, National Bureau of Standards, Washington 25, D.C.

Werner C. Rheinboldt, Director, Computer Science Center, University of Maryland, College Park, Maryland

Olga Taussky, Research Associate, California Institute of Technology, Pasadena, California

John Todd, Professor of Mathematics, California Institute of Technology, Pasadena, California

David M. Young, Jr., Professor of Mathematics and Director, Computation Center, University of Texas, Austin, Texas

Marvin Zelen, Mathematics Research Center, United States Army, University of Wisconsin, Madison, Wisconsin

SURVEY OF
NUMERICAL ANALYSIS

EDITED BY

JOHN TODD

PROFESSOR OF MATHEMATICS
CALIFORNIA INSTITUTE OF TECHNOLOGY
PASADENA, CALIFORNIA

McGRAW-HILL BOOK COMPANY, INC.   1962
New York   San Francisco   Toronto   London

SURVEY OF NUMERICAL ANALYSIS

64919

45678910111213 HDMM 754321098

Preface

Origins

In 1957 a grant was made to the National Bureau of Standards, by the National Science Foundation, for the support of a Training Program in Numerical Analysis for Senior University Staff, under my direction. An objective of this program was to attract mature mathematicians into an area of vital importance which had been largely neglected. The first chapter of this book tries to show that numerical analysis is an attractive subject in which mathematics of practically all sorts can be used significantly, and from which many branches of mathematics can benefit.

After this was concluded it was decided to follow a suggestion of Dr. Olga Taussky and to develop the lectures given there into a book entitled "Survey of Numerical Analysis." Unfortunately, for various reasons not all the speakers who took part in the program participated in the development of the book, and there are some gaps.* In order not to affect the unity of the program, it was decided not to attempt to fill these gaps by including new contributions.† However, ample material is included for an introductory course, as well as representative chapters for advanced courses in numerical analysis and in supporting mathematics.

The authors are grateful to both organizations for the opportunity to present their ideas orally, and to their teachers, colleagues, and pupils for help in the later development.

Activities of Numerical Analysts

It is appropriate to discuss briefly what the activities of a numerical analyst should be. In addition to considering the exploitation of

* Several of the gaps have been covered by excellent monographs which have appeared recently. They cover, for example, such subjects as asymptotics, computability and unsolvability, initial-value problems, and linear programming.

† We note that Dr. Walter Gautschi and Dr. Werner C. Rheinboldt, who took part in the repetition of the Training Program (which took place in 1959, under the direction of Dr. Philip J. Davis), collaborated with Prof. H. A. Antosiewicz on Chapters 9 and 14.

automatic computers in new areas, he should be concerned with the solution of classes of problems: e.g., the solution of systems of linear equations, or the solution of ordinary differential equations.   As well as reexamining old methods in the light of available equipment, he should be devising and evaluating new methods.   Since, in general, it will be impossible for him to give the methods a complete theoretical examination, he should carry out controlled computational experiments, in which, for instance, he compares the observed errors with his theoretical estimates for realism.   These experiments should be recorded and analyzed.   Finally, he should construct and discuss "bad examples."

Such material, when combined with the experience of computers and the intuition of the customer, will be invaluable when the methods are being applied in practice, beyond the regions in which they are secure in the sense of classical mathematics.

The Education of Numerical Analysts

Informal teaching of the use of computers and of numerical analysis can begin at a very early stage.   Formal teaching is appropriate whenever a reasonable background in the calculus and matrix theory is achieved—usually in the junior year.   The contents of Chapter 3 and the first part of Chapter 8 are appropriate in a basic science curriculum.   However, in view of the current tendency to abstraction, it may be necessary to incorporate them in the basic numerical analysis course.   This course should include, in addition, most of the contents of Chapters 1, 2, 4, 5, and 6.   We have covered this material in a two-quarter course, with three lecture hours per week and appropriate machine time.

We believe that there should be no division between theoretical and practical numerical analysis, and that a lecture without numerical examples is a lecture wasted.   The instructor should have had recent machine experience and the supervision of practical work should, as far as possible, not be delegated.   The following general advice was given by Prof. G. Pólya* to prospective high school teachers: "Acquire, and keep up, some aptitude for problem solving."   This is particularly relevant here, and to it we would add the further qualification of experience in making examples.

Our worked examples and problems have an academic flavor, but this is mainly for brevity.   They can be dressed up by the instructor according to his taste; for instance, he can relate the calculations of the zeros of Bessel functions to the eigenvalues of a differential equation and to the frequencies of vibrations of a drumhead.   It is not possible

* G. Pólya, On the Curriculum for Prospective High School Teachers, *Amer. Math. Monthly*, vol. 65, pp. 101–104, 1958.

to include in a survey significant case studies in, for example, reactor engineering, astrophysics, or geophysics. Fortunately, however, monographs on such topics are becoming available.

Only in exceptional circumstances will teaching institutions be able to provide computers and computer organizations at the level of the best of the governmental and commercial installations. Generally, therefore, we recommend that students get experience in such centers as soon as they have completed the basic course. After this they will be in a better position to appreciate advanced courses. Since the practicing numerical analyst meets problems from many different areas, one-quarter courses, such as could be based on the material in the later chapters, are appropriate rather than more extensive treatments of special topics.

Finally, in view of the rapid developments in the field, students must be encouraged from the beginning to get acquainted with the periodical literature; for this purpose we have given ample references in the text and in the problems. The need for critical reading should be emphasized.

Remarks

In a composite work of this character, complete uniformity and freedom from overlap is almost impossible to maintain. The known inconsistencies in notations and terminology should not disturb the reader, and the repetitions are to his advantage. We hope that the errors and inaccuracies which have been overlooked will not be troublesome.

In the last decade, the electronic engineers have increased the power of our computers about a thousandfold; unfortunately there has been no comparable development in the relevant mathematics. We hope that this "Survey" will aid such a development; our views on this point are elaborated in Chapter 1. Although it may well be that the greatest contribution of automatic computers will be outside of the physical sciences, there is no doubt that a thorough grounding in mathematics and numerical analysis is the best initial training for those concerned with the use of computers if they are to avoid the many logical and arithmetic perils which await those who use their machines formally and uncritically.

John Todd

Contents

1

Motivation for Working
in Numerical Analysis*

JOHN TODD

PROFESSOR OF MATHEMATICS

CALIFORNIA INSTITUTE OF TECHNOLOGY

1.1 Introduction

The profession of numerical analysis is not yet so desirable that it is taken up by choice; indeed, although it is one of the oldest professions, it is only now becoming respectable.   Most of those who are now working in this field have been more or less drafted into it, either in World War I or in World War II, or more recently.   The question at issue is, Why have they stayed in this field and not returned to their earlier interests?

The answer is that numerical analysis is an attractive subject in which mathematics of practically all sorts can be used significantly and from which many branches of mathematics can benefit.   We call attention here to the applications of functional analysis by the Russian school led by Kantorovitch [1].   (For a survey of some Western work see Collatz [1a]; see also Altman [90].)   In another direction we recall the developments in analytic number theory by Lehmer and Rademacher which followed MacMahon's computations of $p(n)$ for Hardy and Ramanujan [2].   We note here the contribution of machines to a problem on rearrangements in real variable theory due to D. H. Lehmer [91], to the theory of finite projective geometries and related fields by Hall and his

* This is a slightly revised and extended version of the article, with the same title, which appeared in *Comm. Pure Appl. Math.*, vol. 8, pp. 97–116, 1955, and which was reprinted in "Transactions of the Symposium on Computing, Mechanics, Statistics and Partial Differential Equations," F. E. Grubbs, F. J. Murray, and J. J. Stoker, eds., Interscience Publishers, Inc., New York, 1955.   We are grateful to the publishers for permission to reproduce this here.   A translation of this article into German, by Prof. Dr. E. Kamke, appeared in *Jber. Deutsch. Math. Verein.*, vol. 58, pp. 11–38, 1955; and a Russian version has appeared in *Matematicheskoe prosveshchenie*, vol. 1, pp. 75–86, 1955, and vol. 2, pp. 97–110, 1956.

collaborators (see Chap. 15), to a problem of Taussky [122] in the theory of sequence spaces by Kato [101], and to complex-function theory by Kreyszig and Todd [93] and Kusmina [94].

Before proceeding to a discussion of some individual topics in numerical analysis, some general remarks are in order. We have, on various occasions, distinguished between classical and modern numerical analysis, the latter being material required in connection with the exploitation of high-speed automatic digital computing machines. It now seems desirable to recognize ultramodern numerical analysis, which may be specified as adventures with high-speed automatic digital computing machines (see [50, 51]). There are, of course, no sharp boundaries between these parts of the subject, and there is room for development in the classical phases as well as in the newer areas.

In distinction to the deliberate explorations contemplated in ultramodern numerical analysis, there is much routine work in numerical analysis which must necessarily be of an experimental or empirical nature. It is just not feasible to carry out rigorous error estimates for all problems of significant complication; it is necessary to place considerable reliance, on the one hand, on the experience of those familiar with similar problems and, on the other, on the good judgment of the setter of the problem. To justify this remark, we consider three examples. The solution of systems of 20 or more first-order differential equations is being handled regularly. To see the complication of theoretical error estimates [in which the fact that all numbers handled are finite (binary) decimals is disregarded], we refer to Bieberbach [3]. The complication of a stability analysis in a system of 14 equations is evident from a study carried out by Murray [4]. Again, the extent of a complete error estimate for the problem of matrix inversions is familiar from the work of von Neumann and Goldstine [5, 5a] and Turing [6]. Finally, there are the analysis of the triple-diagonal method for determining the characteristic roots of a symmetric matrix by Givens [7, 7a] and the analysis of the Jacobi diagonalization method by Goldstine, Murray, and von Neumann [26].

What the numerical analyst has to do is to be aware of the precision of results obtained from, for instance, the conformal mapping of an ellipse on a circle by a certain process and, from these results, to extrapolate to cases of regions of comparable shape. On the one hand, he has to examine general error analyses for their realism by comparison with cases where the explicit, exact results are known. On the other hand, he must devote time to the construction and study of bad examples so as to counteract any tendency to too much extrapolation. For a preliminary discussion of matrix inversion in the last two directions, we refer to Newman and Todd [95] and to Todd [76, 77].

The main part of this chapter is devoted to a discussion of some topics in numerical analysis which appear attractive. These have been chosen, among those with which the author is familiar, to point out some of the techniques of the subject and to indicate some of the mathematicians who have made distinguished contributions in the field. In addition, the choice has been controlled by the author's opinion that separation between theoretical and practical numerical analysis is undesirable. The practicality of some of the techniques used is illustrated by computations of the radiation from a simple source which is reflected from a Lambert plane, recently carried out by Henrici [8], where the ideas of Secs. 1.3 and 1.6 were used.

1.2 Evaluation of Polynomials

What is the best way of computing polynomials, for instance,

$$f(x) = a_0 x^n + \cdots + a_{n-1} x + a_n,$$

for a series of values of x, not equally spaced? (In the case where the values of $f(x)$ for a series of equally spaced values of x are required, building up $f(x)$ from its differences might be the most convenient.) The usual answer is to suggest the recurrence scheme:

$$f_0 = a_0,$$
$$f_{r+1} = xf_r + a_{r+1}, \qquad r = 0, 1, \ldots, n - 1,$$

which was known to Newton but is usually ascribed to Horner [9]. In this way we get $f(x)$ by n additions and n multiplications. Is this the best possible algorithm? Consider an alternative, in the case of

$$f(x) = 1 + 2x + 3x^2.$$

If we proceed as follows:

$$2x, x^2, 3x^2, 1 + 2x + 3x^2,$$

we need 3 multiplications and 2 additions compared with the 2 multiplications and 2 additions needed in applying the above algorithm; thus

$$3x, 3x + 2, x(3x + 2), x(3x + 2) + 1.$$

This problem was formulated as one in abstract algebra by Ostrowski, and he showed [9] that the above algorithm was indeed the best for polynomials of degree not exceeding 4. A different approach was made recently by Motzkin [10] (see also Belaga [98]). Not restricting himself to purely rational processes, he showed that algorithms which are more economical in practice can be obtained for larger n, when a sufficiently large number of values of $f(x)$ are required.   We give a simple example in the case $n = 6$.   Consider the evaluation of

$$P = x^6 + Ax^5 + Bx^4 + Cx^3 + Dx^2 + Ex + F.$$

Introduce the following polynomials:

$$P_1 = x^2 + ax,$$
$$P_2 = (P_1 + x + b)(P_1 + c),$$
$$P_3 = (P_2 + d)(P_1 + e),$$

and determine a, b, c, d, e, and f by identifying P and $P_3 + f$.   This can be done by the solution of linear equations and a single quadratic.   This evaluation is done once for all, and then P can be evaluated at the expense of three multiplications only, with a significant economy over the other process if we have to evaluate P for a sufficiently large number of values of x.

The details of the evaluations are as follows.   The result of equating coefficients in P and $P_3 + f$ is

$$3a + 1 = A, \tag{1.1}$$
$$3a^2 + 2a + b + c + e = B, \tag{1.2}$$
$$a^3 + a^2 + 2ab + 2ac + 2ae + c + e = C, \tag{1.3}$$
$$a^2b + a^2c + a^2e + ac + ae + bc + be + ce + d = D, \tag{1.4}$$
$$abc + abe + ace + ad + ce = E, \tag{1.5}$$
$$ebc + de + f = F. \tag{1.6}$$

From (1.1) we find a.   Hence we can rewrite (1.2) and (1.3) in the form

$$b + c + e = B', \tag{1.2'}$$
$$2a(b + c + e) + c + e = C'. \tag{1.3'}$$

(We use primed capitals to indicate new known constants.)   Using (1.2') in (1.3'), we get

$$c + e = C'', \tag{1.3''}$$

which, with (1.2'), gives us b explicitly.   Using $a, b, c + e$, we can write (1.4) as

$$d + ce = D'. \tag{1.4'}$$

Using $a, b, c + e, d + ce$ in (1.5), we find

$$ce = E', \tag{1.5'}$$

which gives d from (1.4').   From (1.3'') and (1.5') we can find c, e by solving a quadratic equation, and then from (1.6) we can find f.

1.3 Increasing the Speed of Convergence of Sequences

The construction of processes which increase the speed of convergence of sequences and series has been a favorite topic for many numerical analysts. For instance, there is the h^2 extrapolation process of Richardson [11], the converging-factor method of Airey [12, 12a], the Euler summation process [13], and a whole subject associated with the name of Chebyshev (see, for example, Chap. 3 and [14]). We shall discuss the δ^2 process which has been popularized in numerical analysis by Aitken [15, e.g.]; it dates back at least to Kummer [16].

If

$$x_n \rightarrow x$$

and

$$x_n - x \doteq A\lambda^n, \qquad |\lambda| < 1, \tag{1.7}$$

then

$$\frac{x_{n+2} - x}{x_{n+1} - x} \doteq \frac{x_{n+1} - x}{x_n - x} \doteq \lambda. \tag{1.8}$$

From (1.8) we find

$$x \doteq x_{n+2} - \frac{(x_{n+2} - x_{n+1})^2}{x_{n+2} - 2x_{n+1} + x_n}.$$

This suggests that the sequence $\{\bar{x}_{n+2}\}$ defined by

$$\bar{x}_{n+2} = x_{n+2} - \frac{(x_{n+2} - x_{n+1})^2}{x_{n+2} - 2x_{n+1} + x_n}, \qquad n = 0, 1, 2, \ldots$$

converges more rapidly to x than the original sequence. This is indeed the case; for if

$$x_n - x = A\lambda^n + o(\lambda^n), \qquad |\lambda| < 1,$$

then it follows that

$$\bar{x}_n - x = o(\lambda^n).$$

Several remarks are in order. First, this process can be iterated to remove successively components in the remainder of the form

$$A\lambda^n, B\mu^n, C\nu^n, \ldots,$$

where $1 > |\lambda| > |\mu| > |\nu| > \cdots$. The cases in which there are equalities such as $|\lambda| = |\mu|$ can be handled by simple modifications. Second, it is important to note that this process can make things worse if the convergence is not geometric as required by (1.7). Here is a simple example involving two of the standard iterative processes for determining the reciprocal of a number N. Consider the sequences

$$y_{n+1} = (1 - N)y_n + 1, \qquad z_{n+1} = z_n(2 - Nz_n).$$

In the case $N = \frac{1}{2}$ with $y_0 = 1$, $z_0 = 1$, we obtain the following table:

y_n		$\bar{y}_n$	z_n		$\bar{z}_n$
1			1		
	.5			.5	
1.5		−.25	1.5		−.125
	.25			.375	
1.75		−.125 2	1.875		−.2578 3.0000
	.125			.1172	
1.875		2	1.9922		2.0455

The sequence $\{\bar{y}_n\}$ appears to converge more rapidly than $\{y_n\}$ while the sequence $\{\bar{z}_n\}$ appears to converge less rapidly than $\{z_n\}$.   These results can be easily established.   First of all, each sequence converges to N^{-1} if $0 < N < 1$ for

$$y_n - N^{-1} = (1 - N)^n(y_0 - N^{-1})$$

and

$$z_n - N^{-1} = -N^{2^n-1}(z_0 - N^{-1})^{2^n}.$$

Thus $\{y_n\}$ satisfies the condition (1.7), while $\{z_n\}$ does not, converging too rapidly.   In the present case we have $\bar{y}_n \equiv N^{-1}$.   On the other hand, it can be shown that

$$\frac{\bar{z}_n - N^{-1}}{z_n - N^{-1}} \to -\infty.$$

Note, however, that to justify the application of this process it is sufficient to show the existence of an expansion of the form (1.7), with $|\lambda| < 1$.

Extensive use of this process was made in experiments in conformal mapping by Blanch and Jackson [17] and by Todd and Warschawski [18].   For instance, in the latter, the mapping of an ellipse (of axis ratio 5:1) on a circle, it was found that about 50 iterations, each requiring about 30 minutes of computing on SEAC, were required to secure directly about 9 correct decimals in the value of the boundary function. It was, however, possible to obtain the same accuracy by a double use of the Aitken process on the first 14 iterants—the extra time required for this being negligible.

1.4   Modified Differences

We shall show here how the use of quadratic interpolation enables the tablemaker to cut down on the size of a table at the expense of some work by the table user.   We shall then show how a further saving in space can be accomplished, at no further expense to the user but at some to the tablemaker, by the use of modified differences.   For simplicity and definiteness, we consider the construction of a table of $\sin x$, to 4 places of decimals, for x in the range $(0, \frac{1}{2}\pi)$.

(a) *Linear Interpolation*

The error involved in linear interpolation, that is, the assumption that

$$f(a + ph) = f(a) + p[f(a + h) - f(a)], \qquad 0 \le p \le 1,$$

can be estimated as

$$h^2 \left| \binom{p}{2} \right| \max |f''(x)|.$$

If this is to be less than $\frac{1}{2} \times 10^{-4}$ an appropriate choice for h is .02. This requires a table of some 80 entries, part of which is shown below:

x	$\sin x$
.00	.0000
.02	.0200
.04	.0400
.06	.0600
.08	.0799
.	.
.	.
.	.
1.20	.9320
1.22	.9391
1.24	.9458
1.26	.9521
1.28	.9580
.	.
.	.
.	.

Interpolation, say for $x = 1.234$, in this table is carried out as follows:

$$\sin 1.234 = .9391 + \tfrac{14}{20}(.9458 - .9391) = .9438.$$

(b) *Cubic Interpolation*

We now consider using the Everett interpolation formula

$$f_p = qf_0 + pf_1 + E_2\delta^2 f_0 + F_2\delta^2 f_1 + E_4\delta^4 f_0 + F_4\delta^4 f_1 + \cdots \quad (1.9)$$

where $f_p = f(a + ph)$ and

$$q = 1 - p, \qquad E_2 = q(q^2 - 1)/6, \qquad F_2 = p(p^2 - 1)/6, \qquad \ldots .$$

If we retain the first four terms the truncation error can be estimated as

$$h^4 \left| \binom{p+1}{4} \right| \max |f^4(x)| \le h^4 \times .024 \times 1.$$

For this to be less than $\frac{1}{2} \times 10^{-4}$ we can conveniently take $h = .2$. The corresponding complete table is given below.

x	$\sin x$	δ^2
.0	.0000	0
.2	.1987	−80
.4	.3894	−155
.6	.5646	−224
.8	.7174	−287
1.0	.8415	−336
1.2	.9320	−371
1.4	.9854	−392
1.6	.9996	−400
1.8	.9738	−387

For interpolation, we now have either to compute the Everett coefficients or to obtain them from a table; we find

$$p = .17, \qquad E_2 = -.0430, \qquad F_2 = -.0275.$$

We then have

$$\sin 1.234 = .9320 + \tfrac{34}{200}(.9854 - .9320)$$
$$+ (.0430)(.0371) + (.0275)(.0392) = .9438.$$

(c) Comrie's Throwback

This device, introduced by Comrie [19], depends essentially on the fact that the ratio

$$k(p) = \frac{E_4}{E_2} = \frac{(p+1)(p-3)}{20}$$

is approximately constant for $0 \leq p \leq 1$. Various ways of choosing a mean value for this have been discussed [20]. The preferred value is $k = -.18393$. With this value of k we rewrite the first four terms of (1.9) as

$$f_p \doteq qf_0 + pf_1 + [E_2(\delta^2 f_0 + k\delta^4 f_0) + F_2(\delta^2 f_1 + k\delta^4 f_1)]. \quad (1.10)$$

Therefore, if we define

$$\delta_m^2 f = \delta^2 f + k\delta^4 f$$

and use these modified second differences in exactly the same way as we used the ordinary second differences in the preceding subsection, we can obtain the desired accuracy of interpolation with a much larger interval. In fact the error in (1.10) is made up of the truncation now bounded by

$$h^6 \left| \binom{p+3}{6} \right| \max |f^6(x)| \leq h^6 \times .0049 \quad (1.11)$$

together with the error caused by the modification. It can be shown that the latter is less than half a unit in the last place if the fourth differences are less than 1000 units (and the fifth less than 70 units).

The condition (1.11) gives $h \leq .46$, which suggests that $h = .5$ might be acceptable. For this value of h, a bound for the fourth difference is

$$(.5)^4 \times \max |f^4(x)| \leq .0625$$

which is acceptable, although the bound for the fifth is not. Nevertheless we shall use $h = .5$ without carrying out a more precise estimate.

The *complete* table is given below:

x	$\sin x$	δ_m^2
.0	.0000	0
.5	.4794	-1225
1.0	.8415	-2154
1.5	.9975	-2552
2.0	.9093	-2326

For interpolation, we first find the Everett coefficients

$$p = .468, \quad E_2 = -.0636, \quad F_2 = -.0609.$$

We then have

$$\sin 1.234 = .8415 + {}^{234}\!/_{500}(.9975 - .8415) + (.0636 \times .2154)$$
$$+ (.0609 \times .2552) = .9145 + .0137 + .0155 = .9437.$$

The discrepancy between the results can be explained either by the marginal choice of h or by rounding errors.

More elaborate types of throwback—for example, of the sixth difference as well as of the fourth—were also given by Comrie. In the past few years a unified account of theory of the throwback was developed, and its relation with expansions in Chebyshev polynomials was established. This is discussed briefly in [21] and in detail by Fox [96]. Some minor disadvantages of modified differences have been discussed by Comrie [19].

1.5 Characteristic Roots of Finite Matrices

Considerable effort has been expended in problems of numerical analysis involving matrices. Bibliographical material is available in [22, 72] and in Householder [103]. The two main problems are the inversion of matrices and the determination of their characteristic values. In both problems the practical determination of bounds for characteristic roots is important (see Chap. 8). In this connection we call attention here to the following lemma of Geršgorin [24], which has many applications:

All the characteristic roots of $A = (a_{ij})$ lie in the union of the circular regions

$$|a_{ii} - z| \leq \sum_{i \neq j} |a_{ij}|, \qquad i = 1, 2, \ldots, n.$$

This is proved by use of the fact that a determinant with dominant main diagonal does not vanish.   This last result has been generalized by many writers; for an account of some of the work, see Taussky [25] and Parodi [111].

One of the preferred and practical methods of getting all the characteristic roots of a symmetric matrix depends on the reduction of the matrix to pure diagonal forms (Goldstine, Murray, and von Neumann [26], Gregory [27]) by superposing orthogonal transformations involving two variables at a time.   Theoretically we obtain

$$TAT' = \text{diag}\,(\lambda_1, \lambda_2, \ldots, \lambda_n),$$

and then $\lambda_1, \lambda_2, \ldots, \lambda_n$ are the exact characteristic values.   In practice we find

$$TAT' = (\epsilon_{ij})$$

where the ϵ_{ij} are small for $i \neq j$.   We then ask, How near are the ϵ_{ii} to the λ_i?   If we disregard the question of the transformation not being truly orthogonal—and therefore of the characteristic roots of (ϵ_{ij}) not being identical with those of (a_{ij})—the answer comes at once from the lemma.   If the ϵ_{ij}, $i \neq j$, are sufficiently small, then

$$|\lambda_i - \epsilon_{ii}| \leq \sum_{i \neq j} |\epsilon_{ij}|, \qquad i = 1, 2, \ldots, n.$$

Allowance can easily be made in this inequality for round-off error in the product TAT'.

1.6   Quadrature, Integral Equations

(a) Quadrature

We begin with an example to show that there is still scope for new ideas in classical numerical analysis.   A typical quadrature formula is

$$\int_a^b f(x)\,dx \doteq \sum p_i f(x_i),$$

and the error

$$E = \left| \int_a^b f(x)\,dx - \sum p_i f(x_i) \right|$$

is estimated as a multiple of a (high) derivative $f^n(x)$ of $f(x)$ at a point in (a,b).   In many cases it is far from convenient to obtain bounds on $f^n(x)$

or to estimate these by computing the corresponding differences manually.   Recently Davis and Rabinowitz [28, 28a] reconsidered this problem in the case when $f(x)$ is analytic in a region including the segment (a,b).   Eberlein [29] has also contributed to this problem.   The case of ellipses $\mathscr{E}$ with foci at the end points, which we normalize to $(1,0), (-1,0)$, can be handled elegantly, in terms of the Chebyshev polynomials

$$(1 - z^2)^{-\frac{1}{2}} \sin [(n + 1) \arccos z]$$

which are orthogonal over the area of such an ellipse.   It can be shown that

$$|E| \le \sigma_{\mathscr{E}} \, \|f\|$$

where $\sigma_{\mathscr{E}}$ is a constant depending only on the ellipse $\mathscr{E}$ and where

$$\|f\| = \int\!\!\int_{\mathscr{E}} | f(z)|^2 \, dx \, dy.$$

(Note that $\|f\|$ increases as $\mathscr{E}$ expands; however, $\sigma_{\mathscr{E}}$ then decreases, and there is a problem of optimal choice of $\mathscr{E}$.)   The $\sigma_{\mathscr{E}}$ can be tabulated once for all, and $\|f\|$ can be estimated in terms, for example, of max $|f|$.

As an example, consider the evaluation of

$$\int_3^4 \Gamma(x) \, dx$$

using a 7-point Gaussian rule.   To evaluate and bound the fourteenth derivative of $\Gamma(z)$ seems rather out of the question.   Simple estimates can be used in the method just described to find

$$|E| \le 2.04 \times 10^{-12}.$$

A comparison of this estimate with that given by the usual one [30, 31],

$$\frac{f^{(2n)}(\xi)(n!)^4}{(2n!)^3(2n + 1)}, \qquad 3 \le \xi \le 4,$$

where the derivative is now estimated by the use of Cauchy's formula, shows that the new one is somewhat better.   For further developments in this vein, see Davis [112].

(b) Integral Equations

Among the basic problems in the numerical analysis of integral equations are the relations between the eigenvalues of a (symmetric) kernel to those of an approximating matrix. A satisfactory account of this was given recently by Wielandt [32] in support of some experiments on conformal mapping [18] which were being carried out on SEAC, the

National Bureau of Standards Eastern Automatic Computer.   The continuous problem is the solution of

$$\int_0^1 K(x,\xi)y(\xi)\ d\xi = ky(x).$$

We make this discrete by introducing a quadrature

$$\int_0^1 f(\xi)\ d\xi \doteq \sum p_\nu f(\xi_\nu) \tag{1.12}$$

and are therefore led to consider the matrix problem

$$\sum_\nu K(\xi_\mu,\xi_\nu)p_\nu y_\nu = \kappa y_\mu.$$

What are the relations between the finite number of κ and the infinity of the k?   We quote a typical result.   If we take for (1.12) the trapezoidal quadrature

$$\int_0^1 f(\xi)\ d\xi = \frac{1}{n}(\tfrac{1}{2}f_0 + f_1 + \cdots + f_{n-1} + \tfrac{1}{2}f_n), \qquad f_i \equiv f\left(\frac{i-1}{n}\right),$$

then, provided K satisfies

$$|K(x,\xi) - K(\alpha,\beta)| \le L(|x - \alpha| + |y - \beta|),$$

where α, β run through the points $(i/n, j/n)$ and where $|x - \alpha| < \tfrac{1}{2}n^{-1}$, $|y - \beta| < \tfrac{1}{2}n^{-1}$, we have

$$|k - \kappa| \le \frac{CL}{n-1},$$

where the constant $C = \tfrac{1}{4} + \sqrt{\tfrac{1}{12}}$ is best possible.

(c) Convergence and Stability

Problems of convergence and stability in the numerical solution of ordinary and partial differential equations lead to interesting and subtle questions.

Consider first an ordinary differential equation for a function $y = y(x)$. One meaning of a numerical solution is a sequence of values $Y_n \doteq y(x_n)$, at a sufficiently dense set $\{x_n\}$, which approximate $y(x_n)$ to within an assigned tolerance.   [In the case of a characteristic-value problem, we also have to ensure that the characteristic values in the discrete problem are sufficiently near to those of the continuous problem; see also Sec. 1.6(b) above.]   Various prescriptions for finding such values are available.   In general, however, these prescriptions are not carried out rigorously; calculations are made with rounded numbers.   In some cases the effects can be catastrophic (see, e.g., Todd [82]).   An indication of a source of difficulty is the following: we may be attempting to compute a bounded solution of a differential equation which also has an unbounded solution—for instance, e^{-x} in the case of $y'' = y$. An error may introduce a component of the unbounded solution which will soon predominate.

So, apart from the adequateness of the approximation of Y_n to y_n (the problem of convergence), we have to investigate the sensitiveness of the numerical process to the limited digital character of our equipment. Instead of producing Y_n, we actually produce $\bar{Y}_n$; the study of $|Y_n - \bar{Y}_n|$ is the problem of "stability."

Among those who have contributed to this field are Rutishauser [83], Lotkin [89], Dahlquist [118], and Henrici [117].

Similar problems, as well as some new features in those just mentioned, appear in the study of partial differential equations (see Chap. 11). The main new feature is that in many cases restrictions on the shape of the mesh are necessary for convergence [85] and for stability [84, 86, 109]. The convergence restrictions, which can often be motivated physically, are in many cases those which are significant numerically. This connection has been developed by P. Lax and others and has been discussed in the monograph of Richtmyer [108].

A final remark, which we do not elaborate, is the following. It is tempting to base error analyses on the hypothesis that individual errors are random variables. This, of course, is not the case, because the errors are completely determined once the details of the computational process are settled. However, such assumptions often lead to useful and realistic estimates (see, on the one hand, Goldstine and von Neumann [5a] and Rademacher [88] and, on the other, Huskey [87]).

1.7   Game Theory and Related Developments

In game theory there are problems in which the intuition of a geometer can play an essential part; for instance, the theory of polyhedra and convex bodies and fixed-point theory are highly relevant. The foundations of a theory of games were laid down by von Neumann [33, 39, 74, 75], beginning in 1928. The theory of two-person zero-sum games is well developed; but the practical problem of finding the value of such a game and the optimal strategies is difficult, and the solutions available so far are not entirely satisfactory. Among related and essentially equivalent problems are the solution of systems of linear inequalities, the solution of linear programs in the sense of Dantzig, and the Chebyshev problem of determining the minimax "solution" of an inconsistent system of linear equations

$$\eta_j = \sum_{k=1}^{m} a_{jk} x_k + c_j = 0, \qquad j = 1, 2, \ldots, n,$$

that is, the set of values x_k which minimizes the maximum of the residuals $|\eta_j|$ (see, e.g., Stiefel [106]).

Among the methods of attacking these problems are the simplex method [34], the relaxation method [35, 35a], and the double-description method [36]. We shall, however, discuss a very simple example by a natural approach due to Brown [37], the validity of which was established by Robinson [38]. A related continuous solution of this discrete problem has been given by Brown and von Neumann [37a]; we take up this idea of continuous approach to discrete problems again in Sec. 1.9(c).

Consider the following game played between two players, R and C, each of whom has two strategies, which we may interpret as the choice of a row or a column in the pay-off matrix $P = (p_{ij})$:

$$P = \begin{pmatrix} 1 & 3 \\ 4 & 2 \end{pmatrix}.$$

If R chooses the ith row and C chooses the jth column, then R gets p_{ij} from C. This is manifestly an unfair game, and R should pay to play it.

The value of this game is 2.5, and the optimal strategies are the following: R should choose 1 and 2 each with probability $\frac{1}{2}$; C should choose 1 with probability $\frac{1}{4}$ and 2 with probability $\frac{3}{4}$. The significance of these statements is the following: if R plays in this way, his expected gain is not less than 2.5, whereas if C plays this way, his expected loss is not greater than 2.5.

To prove this statement is simple. Let R play 1 with probability $r \geq 0$ and 2 with probability $1 - r \geq 0$; let C play 1 with probability $c \geq 0$ and 2 with probability $1 - c \geq 0$. Then the expectation of R is

$$E = 1 \times rc + 4(1 - r)c + 3r(1 - c) + 2(1 - r)(1 - c).$$

We have

$$E = -4(r - \tfrac{1}{2})(c - \tfrac{1}{4}) + \tfrac{5}{2}.$$

This shows that when $r = \frac{1}{2}$ then $E = \frac{5}{2}$ for any c and that when $r \neq \frac{1}{2}$ then c can be chosen to make $E < \frac{5}{2}$; similarly, if $c = \frac{1}{4}$, then $E = \frac{5}{2}$, and if $c \neq \frac{1}{4}$, then r can be chosen to make $E > \frac{5}{2}$ (see McKinsey [39]).

How can we arrive at these results, or approximations to them?

We shall describe an algorithm for an *alternating* choice of strategies by R and C which can be interpreted as follows: each chooses that strategy which is better in comparison with the observed behavior to date of his opponent.

After n plays, suppose C has chosen 1 in $c_1^{(n)} \times n$ plays and 2 in the remaining $c_2^{(n)} \times n$ plays. (For convenience, from now on, we shall drop the superscripts.) If C continues this pattern, the expectation of R in the next play is

$$e_1 = c_1 + 3c_2 \qquad \text{if he chooses 1,}$$
$$e_2 = 4c_1 + 2c_2 \qquad \text{if he chooses 2.}$$

R therefore chooses 1 or 2 according to whether $e_1 \geq e_2$ or $e_1 < e_2$. Similarly, if R has chosen 1 in $r_1^{(n)} \times n$ plays and 2 in the remaining $r_2^{(n)} \times n$ plays, then C chooses 1 or 2 according to the expected size of his loss, which is

$$f_1 = r_1 + 4r_2 \qquad \text{if he chooses 1,}$$
$$f_2 = 3r_1 + 2r_2 \qquad \text{if he chooses 2.}$$

Specifically C chooses 1 if $f_1 \leq f_2$ and 2 if $f_1 > f_2$.

We have used the word "play" loosely in the preceding paragraph. We actually describe an algorithm for a choice of strategies by R and C alternately.   A sequence of strategies is determined after we make an arbitrary choice of an initial strategy for R, say 1.   The resultant sequence can be combined in pairs to give a sequence of plays in the proper sense:

(1,1), (2,1), (2,2), (2,2), (2,2), (2,2), (2,2), (2,2), (1,2), (1,2), (1,2),
(1,2), (1,2), (1,1), (1,1), (2,1), (2,2), (2,2), (2,2), (2,2), (1,2), (1,2), (1,2),
(1,1), (1,1), (2,1), (1,1), (2,1), (2,2), (2,2), (2,2), (2,2), (2,2), (2,2), (2,2),
(2,2), (2,2), (2,2), (2,2), (2,2), (1,2), (1,2), (1,2), (1,2), (1,2), (1,2), (1,2),
(1,2), (1,2), (1,2), ...

It has been shown [38] that, as $n \to \infty$, the sequences $c_1^{(n)}$, $r_1^{(n)}$ converge to the optimal strategy, that is, $c_1^{(n)} \to \frac{1}{4}$, $r_1^{(n)} \to \frac{1}{2}$, and that the average pay-off $p^{(n)}$ converges to the value of the game.   In our case

$$r_1^{(50)} = .48, \qquad c_1^{(50)} = .2, \qquad p^{(50)} = 2.4.$$

The structure of the sequence above, consisting of blocks of identical elements, is typical; this can obviously be used to speed the computations.   For some practical experiments in this field, see [40].   Another algorithm, the convergence of which has also been established, is the following.   We begin with the choice of a play, say (1,1).   Then future plays are determined by the *simultaneous* choice of strategies by R and C according to the previous rule.   The sequence of plays now begins

$$(1,1), (2,1), (2,1), (2,2), ...$$

It has been observed that convergence of the above alternate-choice algorithm is often faster than that arising from genuine simultaneous choice of strategies.

We shall now discuss an application of the theory of games to the so-called assignment problem.   This problem is to assign n square pegs to n round holes in such a way as to maximize the total goodness of fit.   In other words, (a_{ij}) being given, we have to choose a permutation $p(i)$ of $(1, 2, \ldots, n)$ so as to maximize

$$\sum a_{ip(i)}. \tag{1.13}$$

This is trivial theoretically; we have only to find the largest of the $n!$ sums of the form (1.13). In practice, however, this may be out of the question, and so we may have to settle for some approximation to the maximum. One way of doing this (suggested by von Neumann [41]) is to set up an equivalent game-theory problem—it turns out to be a sort of hide-and-seek—and solve this approximately by the method just discussed. The first player chooses a pair of indices (i,j) $(1 \leq i \leq n,$ $1 \leq j \leq n)$; he has n^2 strategies. The second then elects first to guess the first or second of these two indices, and then guesses it by choosing k $(1 \leq k \leq n)$; he has $2n$ strategies. In the first case if $k = i$, and in the second case if $k = j$, the first player pays the second $(a_{ij})^{-1}$; otherwise there is no pay-off.

Assignment problems for $n = 12$ have been handled by this method. It has, however, been found that a direct approach which regards the assignment problem as a special case of a transportation problem (see [42]) has been very successful. One chooses a permutation matrix (p_{ij}) such that $\sum_{i,j} p_{ij} a_{ij}$ is minimum, and solves this, for instance, by the simplex method [34].

An up-to-date account of this problem and its generalizations has been given by Motzkin [42]. Among these are the transportation problem, the caterer problem, the problem of contract awards, and the traveling-salesman problem [43, 44]. Solutions to problems of this type are now obtained on a routine basis, on high-speed computers, as an aid to management decision in industrial and military situations [45]. Among other problems of this general character, which are in the research stage, are those concerned with organization theory, which have been studied by Marshak and Tompkins [46].

1.8   Monte Carlo

This is a subject with large areas unsoiled by theorems, as can be seen by reference to the reports on various symposia held on the subject [67, 68]. For instance, during the last four years we have been generating millions of pseudo-random numbers on SEAC, using such relations as

$$r_n = 2^{-42} x_n, \qquad x_{n+1} \equiv \rho x_n (\bmod 2^{42}), \qquad x_0 = 1, \qquad \rho = 5^{17}$$

or

$$r_n = 2^{-44} x_{2n}, \qquad x_{n+1} \equiv x_n + x_{n-1} (\bmod 2^{44}), \qquad x_0 = 0, \qquad x_1 = 1.$$

See, for instance, Chap. 4, Taussky and Todd [68, pp. 15–28], and Todd [81]. The r_n behave as if they came from a uniform distribution in the interval $(0, 1)$. The results we obtained were satisfactory in all cases where we had independent checks. We have, however, no theorems at all about the "randomness" of these sequences or about the distributions in blocks of the size used in our calculations.

We mention here also the quasi-Monte Carlo processes studied by Peck and Richtmyer [47, 48]. Here high-power algebraic number theory is used to evaluate the error committed by replacing integrals by sums of the integrands at points determined by certain algebraic numbers. See also Halton [92] and Hammersley [120].

1.9 Recent Activity in Numerical Analysis

A few areas are mentioned here with which the author is familiar and which he has found interesting. This personal selection omits reference to many areas in which there have been important advances (e.g., meteorology) and to areas which have been discussed elsewhere in this volume.

(a) Ultramodern Numerical Analysis

One class of experiments may be described as follows. It has been usual in discussing properties of matter to regard the medium as continuous, to set up differential equations, look at them for a while, give up, and replace them by difference equations. These difference equations are then solved, and no attention is paid to their physical significance, if any.

An alternative approach is to handle the problem discretely from the beginning, lumping the "molecules" together in groups as small as the computing equipment can handle.

Among those who have handled problems in this general way are Seeger, von Neumann, and Polachek (see Seeger [49]), who were concerned with shock-wave phenomena. Pasta and Ulam [50] have studied the mixing of fluids and the motions of star clusters in this way. Metropolis and Fermi [51] have investigated the equations of state of individually interacting particles forming an idealized liquid. Fröberg [78] has studied a model of a photographic emulsion.

(b) Biological Applications

There has been pioneering work by Turing [52] on the problem of morphogenesis. Turing constructs a mathematical model of a growing embryo and shows how well-known physical laws are sufficient to account for many of the facts about the development of its anatomical structure.

Another application has been the study of the reaction of nerve fibers to electric stimuli. These phenomena are governed by a system of four nonlinear ordinary differential equations (Hodgkin-Huxley). The system has been studied by Antosiewicz, Cole, FitzHugh, and Rabinowitz, and, in particular, the threshold value of the input current has been determined. The agreement with the results of many experiments indicates the reliability of the model and encourages further investigation (see [53]).

Barricelli has studied numerical analogues of genetic and evolutionary processes.

(c) Combinatorial Analysis

Combinatorial analysis is an obvious source of problems.   There have been recent reports on this topic by Cairns [54] and Tompkins [55]. The numerical analyst, however, soon finds himself out of his depth if he uses straightforward approaches.

One new idea which was tried is that of a continuous approach to discrete problems, in particular to the search for perfect difference sets. A perfect difference set is a set of $n + 1$ integers whose $n(n + 1)$ differences take on all nonzero values mod $n^2 + n + 1$.   For example, the differences of 1, 2, 4 are ± 1, ± 2, ± 3; that is, all nonzero values mod 7, and so 1, 2, 4 form a perfect difference set mod 7.

A perfect difference set $\mathscr{S}$ can be specified by $N = n^2 + n + 1$ constants x_r, where $x_r = 1$ if $r \in \mathscr{S}$, $x_r = 0$ otherwise.   In this case we have

$$y_0 = \sum_r x_r^2 = n + 1,$$

$$y_s = \sum_r x_r x_{r+s} = 1, \qquad s = 1, 2, \ldots, N - 1$$

(the subscript $r + s$ is to be understood mod N); hence

$$\sum_r y_r = (n + 1)^2. \tag{1.14}$$

It follows, therefore, that such a set x_r minimizes

$$J = (n + 1) \sum_s y_s^2 - n y_0^2$$

for, in view of (1.14), J differs by a constant from

$$[y_0 - (n + 1)]^2 + (n + 1) \sum_{s>0} (y_s - 1)^2.$$

This suggests an attempt to obtain a set of x_r by minimizing J, now regarded as a function of the N continuous real variables x_r, subject to (1.14) (and perhaps to other relations such as $0 \le x_r \le 1$).   Such an attempt was made on SWAC, the National Bureau of Standards Western Automatic Computer, by a steepest-descent process.   Although admissible values of y were obtained rapidly, the corresponding values of x were not integers.   See also Chap. 15 and [115].

(d) Number Theory and Algebra

The subjects of number theory and algebra are natural sources of problems, and there have been many applications of high-speed computers in these areas, particularly in elementary, algebraic, and analytic number theory, as well as some in algebra proper [55a, 56].

Recent work on SWAC, mainly on elementary number theory by D. H. Lehmer, E. Lehmer, and their collaborators, has been discussed by E. Lehmer [57].

Among other work has been a study of the divisibility of $[(p - 1)! + 1]/p$ by p. This was known to be the case for $p = 5, p = 13$; Goldberg [58] found that it was also the case for $p = 563$ and for no other $p < 10000$.

Problems in algebraic number theory are more complicated to handle. A survey of computational problems in this field has been given by Taussky [59]. Since then there has been work by Cohn and Gorn on units in cubic fields (see Cohn [60]).

There have been various attempts to study the zeros of the Riemann zeta function; among those is the work of Turing [61].

The studies in algebra proper include the work of Paige and Tompkins [55a] on the systematic generation of permutations, with applications to group theory, and that of Goldberg [56] on the Baker-Campbell-Hausdorff formula. Forsythe [80] has enumerated all the 126 semigroups of order 4. The characters of symmetric groups have been investigated by Bivins and others [79] and by Comét [107].

(e) Topology

It is clear that approximate computations of quantities known to be integers serve to define them if the absolute value of the error is known to be less than $\frac{1}{2}$. This is used in the work on $p(n)$ mentioned earlier. Pasta and Ulam [50] have suggested that further applications can be made in an essentially topological problem—for example, the structure of the lines of force caused by current in two infinite straight wires which are skew.

A simple application of this is to the location of the zeros of a polynomial $P(z)$. We use the fact that

$$n = \frac{1}{2\pi i} \int_C \frac{P'(z)}{P(z)} \, dz,$$

where n is the number of zeros inside the simple closed rectifiable curve C. It is possible to choose C to be a square so large as to contain all the zeros of $P(z)$ and then, by process of quadrisection, to locate the zeros approximately. The quadrature must be accomplished with absolute error less than $\frac{1}{2}$; if this proves difficult because of the vanishing or near vanishing of $P(z)$ on the boundary, then we know that we are in the neighborhood of a zero and can act accordingly. A constructive proof of the fundamental theorem of algebra along these lines has been given by Rosenbloom [62]. See also Tompkins [104].

1.10   Theory of Machines or Automata

Among those who have contributed to basic research in machine theory have been Turing [63], Shannon [64], and von Neumann [65]. There have been some efforts of a supporting-research character: the use of machines to design circuits for better machines, the design of self-correcting codes, and improvements in the use of machines—for example, more automatic coding.   Much of this belongs more to the domain of logicians than to that of the numerical analyst.   For recent work in these areas, see, for example, [99, 100, 102, 105].   A bibliography is given by Carr [116].

REFERENCES

1. L. Kantorovitch, Functional Analysis and Applied Mathematics, *Uspehi Mat. Nauk*, vol. 3, pp. 89–185, 1948.

1a. L. Collatz, Einige Anwendungen funktionalanalytischer Methoden in der praktischen Analysis, *Z. Angew. Math. Phys.* vol. 4, pp. 327–357, 1953.

2. G. H. Hardy, "Ramanujan," Cambridge University Press, London, 1940.

3. L. Bieberbach, On the Remainder of the Runge-Kutta Formula in the Theory of Ordinary Differential Equations, *Z. Angew. Math. Phys.*, vol. 2, pp. 233–248, 1951.

4. F. J. Murray, Planning and Error Consideration for the Numerical Solution of a System of Differential Equations on a Sequenced Calculator, *Math. Tables Aids Comput.*, vol. 4, pp. 133–144, 1950.

5. J. von Neumann and H. H. Goldstine, Numerical Inverting of Matrices of High Order, *Bull. Amer. Math. Soc.*, vol. 53, pp. 1021–1099, 1947.

5a. H. H. Goldstine and J. von Neumann, Numerical Inverting of Matrices of High Order, *Proc. Amer. Math. Soc.*, vol. 2, pp. 188–202, 1951.

6. A. M. Turing, Rounding-off Errors in Matrix Processes, *Quart. J. Mech. Appl. Math.*, vol. 1, pp. 287–308, 1948.

7. W. Givens, "Numerical Computation of the Characteristic Values of a Real Symmetric Matrix," Oak Ridge National Laboratory Report 1574, 1954.

7a. W. Givens, A Method of Computing Eigenvalues and Eigenvectors Suggested by Classical Results on Symmetric Matrices, in [72], pp. 117–122.

8. P. Henrici, Application of Two Methods of Numerical Analysis to the Computation of the Reflected Radiation of a Point Source, *J. Washington Acad. Sci.*, vol. 45, pp. 38–45, 1955.

9. A. M. Ostrowski, On Two Problems in Abstract Algebra Connected with Horner's Rule, in "Studies in Mathematics and Mechanics Presented to R. von Mises," pp. 40–48, Academic Press, Inc., New York, 1954.

10. T. S. Motzkin, Evaluation of Polynomials and Evaluation of Rational Functions, *Bull. Amer. Math. Soc.*, vol. 61, p. 163, 1955.

11. L. F. Richardson, The Deferred Approach to the Limit, *Philos. Trans. Roy. Soc. London. Ser. A*, vol. 226, pp. 299–350, 1927.

12. J. R. Airey, The Converging Factor in Asymptotic Series and the Calculation of Bessel, Laguerre and Other Functions, *Phil. Mag.*, ser. 7, vol. 24, pp. 521–552, 1937.

12a. J. C. P. Miller, A Method for the Determination of Converging Factors, Applied to the Asymptotic Expansions for the Parabolic Cylinder Functions, *Proc. Cambridge Philos. Soc.*, vol. 48, pp. 243–254, 1952.

13. J. Barkley Rosser, Transformations to Speed the Convergence of Series, *J. Res. Nat. Bur. Standards*, vol. 46, pp. 56–64, 1951.

14. C. Lanczos, Introduction to "Tables of Chebyshev Polynomials," National Bureau of Standards Applied Mathematics Series, vol. 9, 1952; "Applied Analysis," Prentice-Hall, Inc., Englewood Cliffs, N.J., 1956.

15. A. C. Aitken, Studies in Practical Mathematics, 6: On the Factorization of Polynomials by Iterative Methods, *Proc. Roy. Soc. Edinburgh. Sect. A.*, vol. 63, pp. 174–191, 1951.

16. E. E. Kummer, Eine neue Methode, die numerische Summen langsam convergierender Reihen zu berechnen, *J. Reine Angew. Math.*, vol. 16, pp. 206–214, 1837.

17. G. Blanch and L. K. Jackson, Computation of Harmonic Measure by L. Ahlfors' Method, in [71], pp. 53–61.

18. J. Todd and S. E. Warschawski, On the Solution of the Lichtenstein-Gerschgorin Integral Equation in Conformal Mapping, II, in [71], pp. 31–44.

19. L. J. Comrie, in "British Association for the Advancement of Science Mathematical Tables," 3d ed., vol. 1, pp. xiii–xiv, Cambridge University Press, London, 1951.

20. M. Abramowitz, Note on Modified Second Differences for Use with Everett's Interpolation Formula, in "Tables of Bessel Functions of Fractional Order," I, National Bureau of Standards Columbia University Press Series, vol. 10, pp. xxxiii–xxxvi, 1948.

21. "Interpolation and Allied Tables," H.M. Stationery Office, London, 1956.

22. G. E. Forsythe, Solving Linear Equations Can Be Interesting, *Bull. Amer. Math. Soc.*, vol. 59, pp. 299–329, 1953.

23. M. R. Hestenes, Iterative Computational Methods, in [66], pp. 85–96.

24. S. Geršgorin, Über die Abgrenzung der Eigenwerte einer Matrix, *Izv. Akad. Nauk SSSR. Ser. Mat.*, vol. 7, pp. 749–754, 1941.

25. O. Taussky, A Recurring Theorem on Determinants, *Amer. Math. Monthly*, vol. 56, pp. 672–676, 1949.

26. H. H. Goldstine, F. J. Murray, and J. von Neumann, The Jacobi Method for Real Symmetric Matrices, *J. Assoc. Comput. Mach.*, vol. 6, pp. 59–95, 1959.

27. R. T. Gregory, Computing Eigenvalues and Eigenvectors of a Symmetric Matrix on the ILLIAC, *Math. Tables Aids Comput.*, vol. 7, pp. 215–220, 1953.

28. P. Davis and P. Rabinowitz, On the Estimation of Quadrature Errors for Analytic Functions, *Math. Tables Aids Comput.*, vol. 8, pp. 193–203, 1954.

28a. P. Davis, Errors of Numerical Approximation for Analytic Functions, *J. Rational Mech. Anal.*, vol. 2, pp. 303–313, 1953.

29. W. F. Eberlein, Theory of Numerical Integration, I: Preliminary Report, *Bull. Amer. Math. Soc.*, vol. 60, pp. 366–367, 1954.

30. G. Szegö, "Orthogonal Polynomials," American Mathematical Society Colloquium Publications, vol. 23, 1959.

31. A. N. Lowan, N. Davids, and A. Levenson, Table of the Zeros of the Legendre Polynomials . . . , *Bull. Amer. Math. Soc.*, vol. 48, pp. 739–743, 1942.

32. H. Wielandt, Error Bounds for Eigenvalues of Symmetric Integral Equations, in [70], pp. 261–282.

33. J. von Neumann and O. Morgenstern, "Theory of Games and Economic Behavior," 2d ed., Princeton University Press, Princeton, N.J., 1947.

34. G. B. Dantzig, Maximization of a Linear Function of Variables Subject to Linear Inequalities, in [121], pp. 339–347.

35. S. Agmon, The Relaxation Method for Linear Inequalities, *Canad. J. Math.*, vol. 6, pp. 382–392, 1954.

35a. T. S. Motzkin and I. J. Schoenberg, On the Relaxation Method for Linear Inequalities, *Canad. J. Math.*, vol. 6, pp. 393–404, 1954.

36. T. S. Motzkin, H. Raiffa, G. L. Thompson, and R. M. Thrall, The Double Description Method, in [75], pp. 5–73.

37. G. W. Brown, Iterative Solution of Games by Fictitious Play, in [121], pp. 374–376.

37a. G. W. Brown and J. von Neumann, Solution of Games by Differential Equations, in [74], pp. 73–79.

38. J. Robinson, An Iterative Method of Solving a Game, *Ann. of Math.*, vol. 54, pp. 296–301, 1951.

39. J. C. C. McKinsey, "Introduction to the Theory of Games," McGraw-Hill Book Company, Inc., New York, 1952.

40. A. J. Hoffman, M. Mannos, D. Sokolowsky, and N. Wiegmann, Computational Experience in Solving Linear Programs, *J. Soc. Indust. Appl. Math.*, vol. 1, pp. 17–34, 1 53.

41. J. von Neumann, A Certain Zero-sum Two-person Game Equivalent to the Assignment Problem, in [74], pp. 5–12.

42. T. S. Motzkin, The Assignment Problem, in [70], pp. 109–125.

43. W. W. Jacobs, The Caterer Problem, *Naval Res. Logist. Quart.*, vol. 1, pp. 154–165, 1954; J. W. Gaddum, A. J. Hoffman, and D. Sokolowsky, On the Solution of the Caterer Problem, *ibid.*, pp. 223–229.

44. G. B. Dantzig, R. Fulkerson, and S. Johnson, Solution of a Large Scale Traveling Salesman Problem, *Operations Res.*, vol. 2, pp. 393–404, 1954.

45. L. Gainen, D. Honig, and E. D. Stanley, Linear Programming in Bid-evaluation, *Naval Res. Logist. Quart.*, vol. 1, pp. 48–54, 1954.

46. C. B. Tompkins, Notes on computational aspects of a problem in organizational theory formulated by J. Marshak (1952, unpublished).

47. L. G. Peck, On Uniform Distribution of Algebraic Numbers, *Proc. Amer. Math. Soc.*, vol. 4, pp. 440–443, 1953.

48. R. D. Richtmyer, "The Evaluation of Definite Integrals and a Quasi-Monte Carlo Method Based on the Properties of Algebraic Numbers," Los Alamos Scientific Laboratory Report LA1342, 1951–1952.

49. R. J. Seeger, On Computational Techniques for Certain Problems in Fluid Dynamics, in "Proceedings of a Symposium on Large-scale Digital Calculating Machinery," Annals of the Computation Laboratory of Harvard University, vol. 16, pp. 157–168, 1948.

50. J. Pasta and S. M. Ulam, "Heuristic Studies in Problems of Mathematical Physics on High Speed Computing Machines," Los Alamos Scientific Laboratory Report LA1557, 1953; Heuristic Numerical Work in Some Problems of Hydrodynamics, *Math. Tables Aids Comput.*, vol. 13, pp. 1–12, 1959.

51. N. Metropolis, Some Topics in Experimental Mathematics, in "Proceedings of Symposium . . . ," Argonne National Laboratory Report ANL5181, pp. 265–270, 1953.

52. A. M. Turing, The Chemical Basis of Morphogenesis, *Philos. Trans. Roy. Soc. London. Ser. B*, vol. 237, pp. 37–72, 1952.

53. R. FitzHugh and H. A. Antosiewicz, Automatic Computation of Nerve Excitation, *J. Soc. Indust. Appl. Math.*, vol. 7, pp. 447–458, 1959.

54. S. S. Cairns, Computational Attacks on Discrete Problems, *Amer. Math. Monthly*, vol. 61, no. 7, pt. II, pp. 29–31, 1954.

55. C. B. Tompkins, Machine Attacks on Problems Whose Variables Are Permutations, in [70], pp. 195–211.

55a. L. J. Paige and C. B. Tompkins, Systematic Generation of Permutations on an Automatic Computer and an Application to a Problem Concerning Finite Groups (1954, unpublished).

56. K. Goldberg, log $e^x e^y$ in a Free Associative Ring, *Bull. Amer. Math. Soc.*, vol. 60, pp. 332–333, 1954.

57. E. Lehmer, Number Theory on the SWAC, in [70], pp. 103–108.

58. K. Goldberg, A Table of Wilson Quotients and the Third Wilson Prime, *J. London Math. Soc.*, vol. 28, pp. 252–256, 1953.

59. O. Taussky, Some Computational Problems in Algebraic Number Theory, in [70], pp. 187–193; see also Chap. 8 below.

60. H. Cohn, Numerical Study of Signature Rank of Cyclic Cyclotomic Units, *Math. Tables Aids Comput.*, vol. 8, pp. 186–188, 1954.

60a. H. Cohn, Some Experiments in Ideal Factorization on the MIDAC, *J. Assoc. Comput. Mach.*, vol. 2, pp. 111–118, 1955.

61. A. M. Turing, Some Calculations of the Riemann Zeta-function, *Proc. London Math. Soc.*, ser. 3, vol. 3, pp. 99–117, 1953.

62. P. C. Rosenbloom, An Elementary Constructive Proof of the Fundamental Theorem of Algebra, *Amer. Math. Monthly*, vol. 52, pp. 562–570, 1945.

63. A. M. Turing, On Computable Numbers with an Application to the Entscheidungsproblem, *Proc. London Math. Soc.*, ser. 2, vol. 42, pp. 230–265, 1936, and vol. 43, pp. 544–546, 1937.

64. C. Shannon, Computers and Automata, *Proc. IRE*, vol. 41, pp. 1234–1241, 1953.

65. J. von Neumann, The General and Logical Theory of Automata, in L. A. Jeffries, ed., "Cerebral Mechanisms in Behavior," John Wiley and Sons, Inc., New York, 1951.

66. F. E. Grubbs, F. J. Murray, and J. J. Stoker, eds., "Transactions of the Symposium on Computing, Mechanics, Statistics and Partial Differential Equations," Interscience Publishers, Inc., New York, 1955.

67. A. S. Householder, G. E. Forsythe, and H. H. Germond, eds., "Monte Carlo Method," National Bureau of Standards Applied Mathematics Series, vol. 12, 1951.

68. H. A. Meyer, ed., "Symposium on Monte Carlo Methods," John Wiley & Sons, Inc., New York, 1956.

69. G. Birkhoff, K. O. Friedrichs, and T. E. Sterne, eds., "Transactions of the Symposium on Fluid Mechanics and Computing," Interscience Publishers, Inc., New York, 1954.

70. J. H. Curtiss, ed., "Numerical Analysis: Proceedings of Symposia in Applied Mathematics—Volume VI," McGraw-Hill Book Company, Inc., New York, 1956.

71. J. Todd, ed., "Experiments in the Computation of Conformal Maps," National Bureau of Standards Applied Mathematics Series, vol. 42, 1954.

72. L. J. Paige and O. Taussky, eds., "Simultaneous Linear Equations and the Determination of Eigenvalues," National Bureau of Standards Applied Mathematics Series, vol. 29, 1953.

73. O. Taussky, ed., "Contributions to the Solution of Systems of Linear Equations and the Determination of Eigenvalues," National Bureau of Standards Applied Mathematics Series, vol. 39, 1954.

74. H. W. Kuhn and A. W. Tucker, eds., "Contributions to the Theory of Games," I, II, Annals of Mathematics Studies, vols. 24, 28, Princeton University Press, Princeton, N.J., 1950, 1953.

75. M. Dresher, A. W. Tucker, and P. Wolfe, eds., "Contributions to the Theory of Games," III, Annals of Mathematics Studies, vol. 39, Princeton University Press, Princeton, N.J., 1957.

75a. R. D. Luce and A. W. Tucker, eds., "Contributions to the Theory of Games," IV, Annals of Mathematics Studies, vol. 40, Princeton University Press, Princeton, N.J., 1959.

76. J. Todd, On the Condition of Matrices, II, *Arch. Math.*, vol. 5, pp. 249–257, 1954.

77. J. Todd, The Condition of the Finite Segments of the Hilbert Matrix, in [73], pp. 109–116.

78. C.-E. Fröberg, On a Mathematical Model of a Photographic Emulsion, *Ark. Fys.*, vol. 7, pp. 497–502, 1954.

79. R. L. Bivins, N. Metropolis, P. R. Stein, and M. B. Wells, Characters of the Symmetric Groups of Degree 15 and 16, *Math. Tables Aids Comput.*, vol. 8, pp. 212–216, 1954.

80. G. E. Forsythe, SWAC Computes 126 Distinct Semi-groups of Order 4, *Proc. Amer. Math. Soc.*, vol. 6, pp. 443–447, 1955.

81. J. Todd, Experiments in the Solution of Differential Equations by Monte Carlo Methods, *J. Washington Acad. Sci.*, vol. 44, pp. 377–381, 1954.

82. J. Todd, Notes on Modern Numerical Analysis, I, *Math. Tables Aids Comput.*, vol. 4, pp. 39–44, 1950.

83. H. Rutishauser, Über die Instabilität von Methoden zur Integration gewöhnlichen Differentialgleichungen, *Z. Angew. Math. Phys.*, vol. 3, pp. 65–74, 1953.

84. J. Todd, A Direct Approach to the Problem of Stability in the Numerical Solution of Partial Differential Equations, *Comm. Pure Appl. Math.*, vol. 9, pp. 597–612, 1956.

85. R. Courant, K. Friedrichs, and H. Lewy, Über die partiellen Differenzengleichungen der mathematischen Physik, *Math. Ann.*, vol. 100, pp. 32–74, 1928.

86. G. G. O'Brien, M. A. Hyman, and S. Kaplan, A Study of the Numerical Solution of Partial Differential Equations, *J. Math. Phys.*, vol. 29, pp. 223–252, 1951.

87. H. D. Huskey, On the Precision of a Certain Process of Numerical Integration (with an appendix by D. R. Hartree), *J. Res. Nat. Bur. Standards*, vol. 42, pp. 57–62, 1949.

88. H. Rademacher, On the Accumulation of Error in Processes of Integration, in "Proceedings of Symposia on Large-scale Digital Calculating Machines," Annals of the Computation Laboratory of Harvard University, vol. 16, pp. 176–185, 1948.

89. M. Lotkin, The Propagation of Error in Numerical Integration, *Proc. Amer. Math. Soc.*, vol. 5, pp. 869–887, 1954.

90. M. Altman, "Approximation Methods in Functional Analysis," California Institute of Technology, Pasadena, Calif., 1959–1960.

91. D. H. Lehmer, On a Problem of Hardy and Littlewood, *J. London Math. Soc.*, vol. 34, pp. 395–396, 485, 1959.

92. J. H. Halton, On the Efficiency of Certain Quasi-random Sequences of Points in Evaluating Multi-dimensional Integrals, *Numer. Math.*, vol. 2, pp. 84–90, 1960.

93. E. O. A. Kreyszig and J. Todd, The Radius of Univalence of the Error Function, *Numer. Math.*, vol. 1, pp. 78–89, 1959; On the Radius of Univalence of the Function $\exp z^2 \int_0^z \exp(-t^2)\, dt$, *Pacific J. Math.*, vol. 9, pp. 123–127, 1959; The Radius of Univalence of Bessel Functions, I, *Illinois J. Math.*, vol. 4, pp. 143–149, 1960.

94. G. V. Kusmina, Numerical Determination of the Radius of Univalence of Analytic Functions, *Trudy Mat. Inst. Steklov.*, vol. 53, pp. 192–235, 1959 (in Russian).

95. M. Newman and J. Todd, The Evaluation of Matrix Inversion Programs, *J. Soc. Indust. Appl. Math.*, vol. 6, pp. 466–476, 1958.

96. L. Fox, "The Use and Construction of Mathematical Tables," National Physical Laboratory Mathematical Tables, vol. 1, 1956.

97. Z. Kopal, "Numerical Analysis," John Wiley & Sons, Inc., New York, 1955.

98. E. G. Belaga, Some Problems Involved in the Calculation of Polynomials, *Dokl. Akad. Nauk SSSR*, vol. 123, pp. 775–777, 1958 (in Russian).

99. M. Davis, "Computability and Unsolvability," McGraw-Hill Book Company, Inc., New York, 1958.

100. S. C. Kleene, "Introduction to Metamathematics," D. Van Nostrand Company, Inc., Princeton, N.J., 1952.

101. T. Kato, On the Hilbert Matrix, *Proc. Amer. Math. Soc.*, vol. 8, pp. 73–81, 1957; On Positive Eigenvectors of Positive Infinite Matrices, *Comm. Pure Appl. Math.*, vol. 11, pp. 573–586, 1958.

102. C. E. Shannon and J. McCarthy, eds., "Automata Studies," Annals of Mathematics Studies, vol. 34, Princeton University Press, Princeton, N.J., 1956.

103. A. S. Householder, "Principles of Numerical Analysis," McGraw-Hill Book Company, Inc., New York, 1953; the bibliography is continued in *J. Assoc. Comput. Mach.*, vol. 3, pp. 85–100, 1956.

104. C. B. Tompkins, Computation Using Kronecker Indices, *Notices Amer. Math. Soc.*, vol. 6, p. 163, 1959 (abstract).

105. H. Rodgers, Jr., The Present Theory of Turing Machine Computability, *J. Soc. Indust. Appl. Math.*, vol. 7, pp. 114–130, 1959.

106. E. Stiefel, Note on Jordan Elimination, Linear Programming and Tchebycheff Approximation, *Numer. Math.*, vol. 2, pp. 1–17, 1960.

107. S. Comét, Über die Anwendung von Binärmodellen in der Theorie der Charaktere der symmetrischen Gruppen, *Numer. Math.*, vol. 1, pp. 90–109, 1959.

108. R. D. Richtmyer, "Difference Methods for Initial-value Problems," Interscience Publishers, Inc., New York, 1957.

109. A. N. Lowan, "The Operator Approach to Problems of Stability and Convergence," Scripta Mathematica, New York, 1957.

110. R. E. Langer, ed., "On Numerical Approximation," University of Wisconsin Press, Madison, Wis., 1959.

111. M. Parodi, "La localisation des valeurs caractéristiques des matrices et ses applications," Gauthier-Villars, Paris, 1959.

112. P. Davis, On the Numerical Integration of Periodic Analytic Functions, in [110], pp. 45–59.

113. D. H. Lehmer, Combinatorial Problems with Digital Computers, in "Proceedings of the Fourth Canadian Congress," pp. 160–173, 1957.

114. D. H. Lehmer, Teaching Combinatorial Tricks to a Computer, in [115], pp. 179–193.

115. R. Bellman and M. Hall, Jr., eds., "Combinatorial Analysis: Proceedings of Symposia in Applied Mathematics"—Volume X, American Mathematical Society, Providence, R.I., 1960.

116. J. W. Carr, III, Digital Computer Programming, "Handbook of Automation, Computation, and Control," vol. 2, chap. 2, John Wiley & Sons, Inc., New York, 1959.

117. P. Henrici, A Unified Theory of Propagated Error and Numerical Stability for Some Methods of Integrating Ordinary Differential Equations, *Notices Amer. Math. Soc.*, vol. 5, p. 55, 1958 (abstract).

118. G. Dahlquist, Convergence and Stability in the Numerical Integration of Ordinary Differential Equations, *Math. Scand.*, vol. 4, pp. 33–53, 1956.

119. O. Taussky and J. Todd, Some Discrete Variable Computations, in [115], pp. 201–209.

120. J. M. Hammersley, Monte Carlo Methods for Solving Multivariable Problems, *Ann. New York Acad. Sci.*, vol. 86, pp. 844–874, 1960.

121. T. C. Koopmans, ed., "Activity Analysis of Production and Allocation," John Wiley & Sons, Inc., New York, 1951.

122. O. Taussky, Research Problem 12, *Bull. Amer. Math. Soc.*, Vol. 60, p. 290, 1954; A Remark Concerning the Characteristic Roots of the Finite Segments of the Hilbert Matrix, *Quart. J. Math. Oxford Ser.* (2), vol. 20, pp. 80–83, 1949. See also J. Todd, Computational Problems Concerning the Hilbert Matrix, *J. Res. Nat. Bur. Standards*, vol. 65 *B*, pp. 19–22, 1961.

2

Classical Numerical Analysis

JOHN TODD

PROFESSOR OF MATHEMATICS

CALIFORNIA INSTITUTE OF TECHNOLOGY

2.1 General Introduction

This chapter provides a survey of some of the techniques of classical numerical analysis, by which we mean, approximately, computing with desk machines. Even those who have the freest access to automatic computers and are most adept in their use find desk computers indispensable in various phases of numerical analysis—for instance, in pilot calculations, in checking, and in the preliminary (or final) analyses of results prepared by more powerful equipment. Further, a spell of many-decimal calculation on a desk machine is a helpful approach to the use of automatic computers, on which mistakes will be more costly, if less painful, than on desk equipment.

Ideally, this chapter should include methods appropriate for desk machines for handling all the various topics to which succeeding chapters are devoted. It is, however, restricted to the following topics: interpolation, quadrature and differentiation, ordinary differential equations, miscellaneous devices, and tables.

Although our main concern here is with desk computing, we do not hesitate to digress for elementary discussions of points in automatic computation where this seems advisable.

This chapter should be read with a desk calculator and various standard tables at hand. The reader can easily vary the worked examples to provide exercises which can be checked by reference to standard tables. This will, in addition, induce an acquaintance with tables. Among the particularly suitable tables are the tables of Bessel functions (BAAS 6, 10) and those of the Airy integral (BAAS 12) which were prepared by the Mathematical Tables Committee of the British Association for the Advancement of Science. There is much valuable advice in the introductions to other standard tables, some of which are mentioned in Secs. 2.37 to 2.42; references such as BAAS 12 are explained in these sections.

A convenient collection of tables and formulas is "Interpolation and Allied Tables," H.M. Stationery Office, London, 1956. We shall refer to this as IAT.

The material in this chapter is covered in detail in many well-known textbooks, some of which are listed in Sec. 2.43. We refer to some of these for amplification of our account at various points.

INTERPOLATION

2.2 Introduction

It is not often that one finds the exact information one requires directly in a table; it is usually necessary to interpolate, or to read between the lines. Whether one can do this at all and, in case one can, the accuracy of the interpolation process depends on the "regularity," or "smoothness," of the function under consideration, near the point in question. The meaning of the words in quotation marks is indicated by the form of the error estimates given below.

Consider, for instance, the following table:

x	5	10	15	20	25	30	35	40	45	50	55	...
$f(x)$	5	5	5	5	5	5	7	5	5	5	11	...

This is of no great help in determining $f(x)$ for other (integral) values of x. (This is a table of the greatest prime factor of x.) On the other hand, a table like

x	0	1	2	3	4	5	...
$g(x)$	0	3	12	27	49	76	...

lends itself to interpolation for any value of x when we notice the comparative regularity of the growth of $g(x)$. (This is a table of the integral part of $10^4 \sin^2 x°$.)

2.3 Special Methods

We begin with an account of processes in which some use is made of the particular form of the function—for instance, an addition theorem it satisfies, or its power series expansion. We give several examples.

To compute exp 1.23456 to 6D (6 decimal places) having a 6D table of exp x at an interval of .001 in x, we can proceed as follows:

$$\exp 1.23456 = \exp 1.234 \times \exp .00056$$
$$\doteqdot 3.434942(1 + .00056)$$
$$\doteqdot 3.436866$$

or, as a check, $\exp 1.23456 = \exp 1.235 \times \exp -.00044$
$$\doteqdot 3.438379(1 - .00044)$$
$$\doteqdot 3.436866.$$

Here and elsewhere we use the symbol $\doteqdot$ to indicate approximate equality in a loose sense.   It is possible to give rigorous error estimates in this case, but this is rather exceptional.   The first use of $\doteqdot$ covers the error in the tabular value of exp 1.234 and the error caused by the truncation of the exponential series, replacing e^x by $1 + x$.   The second use of $\doteqdot$ covers the rounding off of the product.   It is clear that the relative error is at most about $\frac{1}{2}(\frac{1}{2} \cdot 10^{-3})^2$, if we compute from the nearer tabular value.

On the whole, we shall simply use the equality sign, where the symbol $\doteqdot$ would be proper, and use the latter for emphasis.

Similarly, we can interpolate in trigonometrical tables using the approximations

$$\sin (x + y) \doteqdot (1 - \tfrac{1}{2} y^2) \sin x + y \cos x$$
$$\cos (x + y) \doteqdot (1 - \tfrac{1}{2} y^2) \cos x - y \sin x$$

when y is small.   Checking can be done as in the preceding case, or, if both functions are needed, we can use

$$\sin^2 \theta + \cos^2 \theta = 1.$$

A word of warning is, however, necessary in the latter case.   This check is not efficient when $\sin \theta$ is near 0 or 1 (see Stegun and Abramowitz [1]).

We can also handle the inverse trigonometrical functions in a similar way.   Consider arctan x.   We have

$$\arctan (x + ph) = \arctan x + \arctan A$$
$$= \arctan x + A - \tfrac{1}{3}A^3 + \ldots, \qquad |A| \le 1,$$

where $A = ph/[1 + x(x + ph)]$.   The first two terms on the right suffice to give 6D accuracy when $h = .01$, $|p| \le 1$.   For instance,

$$\arctan .1234 = \arctan (.12 + .0034)$$
$$= .119429 + .0034/[1 + .12 (.1234)]$$
$$= .122779$$

and, as a check,

$$\text{arctan } .1234 = \text{arctan } (.13 - .0066)$$
$$= .129275 - .0066/[1 + .13 \, (.1234)]$$
$$= .122779.$$

2.4 Recurrence Relations

Another method of interpolation is the use of recurrence relations.   It is known, for instance, that for $N > 0$ and for suitable values of x_0, the sequence defined for $n = 0, 1, 2, \dots$ by

$$x_{n+1} = \tfrac{1}{2}(x_n + Nx_n^{-1}) \qquad (2.1)$$

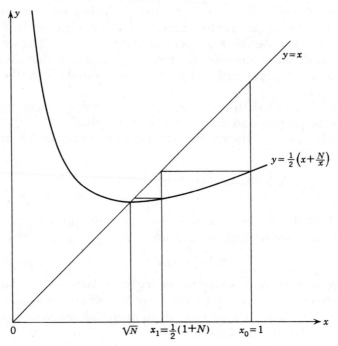

$$y = x$$

$$y = \tfrac{1}{2}\left(x + \tfrac{N}{x}\right)$$

$$0 \qquad \sqrt{N} \quad x_1 = \tfrac{1}{2}(1+N) \qquad x_0 = 1$$

Fig. 2.1   Quadratic convergence to $\sqrt{N}$.

converges to $N^{1/2}$. The convergence is illustrated graphically in the case $x_0 = 1$, $N = .25$ in Fig. 2.1.   Arithmetically we observe that

$$x_{n+1} - N^{1/2} = \tfrac{1}{2}(x_n - N^{1/2})^2 x_n^{-1},$$

which shows that $0 < x_n$ implies $x_{n+1} > N^{1/2}$. Hence, if we choose $x_0 > 0$, we have $x_n > N^{1/2}$ for all $n > 0$. Again, since

$$x_{n+1} - x_n = \tfrac{1}{2}(N - x_n^2)x_n^{-1} < 0,$$

it follows that the sequence $\{x_n\}$ is a monotone decreasing sequence, and since it is bounded below (e.g., by $N^{1/2}$), it has a limit, say l.   Clearly, $l \geq N^{1/2} > 0$.   Passage to the limit in (2.1) gives

$$l = \tfrac{1}{2}(l + Nl^{-1}),$$

so that $l^2 = N$, $l = N^{1/2}$.

The convergence in this case is rapid.   If we write $\epsilon_n = x_n - N^{1/2}$, then $\epsilon_{n+1} = \tfrac{1}{2}\epsilon_n^2 x_n^{-1} = O(\epsilon_n^2)$; in this circumstance the convergence is said to be *quadratic*, and the number of correct decimal places in x_n is about doubled at each iteration.   See Milne-Thomson [2].   In the example chosen, the sequence of approximations is

$$1, \quad .625, \quad .5125, \quad .500152, \quad .500000, \quad \dots$$

If, instead of (2.1), we take

$$x_{n+1} = x_n + \tfrac{1}{2}(N - x_n^2), \tag{2.1'}$$

we can establish that $x_n \uparrow N^{1/2}$, when $0 \leq N \leq 1$, $x_0 = 0$.   We note that the convergence in this case is *linear*:

$$\epsilon_{n+1} = \epsilon_n[1 - \tfrac{1}{2}(N^{1/2} + x_n)].$$

The slowness of the convergence in the case $N = .25$, $x_0 = 0$ is evident from the following sequence of approximations:

$$0, \quad .125, \quad .242188, \quad \dots$$

For $N > 0$ and for suitable x_0, the sequence

$$x_{n+1} = x_n(2 - Nx_n) \tag{2.2}$$

converges *quadratically* to N^{-1} (see Fig. 2.2).   If we take $N = \tfrac{1}{2}, x_0 = 1$, the successive approximations to $N^{-1} = 2$ are

$$1, \quad 1.5, \quad 1.875, \quad 1.992188, \quad 1.999969, \quad 2.000000, \quad \dots$$

If, instead of (2.2), we take

$$x_{n+1} = (1 - N)x_n + 1, \tag{2.2'}$$

we can establish *linear* convergence of x_n to N^{-1}; in fact, $\epsilon_{n+1} = (1 - N)\epsilon_n$ (see Fig. 2.3).   The corresponding approximations are

$$1, \quad 1.5, \quad 1.75, \quad 1.875, \quad \dots$$

The relation (2.2) is the special case $p = 1$ of the recurrence relation

$$x_{n+1} = x_n(p + 1 - Nx_n^p)/p. \tag{2.3}$$

For suitable x_0, N, we have

$$x_n \to N^{-1/p}.$$

These methods are used frequently in automatic computation, and we shall elaborate a little on them.

We first note that each of the relations (2.1), (2.2), and (2.3) is a special case of the Newton-Raphson method.   A modern account of this process is given in Chap. 14.   Here we note the formula

$$x_{n+1} = x_n - f(x_n)/f'(x_n), \qquad (2.4)$$

which is readily motivated geometrically.   For certain f and for suitable x_0, the sequence x_n converges to a zero of f.   We obtain (2.1), (2.2),

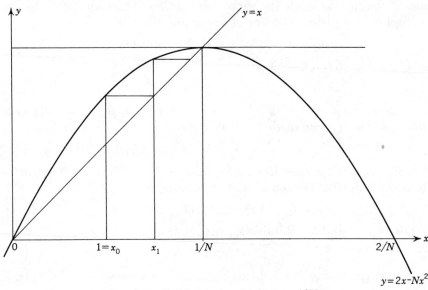

FIG. 2.2   Quadratic convergence to $1/N$.

and (2.3) by taking $f(x) = N - x^2$, $f(x) = N - x^{-1}$, $f(x) = N - x^{-p}$, respectively.

We next note that there can be more than one recurrence relation, with a given order of convergence, for a particular function.   In addition to (2.1), we have

$$y_{n+1} = 2y_n^3/(3y_n^2 - N) \qquad (2.5)$$

and

$$z_{n+1} = z_n(3N - z_n^2)/2N, \qquad (2.6)$$

which converge quadratically to $N^{1/2}$, for suitable initial values.   We can get (2.5) from (2.4) by taking $f(x) = x^3 - Nx$.

The recurrence relation (due to R. Dedekind)

$$x_{n+1} = \frac{x_n^3 + 3Nx_n}{3x_n^2 + N} \qquad (2.7)$$

can be shown to have cubic convergence to $N^{1/2}$.

The relation

$$x_{n+1} = x_n[3(1 - Nx_n) + (Nx_n)^2] \qquad (2.8)$$

has cubic convergence to N^{-1}. The study of this is instructive; convergence takes place when $0 < x_0 < 2N^{-1}$.

In some of the earlier automatic computers there was no division instruction, and the operation of division had to be programmed as a subroutine; a convenient method was the use of a relation such as (2.2) or

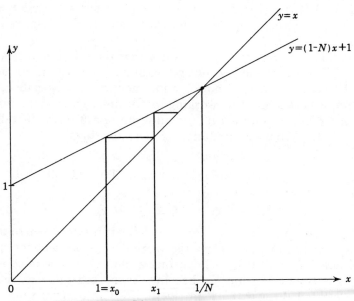

FIG. 2.3   Linear convergence to $1/N$.

(2.8).   Similarly, the relations (2.1), (2.5), and (2.6) could be used to produce square roots; for machines without division (2.6) is particularly convenient.   In practice, quadratically convergent sequences are usually sufficient.

Among the other recurrence relations of interest is the arithmetic geometric relation of Gauss:

If positive x_0, y_0 *are given,* $x_{n+1} = \frac{1}{2}(x_n + y_n)$, $y_{n+1} = \sqrt{x_n y_n}$, *then* $\lim x_n$ *and* $\lim y_n$ *exist and are equal. In particular, if* $x_0 = 1, 0 \leq y_0 \leq 1$, *then*

$$\lim x_n = \lim y_n = \pi/[2K'(y_0)]$$

where
$$K'(k) = \int_0^1 \{(1 - x^2)(1 - (1 - k^2))\}^{-\frac{1}{2}}\, dx.$$

An elaborate discussion of other relations of this form has been given by King [3].

There are similar relations which can be used to generate the elementary transcendental functions (see Hurwitz [4]). Another result, due to Borchardt, is as follows:

If positive x_0, y_0 are given, $x_{n+1} = \frac{1}{2}(x_n + y_n)$, $y_{n+1} = \sqrt{x_{n+1}y_n}$, then $\lim x_n$ and $\lim y_n$ exist and are equal. In particular, if $x_0 = \cos\theta$, $y_0 = 1$, then

$$\lim x_n = \lim y_n = (\sin\theta)/\theta.$$

We note that the convergence proof given above for the sequence defined by (2.1) is academic. In practice (whether with desk machines or automatic computers), we cannot have an infinite descent $x_0 > x_1 > x_2 > \cdots \to N^{1/2}$.

Let us take a simple example to show that the relation $x_0 > x_1$ may be false. The exact method of application of the algorithm and the precise behavior of the computing equipment must be specified. For simplicity, we use a machine working to 2 decimal digits, with multiplication and division rounded by the addition of a 5 to the first digit to be discarded. We use the relation (2.1) in the form

$$x_1 = .50x_0 + .50(N \div x_0).$$

With $N = .01$, $x_0 = .11$, we get $N \div x_0 = .09$ and $.50 \times .11 = .06$; then $.50 \times .09 = .05$, and

$$x_1 = .05 + .06 = .11 = x_0.$$

The full examination of (2.1) is a very delicate matter, even in the case of fixed-point computers. For a thorough discussion, see Householder [5] or Goldstine et al. [6]. The examination in the case of computers with floating-point arithmetic becomes more complicated and was recently carried through by Rumsey [67]. The natural time to stop would be when the sequence $x_0 > x_1 > \cdots$ becomes stationary or turns back, and with an efficient algorithm (and machine) one would expect to obtain at this stage the best possible result. That is to say, if r is the number alleged by the computer to be $N^{1/2}$, then r is the result of rounding $N^{1/2}$ to fit the machine.

That care should be taken in the details of the algorithm is shown by the following example, which we give, for simplicity, in an academic form. Let us suppose we have decided that the first x_n for which $x_n \geq x_{n-1}$ is the approximate square root. Then, if $N = -\frac{1}{2}$ and $x_0 = 1$, we obtain successively

$$1, \quad \frac{1}{4}, \quad -\frac{7}{8}, \quad -\frac{17}{112}, \quad \cdots,$$

and we thus obtain

$$\sqrt{-\frac{1}{2}} = -\frac{17}{112}.$$

Thus any program for evaluating square roots should include an initial check that $N \geq 0$. The omission of such a check is not likely to be serious if one is simply evaluating square roots, for one is not likely to ask for the square root of a negative number; but in more realistic problems, when one is using the program as a subroutine, to evaluate the square root of a calculated quantity which is never displayed, failure to check can cause havoc.

We note, finally, that the scalar recurrence relations discussed in this section can be applied in more general situations, when the real number N is replaced by a matrix or an operator. The use of these generalizations to find (or to improve) an approximate inverse of a matrix or an operator is discussed in Chaps. 6 and 14.

2.5 Reduced Derivatives

A very natural way to interpolate is to use Taylor's series.   If

$$f(a + h) = f(a) + hf'(a) + \frac{h^2}{2!}f''(a) + \cdots, \qquad (2.9)$$

then, if we know $f(a)$ and its successive derivatives $f'(a), f''(a), \ldots$, it will be easy to compute $f(a + h)$ for small h.   For instance, if $f(x) = \sin x$, we have

x	f	f'	f''	f'''
.4	.3894	.9210	$-.3894$	$-.9210$
.5	.4794	.8776	$-.4794$	$-.8776$

and we can find sin .4321 as follows:

$$\sin .4321 = \sin (.4 + .0321) = .3894 + (.0321)(.9210)$$
$$+ \tfrac{1}{2}(.0321)^2(-.3894) + \tfrac{1}{6}(.0321)^3(-.9210) + \cdots = .4188.$$

We can check this value by writing $\sin .4321 = \sin (.5 - .0679)$ and proceeding as before.

In practice, however, it is usual not to tabulate the successive derivatives $f^{(n)}(x)$ themselves but rather the *reduced* derivatives $\tau^n = h^n f^{(n)}(x)/n!$, at an appropriate interval h.   The table above would now appear as

x	f	τ	τ^2	τ^3
.4	.3894	921	-19	-2
.5	.4794	878	-24	1

A table in this form is especially convenient when not only f but also f' is likely to be needed.   For, if we take (2.9) in the form

$$f(a + \theta h) = f(a) + \theta h f'(a) + (\theta^2 h^2/2!)f''(a) + \cdots$$

and differentiate this, we get

$$hf'(a + \theta h) = hf'(a) + 2\theta \frac{1}{2!} h^2 f''(a) + 3\theta^2 \frac{1}{3!} h^3 f'''(a) + \cdots$$

$$= \tau + 2\theta\tau^2 + 3\theta^2\tau^3 + \cdots .$$

For worked examples, we refer to the introductions to standard tables (BAAS 12, NBSAMS 17).

2.6 Lagrangian Methods

In the cases discussed so far we have made use of special properties of the function $f(x)$ under consideration.   We now discuss the Lagrangian method, in which no special properties of $f(x)$ are used.   The basic idea is to obtain a good approximation $L(x)$ for $f(x)$ in terms of simple functions, in particular polynomials, and to evaluate $f(\xi)$ approximately as $L(\xi)$.   The method is founded on the following result from elementary algebra:

There is a unique polynomial of degree n assuming n + 1 arbitrary values f_i at any $(n + 1)$ distinct points $x_0, x_1, \ldots, x_n$.   This polynomial is

$$L_n(x) = L_n(f,x) = \sum_{i=0}^{n} f_i l_i^{(n)}(x)$$

where $l_i^{(n)}(x) = l_i(x) = \prod' [(x - x_j)/(x_i - x_j)]$

and the product is over all $j = 0, 1, \ldots, n; j \neq i$.

The existence of an interpolating polynomial can be shown using the nonvanishing of the Vandermondian.   For simplicity, let us discuss the case $n = 3$, the 4-point case.   We change the notation and ask for the existence of a cubic $\alpha x^3 + \beta x^2 + \gamma x + \delta$ which assumes the values A, B, C, D at distinct points a, b, c, d.   This assumption requires

$$A = \alpha a^3 + \beta a^2 + \gamma a + \delta$$
$$B = \alpha b^3 + \beta b^2 + \gamma b + \delta$$
$$C = \alpha c^3 + \beta c^2 + \gamma c + \delta$$
$$D = \alpha d^3 + \beta d^2 + \gamma d + \delta.$$

This is a set of linear equations for $\alpha, \beta, \gamma, \delta$ which can be solved uniquely, since the determinant of the system is a Vandermondian which does not vanish, a, b, c, d being assumed distinct.   This establishes the existence of an interpolating cubic.   That it is unique follows essentially from the fundamental theorem of algebra, for, if there were two, their difference would be a polynomial of degree 3 at most, which would vanish at a, b, c, d.

It is clear that the $\alpha, \beta, \gamma, \delta$ are linear functions of A, B, C, D, and the same is true for the interpolating cubic $\alpha x^3 + \beta x^2 + \gamma x + \delta$, which we can therefore write as

$$A\mathscr{A}(x) + B\mathscr{B}(x) + C\mathscr{C}(x) + D\mathscr{D}(x),$$

where the polynomials $\mathscr{A}$, $\mathscr{B}$, $\mathscr{C}$, $\mathscr{D}$ are cubics. This shows that tables of $\mathscr{A}$, $\mathscr{B}$, $\mathscr{C}$, $\mathscr{D}$ would greatly facilitate interpolation in tables of any function which allows 4-point interpolation. It is clearly not possible to contemplate tables covering arbitrary a, b, c, d, but the problem becomes practicable if we restrict ourselves to the case when $a - b = b - c = c - d = l$, particularly if we notice that we can assume that $l = -1$ and $a = -1, b = 0, c = 1, d = 2$. Using p as the nondimensional variable, we see that

$$\mathscr{A}(p) = L_{-1}(p) = -p(p - 1)(p - 2)/6$$

$$\mathscr{B}(p) = L_0(p) = (p + 1)(p - 1)(p - 2)/2$$

$$\mathscr{C}(p) = L_1(p) = -(p + 1)p(p - 2)/2$$

$$\mathscr{D}(p) = L_2(p) = (p + 1)p(p - 1)/6.$$

The general case of $(n + 1)$-point interpolation can be treated similarly. However, the result can be established directly by observing that $l_i(x_j) = \delta_{ij}$, so that

$$L_n(f, x_j) = \sum f_i \delta_{ij} = f_j, \qquad j = 0, 1, \ldots, n.$$

The uniqueness follows by the argument used above. We note that, for all x, $\sum l_i(x) = 1$.

The question of the error in interpolation by the Lagrangian formula is significant only when we are given some information about the general behavior of the function. The usual remainder formula is

$$f(x) - L_n(f, x) = \frac{f^{(n+1)}(\xi)}{(n + 1)!} \prod_{i=0}^{n} (x - x_i) \tag{2.10}$$

where f is assumed to have an $(n + 1)$st derivative in an interval including x, x_0, x_1, $\ldots$, x_n and where $\xi = \xi(x)$ is a point in this interval. Note that we do not assume that the nodes x_0, x_1, $\ldots$, x_n are equally spaced. The idea of the proof of this result is fully illustrated by the linear case, which we shall now discuss.

Linear interpolation between a and $b = a + h$ gives, for $f(a + ph)$, $0 \le p \le 1$,

$$f(a + ph) \doteqdot f(a) + p[f(b) - f(a)].$$

We shall show that

$$f(a + ph) - \{f(a) + p[f(b) - f(a)]\} = \tfrac{1}{2}h^2 f''(\xi)p(p - 1).$$

To do this we consider

$$F(p) \equiv f(a + ph) - \{f(a) + p[f(b) - f(a)]\} - Kp(p - 1).$$

We first choose any p_0, $p_0 \neq 0$, $p_0 \neq 1$, and then choose $K = K(p_0)$ so that $F(p_0) = 0$. Then $F(p)$ has three zeros in $[0,1]$: 0, 1, p_0. Hence $F''(\theta) = 0$, $0 \leq \theta \leq 1$. This means

$$h^2 f''(a + \theta h) = 2K,$$

so that

$$f(a + p_0 h) = f(a) + p_0[f(b) - f(a)] + \tfrac{1}{2}h^2(p_0{}^2 - p_0)f''(\xi),$$

where $\xi = a + \theta h$ depends on p_0 through θ. We can now drop the subscript and write

$$f(a + ph) - \{f(a) + p[f(b) - f(a)]\} = \tfrac{1}{2}f''(\xi)[h^2(p^2 - p)],$$

which is of the form (2.10).

If we restrict our attention to the case of equally spaced nodes, say $x_i = a + ih$, $i = 0, 1, \ldots, n$, and consider the error at $x = a + ph$, then (2.10) can be written in the convenient form

$$f(x) - L_n(f,x) = \binom{p}{n+1} h^{(n+1)} f^{(n+1)}(\xi). \tag{2.10'}$$

We shall now discuss these error estimates briefly and academically; we return in Sec. 2.10 to a more practical account. In the linear case we note that for interpolation proper we have $0 \leq p \leq 1$, and so $0 \leq (p - p^2) \leq \tfrac{1}{4}$. Hence

$$f(x) - L_1(x) = -\tfrac{1}{8}\theta h^2 f''(\xi) \tag{2.11}$$

for some θ, $0 \leq \theta \leq 1$.

This means that the maximum error in linear interpolation in a table of $\sin x$, at an interval of .02 radian, is $\tfrac{1}{8}(.02)^2 = \tfrac{1}{2} \cdot 10^{-4}$, so that this method is appropriate for a table to 4D. To see how realistic this estimate is, we consider the evaluation of $\sin .3367$, given

$$\sin .32 = .314567, \qquad \sin .34 = .333487.$$

Linear interpolation gives .330359, whereas the correct 6D value is .330374.

As another application of (2.11), let us determine a range of x for which linear interpolation in a 6D table of $\tan x$ at an interval of .001 radian is appropriate. We have $\tfrac{1}{8}h^2(\tan x)'' = \tfrac{1}{8}(10^{-6}) \cdot 2 \sin x \sec^3 x$. As x increases from 0 to $\tfrac{1}{2}\pi$, $\sin x$ and $\sec x$ both increase, and so the whole error estimate increases. Equating the error estimate to $\tfrac{1}{2} \cdot 10^{-6}$, we see that $\sin x \sec^3 x = 2$, which gives $x = \tfrac{1}{4}\pi$. Linear interpolation is therefore appropriate in the interval $0 \leq x \leq \tfrac{1}{4}\pi$.

The results which correspond to (2.11) in nonlinear cases can be obtained by examining the behavior of $\Pi(x - x_i)$ as x varies. For simplicity we consider the 4-point equally spaced case. We have then to consider the behavior of $(p + 1)p(p - 1)(p - 2)$. This vanishes at $p = -1, 0, 1, 2$ and has minima at $\frac{1}{2}(1 \pm \sqrt{5})$ and a maximum at $\frac{1}{2}$. The extreme values are $-1, -1$, and $\frac{9}{16}$. Thus we have, writing $M = \max |f^{(4)}(x)|$,

$$|f(x) - L_3(x)| \leq \frac{9}{16} \cdot \frac{h^4}{4!} M \qquad \text{if} \quad 0 \leq x \leq h$$

(2.12)

$$|f(x) - L_3(x)| \leq 1 \cdot \frac{h^4}{4!} M \qquad \text{if} \quad -h \leq x \leq 0, \quad h \leq x \leq 2h.$$

The smaller estimate for the central interval is in agreement with our intuition.

These mean that the maximum error in 4-point interpolation in a table of $\sin x$, at an interval of .1 radian, is about 2×10^{-6} in the central interval and about twice that in the outer intervals. As an example, let us find $\sin .123$, given

$$\sin 0 = 0, \qquad \sin .1 = .099833, \qquad \sin .2 = .198669, \qquad \sin .3 = .295520.$$

The appropriate coefficients, which can be obtained from tables (or from the explicit expressions given above), are

$$-.0522445, \quad .8381835, \quad .2503665, \quad -.0363055.$$

We find $\sin .123 = .122689$—the correct value is $.122690$.

For the general results corresponding to (2.11) and (2.12) see the introduction to NBSCUP 4.

An elegant and practical method for reducing an $(n + 1)$-point interpolation to a sequence of $\frac{1}{2}n(n + 1)$ linear interpolations has been given by Aitken. It is convenient for both desk calculators and automatic computers. We describe the 4-point case for simplicity.

Given $f(a) = A, f(b) = B, f(c) = C, f(d) = D$, we show how to find $f(p)$. Interpolate linearly between (a,A), (b,B) to find (p,B_1); then interpolate linearly between (a,A), (c,C) to find (p,C_1) and then between (a,A), (d,D) to find (p,D_1). The next stage is to interpolate linearly between (b,B_1), (c,C_1) to find (p,C_2) and then between (b,B_1), (d,D_1) to find (p,D_2). Finally, interpolate linearly between (c,C_2) and (d,D_2) to find (p,P).

The scheme is illustrated graphically in Fig. 2.4. We note that there is no assumption that the a, b, c, d are equally spaced, and so the method can be applied to the case of inverse interpolation.

We give, without comment, two examples which show how the scheme can be carried out and how labor can be saved by dropping common initial figures. Many extensions of the method have been given by Aitken and Neville.

Given $f(1) = 1, f(2) = 125, f(3) = 729, f(4) = 2197$, find $f(2.5)$.

$1 = a$	$1 = A$			
$2 = b$	$125 = B$	$187 = B_1$		
$3 = c$	$729 = C$	$547 = C_1$	$367 = C_2$	
$4 = d$	$2197 = D$	$1099 = D_1$	$415 = D_2$	$343 = P.$

Here $f(x) = (4x - 3)^3$ and the interpolation is exact, as it should be.

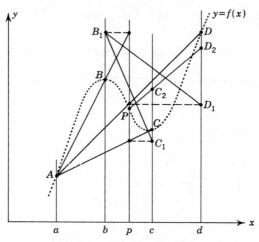

FIG. 2.4   Aitken's algorithm.

Given $f(0) = 47.434165$, $f(1) = 47.539457$, $f(2) = 47.644517$, $f(3) = 47.749346$, find $f(1.4321)$.

0	47.434165				-1.4321
1	.539457	.584954			$- .4321$
2	.644517	682	837		$+ .5689$
3	.749346	517	60	24	$+1.5689$

We find $f(1.4321) = 47.584824$, which agrees with the fact that

$$f(x) = \sqrt{2250 + 10x}.$$

We shall now show generally that the Aitken algorithm leads to the Lagrangian interpolant. We follow a proof of Feller. We want to evaluate $f(p)$, where f is a polynomial of degree n determined by its values at the distinct points $x_0, x_1, \ldots, x_n$. Consider

$$f^{(1)}(x) = \frac{\begin{vmatrix} f(x_0) & x_0 - p \\ f(x) & x - p \end{vmatrix}}{x - x_0}, \qquad x \neq x_0.$$

We observe that $f^{(1)}(x)$ is a polynomial of degree $n - 1$ and that $f^{(1)}(p)$ $= f(p)$.   Hence our problem is equivalent to that of evaluating $f^{(1)}(p)$, where $f^{(1)}$ is determined by its values at $x_1, x_2, \ldots, x_n$.   Repetition of this process according to the scheme

$$
\begin{array}{llll}
x_0 & f(x_0) \\
x_1 & f(x_1) & f^{(1)}(x_1) \\
x_2 & f(x_2) & f^{(1)}(x_2) & f^{(2)}(x_2) \\
\cdot & \cdot & \cdot & \cdot \\
\cdot & \cdot & \cdot & \cdot \\
\cdot & \cdot & \cdot & \cdot \\
x_n & f(x_n) & f^{(1)}(x_n) & f^{(2)}(x_n) \cdots f^{(n)}(x_n) = f(p)
\end{array}
$$

leads to the determination of $f(p)$.

It has been necessary so far to insist on the nodes $x_0, x_1, \ldots, x_n$ being distinct.   It is possible to develop interpolation formulas with coincident nodes: for instance, if x_0 and x_1 coincide, we consider polynomials which have not only an assigned value but an assigned derivative at the double node.   The extreme case occurs when all the nodes coincide at x_0 and we obtain a (finite) Taylor expansion for a polynomial, which, together with its derivatives, has assigned values at x_0.   The most useful case is the hermitian one, when the nodes are all double; an up-to-date discussion of various aspects of this method of osculatory interpolation has been given by Salzer.

A counting argument shows that we may expect to be able to find a unique polynomial $H_{2n+1}(x)$ of degree $2n + 1$ which has assigned values and assigned derivatives at $n + 1$ distinct points $x_0, x_1, \ldots, x_n$.   It is reasonable to expect that, if the assigned values are $f(x_i)$ and $f'(x_i)$ where $f(x)$ is differentiable $2n + 2$ times, then $|H_{2n+1}(f, x) - f(x)|$ is bounded by a multiple of max $|f^{(2n+2)}(x)|$.   All this can be established without the introduction of any new ideas.   Indeed, with the earlier notation,

$$
H_{2n+1}(x) = \sum_{i=0}^{n} [l_i(x)]^2 [1 - 2l_i'(x_i)(x - x_i)] f(x_i) + \sum_{i=0}^{n} [l_i(x)]^2 (x - x_i) f'(x_i)
$$

and $f(x) - H_{2n+1}(x) = f^{(2n+2)}(\xi) \left[\prod_{i=0}^{n} (x - x_i) \right]^2 / (2n + 2)!,$

where $\xi = \xi(x)$ lies in the interval containing $x, x_0, x_1, \ldots, x_n$.

Examples showing the power of this method can easily be constructed. It is particularly appropriate in cases where both f and f' are tabulated alongside each other.   For instance, many tables give $\sin x$ and $\cos x$, $J_0(x)$ and $J_1(x) = -J_0'(x)$, and exp $(-\tfrac{1}{2}x^2)$ and $\int_0^x \exp(-\tfrac{1}{2}t^2)\, dt$ together.

We note that, although the representations of the Lagrangian and hermitian interpolants are valid when the nodes are complex, the error estimates given no longer hold.   This is essentially due to the fact that the usual mean-value theorems are not valid in the complex plane. [For instance, if $f(z) = e^z$, then $f(0) = f(2\pi i) = 1$, but $f'(z) = e^z$ is never zero.]

Suitable estimates can be easily obtained using Cauchy's theorem making use of the following representation of the remainder:

If $\mathscr{C}$ is a rectifiable closed curve, if $f(z)$ is regular in $\mathscr{D}$, the interior of $\mathscr{C}$, and continuous on $\mathscr{C} + \mathscr{D}$, and if x and the distinct points $a_0, a_1, \ldots, a_n$ be in $\mathscr{D}$, then

$$f(x) - L_n(f,x) = \frac{1}{2\pi i} \int_{\mathscr{C}} \frac{f(z) \prod (x - a_i)}{(z - x) \prod (z - a_i)} \, dz, \quad x \neq a_i, i = 0, 1, \ldots, n.$$

There is a simple modification of this available in the case when $f(z)$ is allowed to have a finite set of poles in $\mathscr{D}$.

This representation is useful even when the a_i are real.   The presence of singularities of $f(z)$ off the real axis can affect the efficiency of the approximation of $f(x)$ by $L_n(f,x)$ on the real axis.   This point is elaborated in Chap. 3, where we discuss the Runge example.

2.7 Finite-difference Methods

The calculus of finite differences is a basic tool in numerical analysis. A certain acquaintance with it is convenient in the description and explanation of the many processes of interpolation which involve differences.

The formation of a table of successive differences of a function (tabulated at equal intervals in the argument) is indicated below in the case of a table of cubes.   The notation is as follows.   If we write

x	$f(x)$	Δf	$\Delta^2 f$	$\Delta^3 f$	$\Delta^4 f$
1	1				
		7			
2	8		12		
		19		6	
3	27		18		0
		37		6	
4	64		24		0
		61		6	
5	125		30		0
		91		6	
6	216		36		0
		127		6	
7	343		42		0
		169		6	
8	512		48		0
		217		6	
9	729		54		
		271			
10	1000				

$f(n) = f_n = F(a + nh)$, then we define $\Delta^r F = \Delta_n{}^r F$ to be $\Delta^r f$ where

$$\Delta f(n) = f(n + 1) - f(n), \qquad \Delta^r f(n) = \Delta \, \Delta^{r-1} f(n), \qquad r > 1.$$

This gives

$$\Delta^2 f(n) = \Delta \, \Delta f(n) = [f(n + 2) - f(n + 1)] - [f(n + 1) - f(n)]$$
$$= f(n + 2) - 2f(n + 1) + f(n).$$

We find, using the standard notation for binomial coefficients,

$$\Delta^r f(n) = f(n + r) - \binom{r}{1} f(n + r - 1) + \binom{r}{2} f(n + r - 2)$$
$$+ \cdots + (-1)^{r-1} \binom{r}{1} f(n + 1) + (-1)^r f(n).$$

This table illustrates the following fundamental fact:

The nth differences (at any constant interval) of a polynomial of degree n are constant, and all succeeding differences vanish.

This is readily established by noting that the operation of differencing reduces the degree of a polynomial by unity:

$$\Delta \left(\sum_{r=0}^{n} a_r x^r \right) = \sum_{r=0}^{n} a_r \Delta x^r$$
$$= \sum_{r=0}^{n} a_r [(x + h)^r - x^r]$$
$$= \sum_{r=0}^{n} a_r (rhx^{r-1} + \cdots) = \sum_{r=0}^{n-1} b_r x^r.$$

It is only rarely in practice that we have to deal with exact poly-nomials. The effect of rounding off in a difference table is shown by the following table of $.1x^3$ rounded to the nearest integer.

x	$f(x)$	Δf	$\Delta^2 f$	$\Delta^3 f$	$\Delta^4 f$
1	0				
		1			
2	1		1		
		2		0	
3	3		1		2
		3		2	
4	6		3		−1
		6		1	
5	12		4		−3
		10		−2	
6	22		2		5
		12		3	
7	34		5		−3
		17		0	
8	51		5		0
		22		0	
9	73		5		
		27			
10	100				

The difference which we expect to be constant is oscillatory (and higher differences will get larger).

Let us see what happens in a bad case—for example,

$$f(x) = \tfrac{1}{2} - (-)^n a$$

for a small. The difference tables for $f(x)$ and for $f(x)$ rounded to the nearest integer are as follows:

x	$f(x)$	Δf	$\Delta^2 f$	$\Delta^3 f$	$\Delta^4 f$
0	$\tfrac{1}{2} - a$				
		$2a$			
1	$\tfrac{1}{2} + a$		$-4a$		
		$-2a$		$8a$	
2	$\tfrac{1}{2} - a$		$+4a$		$-16a$
		$2a$		$-8a$	
3	$\tfrac{1}{2} + a$		$-4a$		
		$-2a$			
4	$\tfrac{1}{2} - a$				

x	$f(x)$	Δf	$\Delta^2 f$	$\Delta^3 f$	$\Delta^4 f$
0	0				
		1			
1	1		-2		
		-1		$+4$	
2	0		$+2$		-8
		1		-4	
3	1		-2		
		-1			
4	0				

This shows that we may have a spurious contribution of up to 2^{n-1} units in the nth difference, because of rounding off of the functional values to the nearest unit.

The effect of a change in the length of the (constant) interval of differencing is easily determined: the constant nth difference of x^n at unit interval is $n!$, whereas if we take an interval h, the nth difference is $h^n n!$.

1	1				
		7			
2	8		12		
		19		6	
3	27		18		0
		37		6	
4	64		24		$+1$
		61		7	
5	125		31		-4
		92		3	
6	217		34		$+6$
		126		5	
7	343		43		-4
		169		9	
8	512		48		$+1$
		217		6	
9	729		54		0
		271		6	
10	1000		60		
		331			
11	1331				

The formation of a table of differences is useful in checking a table or locating errors.   The way in which an error propagates is indicated in the repetition opposite of the table on p. 42, with a deliberate error at $x = 6$, where we have written 217 instead of 216.   The pattern of $(1 - 1)^4$ in the fourth column is characteristic.   In practice, however, the exact binomial pattern will be more or less obscured by rounding errors, but it is usually easy to pick out errors, even when several are present and interfering (see Miller [8]).

The binomial pattern can also be established by noting that differencing is a *linear* operation, that the effect of the error is just that of the differences of 0, 0, 0, 0, 0, 1, 0, 0, 0, 0, 0, and that these come immediately from the explicit formula for Δ^n.

So far we have mainly discussed the differences of polynomials.   This is almost enough, for we are concerned with polynomial interpolation, which is applicable only when the function in question is approximately representable by a polynomial.   If $f(x)$ is differentiable, we have

$$\Delta f(x) = f(x + h) - f(x) = hf'(x + \theta h), \qquad 0 \le \theta \le 1.$$

Thus, if f' is continuous and h is small, we have

$$\Delta f(x) \doteq hf'(x).$$

More generally, we can show that, if $f(x)$ has a continuous nth derivative and h is sufficiently small,

$$\Delta^n f(x) \doteq h^n f^{(n)}(x).$$

More precisely, if $f^{(n)}(x)$ is continuous in $[a, a + nh]$, then

$$\Delta^n f(a) = h^n f^{(n)}(\xi), \qquad a \le \xi \le a + nh.$$

This can be proved by induction.   For $n = 1$, it is the first mean-value theorem.   Assuming this true for $n = r$, we consider

$$\Delta^{r+1} f(a) = \Delta^r [f(a + h) - f(a)],$$

and our induction hypothesis applied to $f(x + h) - f(x)$ gives

$$\Delta^{r+1} f(a) = h^r [f^{(r)}(\xi' + h) - f^{(r)}(\xi')], \qquad a \le \xi' \le a + rh.$$

Applying the first mean-value theorem, we now find

$$\Delta^{r+1} f(a) = h^{r+1} f^{(r+1)}(\xi),$$

where $\xi' \le \xi \le \xi' + h$,   so that $a \le \xi \le a + (r + 1)h$

as required.

In addition to the forward difference operator Δ, it is convenient to make use of the following operators: $\nabla, E, \mu, \delta, D$.   These are defined by $\nabla f(r+1) = f(r+1) - f(r)$, $Ef(r) = f(r+1)$, $\mu f(r) = \frac{1}{2}[f(r-\frac{1}{2}) + f(r+\frac{1}{2})]$, $\delta f(r) = f(r+\frac{1}{2}) - f(r-\frac{1}{2})$, $Df(r) = f'(r)$. These operators can be manipulated with reasonable impunity. Among the interrelations between them are

$$E = 1 + \Delta, \qquad E = \exp hD, \qquad \delta = E^{\frac{1}{2}} - E^{-\frac{1}{2}} = 2 \sinh \frac{1}{2}hD.$$

It is convenient to indicate the entries in a difference table in the forward, central, and backward notations:

$$f(-2) = f(a - 2h)$$
$$\Delta_{-2} = \nabla_{-1} = \delta_{-\frac{3}{2}}$$
$$f(-1) = f(a - h) \quad \mu_{-1} \qquad \Delta_{-2}{}^2 = \nabla_0{}^2 = \delta_{-1}{}^2$$
$$\Delta_{-1} = \nabla_0 = \delta_{-\frac{1}{2}} \quad \mu_{-\frac{1}{2}}{}^2 \qquad \Delta_{-2}{}^3 = \nabla_1{}^3 = \delta_{-\frac{1}{2}}{}^3$$
$$f(0) = f(a) \quad \mu_0 \qquad \Delta_{-1}{}^2 = \nabla_1{}^2 = \delta_0{}^2 \qquad \mu_0{}^3 \qquad \Delta_{-2}{}^4 = \nabla_2{}^4 = \delta_0{}^4$$
$$\Delta_0 = \nabla_1 = \delta_{\frac{1}{2}} \quad \mu_{\frac{1}{2}}{}^2 \qquad \Delta_{-1}{}^3 = \nabla_2{}^3 = \delta_{\frac{1}{2}}{}^3$$
$$f(1) = f(a+h) \quad \mu_1 \qquad \Delta_0{}^2 = \nabla_2{}^2 = \delta_1{}^2$$
$$\Delta_1 = \nabla_2 = \delta_{\frac{3}{2}}$$
$$f(2) = f(a + 2h)$$

Little useful purpose is served by explicit evaluations of differences of functions. The following result, easily established by induction, is, however, interesting:

$$\delta^{2n}[\sin (a + ph)] = (-4 \sin^2 \tfrac{1}{2}h)^n \sin (a + ph).$$

This shows that, for $h > \frac{1}{3}\pi$, δ^{2n} need not converge as $n \to \infty$.

We discuss briefly the Newton-Gregory process of interpolation. For positive integral p, we have

$$E^p = (1 + \Delta)^p,$$

that is, $f(p) = f(0) + \binom{p}{1}\Delta f(0) + \cdots + \binom{p}{p-1}\Delta^{p-1}f(0) + \Delta^p f(0)$.

The last relation is an algebraic identity, no matter what f is. If we allow p to have a general value, we obtain the Newton-Gregory formula:

$$f(p) = f(0) + p\,\Delta f(0) + \tfrac{1}{2}p(p-1)\Delta^2 f(0)$$
$$+ \tfrac{1}{6}p(p-1)(p-2)\,\Delta^3 f(0) + \cdots.$$

When f is a polynomial, the differences become zero, the series is a finite one, and we have an algebraic identity. In general, we can obtain an expression for the remainder in the series.

Observe that $S_n(p) = f(0) + \binom{p}{1}\Delta f(0) + \cdots + \binom{p}{n-1}\Delta^{n-1}f(0)$ is a polynomial in p of degree $n-1$. It is almost evident that $S_n(p) = f(p)$, for $p = 0, 1, 2, \ldots, n-1$. Hence $S_n(p) = L_{n-1}(f,p)$, the Lagrangian interpolant being unique.   We can therefore use the remainder already obtained in (2.10′):

$$f(p) - S_n(p) = \binom{p}{n} h^n f^{(n)}(\xi)$$

provided $f^{(n)}$ exists, where ξ lies in the interval containing p, 0, 1, ..., $n - 1$.

It is now clear that, with a table of a function and its differences and a table of binomial coefficients, we are in a position to interpolate.   Although this is not a preferred method, we shall discuss an example in some detail, since it illustrates several general points.

We shall evaluate $f(3.927)$ from the accompanying table [which gives $f(x) = e^x - 50$].   We require the binomial coefficients for argument $.35 = .007/.02$.   These can be computed or obtained from tables and are

$$1, \quad .35, \quad -.11375, \quad .06256, \quad -.04145, \quad ....$$

x	$f(x)$	Δ	Δ^2	Δ^3	Δ^4
3.92	.40044				
		101816			
3.94	1.41860		2057		
		103873		40	
3.96	2.45733		2097		5
		105970		45	
3.98	3.51703		2142		−3
		108112		42	
4.00	4.59815		2184		
		110296			
4.02	5.70111				

We find

$$
\begin{aligned}
f(3.927) &= .40044 + 1.01816 \times .35 + .02057 \times (-.11375) \\
&\quad + .00040 \times .06256 \\
&= .40044 + .35636 - .00234 + .00003 \\
&= .75449. \tag{2.13}
\end{aligned}
$$

For a check on this, we can think of 3.927 as $3.94 - .65 \times .02$ instead of as $3.92 + .35 \times .02$, obtain the binomial expansions for argument $-.65$, and carry on as before.

We note that the behavior of successive terms in (2.13) provides a usually reliable way of deciding on the accuracy of a particular interpolation without recourse to the error estimate which is usually taken in the form $\binom{p}{n} \Delta^n$.   In the present cases it would appear that the contribution from the fourth differences does not affect the fifth decimal place.

We observe that, since $f^{(4)} = f + 50 \doteq 50$, we can expect a fourth difference of about $50 \times (.02)^4 = .8 \times 10^{-5}$, that is, about a unit in the fifth place. We actually found 5, -3. The discrepancies are 4, -4, about one-half the extreme variation possible. It is interesting to check that these are due to the rounding of the tabular values.

We have seen that the Newton-Gregory process is obtained by a mere algebraic rearrangement of the Lagrangian interpolant. Other rearrangements associated with Bessel and Everett which are preferred above the Newton-Gregory one will now be discussed. They can also be generated formally by use of the difference operators.

The Bessel formula is

$$f(p) = f(0) + p\delta_{1/2} + B_2(\delta_0^2 + \delta_1^2) + B_3\delta_{1/2}^3 + B_4(\delta_0^4 + \delta_1^4) + \cdots$$

where the coefficients B_r are

$$B_2(p) = B_2(1 - p) = \tfrac{1}{2}p(p - 1)/2!,$$
$$B_3(p) = -B_3(1 - p) = p(p - 1)(p - \tfrac{1}{2})/3!,$$
$$B_4(p) = B_4(1 - p) = \tfrac{1}{2}p(p + 1)(p - 1)(p - 2)/4!, \ldots.$$

{It would be more reasonable to write the first two terms in the form

$$\tfrac{1}{2}[f(0) + f(1)] + (p - \tfrac{1}{2})\delta_{1/2}.\}$$

The Bessel formula is particularly convenient when $p = \tfrac{1}{2}$, for then the odd coefficients vanish. For example, if we neglect the fourth and higher differences, we obtain

$$f(\tfrac{1}{2}) = \tfrac{1}{2}f(0) + \tfrac{1}{2}f(1) + (-\tfrac{1}{16})[\delta^2 f(0) + \delta^2 f(1)],$$

which can be written in Lagrangian form as

$$f(\tfrac{1}{2}) = \tfrac{1}{16}[-f(-1) + 9f(0) + 9f(1) - f(2)].$$

Perhaps the most useful process is the Everett one:

$$f(p) = \{(1 - p)f(0) + pf(1)\} + \{E_2\delta_0^2 + F_2\delta_1^2\} + \{E_4\delta_0^4 + F_4\delta_1^4\} + \cdots,$$

$$(2.14)$$

where

$$E_2(p) = F_2(1 - p) = -p(p - 1)(p - 2)/3!,$$
$$E_4(p) = F_4(1 - p) = -(p + 1)p(p - 1)(p - 2)(p - 3)/5!, \quad \ldots.$$

Use of the terms within the first pair of braces is equivalent to linear (i.e., 2-point) interpolation; use of the terms within the first two pairs of braces is equivalent to cubic (i.e., 4-point) interpolation; and so on. It follows, from the form of the remainder in the Lagrangian 4-point case, that we can interpolate in a table of $\sin x$ at an interval of .2 and have an error of less than $\tfrac{1}{2} \times 10^{-4}$ if we use the first four terms in (2.14).

We repeat an example from Chap. 1. To find sin 1.234, we use the entries:

x	$\sin x$	δ^2
1.2	.9320	-371
1.4	.9854	-392

The Everett coefficients for $p = .17$ are $E_2 = -.0430, F_2 = -.0275$, and we find

$$\sin 1.234 = (.83 \times .9320 + .17 \times .9854)$$
$$+ (.0430 \times .0371 + .0275 \times .0392)$$
$$= .9438.$$

Owing to the symmetry of the Everett formula, it is not possible to check the computation by using $1.234 = 1.4 - .83(.2)$. It is quite easy to misread the coefficients, or to give them a wrong sign, and so some checking is desirable. We can use the Bessel method. The extra difference (-21) which is required can be obtained mentally. The Bessel coefficients for $p = .17$ are $B_2 = -.0353, B_3 = .0078$, and we find

$$\sin 1.234 = (.83 \times .9320 + .17 \times .9856) + (-.0353)(-.0763)$$
$$+ .0078(-.0021)$$
$$= .9438.$$

We shall now discuss the "throwback" (see Chap. 1 and NPL 1). It was observed that the ratios

$$\frac{E_4}{E_2} = \frac{p^2 - 2p - 3}{20}$$

and
$$\frac{B_4}{B_2} = \frac{p^2 - p - 2}{12}$$

are approximately constant for $0 \leq p \leq 1$. (The reader should draw a rough graph of the two quadratics.) If, therefore, a reasonable mean value k of these ratios is chosen, we can include the fourth-difference contribution by "modifying" the second difference:

$$\delta_m^2 f = \delta^2 f + k\, \delta^4 f.$$

Various ways of choosing k have been discussed, and the preferred value is $k = -.18393$ (see, e.g., Abramowitz [9]).

The use, in practice, of this idea is along the following lines. The tablemaker computes $f, \delta^2 f, \delta^4 f$ but prints only $f, \delta_m^2 f$. If the user treats the $\delta_m^2 f$ just as he treats $\delta^2 f$, he receives a bonus, the major part of the contribution of $\delta^4 f$, without having to obtain the E_4, F_4 or to do the multiplications and additions. The actual error incurred by the modification is less than half a unit if the fourth differences are less than 1000 and the fifth difference less than 70.

If we return to the case of a 4D table of sin x, we now see that an interval of $h = .5$ will practically suffice.   That is to say, the table

x	$\sin x$	δ_m^2
.0	.0000	0
.5	.4794	-1225
1.0	.8415	-2154
1.5	.9975	-2552
2.0	.9093	-2326

will be adequate.   For instance, since for

$$p = \tfrac{1}{2}, \qquad E_2 = -.0625, \qquad F_2 = -.0625,$$

we have

$$\sin 1.25 = .9195 + \tfrac{1}{16}(.2154 + .2552) = .9489.$$

Actually,

$$\sin 1.25 = .9490,$$

and the discrepancy can be explained by round-off or by the marginal choice of h.

2.8   Comparison of Methods

There is a violent transatlantic controversy about the methods discussed in Secs. 2.6 and 2.7.   On the whole, the Americans favor the Lagrangian methods and the Europeans the difference methods.   We shall mention some of the arguments brought up.

There is no doubt that the Lagrangian method should be used only for a guaranteed table; the calculation of the differences required for the other methods provides a check on the reliability of a new or doubtful table and, the differences having been obtained, the use of the difference methods is usually less laborious.   There is, however, the question of what order of interpolation to use.   Only in a few tables is this given, and so, if one does not want to compute differences, one is forced to carry out more than one interpolation and to observe the behavior of the interpolant; for this the Aitken scheme is efficient.   Since the sum of the Lagrangian coefficients is necessarily unity, one can provide a good check in desk computations by accumulating the multipliers as well as the product.   This check is not available in the finite-difference methods (except in the linear case), where the varying orders of magnitude of the multipliers and the differences encourage wrong settings in the calculator. We have already pointed out that it is possible to check the computations in the Bessel case by doing the interpolation for p and for $1 - p$.   Another advantage of the Bessel method is that one can use the exact order which is necessary—the Everett method always gives an even order interpolation.   Neither of these methods is available at the beginning or end of a table, unless the missing differences are supplied (e.g., by guessing or by using properties of the function, e.g., parity); the Newton-Gregory method is suitable for the beginning of a table and is easily modified to handle the end of a table.

2.9   Auxiliary Functions

It has been clear from examples and from the form of the remainders that interpolation becomes awkward in the neighborhood of a singularity of a function or of one of its derivatives.   One of the ways of easing the situation is by the introduction of auxiliary functions, which may be additive or multiplicative.   We choose functions $a(x)$ or $m(x)$, which are already tabulated (or easily computed) and simpler (in the sense of permitting easier interpolation), in such a way that $a(x) + f(x)$, or $m(x)f(x)$, is "smoother" than $f(x)$ itself.

We illustrate this by two simple examples.   Consider cosec x near $x = 0$.   The difficulty in interpolation is evident from the accompanying table for cosec x:

x	cosec x	cosec $x - x^{-1}$			x cosec x			
0	∞	0			1.000000			
			833			4		
.005	200.001	.000833		1	1.000004		9	
			834			13		−1
.010	100.002	.001667		−1	1.000017		8	
			833			21		0
.015	66.6692	.002500		0	1.000038		8	
			833			29		0
.020	50.0033	.003333		1	1.000067		8	
			834			37		1
.025	40.0042	.004167		0	1.000104		9	
			834			46		
.030	33.3383	.005001			1.000150			

However, interpolation in the tables of cosec $x - x^{-1}$ or x cosec x is trivial, and we can obtain the value of cosec x by addition (after reference to a table of reciprocals) or by a division.   The choice of auxiliary functions is usually easy.   In the present case they were suggested by the power series

$$x \text{ cosec } x = 1 + \tfrac{1}{6}x^2 + \tfrac{7}{360}x^4 + \cdots,$$

which is convergent for $|x| < \pi$.

As a slightly more sophisticated example, we discuss the case of

$y = \arcsin x$ near $x = 1$.   The choice of an auxiliary function is motivated as follows.   We have

$$\arcsin (1 - \epsilon) = \tfrac{1}{2}\pi - \arccos (1 - \epsilon) = \tfrac{1}{2}\pi - \arcsin (2\epsilon - \epsilon^2)^{1/2}$$
$$= \tfrac{1}{2}\pi - \sqrt{2\epsilon} + O(\epsilon^{3/2}).$$

Hence $\arcsin x + \sqrt{2(1 - x)} = \tfrac{1}{2}\pi + O[(1 - x)^{3/2}]$.

x	$y = \arcsin x$	$\delta^2 y$	$z = y + \sqrt{2(1 - x)}$	Δz
.94	1.2226		1.5690	
				4
.95	1.2532	32	1.5694	
				4
.96	1.2870	44	1.5698	
				4
.97	1.3252	71	1.5702	
				3
.98	1.3705	135	1.5705	
				2
.99	1.4293	827	1.5707	
				1
1.00	1.5708		1.5708	

To find, for example, sin .9512 from the original table, we have to use at least cubic interpolation, but with the new table we can use linear interpolation and a square-root table to get

$$\arcsin .9512 = 1.5694 + .12 \times .0004 - \sqrt{2} \times .0488$$
$$= 1.2570.$$

In the case of a function which oscillates with a slowly varying amplitude and period, it is appropriate to look for auxiliary functions $A(x)$, $B(x)$ such that

$$f(x) \doteqdot A(x) \cos [B(x) + \epsilon].$$

The appropriate choice is often suggested by asymptotic representation. For instance, the asymptotic expansion for $J_0(x)$ suggests that we represent it in the form

$$J_0(x) = A_0(x) \sin x + B_0(x) \cos x.$$

The efficiency of this is evident on referring to BAAS 6, 10.   A straightforward table for the range 0 to 25 occupies 200 pages, whereas a comparable 8D table giving $A_0(x)$, $B_0(x)$ for the range 25 to 6000 requires 10 pages.

It is appropriate to mention here the use of rational (and, in particular, polynomial) approximations to functions.   Given such an approximation, interpolation is replaced by the calculation of two polynomials (see

Chap. 1). The use of such an approximation has increased with the use of automatic computers, and there is considerable activity in connection with the automatic generation of such approximations. For a severely practical account of these matters, we refer to Hastings [11]. See also NPL 6 and Chap. 3.

It is also appropriate to indicate here how changes in the dependent or independent variable or in both can facilitate tabulation and interpolation. These changes are often suggested by asymptotic expansions.

For instance, consider the tabulation of $\Gamma(x)$ for $x \geq 100$. From the asymptotic expansion it is apparent that

$$f_1(x) = \frac{\Gamma(x)}{x^{x-\frac{1}{2}}e^{-x}(2\pi)^{\frac{1}{2}}}$$

is approximately linear in x^{-1}. A table of $f_1(x)$ for $x^{-1} = 0(.001).01$, for example—together with appropriate auxiliary tables—enables $\Gamma(x)$ to be obtained throughout the range to about 8D.

Another example is the tabulation of $\text{Ei}(x) = \int_{-\infty}^{x} t^{-1}e^{-t} \, dt$ for $10 \leq |x| \leq \infty$. It has been shown that a table of $T(x) = e^{-x}\text{Ei}(x) - x^{-1}$ for $x^{-1} = -.1(.01).1$ is interpolable to about 8D, using the Everett process, with modified second differences (see Fox and Miller [12]).

Finally, consider the tabulation of $J_0(x)$ for large x. We have

$$J_0(x) \sim (2/\pi x)^{\frac{1}{2}}[P_0(x) \cos (x - \tfrac{1}{4}\pi) - Q_0(x) \sin (x - \tfrac{1}{4}\pi)],$$

where $P_0(x)$ and $xQ_0(x)$ are power series in x^{-2}. This suggests the use of x^{-2} as an independent variable; it has been shown by Hartree [13] that this change is very efficient and that a table of 41 entries, in which linear interpolation is good to 7D, covers the range $5 \leq x \leq \infty$.

For further examples see NPL 4 and RSS 3.

2.10 Errors in Interpolation

We shall discuss here the errors which occur when we compute $f(p)$ according to the methods we have described.

In the first place, the argument p may be uncertain, and if the amount of uncertainty is ϵ, the consequential uncertainty in $f(p)$ will be $\epsilon f'(p)$. If f is given analytically, it may be possible to estimate $f'(p)$; otherwise we can estimate it as $h^{-1} \Delta f$. For instance, if $f(x) = \sin x$, the uncertainty in $f(p)$ does not exceed that in p; if $f(x) = \arctan x$, the same is true for all p, but for large p the uncertainty in $f(p)$ is much smaller.

Should this type of uncertainty be present, its effect must be examined first, in order to ensure that an appropriate interpolation method is chosen. It is manifestly uneconomical and misleading to use an interpolation process in which the intrinsic errors are much less than the unavoidable uncertainties.

We have given already an admittedly academic error estimate for the Lagrangian process and therefore for the equivalent difference methods. We now examine an interpolation process more carefully; for simplicity, we discuss linear interpolation in a d-decimal-place table.   We want a value of $f(p)$, being given $f(a), f(b)$.   Now, we are not usually given $f(a)$, $f(b)$, but rather approximations to these, $\overline{f(a)}, \overline{f(b)}$, which are obtained, for example, by rounding the true values.   The difference between

$$\overline{f(a)} + \frac{p-a}{b-a}[\overline{f(b)} - \overline{f(a)}] \quad \text{and} \quad f(a) + \frac{p-a}{b-a}[f(b) - f(a)] = L_1(p)$$

is

$$\frac{p-a}{b-a}[\overline{f(b)} - f(b)] + \frac{b-p}{b-a}[\overline{f(a)} - f(a)].$$

Let us assume that the $\bar{f}$ are obtained by rounding the f, so that the tabular error is at most $\epsilon = \frac{1}{2} \cdot 10^{-d}$.   Then the above difference is at most

$$\epsilon\left(\frac{p-a}{b-a} + \frac{b-p}{b-a}\right) = \epsilon.$$

However, we do not actually compute $\overline{f(a)} + \frac{p-a}{b-a}[\overline{f(b)} - \overline{f(a)}]$, for $(p-a)/(b-a)$ will not be integral in general, and we shall have to incur a rounding error of amount at most ϵ.   Thus the difference between the result of our computation and $L_1(p)$ is in absolute value at most 2ϵ.   In order to find the actual discrepancy, we must add the truncation error; if, as is usual, we arrange for this to be at most ϵ, the total absolute error will be at most 3ϵ (see Ostrowski [14]).

As an example, let us find sin .43 by linear interpolation between sin .42 = .4078, sin .44 = .4259.   We find .4078 + $\frac{1}{2}$ × .0181, which rounds to .4168, whereas sin .43 = .4169.   The values of the data to 6 places are .407760, 425939, and sin .43 = .416871.

Let us now consider what happens in the nonlinear case.   Essentially similar considerations apply in the Lagrangian and difference methods. Assuming p to be given precisely, we have to obtain the Lagrangian or Bessel or Everett coefficients.   In general, these will not be obtained exactly—we may, indeed, have to obtain them by interpolation.   Then there are the errors due to tabular errors in the Lagrangian case and due to these tabular errors and to consequential errors in the differences used in the other cases.

If modified differences are employed, we have to take account both of the errors caused in their calculation and of the additional truncation errors caused by the modification.

It is clear, therefore, that to make full error estimates in an interpolation process is a laborious job.   The results of such estimates are available in the booklet IAT, to which we have referred.

2.11 Inverse Interpolation and Related Topics

It is not often that one has to interpolate in a table given at unequal intervals.   If much interpolation in such a table is required, it is probably best to produce from it an interpolable table at a constant interval.   This can be done by using the original Lagrangian method, although it will now not be possible to obtain the coefficients from tables—they will have to be calculated.   The Aitken process is, of course, very suitable here.

The concept of divided differences is used in these circumstances. Suppose $f(x)$ given at $x_0, x_1, x_2, \ldots$.   The first divided difference is defined by

$$f(x_i, x_{i+1}) = [f(x_{i+1}) - f(x_i)]/(x_{i+1} - x_i).$$

The second divided difference is defined by

$$f(x_i, x_{i+1}, x_{i+2}) = [f(x_{i+1}, x_{i+2}) - f(x_i, x_{i+1})]/(x_{i+2} - x_i).$$

And similarly for higher divided differences.   It can be shown that the nth divided differences of a polynomial of degree at most $(n - 1)$ vanish. Thus the equality of the nth divided differences is a test for a function to coincide with a polynomial of degree at most n.   The approximate equality will indicate that an $(n + 1)$-point interpolation will be appropriate.

We note that, when $x_i = x_0 + ih$, we have

$$f(x_0, x_1, \ldots, x_n) = h^{-n} \, \Delta^n f(0)/n! \, .$$

We shall discuss the calculation of $J_{1/2}(1)$ given $J_0(1)$, $J_{1/4}(1)$, $J_{1/3}(1)$, $J_{2/3}(1)$, $J_{3/4}(1)$, $J_1(1)$.   We begin by forming a table of divided differences:

$12n$	$J_n(1)$			
0	.7652			
		43		
3	.7522		42	
		213		2
4	.7309		24	
		332		2
8	.5979		12	
		392		1
9	.5587		1	
		395		
12	.4401			

We carry out, by the Aitken process, a 5-point interpolation:

0	7652			
3	7522	7392		
4	7309	7138	6630	
8	5979	6397	6795	6712
9	5587	6274	6833	6711	6714

Actually,

$$J_{1/2}(1) = .6713967\ldots.$$

The problem of inverse interpolation is to solve for x the equation

$$f(x) = \alpha,$$

α and a table of $f(x)$ being given; we are evaluating, in fact, $f^{-1}(\alpha)$. This is trivial in case the table permits linear interpolation, for then $x = a + \theta h$, where

$$\alpha = f(a + \theta h) = f(a) + \theta[f(a + h) - f(a)],$$

so that

$$\theta = \frac{\alpha - f(a)}{f(a + h) - f(a)}.$$

If linear interpolation is not permissible, a convenient method is to subtabulate the table (of course, only in the neighborhood of the required x) until a table which is interpolable linearly is obtained. This subtabulation can be done by any of the methods described; if much subtabulation is to be done, it is worthwhile making use of special methods (see [15]). We consider the determination of the zero p of $f(x)$, where

$$f(0) = 9480931, \qquad f(1) = 4286597,$$
$$f(2) = -905580, \qquad f(3) = -6095598.$$

We find that the second differences are large (2157, 2159) but that the third is negligible. We estimate the position of the zero by linear interpolation as

$$p \doteq 1 + \frac{4286597}{5192077} = 1.8255.$$

We compute by 3-point Lagrangian interpolation:

$$f(1.820) = 28853, \qquad f(1.825) = 2895, \qquad f(1.830) = -23062.$$

The second difference is now -1, and so linear inverse interpolation is permissible. We find

$$p = 1.825 + \frac{2895}{25957} \times .005 = 1.82555766.$$

The same example can be carried out by the Aitken process, which can be presented as follows:

```
9480931  0
4286597  1  1.82524478                        5194334
-905580  2         562383  1.82555771         10386511   5192177
-6095598 3         600328          796  1.82555766  15576529  10382195  5190018
```

The numbers on the right are the divisors used. In many cases of direct interpolation it is not necessary to record them explicitly.

A word of caution is necessary here. Unless $n = 2$, it is not true that, if n-point interpolation is permissible in a table, then n-point inverse interpolation is permissible. This is best illustrated by an example. Consider the determination of the zero of $f(x)$ where

$$f(0) = -342, \quad f(1) = -218, \quad f(2) = 386, \quad f(3) = 1854.$$

Actually $f(x) = (4x + 1)^3 - 343$, so that 4-point direct interpolation is exact, and the zero is 1.5. A 4-point inverse interpolation gives

```
-342   0                                -342
-218   1   2.7581                        -218    124
 386   2    .9396   2.1018                386    728    604
1854   3    .4672    .5171   1.9926      1854   2196   2072   1468
```

For another example, see Hartree [16].

Another approach to this problem is the following. We can consider the reversion of the Lagrangian expansion and obtain

$$p = r + a_2 r^2 + a_3 r^3 + \cdots,$$

where the a_i are rational functions of the tabular values and where r also depends on the given value $\alpha = f(p)$. For simplicity, we give the formula in the 4-point case (see Salzer [17]):

$$p = r - r^2 s + r^3(2s^2 - t) + r^4(-5s^3 + 5st) + \cdots$$

where
$$r = 6[f(p) - f(0)]/\Delta,$$
$$s = 3[f(1) - 2f(0) + f(-1)]/\Delta,$$
$$t = [f(2) - 3f(1) + 3f(0) - f(-1)]/\Delta,$$
$$\Delta = -f(2) + 6f(1) - 3f(0) - 2f(-1).$$

In the above case we find, with

$$f(-1) = -342, \quad f(0) = -218, \quad f(1) = 386, \quad f(2) = 1854,$$

that

$$r = 1308/1800, \quad s = 1440/1800, \quad t = 384/1800, \quad \Delta = 1800,$$

which gives

$$p = .7267 - .4224 + .4093 - \cdots.$$

The behavior of the terms here suggests that we are in trouble. It should be contrasted with the behavior of the same formula in a reasonable case.

It is possible to obtain rules for the neglect of the contributions of differences in inverse interpolation. We shall not discuss these in detail, but the reader should refer to the literature cited earlier.

A related problem is the determination of the position $\bar{x}$, of the minimum or maximum of a tabulated function, or, more generally, where a tabulated function has an assigned derivative; this has been discussed thoroughly by Salzer. We discuss directly a 3-point method. We fit a parabola $y = a + bx + cx^2$ to $f(x)$ at $x = -1$, $x = 0$, $x = 1$. Then

$$a = f(0), \qquad b = \tfrac{1}{2}[f(1) - f(-1)], \qquad c = \tfrac{1}{2}[f(1) + f(-1)].$$

We obtain for the abscissa and ordinate of its vertex the expressions

$$\bar{x} \doteq \frac{-b}{2c} = -\tfrac{1}{2}\frac{f(1) - f(-1)}{f(1) - 2f(0) + f(-1)}$$

and
$$f(\bar{x}) \doteq \frac{4ac - b^2}{4c} = f(0) - \tfrac{1}{8}\frac{[f(1) - f(-1)]^2}{f(1) - 2f(0) + f(-1)}.$$

2.12 Multivariate Interpolation

Much of the preceding material on univariate interpolation can be extended to the multivariate case. The naïve approach to the problem of finding $f(p,q)$ in a double-entry table is to do successive univariate interpolation; that is, we find $f(0,q), f(1,q), \ldots$ by interpolation in the y direction and obtain $f(p,q)$ by interpolation in the x direction among these values. If much interpolation is to be done, more efficient methods must be sought. In good tables, advice for interpolation is given, and where interpolation is thought likely to be necessary, the table is planned to make it as comfortable as possible.

An important special case of multivariate interpolation is in tables of regular functions of a complex variable. Here use of the Cauchy-Riemann equations can greatly facilitate matters. We refer to the introductions of the many recent tables of this character for various approaches.

Special methods for functions of particular form are often convenient. For instance, in the case of functions defined by integrals, Gaussian quadratures may be applied (see, e.g., Todd [18]).

The use of the throwback for bivariate interpolation has been discussed by Southard [19].

Multivariate interpolation has been the object of some recent research by Milne and his collaborators and by Thacher [20].

QUADRATURE AND DIFFERENTIATION

2.13 Introduction

The problem with which we are mainly concerned is the numerical evaluation of

$$F(x) = \int_a^x f(t)\, dt$$

for one or more values of x, where $f(t)$ is given analytically, or by a table. A comprehensive bibliography has been given by Stroud [68].

Occasionally the simplest solution to this will be provided by obtaining the indefinite integral analytically and then referring to tables of the functions involved. Among the more elaborate tables of integrals in common use are those of Gröbner and Hofreiter [21], Bierens de Haan [22], Byrd and Friedman [23], and Ryshik and Gradstein [24]. In many cases the explicit analytical form of $F(x)$ may not be very helpful (an example of this is given in [25], p. 130). However, even if this solution is too unwieldy for general use, it may be valuable for checking—for example, the final value.

An account of some of the ways of reducing integrals to more manageable forms is given by Abramowitz [26].

2.14 Lagrangian Formulas

The idea now to be exploited is the following. In order to evaluate

$$I = \int_a^b f(x)\, dx$$

approximately, we shall evaluate the integral of an approximation to $f(x)$. We make use of the results already available about the approximations to functions by polynomials.

For instance, if

$$a \leq x_0 < x_1 < \cdots < x_n \leq b$$

and if

$$L_n(f,x) = \sum f(x_i) l_i^{(n)}(x)$$

is the corresponding Lagrangian polynomial, we can consider

$$Q = \int_a^b L_n(f,x)\, dx = \sum f(x_i) \int_a^b l_i^{(n)}(x)\, dx = \sum A_i f(x_i)$$

as an approximation* to I.   We note that the coefficients A_i do not depend on the particular function being integrated, only on the nodes $x_0, x_1, \ldots, x_n$.   If we take special cases, such as the one in which the nodes are equally spaced, the tabulation of the A_i is feasible, and a convenient solution to the problem is available.   Before dealing with the general case and discussing the errors involved, we take up a few particular cases.

(a) The case in which $n = 1$, when $f(x)$ is approximated by a linear function, gives the following:

$$f(x) \doteq f(a) + \frac{x-a}{b-a}[f(b) - f(a)],$$

so that

$$Q = (b-a)\{\tfrac{1}{2}[f(b) + f(a)]\}.$$

This is the trapezoidal rule: the area under the curve is approximated by the area of the trapezium.

It can be shown that $I - Q = -\delta^2/12$, where δ^2 is the second difference—this statement, and similar ones for other quadratures, are elucidated in a discussion at the end of this section.

It is important to note the power of this simple method in dealing with the numerical integration of periodic functions over a full period.   For a full discussion we refer to Birkhoff, Young, and Zarantonello [61], Davis [31, 62], and Hämmerlin [63].

(b) Consider next the case in which we have the 4 points $-1, 0, 1, 2$ and approximate the integrand by a cubic $C(x)$.   If we take

$$C(x) = f_0 + ax + bx^2 + cx^3,$$

so that $C(0) = f_0$, and require in addition that

$$C(-1) = f_{-1}, \qquad C(1) = f_1, \qquad C(2) = f_2,$$

we can obtain a, b, c as linear combinations of the f_i.   In fact,

$$a = -\tfrac{1}{3}f_{-1} - \tfrac{1}{2}f_0 + f_1 - \tfrac{1}{6}f_2,$$
$$b = \tfrac{1}{2}f_{-1} - f_0 + \tfrac{1}{2}f_1,$$
$$c = -\tfrac{1}{6}f_{-1} + \tfrac{1}{2}f_0 - \tfrac{1}{2}f_1 + \tfrac{1}{6}f_2.$$

---

*Since $L_n(f,x) \equiv f(x)$ if $f(x)$ is a polynomial of degree at most n it follows that $Q = I$ in this case.   This result clearly remains true in the weighted case when we consider the approximation of

$$I = \int_a^b f(x)p(x)\,dx$$

by $Q = \Sigma A_i f(x_i)$ where now

$$A_i = \int_a^b l_i^{(n)}(x)p(x)\,dx.$$

We then have

$$Q = \int_{-1}^{2} C(x)\ dx = 3f_0 + \tfrac{3}{2}a + 3b + \tfrac{15}{4}c$$

$$= \tfrac{3}{8}(f_{-1} + 3f_0 + 3f_1 + f_2).$$

This is called the three-eighths rule. It is of the type known as *closed:* the end ordinates are used.

It can be shown that $I - Q = -3\delta^4/80$, where δ^4 is the fourth difference.

(*c*) Consider next the case when we have 5 points, but approximate the integrand by a quadratic through the 3 interior points.

If we take

$$q(x) = f_0 + ax + bx^2$$

so that $q(0) = f_0$ and require in addition that

$$q(-1) = f_{-1}, \qquad q(1) = f_1,$$

we can obtain a, b as linear combinations of the f_i. We have

$$Q = \int_{-2}^{+2} q(x)\ dx = 4f_0 + \tfrac{16}{3}b = \tfrac{4}{3}(2f_1 - f_0 + 2f_{-1}).$$

It can be shown that $I - Q = \tfrac{14}{45}\delta^4$. This formula has been exploited by Milne. It is of the *open* type: the end ordinates are not used, and it can therefore be used as a *predictor* in the solution of differential equations.

We note that the error incurred in the use of open-type formulas is likely to be larger than that of closed-type formulas. We have pointed out already the growth of the error term in a Lagrangian interpolation as we move away from the center and particularly as we get outside the nodes, that is, when we extrapolate.

(*d*) Another common integration formula is Simpson's rule:

$$\int_{-1}^{+1} f(x)\ dx = \tfrac{1}{3}(f_{-1} + 4f_0 + f_1).$$

This can be derived by integrating a cubic which coincides with $f(x)$ at -1, 0, 1 and, in addition, has the same derivative at $x = 0$ as $f(x)$.

It can be shown that $I - Q = -\delta^4/90$.

(*e*) Among the many other quadrature formulas of this type is Weddle's rule:

$$\int_{0}^{6} f(x)\ dx = \tfrac{3}{10}(f_0 + 5f_1 + f_2 + 6f_3 + f_4 + 5f_5 + f_6).$$

It can be shown that $I - Q = -\delta^6/140$.

(*f*) A collection of these formulas has been made by Bickley [27] (see also IAT).

We return now to more theoretical considerations of quadrature formulas of the Lagrangian type.

We have first of all to estimate the error committed. For clarity we consider an ordinary Lagrangian $(n + 1)$-point scheme for a function $f(x)$ which has a continuous $(n + 1)$st derivative. We know that

$$f(x) = L_n(x) + \frac{f^{(n+1)}(\xi)}{(n + 1)!} (x - x_0)(x - x_1) \cdots (x - x_n).$$

If we consider integrating this with respect to x, we must remember that in general ξ depends on x. About the best we can do is to replace $f^{(n+1)}(\xi)$ by $M_{n+1} = \max_{a \leq x \leq b} |f^{(n+1)}(x)|$. We then find

$$|I - Q_n| \leq \frac{M_{n+1}}{(n + 1)!} \int_a^b |x - x_0| \, |x - x_1| \cdots |x - x_n| \, dx.$$

A crude estimate of the integral is $(b - a)^{n+2}$, so that

$$|I - Q_n| \leq M_{n+1}(b - a)^{n+2}/(n + 1)!$$

This is sufficient to show that $Q_n \to I$ as $n \to \infty$ whenever $f(z)$ is an entire function.

We have given, with each of our formulas, an estimate of the error committed. Such estimates can be obtained in various ways. Perhaps the method due to Peano [28] is the most systematic.

We discuss the Simpson's-rule case only. We begin with the relation

$$\int uv''' \, dt = uv'' - u'v' + u''v - \int u'''v \, dt.$$

Applying this when $u = \frac{1}{6}x(1 - x)^2$, $v = f(x) + f(-x)$, $g = uv'''$, we find

$$\int_0^1 g \, dx = \frac{1}{3}[f(1) + 4f(0) + f(-1)] - \int_0^1 [f(x) + f(-x)] \, dx.$$

So, $$\int_{-1}^{+1} f(x) \, dx = \frac{1}{3}[f(1) + 4f(0) + f(-1)] - \int_0^1 g(x) \, dx.$$

Now if $f^{(4)}(t)$ is continuous, $f'''(x) - f'''(-x) = 2xf^{(4)}(\xi)$, $-x \leq \xi \leq x$. Hence, if $|f^{(4)}(t)| \leq M_4$, we have

$$\left| \int_0^1 g(x) \, dx \right| \leq 2M_4 \frac{1}{6} \int_0^1 x^2(1 - x)^2 \, dx = \frac{M_4}{90}.$$

If we argue more closely we find, in the case of intervals of length h,

$$I - Q = -\frac{h^5}{90} f^{(4)}(\xi).$$

Recalling that the fourth difference, at interval h, is approximately $h^4 f^{(4)}(x)$, this gives

$$I - Q \doteq -h\delta^4/90,$$

where δ^4 is an "average" fourth difference—this is the result stated above.

To clarify the situation, let us take the case of the evaluation of

$$S(.5,.5) = \int_0^{.5} \exp\left(-.5 \sec t\right) dt,$$

using $h = .01$. There will then be 25 intervals, and the error in each will be estimated as $-h \cdot h^4 f^{(4)}(\xi)/90$, so the total error is in absolute value at most

$$\frac{25h^5 M_4}{90} \leq 10^{-10}$$

if $M_4 = \max\limits_{0 \leq x \leq .5} |f^{(4)}(x)| \leq 4$, which seems a reasonable guess. (See Sec. 4.24.)

We note here how we can improve the accuracy of a formula such as Simpson's by applying it to subintervals of $[a,b]$, so that "h" is reduced. For simplicity, we discuss the case in which we consider a double application of the rule. We have to compare

$$I_1 = \tfrac{2}{3}h(f_0 + 4f_2 + f_4)$$

with $\qquad I_2 = \tfrac{1}{3}h(f_0 + 4f_1 + f_2) + \tfrac{1}{3}h(f_2 + 4f_3 + f_4).$

Assuming the same bound M_4 for $f^{(4)}$, the error $|I_1 - Q|$ is approximately $(2h)^5 M_4/90$, whereas $|I_2 - Q|$ is about $2h^5 M_4/90$, an improvement by a factor of $2^4 = 16$.

2.15 Quadratures Using Differences

(a) One of the most efficient quadrature formulas is due to Gauss and uses central differences. The basic relation is

$$h^{-1} \int_0^h f(x)\, dx = \delta D^{-1} f_{\frac{1}{2}}$$

$$= \frac{1}{\mu}\left(\frac{2}{\delta} \sinh^{-1} \frac{\delta}{2}\right)^1 \mu f_{\frac{1}{2}}$$

$$= (1 + \tfrac{1}{4}\delta^2)^{-\frac{1}{2}}\left[\frac{2}{\delta}\left(\frac{\delta}{2} - \frac{1}{2}\cdot\frac{\delta^3}{3.8} + \cdots\right)\right]^{-1} \mu f_{\frac{1}{2}}$$

$$= (1 - \tfrac{1}{8}\delta^2 + \tfrac{3}{128}\delta^4 - \cdots)(1 + \tfrac{1}{24}\delta^2$$

$$\qquad - \tfrac{17}{5760}\delta^4 + \cdots)\mu f_{\frac{1}{2}}$$

$$= (1 - \tfrac{1}{12}\delta^2 + \tfrac{11}{720}\delta^4 - \cdots)\mu f_{\frac{1}{2}}.$$

How this is used in practice is indicated by the following beginning of an evaluation of $I = \int_0^{1/2} (1 - x^2)^{1/2}\, dx$, using an interval $h = .05$. The integrand is tabulated and differenced. The starred entries are not officially available if we restrict ourselves to the given values of the integrand. However, these may be estimated in various ways; for instance, the entries -1, -3 in the last column are within the range ± 24 of errors due to rounding of the initial values, and it is reasonable to assume a zero fifth difference and a difference constant at -22, from which the third difference, -6, and the second difference, -2505, can be obtained.† This being done, the first column to the left of the argument column is computed; it is

$$h(1 - \tfrac{1}{12}\delta^2 + \tfrac{11}{720}\delta^4 - \cdots).$$

From this column, that labeled δI is obtained by averaging, and from the δI column, that for I is obtained by addition.

It is clear that the errors in our estimates of the missing differences are obliterated by the multiplying factors $-h/12$, $+11h/720$, ...

The correct value, obtained analytically, is

$$I = \tfrac{1}{8}\sqrt{3} + \frac{\pi}{12} = .478306.$$

$I(x)$	δI		x	$(1 - x^2)^{1/2}$	δ^2		δ^4	
0		50010	0	1.000000	-2502*		-18*	
	49979				-1251	-9*		-1*
49979		49948	.05	998749	2511		19*	
	49854				3762	28		3*
99833		49760	.10	994987	2539		22	
	49602				6301	50		
149435		49445	.15	988686	2589			
	49223				8890			
198658		49001	.20	979796				

(b) The Gregory method uses only differences which are actually available. The formula is

$$\int_0^n f_p\, d_p = \tfrac{1}{2}f_0 + f_1 + \cdots + f_{n-1} + \tfrac{1}{2}f_n + \tfrac{1}{12}(\Delta_0 - \nabla_n)$$
$$- \tfrac{1}{24}(\Delta_0^2 + \nabla_n^2) + \tfrac{19}{720}(\Delta_0^3 - \nabla_n^3) - \tfrac{3}{160}(\Delta_0^4 + \nabla_n^4) + \cdots.$$

† Thus the starred entries in the table are estimated as:

$$
\begin{array}{ccccc}
-2505 & & -22 & & \\
 & -6 & & 0 & \\
 & & 22 & & \\
 & & & 0 &
\end{array}
$$

Notice that the differences involved are the first and the last which are obtained in differencing the integrand at values within the range of integration. The basis of a formal derivation follows. Since $D = \log(1 + \Delta)$, we have

$$\frac{1}{D} = \frac{1}{\Delta - (\Delta^2/2) + (\Delta^3/3) - \cdots}$$

$$= \frac{1}{\Delta}\left(1 - \frac{\Delta}{2} + \frac{\Delta^2}{3} - \cdots\right)^{-1}$$

$$= \frac{1}{\Delta}\left[1 + \left(\frac{\Delta}{2} - \frac{\Delta^2}{3} + \cdots\right) + \left(\frac{\Delta}{2} - \frac{\Delta^2}{3} + \cdots\right)^2\right.$$

$$\left. + \left(\frac{\Delta}{2} - \frac{\Delta^2}{3} + \cdots\right)^3 + \cdots\right]$$

$$= \frac{1}{\Delta} + \frac{1}{2} - \frac{\Delta}{12} + \frac{\Delta^2}{24} - \cdots .$$

(c) The Euler-Maclaurin formula is often convenient, either for the evaluation of a sum or for the evaluation of an integral. The formula is

$$h^{-1}\int_0^{nh} f(x)\, dx = \int_0^n f_p\, dp = \tfrac{1}{2}f_0 + f_1 + \cdots + f_{n-1} + \tfrac{1}{2}f_n$$
$$- \tfrac{1}{12}h(f_n' - f_0')$$
$$+ \tfrac{1}{720}h^3(f_n''' - f_0''')$$
$$- \tfrac{1}{30240}h^5(f_n^{(5)} - f_0^{(5)})$$
$$\cdots\cdots\cdots\cdots\cdots$$

It can be derived by the use of the finite-difference operators as follows. We note that

$$\frac{1}{\Delta} = \frac{1}{E - 1} = \frac{1}{e^D - 1} = \frac{1}{D} - \frac{1}{2} + \frac{B_1}{2!}D - \frac{B_2}{4!}D^3 + \frac{B_3}{6!}D^5 - \cdots$$

$$= \frac{1}{D} - \frac{1}{2} + \frac{1}{12}D - \frac{1}{720}D^3 + \frac{1}{30240}D^5 - \cdots$$

where the B's are the Bernoulli numbers defined by the generating function

$$\tfrac{1}{2}t \cot \tfrac{1}{2}t = 1 - \frac{B_1}{2!}t^2 - \frac{B_2}{4!}t^4 - \frac{B_3}{6!}t^6 - \cdots$$

A careful discussion of this formula and a derivation of an error estimate can be found in Knopp [29]. For the present we discuss an example, the evaluation of $\Sigma\, n^{-2}$. If we let $n \to \infty$ in the above formula and if all the derivatives $f^{(2p+1)}(n) \to 0$ as $n \to \infty$, we obtain, formally,

$$\sum_1^\infty f(n) = \int_0^\infty f(x)\,dx - \tfrac{1}{2}f(0) - \tfrac{1}{12}f'(0) + \tfrac{1}{720}f'''(0) - \cdots.$$

If we take $f(n) = (10 + n)^{-2}$, we find

$$\sum_1^\infty n^{-2} = (1 + 2^{-2} + \cdots + 10^{-2}) + \sum_1^\infty f(n)$$

$$= 1.54976\ 77312 + \int_{10}^\infty x^{-2}\,dx - \tfrac{1}{2}(10)^{-2} + \tfrac{1}{12}(2!)(10)^{-3}$$

$$- \tfrac{1}{720}(4!)(10)^{-5} - \cdots$$

$$= 1.54976\ 77312 + .10000\ 00000 - .00500\ 00000$$
$$+ .00016\ 66667 - .00000\ 03333 + .00000\ 00024 + \cdots$$

$$= 1.64493\ 40670.$$

This is to be compared with

$$\pi^2/6 = 1.64493\ 40668.$$

A naïve approach to the evaluation of $\sum_1^\infty n^{-2}$ shows that the remainder after n terms is about n^{-1}, so that a direct summation is not feasible.

In a similar way, it is possible to evaluate $\sum_0^\infty (2n + 1)^{-2}$ by applying the Euler-Maclaurin formula to the tail $(21)^{-2} + (23)^{-2} + (25)^{-2} + \cdots$ of the series. We have

$$\int_0^\infty \frac{dx}{(21 + 2x)^2} = \frac{1}{2\cdot 21}$$

and so

$$\sum_0^\infty (2n + 1)^{-2} = (1 + 3^{-2} + \cdots + 19^{-2}) + \frac{1}{2\cdot 21}$$

$$+ \left(\frac{1}{2}\frac{1}{21^2} + \frac{1}{12}\frac{4}{21^3} - \frac{1}{720}\frac{24\cdot 8}{21^5} + \frac{1}{30240}\frac{720\cdot 32}{21^7} + \cdots\right)$$

$$= 1.20872\ 1307 + .02380\ 9524 + .00116\ 9715$$

$$= 1.23370\ 0548,$$

which is to be compared with

$$\pi^2/8 = 1.23370\ 0550.$$

2.16 Gaussian-type Quadratures

We have noted that a Lagrangian $(n + 1)$-point quadrature, with arbitrary nodes, is exact for polynomials of degree at most n. Can we do better than this if we choose the x_i cleverly?

If we consider the equality

$$\int f(x)\,dx = \sum A_i f(x_i)$$

or, more generally,

$$\int f(x)p(x)\,dx = \sum A_i f(x_i), \qquad (2.15)$$

where $p(x)$ is a fixed, positive weight function, we see that there are $(2n + 2)$ constants on the right.   One might expect to evaluate these by requiring that (2.15) be satisfied for $f(x) = x^r$, $r = 0, 1, \ldots, 2n + 1$. In this case, since the operations are linear, there would be equality in (2.15) when f is a polynomial of degree $2n + 1$ at most.   We shall show that this is indeed possible, relying on the general theory of orthogonal polynomials.

Let $f_0, f_1, \ldots, f_n, \ldots$ be the normal orthogonal system constructed from $1, x, \ldots, x^n, \ldots$.   Let $x_i = x_i^{(n)}$, $i = 1, 2, \ldots, n$ be the n real zeros of $f_n(x)$.   Let $f(x)$ be any polynomial of degree $2n + 1$ at most.   Then we can write

$$f(x) = q(x)f_{n+1}(x) + r(x) \qquad (2.15')$$

where the quotient $q(x)$ and the remainder $r(x)$ are each of degree n at most.   We then have

$$\int f(x)p(x)\,dx = \int q(x)f_{n+1}(x)p(x)\,dx + \int r(x)p(x)\,dx.$$

By orthogonality, the first integral on the right vanishes.   Hence

$$\int f(x)p(x)\,dx = \int r(x)p(x)\,dx$$

and, if we use an $(n + 1)$-point Lagrangian quadrature, the integral on the right is exactly

$$\sum A_i r(x_i).$$

But, from (2.15'), since $f_{n+1}(x_i) = 0$ for all i,

$$f(x_i) = r(x_i).$$

Hence

$$\int f(x)p(x)\,dx = \sum A_i f(x_i);$$

that is, the quadrature based on the nodes $\{x_i^{(n+1)}\}$ is exact for f.

The coefficients A_i are often called the Christoffel numbers.   It can be shown that they are always positive.

The fact, just established, that an $(n + 1)$-point Gaussian quadrature is exact for polynomials of degree at most $2n + 1$ suggests that, in the general case, the error might be a multiple of $f^{(2n+2)}(\xi)$. This can be established by integrating the Hermite interpolation formula

$$f(x) = H_{2n+1}(x) + \frac{f^{(2n+2)}(\xi)}{(2n + 2)!} \prod_{i=0}^{n} (x - x_i)^2, \qquad \xi = \xi(x)$$

to get

$$\int_a^b f(x)p(x) \, dx - \sum A_i f(x_i) = \frac{f^{(2n+2)}(\xi')}{(2n + 2)!} \int_a^b \prod_{i=0}^{n} (x - x_i)^2 p(x) \, dx,$$
$$a \le \xi' \le b.$$

The integral on the right does not depend on f and can be evaluated once for all; the values in the classical cases are given in Chap. 3.

The values of the abscissas and the Christoffel numbers or multipliers in various cases have been tabulated adequately (see, e.g., references given in Chap. 3).

We discuss one example, the calculation of $E_1(z) = \int_z^\infty (e^{-u}/u) \, du$, for two cases: (a) for $z = 10$, a real value of z, and (b) for $z = 10 + 5i$. We change the variable and obtain

$$e^z E_1(z) = I_1 - iI_2$$

where

$$I_1 = \int_0^\infty e^{-\rho} \frac{x + \rho}{(x + \rho)^2 + y^2} \, d\rho, \qquad I_2 = \int_0^\infty e^{-\rho} \frac{y}{(x + \rho)^2 + y^2} \, d\rho.$$

The Laguerre quadrature

$$I = \int_0^\infty e^{-t} f(t) \, dt \doteq \sum A_i^{(n)} f(x_i^{(n)}) = Q$$

is applicable. We shall use the values of $A_i^{(n)}$, $x_i^{(n)}$ obtained by Salzer and Zucker and shall use $n = 5$:

$x_i^{(5)}$			$A_i^{(5)}$		
.26356	03197	18	.52175	56105	83
1.41340	30591	07	.39866	68110	83
3.59642	57710	41	.07594	24496	817
7.08581	00058	59	.00361	17586	7992
12.64080	08442	76	.00002	33699	723858

(a) In this case, $I_2 = 0$, and we have

$$I_1 \doteq Q_1 = \sum A_i \frac{1}{10 + x_i}.$$

All that is now required is to make a table of reciprocals of $10 + x_i$ and accumulate the product $A_i(10 + x_i)^{-1}$. We find

$$Q_1 = .09156\ 33319,$$

which is to be compared with

$$I_1 = e^{10}E_1(10) = .09156\ 3334,$$

with an error of about 2×10^{-9}.

(b) In this case, both I_1 and I_2 are different from zero.   We have

$$I_1 \doteq Q_1 = \Sigma A_i \frac{-10 + x_i}{25 + (x_1 - 10)^2}, \qquad I_2 \doteq Q_2 = \Sigma A_i \frac{5}{25 + (x_i - 10)^2},$$

and we begin by making a table of

$$-10 + x_i, \qquad 25 + (x_i - 10)^2, \qquad \lambda_i = A_i/[25 + (x_i - 10)^2]$$

for $i = 1(1)5$. We then obtain the Q_1 and Q_2 by accumulating the products $\Sigma\ \lambda_i(x_i - 10)$ and $\Sigma\ 5\lambda_i$. We find

$$I_1 = -.08475\ 7264,$$
$$I_2 = .04826\ 1807,$$

which are to be compared with the correct values:

$$\text{Re}[\exp\ (-10 + 5i)E_1(-10 + 5i)] = -.08475\ 749$$
$$\text{Im}[\exp\ (-10 + 5i)E_1(-10 + 5i)] = -.04826\ 039.$$

The error is of the order 2×10^{-6}.

It is easy to estimate the error. Indeed, the $2n$th derivatives of $(x + t)/[(x + t)^2 + y^2]$ and $y/[(x + t)^2 + y^2]$ are

$$(n!)^2 r_1^{-2n-1} \cos (2n + 1)\theta \qquad \text{and} \qquad (n!)^2 r_2^{-2n-1} \sin (2n + 1)\theta,$$

where $r_i = [(x + \xi_i)^2 + y^2]^{\frac{1}{2}}$, $0 \le \xi_i \le \infty$; and θ_i is defined by $\cos \theta_i = (x + \xi_i)/r_i$, $\sin \theta_i = y/r_i$. Hence the errors do not exceed

$$\frac{(n!)^2}{(x^2 + y^2)^{n+\frac{1}{2}}}, \qquad x \ge 0; \qquad \text{or} \qquad \frac{(n!)^2}{|y|^{2n+1}}, \qquad x \le 0.$$

We observe that the bound increases as z approaches the negative real axis and that there is an optimum value of n, about $|z|$ in the case $n \ge 0$ and about $|y|$ when $x \le 0$.

For further details see Todd [18]

2.17   Use of Functional Analysis

In all the methods discussed so far, the error estimates depend on a value of a high derivative of the integrand at an intermediate point.   In many cases it is not easy to find reasonable bounds.   An alternative approach, by the methods of functional analysis, has been developing recently: the error is expressed in terms of a norm of the integrand.   For an example, we refer to Chap. 1, Sec. 1.6(a).   The method is elaborated in Chap. 14 and in various papers—for example, those by Davis [30, 31] and Langer [32].

2.18   Comparison of Methods

Many of the arguments given in Sec. 2.8 regarding the relative merits of Lagrangian and finite-difference methods for interpolation apply again in the present context.   Here we have also to evaluate the Gaussian-type methods.   It is clear that the latter are not likely to be very practical when the integrand is tabulated at equal intervals, for preliminary interpolations will be necessary to evaluate the $f(x_i)$, and these may out-balance any gain due to the smaller error estimates.   On the other hand, if the integrand is not tabulated, the Gaussian type may be very convenient; this is certainly so in two cases: (1) when automatic computers are being used and the evaluation of $f(x_i)$ does not depend on the number of decimals in the argument and (2) when $f(x_i)$ is being evaluated experimentally and the x_i are set once for all.

2.19   Multiple Integrals

Many of the points raised in connection with multivariate interpolation are again relevant here.   We can evaluate multiple integrals as repeated integrals, and this is probably the most satisfactory method for occasional use.   However, when much multiple integration has to be done, more powerful methods should be considered.   In addition to Irwin's Tract, there is a considerable body of recent literature—for example, the papers by Hammer and his collaborators [33, 59] and by Thacher [34].

There has been some investigation, particularly by Hsu, of approximating to a multiple integral by a line integral, where the line reconnoiters the region of integration.

2.20   The Monte Carlo Method

This method has been used as a tool in the evaluation of multiple integrals.   It has been used, essentially, as a last resort, and, at most, qualitative error estimates were given.   A computational experiment for a nine-dimensional integral was carried out by Davis and Rabinowitz [35] (see Chap. 4).

2.21 Bad Examples

We mention here some quadratures which present considerable diffi-culties.

(a) Tabulate $I(x) = \int_0^x (1 - t^2)^{-\frac{1}{2}} dt$ for $x = 0(.02)1$, to 6D without using its indefinite integral.   This is to be compared with the discussion of auxiliary functions in Sec. 2.9.   The removal of the singularity by the device

$$I(x) = \int_0^x \{(1 - t^2)^{-\frac{1}{2}} - [2(1 - t)]^{-\frac{1}{2}}\} dt + \int_0^x [2(1 - t)]^{-\frac{1}{2}} dt$$

and the direct integration of the second term leave only the first term on the right to be dealt with; in this the integrand is smooth at $x = 1$.

(b) Tabulate the Airy integral $\mathrm{Ai}(x) = \pi^{-1} \int_0^\infty \cos(\frac{1}{3}xt^3 + xt)\, dt$. This quadrature is not feasible, and an appropriate method is to verify that $\mathrm{Ai}(x)$ satisfies the differential equation $y'' = xy$ and to proceed to solve this equation numerically (see BAAS 12).

(c) Hartree [36] has discussed in detail the evaluation of integrals of the form

$$\frac{C_1}{S_1} = \frac{1}{2\beta} \int_{-\beta}^{+\beta} \frac{\cos}{\sin} (x \cos \theta - y \sin \theta) \cos \theta\, d\theta$$

for a given value of β (about .7) and for x, y varying up to 60 and 40, respectively.

2.22 Integral Equations

We indicate here methods of solving integral equations numerically. For a systematic account, see Fox and Goodwin [37].   See also Prasad [38].

(a) Consider the numerical solution of an integral equation of the Fredholm type

$$f(x) = g(x) + \int_a^b f(t)k(x,t)\, dt$$

for $f(x)$, where $g(x)$ and the kernel $k(x,t)$ are given.   We decide that it will be sufficient if we know the ordinates $f(x_i)$, where $a \le x_1 < x_2 < \cdots < x_n \le b$.   Replacing x by x_i in the above equation and replacing

$$\int_a^b f(t)k(x_i,t)\, dt$$

by a suitable quadrature

$$\sum A_i f(x_i),$$

we obtain a set of n linear equations

$$f(x_i) = g(x_i) + \sum A_i f(x_i), \qquad i = 1, 2, \ldots, n.$$

The solution of this system will give the $f(x_i)$ required.   It is usual to take the x_i as the abscissas of a suitable Gaussian quadrature; the determination of $f(x)$ elsewhere is a problem of interpolation.

For applications in the theory of conformal mapping using automatic computers see Todd and Warschawski [64], Stiefel [65], and Todd [66]. For a discussion of a nonlinear integral equation, in the same area, using desk machines, see Ostrowski [39, 40].

(*b*) Consider now an equation of the form

$$f(x) = g(x) + \int_0^x f(t)k(x,t) \, dt \, .$$

for $f(x)$ where $g(x)$ and $k(x,t)$ are given.   We propose to tabulate $f(x)$ at interval h.   If $f(x)$ is known for $x = 0, h, \ldots, (n-1)h$ and we approximate the integral by the Gregory formula, we get a linear equation for $f(nh)$.   To apply this idea, it is necessary to determine the initial values of $f(x)$, and the number of these required is twice the order of the appropriate Gregory formula.   In many cases it may be possible to obtain a power series expansion for $f(x)$ about the origin which will indicate the appropriate formula and give the required values.   From then on, the process is easy, and various conveniences will suggest themselves, especially in the case when $k(x,t)$ depends only on $x - t$.

As an example, consider the solution of

$$y(x) = 2x + 3 - \int_0^x y(t) \, [2(x - t) + 3] \, dt, \qquad y(0) = 3.$$

It is readily verified that the solution to this is

$$y(x) = 4e^{-2x} - e^{-x},$$

and this can be used to check the numerical solution to be given.   If we differentiate the equation, we obtain $y'(0) = -7$ and, for $n \geq 1$,

$$y^{(n+1)}(0) = -3y^{(n)}(0) - 2y^{(n-1)}(0),$$

so that

$$y(x) = 3 - 7x + \tfrac{15}{2}x^2 - \tfrac{31}{6}x^3 + \tfrac{21}{8}x^4 - \cdots.$$

If we consider working to 5D, at an interval of .1, we find that the use of the Gregory formula, omitting sixth and higher differences, is appropriate.   This means that we must compute $y(x)$ from the series for $x = 0(.1)1$, and the first value to be obtained will be $y(1.1)$.   The values are given in the table below.   We rewrite the relevant Gregory formula in Lagrangian form:

$$\int_0^n f(p)\, dp = \tfrac{1}{2}f(0) + f(1) + \cdots + f(n-1) + \tfrac{1}{2}f(n)$$
$$+ \tfrac{1}{12}\{[f(1) - f(0)] - [f(n) - f(n-1)]\}$$
$$- \tfrac{1}{24}\{[f(2) - 2f(1) + f(0)] + [f(n) - 2f(n-1)$$
$$+ f(n-2)]\}$$
$$+ \tfrac{19}{720}\{[f(3) - 3f(2) + 3f(1) - f(0)] - [f(n)$$
$$- 3f(n-1) + 3f(n-2) - f(n-3)]\}$$
$$- \tfrac{3}{160}\{[f(4) - 4f(3) + 6f(2) - 4f(1) + f(0)]$$
$$+ [f(n) - 4f(n-1) + 6f(n-2) - 4f(n-3)$$
$$+ f(n-4)]\}$$
$$+ \tfrac{863}{60480}\{[f(5) - 5f(4) + 10f(3) - 10f(2) + 5f(1)$$
$$- f(0)] - [f(n) - 5f(n-1) + 10f(n-2)$$
$$- 10f(n-3) + 5f(n-4) - f(n-5)]\}$$
$$= \sum_{i=0}^n a_i f(i)$$

where $a_0 = .31559,$ $a_1 = 1.39218,$ $a_2 = .62398,$
$a_3 = 1.24408,$ $a_4 = .90900,$ $a_5 = 1.01427,$
$a_{n-i} = a_i,$ $i = 0, 1, 2, 3, 4, 5,$
$a_r = 1$ otherwise.

This expression is valid only in the form written for $n \geq 11$.   Applying this to our equation, we find, writing

$$2x + 3 = g(x), \qquad 2(x - t) + 3 = k(x - t)$$

and using an interval h,

$$y_n = g_n - h(a_0 y_0 k_n + a_1 y_1 k_{n-1} + \cdots + a_0 y_n k_0),$$

which gives

$$y_n = (1 + h a_0 k_0)^{-1}[g_n - h(a_0 y_0 k_n + a_1 y_1 k_{n-1} + \cdots$$
$$+ a_2 k_2 y_{n-2} + a_1 k_1 y_{n-1})].$$

In our case, $a_0 = .31559,$ $k_0 = 3,$ $h = .1,$ so that $h a_0 k_0 = .094677.$ A little thought about the progress of the calculation suggests the tabular arrangement below.

x	y	ay	5.4	5.4	1.2
0	3.00000	.94677	5.2	5.2	1.1
.1	2.37009	3.29959	5.0	5.0	1.0
.2	1.86255	1.16219	4.8	4.8	.9
.3	1.45443	1.80943	4.6	4.6	.8
.4	1.12700	1.02546	4.4	4.4	.7
.5	.86499	.87733	4.2	4.2	.6
.6	.65596	.65596	4.05708	4.0	.5
.7	.48980	.48980	3.45762	3.8	.4
.8	.35826	.35826	4.47869	3.6	.3
.9	.25463	.25463	2.12153	3.4	.2
1.0	.17346	.17346	4.45498	3.2	.1
1.1		.11034	.94677	3.0	0
1.2			ak	k	x

We begin our calculation by accumulating the 11 products of adjacent terms in the central columns of our table to get the term in parentheses in the expression

$$y_{11} = \frac{5.2 - .1(.94677 \times 5.2 + 3.29959 \times 5.0 + \cdots + .17346 \times 4.45498)}{1.094677}$$

$$= \frac{5.2 - 5.07922}{1.094677}$$

$$= .11034.$$

We enter this as indicated, and the next step is to displace the right-hand half so that 5.4 is opposite .94677 and 4.45498 opposite .11034. We then obtain

$$y_{12} =$$
$$\frac{5.4 - .1(.94677 \times 5.4 + \cdots + .17346 \times 2.12153 + .11034 \times 4.45498)}{1.094677}$$

$$= .06167.$$

And so on. This should be continued until, say, $x = 3$ and the result compared with the solution

$$y_{30} = .03987.$$

Observe that the values of y should be differenced as they are obtained to ensure that the neglect of the sixth and higher differences of the integrand is legitimate.

2.23 Numerical Differentiation

Various expressions for the derivatives of a tabulated function can be obtained by manipulation of the finite-difference operators. Thus, from $E = \exp hD$, we find

$$hD = \log (1 + \Delta) = \Delta - \tfrac{1}{2}\Delta^2 + \tfrac{1}{3}\Delta^3 - \cdots, \qquad (2.16)$$

and from $\delta = 2 \sinh \ (\tfrac{1}{2}hD)$ we obtain

$$h^2D^2 = \delta^2 - \tfrac{1}{12}\delta^4 + \tfrac{1}{90}\delta^6 - \cdots .$$

These, of course, can be rearranged in Lagrangian form.

Alternatively, take the Newton-Gregory interpolation formula

$$f(p) = f(0) + p\Delta f(0) + \tfrac{1}{2}(p^2 - p)\Delta^2 f(0)$$
$$+ \tfrac{1}{6}(p^2 - 3p^2 + 2p)\Delta^3 f(0) + \cdots, \qquad (2.17)$$

differentiate it with respect to p, and then put $p = 0$,

$$hf'(0) = \Delta f(0) - \tfrac{1}{2}\Delta^2 f(0) + \tfrac{1}{3}\Delta^3 f(0) - \cdots,$$

which is (2.16).   If we include the remainder term in (2.17), which is of the form

$$\frac{h^n}{n!} f^n(\xi),$$

and attempt to differentiate it, we come up against the generally unknown behavior of ξ as a function of p.   It is, however, possible to obtain error estimates in the various differentiation formulas.

Apart from these theoretical difficulties, it is intuitively obvious that numerical differentiation is delicate; the round-off errors in tabular values will be magnified on division by the powers of h on the left in the formula.   This suggests that, the larger the interval used, the better. Actually, of course, there is an optimal size.   This is discussed in detail by Kopal ([41], p. 104).   We outline the arguments.

We regard the total error as built up from that due to round-off and that due to truncation.   The first can be estimated in terms of the precision of the tabulation, and the latter depends on the formula used; but each depends on the interval h of tabulation.   It is clear that the round-off error will depend on a negative power of h, and the truncation error on a positive power; in general, therefore, there will be an optimal choice of h.

To fill in the details of such an argument, we have to specify the precision of our tabulation and the formulas and the error norm used.

DIFFERENTIAL EQUATIONS

2.24   Introduction

In this part of the chapter we discuss briefly the integration of ordinary differential equations of a simple type and the solution of simple difference equations.

We have seen in the two earlier sections of this chapter how the use of auxiliary functions and the removal of singularities facilitate interpolation and quadrature. The same is true in the present context. This was apparent to Jacobi, who wrote, "The principal difficulty in the integration of given differential equations appears to be the introduction of appropriate variables. One must use an inverse process; after finding a noteworthy change of variables, one must try to find problems to which this will apply."

Occasionally the simplest solution will be provided by evaluating the analytical solution, either directly or by the use of tables. The compendium of Kamke [42] is invaluable, followed by reference to the indices of Fletcher, Miller, and Rosenhead [43] and of Lebedev and Fedorova [44]. But it is easy to construct examples (see [25], p. 80 and (b) in Sec. 2.27) where this method is not the most convenient.

2.25   The Picard Method

Some of the existence theorems in theoretical analysis are constructive in character and can be used to provide numerical solutions. For instance, the Picard method for the initial-value problem

$$y' = f(x,y), \qquad y(a) = b$$

suggests the definition of a sequence of function $y_n(x)$ by

$$y_0(x) \equiv b,$$
$$y_{n+1}(x) = b + \int_a^x f[t,y_n(t)] \, dt.$$

Under mild assumptions on $f(x,y)$, it can be proved that the sequence $\{y_n(x)\}$ has a limit which is the unique solution of our problem. Since we have quadrature methods at our disposal, it would be possible to evaluate each y_n in turn until a satisfactory approximate solution is obtained.

A little experience shows that this method is not a very practical one, except in the neighborhood of a. We find that we have essentially a two-dimensional solution to a one-dimensional problem; we have to tabulate *each* $y_n(x)$. It will be seen that modifications of our quadrature process enable us to traverse the interval (a,x) once only.

Consider the solution of $y' = 2xy$, $y(0) = 1$, in particular the determination to 4D of $y(.5)$ and $y(1)$. [The actual solution is $y = \exp(-x^2)$.] Instead of carrying out the quadratures numerically, we can do them analytically in this case and obtain $y_0 = 1$, $y_1 = 1 - x^2$, $y_2 = 1 - x^2 + \frac{1}{2}x^4$, $y_3 = 1 - x^2 + \frac{1}{2}x^4 - \frac{1}{6}x^6, \ldots$, the initial segments of the power series for y. It is clear then that, even if our quadratures were exact, it would take about four quadratures to get $y(.5)$ and about eight to get $y(1)$ to the required accuracy.

2.26   Local Taylor Series

Whenever the differential equation is such that it is easy to obtain the nth derivative of the solution—for example, by a recurrence relation—the following method is very suitable.   It has checks at every stage, and large intervals can be used.   We discuss two examples.

(a) $$y' = y - x^2, \qquad y(0) = 3.$$

The solution is $y = e^x + x^2 + 2x + 2$.   Here

$$y' = y - x^2, \quad y'' = y - x^2 - 2x, \quad y^{(3)} = y^{(4)} = \cdots = y - x^2 - 2x - 2.$$

We use an interval $h = .3$ and compute to 5D:

	$x = 0$	$x = .3$	$x = .6$
y	3.00000	4.03986	5.38212
hy'	.90000	1.18496	1.50664
$h^2 y''/2!$	.13500	.15074	.17200
$h^3 y^{(3)}/3!$	.00450	.00607	.00820
$h^4 y^{(4)}/4!$	.00034	.00046	.00061
$h^5 y^{(5)}/5!$	.00002	.00003	.00004
$\Sigma\, h^n y^{(n)}/n!$	4.03986	5.38212	7.06961
$\Sigma\, (-h)^n y^{(n)}/n!$	2.23082	3.00000	4.03985

Adding the first six entries in the first column we get $y(.3)$; if we add with alternate signs, we get $y(-.3)$.   From the computed value of $y(.3)$, we obtain the first six entries in the second column, using the expressions for $y^{(n)}$.   We then obtain $y(.6)$ and $y(0)$—the latter checks with the initial value.   From $y(.6)$ we build up the third column, and so on.

If we attempt to use a larger interval, say $h = 1.5$, we find we need to take 11 terms instead of 6.

(b) $$(x^2 - 1)y'' + 2xy' - 6y = 0, \qquad y(6) = .00063\ 2330,$$
$$y'(6) = -.00032\ 1299.$$

The solution to this is $y = Q_2(x) = (\tfrac{3}{2}x^2 - \tfrac{1}{2}) \log [(x + 1)/(x - 1)] - \tfrac{3}{2}x$.   Writing $\tau_n = h^n y^{(n)}/n!$, we find

$$(x^2 - 1)\tau_{n+2} + [2hx(n + 1)/(n + 2)]\tau_{n+1}$$
$$+ [h^2(n - 2)(n + 3)/(n + 1)(n + 2)]\tau_n = 0.$$

We can use $h = .1$ and integrate from $x = 6$ to $x = 7$ and compare the results obtained with the correct solution:

$$y(7) = .00039\ 5644, \qquad y'(7) = -.00017\ 1573.$$

In this case, in addition to computing $\Sigma\,(\pm 1)^n \tau_n$ to predict and to correct y, we have to compute $\Sigma\, n(\pm 1)^n \tau_n$ to predict and correct y', for our recurrence relations are three-term ones.

2.27   Predictor-Corrector Methods

We describe a rather primitive method of the predictor-corrector type, which shows the idea; for more elaborate methods, see, for example, Milne [45].

If we write $I(n) = \int_0^{nh} f(t)\,dt$ and $f(n) = f(nh)$, two earlier results can be stated in the following form:

Milne: $I(4) - I(0) = 4h[2f(1) - f(2) + 2f(3)]/3,$

with an error of $14 M_4' h^5/45,$

Simpson: $I(4) - I(0) = 2h[f(0) + 4f(2) + f(4)]/3,$

with an error of $-16 M_4'' h^5/45,$

where M_4', M_4'' are values of $f^{(4)}(x)$ at some intermediate points.   Consider the differential equation

$$y'(x) = f(x,y), \qquad y(0) = I(0)$$

and suppose that we have obtained (adequate approximations to) $f(1) = f(h,y(h)), f(2), f(3)$.   Then, using the first formula, we can predict $I(4) = y(4)$.   Using this, we can compute $f(4)$ and then use the second formula to obtain another estimate for $y(4)$.   If the two values of $y(4)$ do not disagree too violently, we can accept their mean as a final value—for the errors are almost equal and opposite—and proceed.   In the event of violent disagreement, a change to a smaller h is indicated.

We discuss two examples.

(a) Solve $y' = x + y, y(0) = 1$ for $0 \le x \le 1$, to 4D.   The correct solution is $y = 2e^x - 1 - x$, so that $y(1) = 2e - 2 = 3.43656\ldots$.   Using an interval $h = .1$ and assuming that $y(.1), y(.2), y(.3)$ are known, our computation begins as follows:

x	y		$y' = f(x,y) = x + y$
0	1.0000		1.0000
.1	1.1103		1.2103
.2	1.2428		1.4428
.3	1.3997		1.6997
.4	1.5836	1.5836	1.9836
.5	1.7974	1.7974	2.2974
.6	2.0442		2.6442
.7			
.8			
.9			
1.0			

(b) Solve the equation $y' = x^2 - y^2, y(0) = 1$, for $0 \leq x \leq 1$.   It can be shown that

$$y(x) = x \frac{\Gamma(\frac{1}{4})I_{3/4}(\frac{1}{2}x^2) + 2\Gamma(\frac{3}{4})I_{3/4}(\frac{1}{2}x^2)}{\Gamma(\frac{1}{4})I_{1/4}(\frac{1}{2}x^2) + 2\Gamma(\frac{3}{4})I_{1/4}(\frac{1}{2}x^2)},$$

and using tables of the fractional Bessel functions (NBSCUP 10, 11), we find

$$y(1) = .75001\ 5703.$$

Instead of using the corrector noted above, we could use

$$I(4) - I(2) = h[f(2) + 4f(3) + f(4)]/3 \qquad \text{with an error of } -M_4'''h^5/90.$$

We can now observe that, if the difference between the predictor and the corrector does not exceed 15 units (in the last place, e.g.), then the error in the corrector may be estimated as about half a unit.

These methods can be applied to vectorial equations.   For simplicity, consider the system

$$\dot{x} = yf_2(t), \qquad \dot{y} = xf_1(t), \qquad x(0), y(0) \text{ given,}$$

where dots indicate differentiation with respect to t.   We assume that $x, \dot{x}, y, \dot{y}$ are known for $t = 0, 1, 2, 3$.   Then we proceed as follows:

1. Predict $x(4)$ by Milne.
2. Compute $\dot{y}(4)$ from $\dot{y} = xf_1(t)$.
3. Predict $y(4)$ by Milne.
4. Check $y(4)$ by Simpson.
5. Compute $\dot{x}(4)$ from $\dot{x} = yf_2(t)$.
6. Check $x(4)$ by Simpson.

2.28 Euler, Heun, and Runge-Kutta Methods

One of the most naïve approaches to the numerical solution of $y' = f(x,y), y(x_0) = y_0$ is associated with Euler.   It consists in defining the solution by the relation

$$y(n + 1) = y(n) + hf(nh, y(n)), \qquad n \geq 0; \qquad y(0) = y_0. \quad (2.18)$$

If we assume that y can be expanded as a power series in h, it is clear that the local error is $O(h^2)$.   This means that we might expect a total error of about $O(h)$, for over a fixed range we would have $O(h^{-1})$ steps, and if we assume the errors additive, we have $O(h^{-1})O(h^2) = O(h)$.   This is therefore not a very practical method; we note, however, that it requires no special starting devices.

A slightly more complicated method is due to Heun; it has a smaller error but retains the advantages of requiring no special starting devices. It consists of the following scheme, for $n \geq 0$:

$$\begin{aligned} y^*(n + 1) &= y(n) + hf(nh, y(n)), \\ y^{**}(n + 1) &= y(n) + hf((n + 1)h, y^*(n + 1)), \qquad (2.19) \\ y(n + 1) &= \tfrac{1}{2}(y^*(n + 1) + y^{**}(n + 1)). \end{aligned}$$

Again, assuming the existence of a power series expansion for y, we find that the local error is $O(h^3)$; more specifically, it does not exceed

$$\tfrac{1}{12}h^3 \, |y'''(\xi)|, \qquad nh \leq \xi \leq (n+1)h,$$

if we assume that $f(x,y)$ is independent of y, that is, that we are carrying out an indefinite integration. If we allow for the dependence on y, the above bound must be replaced by

$$\tfrac{1}{12}h^3 \left| y'''(\xi) - 3y''(\xi) \left(\frac{\partial f}{\partial y} \right)_{(\xi,\eta)} \right|.$$

This means that the total error, in favorable cases, is $O(h^2)$, which makes the scheme a feasible one.

We note that this scheme is likely to be more efficient than a straightforward generalization of the Euler process. For if we used

$$y(n+1) = y(n) + hf(nh,y(n)) + \tfrac{1}{2}h^2\{f_x(nh,y(n)) + f_y(nh,y(n))f(nh,y(n))\},$$

we should have to evaluate f, f_x, f_y at each step instead of f twice if we used (2.19).

The above error estimates do not hold whenever the solution cannot be expanded as a power series. If we take a trivial case

$$y' = x^{1/2},$$

we see that the local error is $O(h^{3/2})$, not $O(h^3)$. It is instructive to study the following classical example in the range $[0,1]$,

$$y' = \sqrt{x} + \sqrt{y}, \qquad y(0) = 0, \tag{2.20}$$

which has a solution of the form

$$y = \tfrac{2}{3}x^{3/2} + \tfrac{4}{7}(\tfrac{2}{3})^{1/2}x^{7/4} + \tfrac{1}{7}x^2 + \tfrac{1}{49}(\tfrac{2}{3})^{1/2}x^{9/4} - \tfrac{2}{1715}x^{5/2} + \cdots.$$

For a recent discussion, see Richter [46]. In order to make use of automatic computers which recognize numbers x, $|x| < 1$ only, we change the scale in each variable in (2.20) by a factor 4, and we shall discuss, instead of (2.20),

$$y' = \tfrac{1}{2}\sqrt{x} + \tfrac{1}{2}\sqrt{y}, \qquad y(0) = 0$$

in the range $0 \leq x \leq .25$. We consider the use of Heun's method, with a variable h. The results of this integration, for $4000h = 1, 5, 10, 50$, have been recorded in Sec. 4.22.

Should the Heun method be unsatisfactory, it is natural to try to get a similar method with a smaller local error. One such method is the Runge-Kutta method, which consists in writing

$$y(n+1) = y(n) + \tfrac{1}{6}[K(1,n) + 2K(2,n) + 2K(3,n) + K(4,n)]$$

where $\qquad K(1,n) = hf[nh, y(n)]$

$$K(2,n) = hf[(n + \tfrac{1}{2})h, y(n) + \tfrac{1}{2}K(1,n)]$$
$$K(3,n) = hf[(n + \tfrac{1}{2})h, y(n) + \tfrac{1}{2}K(2,n)]$$
$$K(4,n) = hf[(n + 1)h, y(n) + K(3,n)].$$

This method is discussed in detail in Chap. 9 (see also Gill [48] and Martin [47]). For the moment, we observe that, when f is independent of y, it specializes to the use of the Simpson rule for the quadrature, that the local error is $O(h^5)$, and that four evaluations of $f(x,y)$ are required in each step. Thus the error here is of the same order as that of the predictor-corrector methods discussed in Sec. 2.27. We can give here a rough comparison between the methods.

First of all, it can be shown that in many representative cases the h appropriate for the Runge-Kutta method is much greater than twice that appropriate for the Heun method, so that the Runge-Kutta method is more efficient, although it requires about twice as much calculation per step. To compare the Runge-Kutta method and the Simpson-Milne method, we note that the local errors in the first can be estimated as $h^5 y^{(5)}(\xi)/2880$ (when f does not depend on y), which is to be compared with $-h^5 y^{(5)}(\xi)/90$ in the second method. The factor of 32 by which they differ implies that the interval h in the first case can be about twice that in the second. This means that the total amount of calculation required is about the same.

Summarizing, we may say that, although the Runge-Kutta method has no checks, it is probably to be preferred for automatic calculators, whereas the Simpson-Milne method is to be preferred for desk computers because of its checks, despite the difficulties at the beginning (which reappear if the interval has to be decreased in the course of the calculation). However, if many desk calculations have to be done, it will be worthwhile investigating some of the more powerful finite-difference methods, such as those discussed in IAT.

We note that it is possible to try the h^2 extrapolation discussed in Sec. 2.33. We can carry out a Heun integration at interval h, then one at interval $\tfrac{1}{2}h$, say, and then improve each ordinate by eliminating the h^2 component in the error.

2.29   Boundary-value Problems

So far we have discussed initial-value problems only. There are, however, various boundary problems for ordinary differential equations which are of practical importance. Many of these are discussed in detail in the texts of Collatz and Fox. We mention briefly two problems.

(*a*) Find a value of λ such that there is a nontrivial solution of the equation

$$y'' + \lambda x y = 0, \qquad y(0) = 0 = y(1).$$

One method of trial and error for this is to guess a value of λ, say λ_1, and solve the resulting initial-value problem, obtaining a value f_1 at $x = 1$. We need to choose some initial slope, which we may take to be $y_1 = 1$.

A reasonable guess for λ_1 can be obtained in the following way. Discretize the problem at interval $h = \frac{1}{4}$ to get

$$y(0) - 2y(\tfrac{1}{4}) + y(\tfrac{1}{2}) = -\tfrac{1}{16} \cdot \tfrac{1}{4} y(\tfrac{1}{4}) \lambda$$
$$y(\tfrac{1}{4}) - 2y(\tfrac{1}{2}) + y(\tfrac{3}{4}) = -\tfrac{1}{16} \cdot \tfrac{1}{2} y(\tfrac{1}{2}) \lambda$$
$$y(\tfrac{1}{2}) - 2y(\tfrac{3}{4}) + y(1) = -\tfrac{1}{16} \cdot \tfrac{3}{4} y(\tfrac{3}{4}) \lambda,$$

where we put $y(0) = y(1) = 0$. This gives a cubic for λ (see Collatz [49a], p. 373; [49c], p. 299).

Having obtained f_1 from λ_1, we take another λ_2 and compute the corresponding f_2. Using these two values, we interpolate and get a new approximation λ_3 for λ. We then obtain f_3 and carry on in this manner.

The exact solution to our problem can be obtained in the following way. The solution to the problem satisfying the left-hand boundary condition only is

$$y = x^{1/2} J_{1/3}(\tfrac{2}{3}\sqrt{\lambda} x^{3/2})$$

If this is to vanish for $x = 1$, we must have (NBSCUP 10, p. 385)

$$\tfrac{2}{3}\sqrt{\lambda} = 2.9025 \ldots, 6.0327 \ldots, \ldots .$$

The least value of λ is therefore

$$\lambda = (4.3438)^2 = 18.9563 \ldots .$$

(*b*) Find the least value of λ for which there is a nontrivial solution of the relations

$$y'' + \lambda y = 0, \qquad y(0) = 0 = y(\pi).$$

It can be shown that, if $u(x)$ is a function satisfying the boundary conditions, then the required value of $\lambda^{1/2}$ is the minimum value of the Rayleigh quotient,

$$R(u) = -\int_0^\pi u u'' \, dx \Big/ \int_0^\pi u^2 \, dx,$$

and the function u which minimizes $R(u)$ is the required solution. Thus, if

$$u_1 = \sin x, \qquad \text{we get} \qquad R(u_1) = 1;$$

if we take

$$u_2 = x(x - \pi), \qquad \text{we get} \qquad R(u_2) = 10/\pi^2 > 1;$$

and if we take

$$u_3 = x(x + \pi)(x - \pi), \qquad \text{we get} \qquad R(u_3) = 21/2\pi^2 > 1.$$

The development of this idea into a practical method requires considerable experience.

2.30 Stability of Numerical Processes for the Solution of Ordinary Differential Equations

The stability of numerical solutions for differential equations is a rather delicate subject and will be treated in more detail in Chap. 9. It is, however, important that the possibilities of catastrophes should always be borne in mind, and it is our purpose to illustrate this in a simple case. It is convenient to interpolate a brief account of the solution of ordinary difference equations with constant coefficients.

There is a vast theory of difference equations, and some of it is parallel to the theory of ordinary differential equations. In particular, the familiar theory of ordinary differential equations with constant coefficients carries over in a natural way.

The solution to the first-order difference equation

$$u_{n+1} = ku_n, \qquad u_0 \text{ given}$$

is manifestly

$$u_n = u_0 k^n.$$

A second-order difference equation can be written, without loss of generality, in the form

$$u_{n+2} - (\alpha + \beta)u_{n+1} + \alpha\beta u_n = 0,$$

which can be rearranged as

$$(u_{n+2} - \alpha u_{n+1}) - \beta(u_{n+1} - \alpha u_n) = 0 \qquad (2.21)$$

or

$$(u_{n+2} - \beta u_{n+1}) - \alpha(u_{n+1} - \beta u_n) = 0.$$

We must now distinguish between (a) the case in which $\alpha \neq \beta$ and (b) the case in which $\alpha = \beta$. In case (a) we can regard (2.21) as a first-order equation for $v_n = u_{n+1} - \alpha u_n$, so that we find

$$u_{n+1} - \alpha u_n = v_0 \beta^n \qquad (2.22)$$

Similarly, we can regard (2.21) as a first-order equation for $w_n = u_{n+1} - \beta u_n$ and obtain

$$u_{n+1} - \beta u_n = w_0 \alpha^n. \qquad (2.23)$$

Eliminating u_{n+1} from (2.22) and (2.23), we find

$$u_n = A\alpha^n + B\beta^n.$$

This method breaks down in case (b). We now obtain only one equation in place of the pair (2.22) and (2.23):

$$u_{n+1} - \alpha u_n = v_0 \alpha^n \qquad (2.24)$$

If we now introduce $w_n = u_n \alpha^{-n}$, this becomes

$$w_{n+1} - w_n = v_0 \alpha^{-1} \qquad (2.25)$$

Summing these last equations, we find

$$w_n - w_0 = n v_0 \alpha^{-1},$$

so that

$$w_n = A + Bn$$

and

$$u_n = (A + Bn)\alpha^n.$$

The extension of these results to equations of higher order is evident. The solution of an initial-value problem

$$y'' = -y, \qquad y(0) = 0, \qquad y'(0) = 1 \qquad (2.26)$$

is essentially reduced to the solution of a recurrence relation for $y(n) = y(nh)$. We can replace the continuous problem (2.26) by a discrete one if we replace the second derivative by $h^{-2}[y(n+2) - 2y(n+1) + y(n)]$:

$$y(n+2) = (2 - h^2)y(n+1) - y(n), \qquad y(0) = 0, \qquad (2.27)$$

where a suitable value of $y(1)$ is to be assigned.

The solution of (2.27) for $h = 1$ with $y(1) = 1$ is

$$y(n) = 0, 1, 1, 0, -1, -1, 0, 1, 1, 0, \ldots.$$

If we take $h = .1$ and $y(1) = \sin .1 = .09983$ and work to 5D, we get the results in column (2) of the table below, which are to be compared with the 10D values of $\sin x$ in column (1). We are therefore getting about 3D accuracy.

If we require more accurate results, it seems natural to take a better approximation than the simple $h^2 y'' = \delta^2 y$ which led to (2.27). If we use

$$h^2 y'' = (\delta^2 - \tfrac{1}{12}\delta^4)y, \qquad (2.28)$$

we get, for $h = .1$:

$$y(n+4) = 16y(n+3) - 29.88y(n+2) + 16y(n+1) - y(n),$$
$$y(0) = 0, \qquad (2.29)$$

where suitable starting values of $y(1), y(2), y(3)$ must be assigned.

In column (3) we have taken $y(i) = \sin i/10$, $i = 1, 2, 3$ and worked to 10D, and in column (4) we have again taken the correct starting values but worked to 5D. These are the catastrophes at which we have hinted and which we shall discuss presently.

Another method replaces the δ^4 in (2.28) by its approximate value $-h^2\delta^2$; in this way we obtain a three-term recurrence,

$$(12 + h^2)\delta^2 y = -12h^2 y,$$

which, in the case $h = .1$, is

$$y(n + 2) = 1.99000\ 83333 y(n + 1) - y(n).$$

The results obtained by the use of this method are recorded in column (5) and are good to 6D.

	(1)	(2)	(3)	(4)	(5)
0	.00000 00000	.00000	.00000 00000	.00000	.00000 00000
.1	.09983 34166	.09983	.09983 34166	.09983	.09983 34166
.2	.19866 93308	.19866	.19866 93308	.19867	.19866 93310
.3	.29552 02067	.29550	.29552 02067	.29552	.29552 02077
.4	.38941 83423	.38939	.38941 83685	.38934	.38941 83450
.5	.47942 55386	.47939	.47942 59960	.47819	.47942 55440
.6	.56464 24734	.56460	.56464 90616	.54721	.56464 24828
.7	.64421 76872	.64416	.64430 99144	.40096	.64421 77021
.8	.71735 60909	.71728	.71864 22373	−2.67357	.71735 61128
.9	.78332 69096	.78323	.80125 45441		.78332 69403
1.0	.84147 09848	.84135	1.09135 22239		.84147 10261
1.1	.89120 73601	.89106	4.37411 56871		.89120 74139
1.2	.93203 90860	.93186			.93203 91543
1.3	.96355 81854	.96334			.96355 82701
1.4	.98544 97300	.98519			.98544 98328
1.5	.99749 49866	.99719			.99749 51092
1.6	.99957 36030	.99922			.99957 37469

A detailed examination of these results has been given by Todd [51]. At present we note only that the solution of the difference equation (2.29) is of the form

$$y(n) = A\alpha^n + B\alpha^{-n} + C \cos n\theta + D \sin n\theta$$

where, to four figures,

$$\alpha = 13.94, \qquad \theta = .1000.$$

The required solution is that in which $A = B = C = 0$, $D = 1$. However, it is clear that, if any component of the solution $A\alpha^n$ enters, it will swamp all the rest. This is indeed what has occurred in (3) and (4); in one case, we get a component with an $A > 0$, and in the other, one with an $A < 0$. These are brought in during the determination of $y(4)$.

MISCELLANEOUS DEVICES

2.31   Introduction

Several interesting processes have been devised to facilitate computations—for example, the Aitken δ^2 process mentioned in Chap. 1.   These were originally conceived for use with desk calculators, but as the customers of the automatic computer became more demanding, such processes have been taken over by the more powerful equipment, and the methods have been developed further.   In addition to the work described here, there have been many investigations by Airey, Bickley, Miller, and Wynn.

2.32   The Aitken δ^2 Process

The Aitken δ^2 process is described in Chap. 1.   We note here that it has been developed recently by Shanks, Lubkin, and Wynn.

The following example is suggested for study.   Find the first few convergents for $\sqrt{19} - 4.3588989 \cdots$ from the (periodic) continued fraction

$$\sqrt{19} = 4 + \frac{1}{2+} \frac{1}{1+} \frac{1}{3+} \frac{1}{1+} \frac{1}{2+} \frac{1}{8+} \cdots$$

and apply the δ^2 method to them.

2.33   Richardson's h^2 Extrapolation, or Deferred Approach to the Limit

The idea of Richardson's h^2 extrapolation is somewhat similar to that of the Aitken scheme.   In general, let $\phi(x)$ be the solution to a continuous problem and $\phi(x,h)$ be the solution to a discrete version of the problem, where h indicates the mesh size.   In some circumstances, we may have

$$\phi(x,h) = \phi(x) + h^2\phi_2(x) + R_2$$

and if R_2 is negligible and if we solve the discrete problem for two values of h, say h_1 and h_2, we have

$$\phi(x,h_1) = \phi(x) + h_1{}^2\phi_2(x)$$
$$\phi(x,h_2) = \phi(x) + h_2{}^2\phi_2(x).$$

From these we can eliminate ϕ_2 to get

$$\phi(x) = \frac{h_2{}^2\phi(x,h_1) - h_1{}^2\phi(x,h_2)}{h_2{}^2 - h_1{}^2} .$$

This plausible device can be applied in other contexts—for instance, when ϕ is a constant or when ϕ is a function of several variables.   We discuss a simple example.

Consider the extrapolation for the circumference of a circle of radius unity, from the lengths of the inscribed squares and hexagon.   We have an estimate of $4\sqrt{2}$ corresponding to a mesh length of $\frac{1}{4}$ and an estimate of 6 corresponding to a mesh length of $\frac{1}{6}$.   This leads to

$$\frac{\frac{1}{36}(4\sqrt{2}) - \frac{1}{16}(6)}{2(\frac{1}{36} - \frac{1}{16})} \doteq 3.1373$$

as an estimate for π.

We note that this method can be applied in the case of the partial differential equation discussed in Chap. 4.   It cannot be applied in the case of the ordinary differential equation discussed in Sec. 2.28 above. For a discussion of other cases when the method is inapplicable, see Wasow [52].

2.34   The Euler Transformation

The Euler summation method is essentially a transformation of one infinite series into another.   It is most convenient to exhibit it in the case of an alternating series.   We proceed formally, using the finite-difference operators:

$$\begin{aligned} u_0 - u_1 + u_2 - \cdots &= (1 - E + E^2 - \cdots)u_0 = (1 + E)^{-1}u_0 \\ &= (2 + \Delta)^{-1}u_0 = \frac{1}{2}(1 + \frac{1}{2}\Delta)^{-1}u_0 \\ &= \frac{1}{2}u_0 - \frac{1}{4}\Delta u_0 + \frac{1}{8}\Delta^2 u_0 - \frac{1}{16}\Delta^3 u_0 + \cdots . \end{aligned}$$

We show the efficacy of this by considering the evaluation of $\ln 2$ from the power series: $\ln 2 = 1 - \frac{1}{2} + \frac{1}{3} - \cdots$.   It is possible to apply the Euler transformation directly to this series, but it is more convenient to apply it to the tail.   We obtain

$$1 - \frac{1}{2} + \cdots - \frac{1}{8} = .63452\ 3809,$$

and we difference the sequence $\frac{1}{9}, \frac{1}{10}, \frac{1}{11}, \frac{1}{12}, \ldots$ thus:

```
.11111 1111
               -.01111 1111
.10000 0000                   +.00202 0202
               -.00909 0909                  -.00050 5051
.09090 9091                   +.00151 5151                  +.00015 5402
               -.00757 5758                  -.00034 9649                  -.00005 5505
.08333 3333
      .
      .
      .
```

The next leading differences are $+.00002\ 2212$, $-.00000\ 9740$, $\ldots$. Using all of these, we find

$$\sum_9^\infty (-1)^{n-1}/n = .05555\ 5556 + .00277\ 7778 + .00025\ 2525 + .00003\ 1566$$
$$+ .00000\ 4856 + .00000\ 0867 + .00000\ 0174 + .00000\ 0038,$$

giving
$$\ln 2 = .69314\ 7169,$$
which we compare with the true value
$$\ln 2 = .69314\ 7181.$$

There does not seem to have been any study of the optimal division of a series into a head and a tail.

We remark that the transformed series always converges if the original one does, but not necessarily more rapidly.

2.35   Asymptotic Expansions

The concept of asymptotic series is used essentially in numerical analysis. We shall discuss a rather primitive case in some detail. The subject is discussed incidentally in many books, and there are several monographs available (see, e.g., Erdélyi [53]).

Whenever the (numerical) behavior of a function over an infinite range, say $0 \leq x < \infty$, is sought, a direct tabulation does not come in question. One answer to this problem is to change the dependent variable—for example, to x^{-1} or x^{-2} (see Sec. 2.9). Another is to obtain a simple approximation to it, valid for large x, say $x \geq x_0$, from which the behavior is obvious and from which the function can be readily calculated to the relevant precision; this analytical expression will replace the tabulation in the infinite range $x_0 \leq x$.

Consider
$$f(x) = \int_x^\infty t^{-1} e^{x-t}\ dt = -e^x \mathrm{Ei}(-x)$$

for $x > 0$, where the integral is manifestly convergent. By successive integration by parts, we find
$$f(x) = \frac{1}{x} - \frac{1}{x^2} + \cdots + \frac{(-1)^{n-1}(n-1)!}{x^n} + (-1)^n n! \int_x^\infty t^{-n-1} e^{x-t}\ dt.$$

If $S_n(x)$ is the sum of the first n terms on the right and $r_n(x)$ is the last term, we have
$$|r_n(x)| = |f(x) - S_n(x)| = n! \int_x^\infty t^{-n-1} e^{x-t}\ dt$$
$$= n!\ x^{-n-1} \int_x^\infty (tx^{-1})^{-n-1} e^{x-t}\ dt$$
$$\leq n!\ x^{-n-1} \int_x^\infty e^{x-t}\ dt$$
$$= n!\ x^{-n-1} [-e^{x-t}]_x^\infty$$
$$= n!\ x^{-n-1}.$$

We want to study this estimate for $r_n(x)$.   First, it is clear that, if we fix n, we can make this remainder as small as we please if we take x sufficiently large.   Secondly, consider, more practically, the behavior of our estimate as a function of n, with x being fixed.   We have

$$n! \, x^{-n-1} = (nx^{-1})[(n-1)! \, x^{-n}],$$

so that our estimate for $|r_n(x)|$ decreases as n increases from 1 to $[x]$, the integral part of x, and then increases to ∞.   Thus, for a fixed value of x, there is a limit to the (estimate for the) accuracy by which we can approximate $f(x)$ by taking a number of terms of the series

$$\sum (-1)^n n! \, x^{-n-1}. \tag{2.30}$$

This is to be carefully distinguished from what happens in the case of a convergent series

$$\sum u_r(x) = S_n(x) + r_n(x),$$

where $|r_n(x)|$ can be made arbitrarily small by taking n sufficiently large. Indeed the series (2.30) is not convergent for any x, since its general term does not tend to zero.   The series has the property that

$$\lim_{x \to \infty} x^n[f(x) - S_n(x)] = 0, \qquad n = 1, 2, \ldots, x > 0.$$

Such a series is said to be asymptotic in the sense of Poincaré, and the relation is denoted by

$$f(x) \sim x^{-1} - x^{-2} + 2! \, x^{-3} - 3! \, x^{-4} + \cdots.$$

In general we write

$$F(x) \sim A_0 + A_1 x^{-1} + A_2 x^{-2} + \cdots, \qquad x \to \infty,$$

whenever

$$\lim x^n[F(x) - (A_0 + A_1 x^{-1} + \cdots + A_n x^{-n})] = 0,$$
$$n = 0, 1, 2, \ldots, x > 0.$$

When this is the case, it is clear that

$$\lim F(x) \qquad\qquad\qquad - A_0$$
$$\lim x[F(x) - A_0] \qquad\qquad = A_1$$
$$\lim x^2[F(x) - A_0 - A_1 x^{-1}] = A_2$$
$$\cdots\cdots\cdots\cdots\cdots\cdots\cdots$$

One of the most useful asymptotic formulas is that of Stirling, which is properly written in the form

$$\log \Gamma(z) - (z - \tfrac{1}{2}) \log z + z \sim \tfrac{1}{2} \log 2\pi + \sum_{r=1}^{\infty} \frac{(-1)^{r-1} B_r}{2r(2r-1) z^{2r-1}}.$$

It is conventional to write this as

$$\log \Gamma(z) \sim (z - \tfrac{1}{2}) \log z - z + \tfrac{1}{2} \log 2\pi + \sum_{r=1}^{\infty} \frac{(-1)^{r-1} B_r}{2r(2r-1) z^{2r-1}}$$

or

$$\Gamma(z) \sim e^{-z} z^z \sqrt{\frac{2\pi}{z}} \left(1 + \frac{1}{12z} + \frac{1}{288z^2} - \cdots \right).$$

The latter is valid for complex z, provided

$$|\arg z| \leq \pi - \delta, \qquad \text{for some } 0 < \delta < \pi.$$

Asymptotic series can be manipulated fairly freely, but precautions are

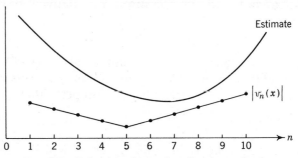

FIG. 2.5   Behavior of actual and estimated error.

necessary.   One of the unexpected phenomena is that of nonuniqueness, because, for instance,

$$e^{-x} \sim 0 + 0 \cdot x^{-1} + 0 \cdot x^{-2} + \cdots.$$

One of the standard methods of deriving asymptotic series is that of integration by parts.   For other methods we have to refer to the literature.

We note that in some cases, in particular the one discussed above, the error at any stage is less than the first omitted term.   We note also that the optimal value of n obtained by consideration of the behavior of our estimate for $|r_n(x)|$ need not be the real optimal.   This is made clear by Fig. 2.5.

To summarize our discussion: it is clear that asymptotic series can be a useful device in the evaluation of functions provided they can give the required precision but, if this is not available, other methods must be used.

We shall now examine a numerical case, $f(x)$, for $x = 15$.   We record on the left the multiplier $n/x = n/15$, which produces the $(n + 1)$st term from the nth.   In the center the actual terms are recorded and on the right the partial sums.

$.0\dot{6}$	.06666 66667	.06666 66667
$.1\dot{3}$	$-.00444\ 44444$	.06222 22223
$.2$	$+.00059\ 25926$	.06281 48149
$.2\dot{6}$	$-.00011\ 85185$	.06269 62964
$.\dot{3}$	$+.00003\ 16049$	.06272 79013
$.4$	$-.00001\ 05350$	.06271 73663
$.4\dot{6}$	$+.00000\ 42140$	.06272 15803
$.5\dot{3}$	$-.00000\ 19665$	.06271 96138
$.6$	$+.00000\ 10488$	.06272 06626
$.\dot{6}$	$-.00000\ 06293$	.06272 00333
$.7\dot{3}$	$+.00000\ 04195$	.06272 04528
$.8$	$-.00000\ 03077$	.06272 01451
$.8\dot{6}$	$+.00000\ 02461$	.06272 03912
$.9\dot{3}$	$-.00000\ 02133$	.06272 01779
$1.$	$+.00000\ 01991$	.06272 03770
$1.0\dot{6}$	$-.00000\ 01991$	.06272 01779
$1.1\dot{3}$	$+.00000\ 02124$	.06272 03903
	$-.00000\ 02407$	.06272 01496

Our arguments suggest that the best estimate for $f(x)$ is that given on the fifteenth line.   As a check on our arithmetic, we can compute the last term directly as

$$\frac{14!}{15^{15}} = \frac{.8718 \times 10^{11}}{4.3790 \times 10^{17}} = 1.9909 \ldots \times 10^{-7},$$

which checks the recorded one.
   The value given in NBSAMS 51 is

$$.062720$$

and that obtained from Coulson and Duncanson [58] is

$$.00000\ 00191\ 8628 \ldots \times 3269017.372 \ldots = .06272\ 028 \ldots.$$

Experiments showed that the Euler process applied to asymptotic series gave sensible results.   We find, for instance, that the sum of the first four terms in $f(15)$ is 0.06269 62966 and that the Euler sum of the tail is .00002 39226, which gives

$$f(15) = .06272\ 02190.$$

If we sum the first eight terms before applying the Euler process, we find

$$f(15) = .06272\ 02790.$$

These processes were justified by Rosser in a paper which contains much other valuable material [54].

For another worked example, see Goodwin and Staton [55].

2.36   Recurrence Relations

The Bessel functions $J_n(x)$ satisfy the recurrence relation

$$J_{n+1}(x) = 2nx^{-1}J_n(x) - J_{n-1}(x).$$

Let us consider the evaluation of $J_{20}(1)$ from this, starting from the values of $J_0(1)$, $J_1(1)$. We find in succession

$$
\begin{aligned}
J_0 &= .76519\ 76866 \\
J_1 &= .44005\ 05857 \\
J_2 &= .11490\ 36848 \\
J_3 &= .01956\ 33535 \\
J_4 &= .00247\ 66362 \\
J_5 &= .00024\ 97381 \\
J_6 &= +.00002\ 09504 \\
J_7 &= -.00000\ 16456
\end{aligned}
$$

To go farther is pointless, for $J_7(1) = +.00000\ 15$. The reason for this loss of significance is the factor $2nx^{-1}$ (any error in $J_1(x)$ is multiplied by 2 in obtaining J_2, the error in J_2 is multiplied by 4 in obtaining J_3, and so on) together with a cancellation effect.

It was observed by Miller (BAAS 10) that sensible results can be obtained by using the recurrence relation backward, that is, in the form

$$J_{n-1} = 2nJ_n - J_{n+1},$$

even though we begin with arbitrary values for J_n, J_{n+1} for a large n. We shall illustrate this.

If we choose, for example, "J"$_{40} = 0$, "J"$_{39} = 1 \times 10^{-8}$, we obtain successively

$$
\begin{aligned}
"J"_{40} &= 0 \\
"J"_{39} &= .00000\ 001 \\
"J"_{38} &= .00000\ 078 \\
"J"_{37} &= .00005\ 927 \\
"J"_{36} &= .00438\ 520 \\
"J"_{35} &= .31567\ 513
\end{aligned}
$$

$$
\vdots
$$

$$"J"_{20} = .43716\ 258 \times 10^{26}.$$

This is, of course, not the correct result, because any multiple of the Bessel functions satisfies the recurrence relation, since it is homogeneous.

To determine the appropriate scale factor, we can consider continuing the recurrence down to obtain "J"$_0$. Comparison of this value with the actual value of J_0 indicates what scale factor is appropriate. This gives

$$J_{20} = 3.87350\ 30 \times 10^{-25}.$$

Another way of determining the scale factor is to use the relation

$$J_0(x) + 2 \sum_{m=1}^{\infty} J_{2m}(x) = 1.$$

This method is applicable in many circumstances and is convenient for use on automatic computers, not only for the Bessel function $J_n(x)$ but for various related functions and for such functions as the Coulomb wave function (see Stegun and Abramowitz [56, 57] and Gautschi [60]).

MATHEMATICAL TABLES

2.37 Introduction

The purpose of this section is to give some advice on the choice and use of mathematical tables. Although it is clearly not possible to cover the detailed needs of all scientists—mathematicians, physicists, chemists, engineers, astronomers, and statisticians, for instance—it seems possible to give information which will satisfy most users of tables and to indicate sources from which they may obtain either more elaborate or less elaborate tables, along with appropriate instructions for their use.

Our main concern is with mathematical tables in the strict sense. We have confined our references to reasonably accessible publications. We have also restricted ourselves, on the whole, to first-class tables. Among the qualities desirable in a table are:

1. Reliability. Various standards of precision are admissible, but these should be stated and maintained.

2. Legibility. This depends on the method of reproduction, the compositor or designer, and the type available.

3. Convenience. Here we are concerned with the arrangement and the ease of interpolation: information should be given about recommended methods and the degree of accuracy which they provide.

It is convenient to distinguish among the books which should be immediately available (i.e., on one's desk), those which should be available in a local library, and those which one should know exist and should know how to obtain on loan. These can roughly be classified as follows:

1. Collections of miscellaneous 3D to 6D tables, together with more extensive tables of special interest. Bibliographical material.

2. Tables of medium accuracy, 6D to 8D. Bibliographical material.

3. Fundamental tables to 8D or more and tables of very special functions.

Many computers find it convenient to use fundamental tables because the fine argument interval may make it possible to avoid interpolation.

2.38 Short List

In the first class we include the following:

P. Barlow, "Tables of Squares, Cubes, . . . ," L. J. Comrie, ed., London, 1941.

E. Jahnke, F. Emde, and F. Lösch, "Tafeln höherer Funktionen," Stuttgart, New York, 1960.

L. J. Comrie, "Chamber's Six-figure Mathematical Tables," vol. II, New York–London, 1949.

or

"Chamber's Shorter Six-figure Mathematical Tables," New York–London, 1950.

or

F. Lösch, "Siebenstellige Tafeln der elementaren transzendenten Funktionen," Berlin, 1954.

There is in preparation a comprehensive volume,

"Handbook of Functions," M. Abramowitz and I. A. Stegun, eds.,

which will appear in the National Bureau of Standards Applied Mathematics Series.

Those who are at all concerned with statistics, either in the design of experiments or in the analysis of the results of experiments, will add to this list such collections as:

R. A. Fisher and F. Yates, "Statistical Tables for Biological, Agricultural and Medical Research," London, 1943.

A. Hold, "Statistical Tables and Formulas," New York, 1952.

E. S. Pearson and H. O. Hartley, "Biometrika Tables for Statisticians," vol. I, London, 1954.

2.39 Bibliographical Material

Every organization which is at all concerned with computation should have available:

A. Fletcher, J. C. P. Miller, and L. Rosenhead, "An Index of Mathematical Tables," London–New York, 1946.

This volume, to which we shall refer as FMR, gives a comprehensive bibliography of mathematical tables, up to 1944.   A revised edition is in preparation.

In 1956 there appeared a Russian index:

A. V. Lebedev and R. M. Federova, "Spravochnik po matematicheskim tablitsiam."

In 1959 a supplement to this was issued:

N. M. Burunova, "Dopolnenie," no. 1.

These can be used even with a very small knowledge of Russian.
The specialist in number theory will require:

D. H. Lehmer, "Guide to Tables in the Theory of Numbers," U.S. National Research Council *Bulletin* 105, 1941.

"An Index of Tables for Statisticians," J. A. Greenwood and H. O. Hartley, eds., is in preparation. It will be divided into Part I, Statistical Tables, and Part II, Selection of Mathematical Tables of Interest to Statisticians.
Mathematical tables are covered by the standard reviewing journals:
Zentralblatt für Mathematik, 1931–
Mathematical Reviews, 1940–
Referativnyĭ Žurnal, 1955–
Computing Reviews, 1960–
but above all in the U.S. National Research Council quarterly,
Mathematical Tables and Other Aids to Computation, 1943–1959,
which has been renamed
Mathematics of Computation, 1960–.
The last journal,
Communications, Assoc. Comput. Mach., 1958–,
and *Numerische Mathematik*, 1959–,
include special accounts of essential equivalents to tables: (rational) approximations to functions, and basic subroutines for automatic computers. Another feature of *Math. Comp.* is monographs on special classes of functions; for example:

H. Bateman and R. C. Archibald, A Guide to Tables of Bessel Functions, *Math. Tables Aids Comput.*, vol. 1, pp. 205–308, 1943–1945.
A. Fletcher, Guide to Tables of Elliptic Functions, *Math. Tables Aids Comput.*, vol. 3, pp. 229–281, 1948.

2.40   Notation

A convenient notation for the contents of a table has been established. By

$$f(x), \qquad x = a(h)b, \qquad 6D$$

we understand a table of $f(x)$ to 6 places of decimals, for values of x at intervals h, between a and b inclusive.   Thus a table of sin x, $x = 0(.02)1$, 6D begins in one of the following forms:

x	sin x	sin x	10^6 sin x
0	.000000	000000	000000
.02	.019999	019999	019999
.04	.039989	039989	039989
.06	.059964	059964	059964
.08	.079915	079915	079915
.10	.099833	099833	099833
.12	.119712	119712	119712

Occasionally, we find

$$f(x), \qquad x = a(h)b, \qquad 8S,$$

indicating that the function is given to 8 significant figures.

The following is the beginning of a table to 8S of $\Gamma(n + \tfrac{1}{2})$ for $n = 1(1)1000$.

n	$\Gamma(n + \tfrac{1}{2})$	
0	1.77245 39	(0)†
1	8.86226 93	(−1)
2	1.32934 04	(0)
3	3.32335 10	(0)
4	1.16317 28	(1)
5	5.23427 78	(1)
6	2.87885 28	(2)

The meaning of extensions of this notation, such as

$$f(x), \qquad x = 0(.001)1(.01)2(.1)3(1)50 \text{ (various) } 1000$$

is apparent.   In FMR a notation has been established which indicates what provision is made for interpolation—whether proportional parts, reduced derivatives, central differences, or modified differences.

Apart from tables in this conventional form, we call attention to the existence of "critical" tables which are appropriate for the quantitative description of slowly varying functions.   The table of contents of a book is essentially a critical table, with the page number as argument.   We

† The figures in parentheses indicate the power of 10 by which the given value must be multiplied.   Thus

$$\Gamma(\tfrac{3}{2}) = .88622693,$$

$$\Gamma(\tfrac{13}{2}) = 287.88528.$$

give here an example of a critical table, to 3 decimal places, of the Everett coefficient E_2.

p	$-E_2$	p	$-E_2$
.0000		.0137	
	.000		.005
.0015		.0169	
	.001		.006
.0045			
	.002		
.0075			
	.003		
.0106			
	.004		
.0137			

This indicates that for values of p satisfying $.0106 \le p < .0075$, we have $-E_2(p) = .003$. The inequality on the right is usually explained by the statement, "In critical cases, ascend."

Standard round-off practice is illustrated by the following examples:

$$.34, \quad .56, \quad .15, \quad .25,$$

which become, when rounded to one place,

$$.3, \quad .6, \quad .2, \quad .2.$$

In words, a contribution of less than half a unit in the last place retained is ignored, a contribution greater than half a unit is counted as a unit, and a contribution of exactly half a unit is ignored or counted as a unit, according as the preceding digit is even or odd. In some tables special devices are introduced to give some indication of the amount of round-off.

Italics are often used to indicate a change in suppressed leading figures in a table; an alternative notation is the use of an asterisk.

In some tables in which linear interpolation is usually permissible, it is the custom to print first differences in italics whenever linear interpolation is not permissible, according to the standards adopted. For instance:

x	$f(x)$	
7.5	.000553	
		−53
7.6	500	
		−47
7.7	453	
		−43
7.8	410	
		−39
7.9	371	

2.41 Collections

There are several collections of tables, some prepared by organizations and others by individuals, which should be accessible.   Most of these belong to the second class, though some are more appropriate in the third class.

British Association for the Advancement of Science

A Mathematical Tables Committee of the British Association for the Advancement of Science was active from 1873 until 1939, when its activities were transferred to the Royal Society Tables Committee.   The publications of the first committee will be denoted by BAAS 1, . . . , and those of its successor by RS 1, ...   A series of shorter mathematical tables is also being issued by the new committee; they will be denoted by RSS 1, ...   All volumes are now published by the Cambridge University Press, London.

BAAS   1   "Circular and Hyperbolic Functions," 1951.
BAAS   2   "Emden Functions," D. H. Sadler and J. C. P. Miller, 1932.
BAAS   3   "Minimum Decompositions into Fifth Powers," L. E. Dickson, 1933.
BAAS   4   "Cycles of Reduced Ideals in Quadratic Fields," E. L. Ince, 1934.
BAAS   5   "Factor Table, Giving the Complete Decompositions of All Numbers Less than 100,000," 1935.
BAAS   6   "Bessel Functions," pt. 1: "Functions of Orders Zero and Unity," 1950.
BAAS   7   "The Probability Integral," 1939.
BAAS   8   "Number-Divisor Tables," 1940.
BAAS   9   "Tables of Powers Giving Integral Powers of Integers,"1940.
BAAS 10   "Bessel Functions," pt. 2: Functions of Positive Integer Order, 1952.
BAAS 11   "Legendre Polynomials," 1946.
BAAS 12   "Airy Integral," J. C. P. Miller, 1946.

Royal Society

RS 1   "Farey Series of Order 1025," E. H. Neville, 1950.
RS 2   "Rectangular-Polar Conversion Tables," E. H. Neville, 1956.
RS 3   "Binomial Coefficients," 1956.
RS 4   "Tables of Partitions," H. Gupta, C. E. Gwyther, and J. C. P. Miller, 1958.
RS 5   "Representations of Primes by Quadratic Forms," 1960.
RS 6   "Tables of the Riemann Zeta-function," 1960.
RS 7   "Bessel Functions," pt. 3: "Zeros and Associated Values," 1960.

RS 8   "Mansell's Tables of Logarithms," in preparation.
RS 9   "Indices and Primitive Roots," A. E. Western and J. C. P.
         Miller, in press.

Royal Society Shorter Mathematical Tables

RSS 1   "A Short Table for the Bessel Functions $I_{n+\frac{1}{2}}(x), \frac{2}{\pi} K_{n+\frac{1}{2}}(x)$,"
          C. W. Jones, 1952.
RSS 2   "Bessel Functions and Formulae," 1953.   (This is a reprint of
          the introductory material in [BAAS 10]).
RSS 3   "A Short Table for Bessel Functions of Integer Orders and
          Large Arguments," L. Fox, 1954.

National Physical Laboratory

   A new series of shorter mathematical tables has been started by the
National Physical Laboratory.   We denote these by NPL 1, ...

NPL 1   "The Use and Construction of Mathematical Tables," L. Fox,
          1956.
NPL 2   "Tables of Everett Interpolation Coefficients," L. Fox, 1958.
NPL 3   "Tables of Generalized Exponential Integrals," G. F. Miller,
          1960.
NPL 4   "Tables of Weber Parabolic Cylinder Functions and Other
          Functions for Large Arguments," L. Fox, 1960.
NPL 5   "Chebyshev Series for Mathematical Functions," C. W. Clen-
          shaw, in press.
NPL 6   "Tables for Bessel Functions of Moderate or Large Orders,"
          F. W. J. Olver, in press.

Harvard University Computation Laboratory

   This organization issues its tables in series of volumes called the Annals
of the Computation Laboratory of Harvard University, published since
1945 by the Harvard University Press, Cambridge, Mass.   We denote
these by Harvard 1, ...
   The main achievement to date is the series Harvard 3–14, published
from 1947 to 1951, a tabulation of the Bessel functions $J_n(x)$ for x between
0 and 100 for $n = 0(1)135$.   The first two volumes are to 18 decimals
and the later volumes are to 10 decimals.   In the earlier volumes the
interval is usually .001, and in the later it is usually .01.   The series also
includes:

Harvard   2   "Tables of the Modified Hankel Functions of Order One-
                 third and of Their Derivatives," 1945.
Harvard 17   "Table for the Design of Missiles," 1948.

Harvard 18,   "Tables of the Generalized Sine- and Cosine-Integral
    19   Functions," pt. I, pt. II, 1949.
Harvard 20   "Tables of Inverse Hyperbolic Functions," 1948.
Harvard 21   "Tables of the Generalized Exponential-Integral Func-
        tions," 1949.
Harvard 22   "Tables of Sine ϕ/ϕ and Its First Eleven Derivatives,"
        1949.
Harvard 23   "Tables of the Error Function and of Its First Twenty
        Derivatives," 1952.
Harvard 35   "Tables of the Cumulative Binomial Probability Distri-
        bution," 1955.
Harvard 40   "Tables of the Function arcsin z," 1956.

The series also includes two volumes of "Proceedings of Symposia on Large-scale Digital Calculating Machines," Harvard 16 and Harvard 26, and four volumes concerned with the machinery at the Harvard Computation Laboratory and the techniques used in its design and operation, Harvard 1, 24, 25, 27.   Harvard 1 contains an extensive bibliography of numerical analysis.

Tracts for Computers

A series of tracts for computers was instituted by K. Pearson in 1919 and is now being edited by E. S. Pearson.   The volumes are denoted by Tract 1, ...   Many volumes in this series are of greatest interest to statisticians:

Tract   1   "Tables of the Digamma and Trigamma Functions," E.
        Pairman, 1919.
Tract   2   "On the Construction of Tables and on Interpolation,"
        pt. 1: "Univariate Tables," K. Pearson, 1920.
Tract   3   "On the Construction of Tables and on Interpolation,"
        pt. 2: "Bivariate Tables," K. Pearson, 1920.
Tract   4   "Tables of the Logarithms of the Complete Γ-function,"
        1921.
Tract   5   "Table of Coefficients of Everett's Central Difference Inter-
        polation Formula," A. J. Thompson, 1943.
Tract   6   "Smoothing," E. C. Rhodes, 1921.
Tract   7   "The Numerical Evaluation of the Incomplete B-function,"
        H. E. Soper, 1921.
Tract   8   "Table of the Logarithms of the Complete Γ-function,"
        E. S. Pearson, 1922.
Tract   9   "Table of log $\Gamma(x)$," J. Brownlee, 1923.
Tract 10   "On Quadrature and Cubature," J. O. Irwin, 1923.
Tracts 11, 14, 16–22 have been combined and issued as A. J. Thomp-
        son, "Logarithmetica Britannica," 2 vols., 1952.

Tract 12   "Bibliotheca tabularum mathematicarum," pt. 1: "Loga-
               rithmic Tables," A: Logarithms of Numbers, J. Henderson,
               1926.
Tract 13   "Tables of the Probable Error of the Coefficients of Corre-
               lation," K. J. Holzinger, 1925.
Tract 15   "Random Sampling Numbers," L. H. C. Tippett, 1927.
Tract 23   "Tables of $\tan^{-1} x$ and $\log (1 + x^2)$," L. J. Comrie, 1938.
Tract 24   "Tables of Random Sampling Numbers," M. G. Kendall
               and B. Babington Smith, 1946.
Tract 25   "Random Normal Deviates," H. Wold, 1948.

Biometrika

In this section we list various tables prepared under the Pearsonian
influence and call attention to various tables (many of interest to statisticians) which have been published in *Biometrika* and of which copies are
available. All are published by the *Biometrika* office.

"Tables of Incomplete Γ-function," K. Pearson, 1934.
"Tables of the Incomplete Beta Function," K. Pearson, 1934.
"Tables of the Complete and Incomplete Elliptic Integral," A. M.
   Legendre, 1934.

National Bureau of Standards

The tables prepared directly or indirectly by the National Bureau of
Standards have been issued in three series: (1) the Mathematical
Tables Series, denoted by NBSMT; (2) the Columbia University Press
Series, denoted by NBSCUP; and (3) the Applied Mathematics Series,
denoted by NBSAMS, in which revised editions of the first are being
incorporated.

Mathematical Tables Series:

NBSMT   1   "Table of the First Ten Powers of the Integers from 1 to
                1000," 1939.
NBSMT   5   "Tables of Sine, Cosine and Exponential Integrals," vol.
                I, 1940.
NBSMT   6   "Tables of Sine, Cosine and Exponential Integrals," vol.
                II, 1940.
NBSMT   7   "Tables of Natural Logarithms," vol. I, 1941.
NBSMT   9   "Tables of Natural Logarithms," vol. II, 1941.
NBSMT 11   "Tables of the Moments of Inertia and Section Moduli of
                Ordinary Angles, Channels, and Bulb Angles with
                Certain Plate Combinations," 1941.
NBSMT 17   "Miscellaneous Physical Tables: Planck's Radiation
                Functions, and Electronic Functions," 1942.

NBSMT 18–37 is a series of smaller tables.   Some of these have been reissued (together with certain unpublished smaller tables) in NBSAMS 37.

Columbia University Press Series:

NBSCUP 1   "Table of Reciprocals of the Integers from 100,000 through 200,009," 1943.

NBSCUP 2   "Table of the Bessel Functions $J_0(z)$ and $J_1(z)$ for Complex Arguments," 1947.

NBSCUP 3   "Table of Circular and Hyperbolic Tangents and Cotangents for Radian Arguments," 1947.

NBSCUP 4   "Tables of Lagrangian Interpolation Coefficients," 1948.

NBSCUP 5   "Tables of Arcsin x," 1945.

NBSCUP 6   "Tables of Associated Legendre Functions," 1945.

NBSCUP 7   "Tables of Fractional Powers," 1946.

NBSCUP 8   "Tables of Spherical Bessel Functions," vol. I, 1947.

NBSCUP 9   "Tables of Spherical Bessel Functions," vol. II, 1947.

NBSCUP 10   "Tables of Bessel Functions of Fractional Order," vol. I, 1948.

NBSCUP 11   "Tables of Bessel Functions of Fractional Order," vol. II, 1949.

NBSCUP 12   "Table of the Bessel Functions $Y_0(z)$ and $Y_1(z)$ for Complex Arguments," 1950.

NBSCUP 13   "Tables Relating to Mathieu Functions," 1951.

Applied Mathematics Series:

NBSAMS 2   "Tables of Coefficients for Obtaining the First Derivative without Differences," H. E. Salzer, 1948.

NBSAMS 3   "Table of the Confluent Hypergeometric Function $F(\frac{1}{2}n, \frac{1}{2}; x)$ and Related Functions," 1949.

NBSAMS 4   "Tables of Scattering Functions for Spherical Particles," 1948.

NBSAMS 5   "Table of Sines and Cosines to 15 Decimal Places at Hundredths of a Degree," 1948.

NBSAMS 6   "Tables of Binomial Probability Distribution," 1950.

NBSAMS 7   "Tables to Facilitate Sequential t-tests," 1951.

NBSAMS 8   "Tables of Powers of Complex Numbers," H. E. Salzer, 1950.

NBSAMS 9   "Tables of Chebyshev Polynomials $S_n(x)$ and $C_n(x)$," 1952.

NBSAMS 10   "Tables for Conversion of X-ray Diffraction Angles to Interplanar Spacing," 1950.

NBSAMS 11   "Table of Arctangents of Rational Numbers," J. Todd, 1951.

NBSAMS 12   "Monte Carlo Method," A. S. Householder, G. E. Forsythe, and H. H. Germond, eds., 1951.

NBSAMS 13   "Tables for the Analysis of Beta Spectra," 1951.

NBSAMS 14   "Tables of the Exponential Function e^x," 1951.

NBSAMS 15   "Problems for the Numerical Analysis of the Future," 1951.

NBSAMS 16   "Tables of $n!$ and $\Gamma(n + \frac{1}{2})$ for the First Thousand Values of n," H. E. Salzer, 1951.

NBSAMS 17   "Tables of Coulomb Wave Functions," vol. I, 1952.

NBSAMS 18   "Construction and Applications of Conformal Maps," E. F. Beckenbach, ed., 1952.

NBSAMS 19   "Hypergeometric and Legendre Functions with Applications to Integral Equations of Potential Theory," C. Snow, 1952.

NBSAMS 20   "Tables for Rocket and Comet Orbits," S. Herrick, 1953.

NBSAMS 21   "A Guide to Tables of the Normal Probability Integral," 1952.

NBSAMS 22   "Probability Tables for the Analysis of Extreme-value Data," 1952.

NBSAMS 23   "Tables of Normal Probability Functions," 1952.

NBSAMS 24   "Introduction to the Theory of Stochastic Processes Depending on a Continuous Parameter," H. B. Mann, 1952.

NBSAMS 25   "Table of the Bessel Functions $Y_0(x)$, $Y_1(x)$, $K_0(x)$, $K_1(x)$, $0 \leq x \leq 1$," 1952.

NBSAMS 26   "Table of Arctan x," 1953.

NBSAMS 27   "Table of 10^x," 1953.

NBSAMS 28   "Table of Bessel-Clifford Functions of Order Zero and One," 1952.

NBSAMS 29   "Linear Simultaneous Equations and the Determination of Eigenvalues," L. J. Paige and O. Taussky, eds., 1952.

NBSAMS 30   "Tables of Coefficients for the Numerical Calculation of Laplace Transforms," H. E. Salzer, 1953.

NBSAMS 31   "Table of Natural Logarithms for Arguments between Zero and Five to Sixteen Decimal Places," 1952.

NBSAMS 32   "Table of Sine and Cosine Integrals for Arguments from 10 to 100," 1953.

NBSAMS 33   "The Statistical Theory of Extreme Values and Some Practical Applications," E. J. Gumbel, 1954.

NBSAMS 34   "Table of the Gamma Function for Complex Arguments," 1954.

NBSAMS 35   "Tables of Lagrangian Coefficients for Sexagesimal Interpolation," 1954.

NBSAMS 36   "Tables of Circular and Hyperbolic Sines and Cosines for Radian Arguments," 1953.

NBSAMS 37   "Tables of Functions and of Zeros of Functions: Collected Short Tables of the Computation Laboratory," 1954.

NBSAMS 38   "Magnetic Fields of Cylindrical and Annular Coils," C. Snow, 1954.

NBSAMS 39   "Contributions to the Solution of Systems of Linear Equations and the Determination of Eigenvalues," O. Taussky, ed., 1954.

NBSAMS 40   "Table of Secants and Cosecants to Nine Significant Figures at Hundredths of a Degree," 1954.

NBSAMS 41   "Tables of the Error Function and Its Derivatives," 1954.

NBSAMS 42   "Experiments in the Computation of Conformal Maps," J. Todd, ed., 1955.

NBSAMS 43   "Tables of Sines and Cosines for Radian Arguments," 1955.

NBSAMS 44   "Table of Salvo Kill Probabilities for Square Targets," 1954.

NBSAMS 45   "Table of Hyperbolic Sines and Cosines, $x = 2$ to $x = 10$," 1955.

NBSAMS 46   "Table of the Descending Exponential, $x = 2.5$ to $x = 10$," 1955.

NBSAMS 47   "Contributions on Partially Balanced Incomplete Block Designs with Two Associate Classes," W. H. Clatworthy, 1956.

NBSAMS 48   "Fractional Factorial Experiment Designs for Factors at Two Levels," Statistical Engineering Laboratory, 1957.

NBSAMS 49   "Further Contributions to the Solution of Simultaneous Linear Equations and the Determination of Eigenvalues," 1958.

NBSAMS 50   "Tables of the Bivariate Normal Distribution Function and Related Functions," 1959.

NBSAMS 51   "Table of the Exponential Integral for Complex Arguments," 1958.

NBSAMS 52   "Integrals of Airy Functions," 1958.

NBSAMS 53   "Tables of Natural Logarithm for Arguments between Five and Ten to Sixteen Decimal Places," 1958.

NBSAMS 54 "Fractional Factorial Experiment Designs for Factors at Three Levels," W. S. Connor and M. Zelen, 1959.

NBSAMS 56 "Tables of Osculatory Interpolation Coefficients," H. E. Salzer, 1959.

NBSAMS 57 "Basic Theorems in Matrix Theory," M. Marcus, 1960.

Akademia Nauk SSSR

A series of excellent tables is being produced in Russia. Among these are:

"Tables of Logarithms of Complex Numbers," 1952.

A. A. Abramov, "Tables of ln $\Gamma(z)$ in the Complex Domain," 1953.

"Tables of Fresnel Integrals," 1953.

K. A. Karpov, "Tables of the Function $w(z) = e^{-z} \int_0^z e^{x^2} dx$ in the Complex Domain," 1954.

"Tables of Sine and Cosine Integrals," 1954.

"Tables of the Exponential Integral," 1954.

L. N. Karmazina, "Tables of the Jacobi Polynomials," 1954.

"Tables of e^x and e^{-x}," 1955.

A. D. Smirnov, "Tables of Airy Functions," 1955.

K. A. Karpov and S. N. Razumovskii, "Tables of the Logarithmic Integral," 1956.

E. N. Dekanosidze, "Table of Cylinder Functions of Two Variables," 1956.

L. N. Karmazina and L. V. Kurochkina, "Table of Interpolation Coefficients," 1956.

A. I. Vzorova, "Tables for Solution of the Laplace Equation in Elliptic Domains," 1957.

K. A. Karpov, "Tables of the Function $F(z) = \int_0^z e^{x^2} dx$ in the Complex Domain," 1958.

E. A. Chistova, "Tables of Bessel Functions of Real Arguments and Their Integrals," 1958.

L. N. Karmazina and E. A. Chistova, "Tables of Bessel Functions of Imaginary Arguments and Their Integrals," 1958.

V. I. Pagurova, "Tables of the Integral-exponential Function $E_\nu(x) = \int_1^\infty e^{-xu} u^{-\nu} du$," 1959.

I. E. Kireeva and K. A. Karpov, "Tables of the Weber Functions," vol. 1, 1959.

M. I. Žurina and L. N. Karmazina, "Tables of the Legendre Functions $P_{-1/2+i\tau}(x)$," vol. 1, 1960.

L. N. Nosova, "Table of Kelvin Functions and Their First Derivatives," 1960.

The following important table was published in Russian but is not in the series of the Akademia Nauk:

V. N. Faddeeva and N. M. Terentiev, "Tables of the Values of the Probability Integral of Complex Arguments," 1954.

2.42 Individual Authors

In addition to the tables in the series described in the preceding section, there are certain individuals who have produced or directed the production of tables of importance for the general worker or the specialist. Among these are J. Peters, L. J. Comrie, J. C. P. Miller, H. T. Davis, and K. Hayashi.

The tables of general use in this category include the following:

L. M. Milne-Thomson, "Jacobian Elliptic Functions," New York, 1950.
E. Cambi, "Eleven and Fifteen Place Tables of Bessel Functions of the First Kind, to All Significant Orders," New York, 1948.

An elaborate collection of constants to many decimals, by J. Peters, J. Stein, and G. Witt, is given in the appendix of the following work:

J. Peters, "Ten-place Logarithm Table," vol. I: "Ten-place Logarithms of the Numbers from 1 to 100,000 together with an Appendix of Mathematical Tables," New York, 1957.

2.43 Texts and Treatises on Numerical Analysis

There follows a short list of books on numerical analysis which are currently available

1. N. I. Achieser, "Vorlesungen über Approximationstheorie," Akademie-Verlag G.m.b.H., Berlin, 1953.
2. D. N. de G. Allen, "Relaxation Methods," McGraw-Hill Book Company, Inc., New York, 1954.
3. F. L. Alt, "Electronic Digital Computers," Academic Press, Inc., New York, 1958.
4. E. F. Beckenbach, ed., "Modern Mathematics for the Engineer," McGraw-Hill Book Company, Inc., New York, First Series, 1956; Second Series, 1961.
5. E. F. Beckenbach, ed., "Construction and Applications of Conformal Maps," National Bureau of Standards, Applied Mathematics Series; vol. 18, 1952.
6. A. A. Bennett, W. E. Milne, and H. Bateman, "Numerical Integration of Differential Equations," Dover Publications, New York, 1956.
7. E. Bodewig, "Matrix Calculus," North Holland Publishing Company, Amsterdam, 1956.

8. A. D. Booth, "Numerical Methods," Academic Press, Inc., New York, 1958.

9. R. A. Buckingham, "Numerical Methods," Sir Isaac Pitman & Sons, Ltd., London, 1957.

10. H. F. Bueckner, "Die praktische Behandlung von Integralgleichungen," Springer-Verlag, Berlin, 1952.

11. L. Collatz, "Eigenwertaufgaben mit technischen Anwendungen," Akademische Verlagsgesellschaft, m.b.H., Leipzig, 1949.

12. L. Collatz, "Handbuch der Physik," II, pp. 369–470, "Numerische und graphische Methoden," Springer-Verlag, Berlin, 1955.

13. L. Collatz, "Eigenwertprobleme und ihre numerische Behandlung," Akademische Verlagsgesellschaft m.b.H., Leipzig, 1945.

14. L. Collatz, "The Numerical Treatment of Differential Equations," Springer-Verlag, Berlin, 1960.

15. S. H. Crandall, "Engineering Analysis," McGraw-Hill Book Company, Inc., New York, 1956.

16. American Mathematical Society, "Numerical Analysis: Proceedings of Symposia in Applied Mathematics—Volume VI," J. H. Curtiss, ed., McGraw-Hill Book Company, Inc., New York, 1956.

17. P. S. Dwyer, "Linear Computations," John Wiley & Sons, Inc., New York, 1951.

18. Engineering Research Associates, "High-speed Computing Devices," W. W. Stifler, Jr., ed. McGraw-Hill Book Company, Inc., New York, 1950.

19. V. N. Faddeeva, "Computational Methods in Linear Algebra," C. D. Benster, tr., Dover Publications, New York, 1959.

20. G. E. Forsythe, Contemporary State of Numerical Analysis, in "Surveys of Applied Mathematics," vol. 5, John Wiley & Sons, Inc., New York, 1958.

21. G. E. Forsythe and W. A. Wasow, "Finite-difference Methods for Partial Differential Equations," John Wiley & Sons, Inc., New York, 1960.

22. L. Fox, "Numerical Solution of Two-point Boundary Problems," Clarendon Press, Oxford, 1957.

23. R. A. Frazer, W. J. Duncan, and A. R. Collar, "Elementary Matrices," Cambridge University Press, London, 1938.

24. D. Gibb, "Interpolation and Numerical Integration," George Bell & Sons, Ltd., London, 1915.

25. V. I. Goncarov, "Interpolation and Approximation," 1954 (in Russian).

26. E. M. Grabbe, S. Ramo, D. E. Wooldridge, eds., "Handbook of Automation, Computation and Control," vols. I–III, John Wiley & Sons, Inc., New York, 1958–1961.

27. D. R. Hartree, "Numerical Analysis," Clarendon Press, Oxford, 1958.
28. C. Hastings, Jr., "Approximations for Digital Computers," Princeton University Press, Princeton, N.J., 1955.
29. F. B. Hildebrand, "Introduction to Numerical Analysis," McGraw-Hill Book Company, Inc., New York, 1956.
30. A. S. Householder, "Principles of Numerical Analysis," McGraw-Hill Book Company, Inc., New York, 1953.
31. "Interpolation and Allied Tables," H. M. Stationery Office, London, 1956.
32. H. Jeffreys and B. S. Jeffreys, "Methods of Mathematical Physics," Cambridge University Press, London, 1956.
33. F. John, Advanced Numerical Analysis, lecture notes, New York University, New York, 1956.
34. C. Jordan, "Calculus of Finite Differences," Chelsea Publishing Company, New York, 1947.
35. L. V. Kantorovitch and V. I. Krylov, "Approximate Methods of Higher Analysis," C. D. Benster, tr., Interscience Publishers, Inc., New York, 1958.
36. Z. Kopal, "Numerical Analysis," John Wiley & Sons, Inc., New York, 1955.
37. J. Kuntzmann, "Méthodes numériques: Interpolation, dérivées," Dunod, Paris, 1959.
38. K. S. Kunz, "Numerical Analysis," McGraw-Hill Book Company, Inc., New York, 1957.
39. C. Lanczos, "Applied Analysis," Prentice-Hall, Inc., Englewood Cliffs, N.J., 1956.
40. R. E. Langer, ed., "On Numerical Approximation," University of Wisconsin Press, Madison, Wis., 1959.
41. H. Levy and E. A. Baggott, "Numerical Studies in Differential Equations," Dover Publications, New York, 1950.
42. M. Marcus, "Basic Theorems in Matrix Theory," National Bureau of Standards Applied Mathematics Series, vol. 57, 1960.
43. H. A. Meyer, Symposium on Monte Carlo Methods, John Wiley & Sons, Inc., New York, 1956.
44. S. E. Mikeladze, "Numerical Methods in Mathematical Analysis," 1953 (in Russian).
45. W. E. Milne, "Numerical Calculus," Princeton University Press, Princeton, N.J., 1950.
46. W. E. Milne, "Numerical Solution of Differential Equations," John Wiley & Sons, Inc., New York, 1953.
47. L. M. Milne-Thomson, "Calculus of Finite Differences," Macmillan & Co., Ltd., London, 1933.

48. H. Mineur, "Techniques de calcul numérique," Béranger, Paris, 1952.
49. "Modern Computing Methods," H. M. Stationery Office, London, 1961.
50. I. P. Natanson, "Konstruktive Funktionentheorie," Akademie-Verlag G.m.b.H., Berlin, 1955.
51. K. J. Nielsen, "Methods in Numerical Analysis," The Macmillan Company, New York, 1956.
52. N. E. Nörlund, "Differenzenrechnung," Springer-Verlag, Berlin, 1924.
53. A. M. Ostrowski, "Vorlesungen über Differential- und Integral-rechnung," vol. 2, Birkhauser, Basel, 1951.
54. A. M. Ostrowski, "Theory of the Solution of Equations and Systems of Equations," Academic Press, Inc., New York, 1960.
55. L. J. Paige and O. Taussky, eds., "Simultaneous Linear Equations and the Determination of Eigenvalues," National Bureau of Standards Applied Mathematics Series, vol. 29, 1953.
56. A. Ralston and H. S. Wilf, eds., "Mathematical Methods for Digital Computers, John Wiley & Sons, Inc., New York, 1960.
57. R. D. Richtmyer, "Difference Methods for Initial Value Problems," Interscience Publishers, Inc., New York, 1958.
58. C. Runge and H. König, "Vorlesungen über numerische Rechnen," Springer-Verlag, Berlin, 1924.
59. J. B. Scarborough, "Numerical Mathematical Analysis," Johns Hopkins Press, Baltimore, 1958.
60. F. S. Shaw, "Introduction to Relaxation Methods," Dover Publications, New York, 1953.
61. R. V. Southwell, "Relaxation Methods in Engineering Science," Clarendon Press, Oxford, 1940.
62. R. V. Southwell, "Relaxation Methods in Theoretical Physics," Clarendon Press, Oxford, 1946.
63. J. F. Steffensen, "Interpolation," Chelsea Publishing Company, New York, 1927.
64. E. L. Stiefel, P. Henrici, and H. Rutishauser, "Further Contributions to the Solution of Simultaneous Linear Equations and the Determination of Eigenvalues," National Bureau of Standards Applied Mathematics Series, vol. 49, 1958.
65. "Subtabulation," H. M. Stationery Office, London, 1958.
66. O. Taussky, ed., "Contributions to the Solution of Systems of Linear Equations and the Determination of Eigenvalues," National Bureau of Standards Applied Mathematics Series, vol. 39, 1954.
67. J. Todd, ed., "Experiments in the Computation of Conformal Maps," National Bureau of Standards Applied Mathematics Series, vol. 42, 1955.

68. R. S. Varga, "Iterative Numerical Analysis," Prentice-Hall, Inc., Englewood Cliffs, N.J., to appear.
69. E. T. Whittaker and G. Robinson, "Calculus of Observations," Blackie & Son, Ltd., Glasgow, 1946.
70. F. A. Willers, "Methoden der praktischen Analysis," Walter De Gruyter & Co., Berlin, 1950.
71. F. A. Willers, "Practical Analysis," R. T. Beyer, tr., Dover Publications, New York, 1948.
72. R. Zurmühl, "Matrizen," Springer-Verlag, Berlin, 1950.
73. R. Zurmühl, "Praktische Mathematik," Springer-Verlag, Berlin, 1957.
74. A. O. Gelfond, "Differenzenrechnung," D. Verlag Wiss., Berlin, 1958 (translation of Russian edition, 1952).
75. A. Korganoff, with the collaboration of L. Bossett, J. L. Groboillot and J. Johnson, "Méthodes de calcul numérique," tome 1: Algèbre non-linéaire, Dunod, Paris, 1961.
76. D. K. Faddeev and V. N. Faddeeva, "Computational Methods of Linear Algebra," Moscow, 1960 (in Russian).   (This is an extended version of 19.)
77. G. N. Lance, "Numerical Methods for High Speed Computers," Iliffe, London, 1960.
78. F. L. Alt, ed., "Advances in Computers," Academic Press, New York.   This is intended to be a continuing publication, the first volume of which appeared in 1960.
79. I. S. Berezin and N. P. Židkov, "Computational Methods," 2 vols., Moscow, 1959 (in Russian).

PROBLEMS

2.1. If $a_0 = 1$, $b_0 = .2$ and if, for $n \geq 0$,

$$a_{n+1} = \tfrac{1}{2}(a_n + b_n), \qquad b_{n+1} = \sqrt{a_n b_n},$$

calculate $a_1, a_2, \ldots$ and $b_1, b_2, \ldots$, working to 10D.
Repeat the calculation working to double precision.

2.2. If $x_0 = .5$, $y_0 = 1$ and if, for $n \geq 0$,

$$x_{n+1} = \tfrac{1}{2}(x_n + y_n), \qquad y_{n+1} = \sqrt{x_{n+1} y_n},$$

calculate $x_1, x_2, \ldots$ and $y_1, y_2, \ldots$, working to 10D.
Repeat the calculation working to double precision.

2.3. Check the results of Probs. 2.1, 2.2 from tables using the values of the limits given in the text.

2.4. Using the Newton process on $f(x) = x^{-p} - N$, obtain a recurrence relation which converges to $N^{-1/p}$.

For what range of initial values does it converge if, for example, $p = 3$?
Use this to determine $(1.2345678)^{-1/3}$ to at least 7D.

2.5. Evaluate in the form arctan (m/n), where m, n are integers,

$$2 \arctan 1 - \arctan 2 + \arctan 4 + \arctan 5$$
$$+ \arctan 34 - \arctan 208 - \arctan 479.$$

(For further examples of this kind see Todd, NBSAMS 11.)

2.6. (Etherington) Evaluate the determinants

$$\begin{vmatrix} -73 & 78 & 24 \\ 92 & 66 & 25 \\ -80 & 37 & 10 \end{vmatrix}, \qquad \begin{vmatrix} -73 & 78 & 24 \\ 92 & 66 & 25 \\ -80 & 37 & 10.01 \end{vmatrix}.$$

2.7. Evaluate $\theta_n(x)$ for $x = .1$ and $x = 1$ and for $n = 2(1)\ 8$ where

$$\theta_0(.1) = .99750\ 156207, \qquad \theta_0(1) = .76519\ 768656,$$
$$\theta_1(.1) = .04993\ 752604, \qquad \theta_1(1) = .44005\ 058575,$$

and where, for $n \geq 1$,

$$x\theta_{n+1}(x) = 2n\theta_n(x) - x\theta_{n-1}(x).$$

Evaluate also

$$r_n(x) = \theta_n(x) - J_n(x)$$

where $J_n(x)$ is the Bessel function of order n.

2.8. Evaluate $J_0(5)$, $J_0(10)$, $J_0(20)$ using the asymptotic formula

$$J_0(x) \sim \sqrt{\frac{2}{\pi x}}\ [P_0(x) \cos (x - \tfrac{1}{4}\pi) - Q_0(x) \sin (x - \tfrac{1}{4}\pi)]$$

where

$$P_0 \equiv 1 - \frac{1^2 \cdot 3^2}{2! \cdot (8x)^2} + \frac{1^2 \cdot 3^2 \cdot 5^2 \cdot 7^2}{4! \cdot (8x)^4} - \cdots,$$

$$Q_0 = -\frac{1^2}{1! \cdot (8x)} + \frac{1^2 \cdot 3^2 \cdot 5^2}{3! \cdot (8x)^3} - \cdots.$$

Compare the results you obtain with the values given in standard tables.

2.9. The following is part of a table of sin θ, at a constant interval, with its differences.   Complete the table and check the final value θ_9 from a standard table.

θ_0	.43313 47858 66963				
		873933 05476			
θ_1	.43322 21791 72439			-4073056	
		873892 32420			-822
θ_2					
					0
θ_3					
					2
θ_4					
					-3
θ_5					
					$+2$
θ_6					
					0
θ_7					
					-1
θ_8					
θ_9					

2.10. Check the following table by differencing:

x	$f(x)$
213	310 87274
214	527 79587
215	745 55816
216	964 16123
217	1283 60670
218	1403 89609
219	1625 30132
220	1847 01371
221	2069 84498
222	2293 52675

2.11. Check the following table by differencing:

x	$f(x)$
-3	4593 46961
-2	19046 00625
-1	33551 77121
0	48211 85121
1	63027 33681
2	77999 32214
3	93128 90625
4	1 08417 19041
5	1 23865 28081
6	1 39474 28721
7	1 55245 32321

Correct it and obtain $f(.5)$ by the following methods:

a. Linear interpolation
b. Bessel
c. Everett
d. Lagrange 4-point
e. Bessel or Everett with fourth-difference contribution
f. Bessel or Everett with modified differences.

2.12. Use the Aitken process to find a zero of $\mathrm{Bi}(-x)$ given the values:

$$\mathrm{Bi}(-.9) = .16263895$$
$$\mathrm{Bi}(-1.0) = .10399739$$
$$\mathrm{Bi}(-1.1) = .04432659$$
$$\mathrm{Bi}(-1.2) = -.01582137$$
$$\mathrm{Bi}(-1.3) = -.07576964$$
$$\mathrm{Bi}(-1.4) = -.13472406.$$

Check your result from tables.

2.13. Illustrate Aitken's method of linear interpolation by determining the zero of $J_0(x)$ between 5.515 and 5.525, being given the following values:

x	5.505	5.515	5.525	5.535
$10^7 J_0(x)$	-51374	-17287	$+16740$	$+50704$

Check your results from tables.

2.14. Use the following extract from a table of $\mathrm{Bi}(x)$ and its reduced derivatives to calculate (and check) the values of $\mathrm{Bi}(2.45)$, $\mathrm{Bi}'(2.45)$

x	$\mathrm{Bi}(x)$	τ	τ^2	τ^3	τ^4	τ^5
2.4	5.61577	79418	6739	411	20	1
2.5	6.48166	94214	8102	501	25	1

2.15. Illustrate various methods of interpolation (linear, Lagrangian, Bessel, Everett) by finding $f(2.5)$ where f is given by the following table:

x	0	1	2	3	4	5
$f(x)$	789	1356	2268	3648	5819	9304

2.16. Tabulate $\ln \Gamma(x) - (x - \tfrac{1}{2}) \ln x + x$, for $x^{-1} = .1(-.01)0$. To how many places is linear interpolation good?
Evaluate $\ln \Gamma(x)$ and $\Gamma(x)$ for $x = 40$ using this table.

2.17. Construct an example to show that the error in interpolation in an "outer" interval in a 4-point Lagrangian interpolation can be significantly larger than that in the "center" interval.

2.18. Evaluate $\int_0^{12} f(x)\,dx$ by various methods where $f(x)$ is given by

x	$10^5 f(x)$	x	$10^5 f(x)$
0	37500	7	−41206
1	33794	8	−23300
2	23200	9	+20794
3	7294	10	100000
4	−11300	11	224294
5	−28906	12	404700
6	−40800		

What is the exact result? [Use, for example, Simpson, (Milne)[3], (3/8)[4], (Weddle)[2], Gregory, central differences (Gauss).] (See BAAS 11.)

2.19. Evaluate $\int_0^{1/2} (1 - x^2)^{1/2}\,dx$ by various methods—in particular, by (a) finding the indefinite integral, (b) Simpson's rule, (c) Gregory's formula, and (d) Gauss' central-difference method.

2.20. Discuss the evaluation of

$$J = \int_{-\infty}^{+\infty} \frac{e^{-x^2}}{1 + x^2}\,dx$$

using the Hermite quadrature. (See J. Barkley Rosser, Note on Zeros of the Hermite Polynomials and Weights for Gauss Mechanical Quadrature Formula, *Proc. Amer. Math. Soc.*, vol. 1, pp. 388–389, 1950.)

2.21. Discuss the approximation to the integral J in Prob. 2.20 by the infinite series

$$h \sum_{n=-\infty}^{\infty} e^{-n^2 h^2}/(1 + n^2 h^2)$$

for varying values of h. (See E. T. Goodwin, The Evaluation of Integrals of the Form $\int_{-\infty}^{+\infty} f(x)e^{-x^2}\,dx$, *Proc. Cambridge Philos. Soc.*, vol. 45, pp. 241–245, 1949.)

2.22. Verify *numerically* that $\mathrm{Ai}(x)$ satisfies the differential equation $y'' = xy$ at $x = 1.4$, being given

x	$\mathrm{Ai}(x)$
1.1	.12004 943
1.2	.10612 576
1.3	.09347 467
1.4	.08203 805
1.5	.07174 950
1.6	.06253 691
1.7	.05432 479

2.23. Verify *numerically* that $J_0(x)$ satisfies the differential equation

$$x^2 y'' + xy + x^2 y = 0,$$

for, say, $x = 5$, $x = 20$, and investigate the effect of varying the interval h. [Obtain from tables the values for $x = \ldots, 4.999, 5.000, 5.001, \ldots; x = \ldots, 4.95, 5.00, 5.05, \ldots; x = \ldots, 4.9, 5.0, 5.1, \ldots; \ldots$ Similarly for $x = \ldots, 19.99, 20.00, 20.01, \ldots; x = \ldots, 19.95, 20.00, 20.05, \ldots; x = \ldots, 19.9, 20.0, 20.1, \ldots; \ldots$ Use values of $J_0(x)$ to appropriate precision.]

2.24. Apply the δ^2 method *twice* to the following sequence: 2.01761, 3.76481, 2.70015, 3.36391, 2.94210, 3.21407, 3.03687, 3.15317, 3.07645.   (See Todd and Warschawski [64], p. 41.)

2.25. Apply a backward recurrence scheme to obtain values of the spherical Bessel function

$$j_n(x) = \sqrt{\pi/2x}\, J_{n+\frac{1}{2}}(x)$$

for $x = 10$, $n = 20$, using the relation

$$j_0(x) = \sin x/x$$

to obtain the scale factor.   Check your result from tables.

2.26. (Fox-Sadler) Prepare a table to 6D or more of

$$f(x) = \int_0^\infty (x + t)^{-\frac{1}{2}} \sin t\, dt$$

describing checking procedures and suggesting interpolation methods.

Hints:

a.   Express $f(x)$ in terms of the Fresnel integrals

$$S(y) = \int_0^y \sin \tfrac{1}{2}\, \pi t^2\, dt, \qquad C(y) = \int_0^y \cos \tfrac{1}{2}\, \pi t^2\, dt.$$

Obtain tables of these integrals and use them for spot checking.

b.   Obtain a power series representation and determine over what range it is convenient for tabulation:

$$f(x) = \sqrt{\pi/2}(\cos x - \sin x) + \sum_0^\infty \frac{(-1)^r (2r + 1)!\, 2^{4r+3}\, x^{2r+\frac{3}{2}}}{(4r + 3)!}\,.$$

c.   Obtain an asymptotic expansion in the form

$$f(x) \sim \frac{1}{\sqrt{x}}\left(1 - \frac{1\cdot 3}{2\cdot 2}\frac{1}{x^2} + \frac{1\cdot 3\cdot 5\cdot 7}{2\cdot 2\cdot 2\cdot 2}\frac{1}{x^4} - \cdots\right)$$

and determine over what range it is convenient for tabulation.

d.   Obtain the differential equation

$$f'' + f = x^{-\frac{1}{2}}$$

and determine over what range this is convenient for tabulation.

2.27. Explain in detail the derivation of the number 3.3 on the ninth line and 1.05 on the eleventh line of the $h^2 f_0''$ column of IAT, p. 62.

REFERENCES

1. I. A. Stegun and M. Abramowitz, Pitfalls in Computation, *J. Soc. Indust. Appl. Math.*, vol. 4, pp. 207–219, 1956.

2. L. M. Milne-Thomson, "Standard Tables of Square Roots," George Bell & Sons Ltd., London, 1929.

3. L. V. King, "On the Direct Numerical Calculation of Elliptic Functions and Integrals," Cambridge University Press, London, 1926.

4. A. Hurwitz, Über die Einführung der elementaren transzendenten Funktionen in der algebraischen Analysis, *Math. Ann.*, vol. 70, pp. 33–47, 1911; reprinted in "Mathematische Werke," vol. 1, pp. 706–721, Birkhauser, Basel, 1932.

5. A. S. Householder, "Principles of Numerical Analysis," McGraw-Hill Book Company, Inc., New York, 1953.

6. H. H. Goldstine, F. J. Murray, and J. von Neumann, The Jacobi Method for Real Symmetric Matrices, *J. Assoc. Comput. Mach.*, vol. 6, pp. 59–96, 1959.

7. H. E. Salzer, "Tables of Osculatory Interpolation Coefficients," National Bureau of Standards Applied Mathematics Series, vol. 56, 1959.

8. J. C. P. Miller, Checking by Differences, I, *Math. Tables Aids Comput.*, vol. 4, pp. 3–11, 1950.

9. M. Abramowitz, Note on Modified Second Differences for Use with Everett's Interpolation Formula, in "Tables of Bessel Functions of Fractional Order," National Bureau of Standards Columbia University Press Series, vol. 10, pp. xxxiii–xxxvi, 1948.

10. W. G. Bickley and J. C. P. Miller, Numerical Differentiation near the Limits of a Difference Table, *Phil. Mag.*, ser. 7, vol. 33, pp. 1–14, 1942.

11. C. Hastings, Jr., "Approximations for Digital Computers," Princeton University Press, Princeton, N.J., 1955.

12. L. Fox and J. C. P. Miller, Table-making for Large Arguments: The Exponential Integral, *Math. Tables Aids Comput.*, vol. 5, pp. 163–167, 1951.

13. D. R. Hartree, The Tabulation of Bessel Functions for Large Arguments, *Proc. Cambridge Philos. Soc.*, vol. 45, pp. 556–557, 1949.

14. A. M. Ostrowski, On the Rounding-off of Difference Tables for Linear Interpolation, *Math. Tables Aids Comput.*, vol. 6, pp. 212–214, 1952.

15. "Subtabulation," a companion booklet to "Interpolation and Allied Tables," H. M. Stationery Office, London, 1958.

16. D. R. Hartree, "Numerical Analysis," Clarendon Press, Oxford, 1958.

17. H. E. Salzer, A New Formula for Inverse Interpolation, *Bull. Amer. Math. Soc.*, vol. 50, pp. 513–516, 1946.

18. J. Todd, Evaluation of the Exponential Integral for Large Complex Arguments, *J. Res. Nat. Bur. Standards*, vol. 52, pp. 313–317, 1956.

19. T. H. Southard, Everett's Formula for Bivariate Interpolation and Throw-back of Fourth Differences, *Math. Tables Aids Comput.*, vol. 10, pp. 216–223, 1956.

20. H. C. Thacher, Derivation of Interpolation Formulas in Several Independent Variables, *Ann. New York Acad. Sci.*, vol. 86, pp. 758–775, 1960.

21. W. Gröbner and N. Hofreiter, "Integraltafel," I, II, Springer-Verlag, Vienna, 1949–1950.

22. D. Bierens de Haan, "Nouvelles tables d'intégrales définies," G. E. Stechert & Company, New York, 1957; see also C. F. Lindman, "Examen des nouvelles tables d'intégrales définies de M. Bierens de Haan," G. E. Stechert & Company, New York, 1944.

23. P. F. Byrd and M. D. Friedman, "Handbook of Elliptic Integrals for Engineers and Physicists," Springer-Verlag, Berlin, 1954.

24. I. M. Ryshik and I. S. Gradstein, "Summen-, Produkt- und Integraltafeln," D. Verlag Wiss., Berlin, 1957 (translation from Russian edition, 1951).

25. "Modern Computing Methods," H. M. Stationery Office, London, 1961.

26. M. Abramowitz, On the Practical Evaluation of Integrals, *J. Soc. Indust. Appl. Math.*, vol. 2, pp. 20–35, 1954.

27. W. G. Bickley, Formulae for Numerical Integration, *Math. Gaz.*, vol. 23, pp. 352–359, 1939; Formulae for Numerical Differentiation, *Math. Gaz.*, vol. 25, pp. 19–27, 1941.

28. G. Peano, Residue in formulas de quadratura, *Mathesis*, vol. 34, pp. 1–10, 1916; reprinted in "Opera Scelte," I, pp. 419–425, Edizioni Cremonese, Rome, 1957.

29. K. Knopp, "Theory and Application of Infinite Series," Blackie & Sons, Ltd., Glasgow, 1928.

30. P. J. Davis and P. Rabinowitz, On the Estimation of Quadrature Errors for Analytic Functions, *Math. Tables Aids Comput.*, vol. 8, pp. 193–203, 1954.

31. P. J. Davis, On the Numerical Integration of Periodic Analytic Functions, in [32], pp. 45–60.

32. R. E. Langer, ed., "On Numerical Approximation," University of Wisconsin Press, Madison, Wis., 1959.

33. P. C. Hammer, Numerical Evaluation of Multiple Integrals, in [32], pp. 99–116.

34. H. C. Thacher, Optimal Quadrature Formulas in *s* Dimension, *Math. Tables Aids Comp.*, vol. 11, pp. 189–196, 1957.

35. P. J. Davis and P. Rabinowitz, Some Monte Carlo Experiments in Computing Multiple Integrals, *Math. Tables Aids Comput.*, vol. 10, pp. 1–7, 1956.

36. D. R. Hartree, The Evaluation of a Diffraction Integral, *Proc. Cambridge Philos. Soc.*, vol. 50, pp. 567–576, 1954.

37. L. Fox and E. T. Goodwin, The Numerical Solution of Non-singular Integral Equations, *Philos. Trans. Roy. Soc. London. Ser. A*, vol. 245, pp. 501–539, 1953.

38. G. Prasad, On the Numerical Solution of Integral Equations, in "Proceedings of the International Congress on Mathematics," pp. 46–59, Toronto, 1924.

39. A. M. Ostrowski, On a Discontinuous Analogue of Theodorsen's and Garrick's Method, in E. F. Beckenbach, ed., "Construction and Application of Conformal Maps," National Bureau of Standards Applied Mathematics Series, vol. 18, pp. 149–164, 1952.

40. A. M. Ostrowski, Theodorsen's and Garrick's Method for Conformal Mapping of the Unit Circle into an Ellipse, in J. Todd, ed., "Experiments in the Computation of Conformal Maps," National Bureau of Standards Applied Mathematics Series, vol. 42, pp. 3–5, 1955.

41. Z. Kopal, "Numerical Analysis," John Wiley & Sons, Inc., New York, 1955.

42. E. Kamke, "Differentialgleichungen, Lösungsmethoden und Lösungen," I, II, Akademische Verlagsgesellschaft, Leipzig, 1944, 1950.

43. A. Fletcher, J. C. P. Miller, and L. Rosenhead, "An Index to Mathematical Tables," McGraw-Hill Book Company, Inc., New York, 1946.

11. A. V. Lebedev and R. M. Fedorova, "Spravochnik po matematicheskim tablitsiam," Izdatel'stvo Akademii Nauk SSSR, Moscow, 1956; see also the supplement to this: N. M. Buronova, "Dopolnenie," no. 1, 1959.

45. W. E. Milne, "Numerical Calculus," Princeton University Press, Princeton, N.J., 1950; "Numerical Solution of Differential Equations," John Wiley & Sons, Inc., New York, 1953.

46. W. Richter, Estimation de l'erreur commise dans la méthode de M. W. E. Milne pour l'intégration d'un système de *n* équations différentielles du premier ordre, *Bull. Soc. Neuchateloise Sci. Nat.*, vol. 75, pp. 1–43, 1952.

47. D. W. Martin, Runge-Kutta Methods for Integrating Differential Equations on High Speed Digital Computers, *Comput. J.*, vol. 1, pp. 118–123, 1958.

48. S. Gill, A Process for the Step-by-step Integration of Differential Equations on an Automatic Digital Computing Machine, *Proc. Cambridge Philos. Soc.*, vol. 47, pp. 96–108, 1951.

49a. L. Collatz, "Eigenwertaufgaben mit technischen Anwendungen," Akademische Verlagsgesellschaft m.b.H., Leipzig, 1949.

49b. L. Collatz, "The Numerical Treatment of Differential Equations," Springer-Verlag, Berlin, 1960.

49c. L. Collatz, "Eigenwertprobleme and ihre numerische Behandlung," Akademische Verlagsgesellschaft m.b.H., Leipzig, 1945.

50. L. Fox, "Numerical Solutions of Two-point Boundary Problems," Clarendon Press, Oxford, 1957.

51. J. Todd, Notes on Modern Numerical Analysis, I, *Math. Tables Aids Comput.*, vol. 4, pp. 39–44, 1950.

52. W. Wasow, Discrete Approximations to Elliptic Differential Equations, *Z. Angew. Math. Phys.*, vol. 6, pp. 81–97, 1955.

53. A. Erdélyi, "Asymptotic Expansions," Dover Publications, New York, 1956.

54. J. Barkley Rosser, Transformations to Speed the Convergence of Series, *J. Res. Nat. Bur. Standards*, vol. 46, pp. 56–64, 1951.

55. E. T. Goodwin and J. Staton, Table of $\int_{0}^{\infty} (\exp -u^2)(u + x)^{-1} du$, *Quart. J. Mech. Appl. Math.*, vol. 1, pp. 319–326, 1948.

56. I. A. Stegun and M. Abramowitz, Generation of Coulomb Wave Functions by Means of Recurrence Relations, *Phys. Rev.*, vol. 98, pp. 1851–1852, 1955.

57. I. A. Stegun and M. Abramowitz, Generation of Bessel Functions on High Speed Computers, *Math. Tables Aids Comput.*, vol. 11, pp. 255–257, 1957.

58. C. A. Coulson and W. E. Duncanson, Some New Values for the Exponential Integral, *Phil. Mag.*, ser. 7, vol. 33, pp. 756–761, 1942.

59. A. H. Stroud, Quadrature Methods for Functions of More Than One Variable, *Ann. New York Acad. Sci.*, vol. 86, pp. 776–791, 1960.

60. W. Gautschi, Recursive Computation of the Repeated Integrals of the Error Function, *Math. Comp.*, vol. 15, pp. 227–232, 1961.

61. G. Birkhoff, D. M. Young, and E. H. Zarantonello, Numerical methods in conformal mapping, in Proceedings of Symposia in Applied Mathematics, vol. IV, McGraw-Hill Book Company, Inc., 1953, pp. 117–140.

62. P. J. Davis, Errors of Numerical Approximation for Analytic Functions, *J. Rat. Mech. Anal.* 2, pp. 303–313, 1953.

63. G. Hämmerlin, Zur numerischen Integration periodischen Funktionen, *Z. Angew. Math. Mech.*, vol. 39, pp. 80–82, 1959.

64. J. Todd and S. E. Warschawski, On the Solution of the Lichtenstein-Gerschgorin Integral Equation in Conformal Mapping, II, pp. 31–44 in NBSAMS 42.

65. E. L. Stiefel, On Solving Fredholm Integral Equations, Applications to Conformal Mapping and Variational Problems of Potential Theory, *J. Soc. Indust. Appl. Math.*, vol. 4, pp. 63–85, 1956.

66. J. Todd, The Condition of Certain Integral Equations, pp. 306–311, in Symposium, Provisional International Computation Center, Birkhauser, Basel, 1961.

67. H. C. Rumsey, personal communication.

68. A. H. Stroud, A Bibliography on Approximate Integration, *Math. Comp.*, vol. 15, pp. 52–80, 1961.

3

The Constructive Theory of Functions

JOHN TODD

PROFESSOR OF MATHEMATICS
CALIFORNIA INSTITUTE OF TECHNOLOGY

3.1 Introduction

In this chapter we present, in outline, an introduction to the constructive theory of functions. This theory can be developed on theoretical lines, independent of numerical applications, but it can also be integrated into courses in numerical analysis.

The term *constructive theory of functions* is due to the Russian mathematician S. N. Bernstein (1880–   ). The subject derives from the work of Chebyshev (1821–1894) and his pupils—for example, Korkine, Zolotareff, and the brothers Markoff. It was set up as an independent discipline by Bernstein, to whom and to whose pupils much of its later development is due.

Basically our subject is concerned with the approximate representation of functions in terms of simpler ones. Two examples are:

1. *Functions $f(x)$ continuous on an interval $[a,b]$ in terms of polynomials*

$$\sum_{i=1}^{k} a_i x^i$$

2. *Continuous periodic functions $F(x)$ with $F(x) = F(x + 2\pi)$ in terms of trigonometrical polynomials*

$$\sum_{i=0}^{k} (a_i \cos ix + b_i \sin ix).$$

This subject, therefore, is likely to be of considerable use in the various applications, but it also turns out to be an intrinsically interesting area of mathematics that includes many sharp and appealing results which are easily accessible.

A vital question is how the goodness of our approximations is to be measured, and there are widely different theories, according to which norm we use.   The following two expansions can be developed formally, for the interval $-1 \leq x \leq 1$:

$$|x| = \frac{1}{2} \sum_{n=1}^{\infty} (-1)^{n+1} \frac{(2n-2)!}{(n-1)!\,(n+1)!} \frac{4n+1}{2^{2n}} P_{2n}(x), \quad (3.1)$$

$$|x| = \frac{2}{\pi} + \frac{4}{\pi} \sum_{n=1}^{\infty} \frac{(-1)^{n+1}}{4n^2-1} T_{2n}(x), \quad (3.2)$$

where $P_n(x)$, $T_n(x)$ are the usual Legendre and Chebyshev polynomials. If we truncate these, we obtain the following series of approximations:

$$\frac{1}{2}, \quad 3(5x^2+1)/16, \quad 15(-7x^4+14x^2+1)/128, \quad \ldots \quad (3.3)$$

and

$$2/\pi, \quad 2(4x^2+1)/3\pi, \quad 3(-16x^4+36x^2+3)/15\pi, \quad \ldots \quad (3.4)$$

Another sequence of approximations (see Remez [32]) is

$$\frac{1}{2}, \quad x^2 + \frac{1}{8}, \quad -1.065537x^4 + 1.930297x^2 + .067621, \quad \ldots \quad (3.5)$$

It is instructive to compare the errors—for instance, in the constant and quadratic cases—between $|x|$ and the expressions in Eqs. (3.3) to (3.5), using the following norms:

M_∞: $\qquad\qquad\qquad\qquad$ max $|e(x)|$,

M_1: $\qquad\qquad\qquad\qquad \int_{-1}^{1} |e(x)|\,dx$,

M_2: $\qquad\qquad\qquad\qquad \left[\int_{-1}^{+1} e(x)^2\,dx\right]^{\frac{1}{2}}$.

In this chapter we are concerned mostly with the Chebyshev, or maximum, norm M_∞, although we have something to say about the rms norm M_2; the norm M_1 is difficult to handle.   However, it is obviously reasonable to try to build up an abstract theory of approximation in normed spaces (see, e.g., Buck [3]).

The following notations are useful in this chapter.   By $p_n(x)$ we understand a polynomial of degree n; if the leading coefficient a_n of $p_n(x)$ is not zero, we define

$$\tilde{p}_n(x) = (a_n)^{-1} p_n(x) = x^n + \cdots,$$

so that $\tilde{p}_n(x)$ has its leading coefficient unity.

3.2   The Theorems of Weierstrass

Theorem 3.1.   If $f(x)$ is continuous in $[a,b]$, then, given any $\epsilon > 0$, there is a polynomial $p = p_\epsilon(x)$ such that

$$|f(x) - p(x)| \leq \epsilon, \qquad a \leq x \leq b.$$

This was established by Weierstrass in 1885.   Another form of this is

Theorem 3.2.   *If $f(x)$ is continuous in $[a,b]$, there is a series of polynomials $\Sigma\, q_n(x)$ which is uniformly convergent to $f(x)$ in $[a,b]$.*

There are analogous theorems for continuous functions which are periodic in an interval which we can take to be $[0,2\pi]$.   These can be established directly, or indirectly, by showing that they are equivalent to the above results.   The analogue of Theorem 3.1 is as follows.

Theorem 3.3.   *If $F(\theta)$ is a continuous function which has period 2π, then, given any $\epsilon > 0$, there is a trigonométrical polynomial $T = T_\epsilon$:*

$$T(\theta) = \tfrac{1}{2}a_0 + \sum_{r=1}^{n} (a_r \cos r\theta + b_r \sin r\theta)$$

such that

$$|F(\theta) - T(\theta)| \leq \epsilon, \qquad all\ \theta.$$

There are many proofs of these theorems.   We describe briefly two of the simpler ones, due, respectively, to Lebesgue (1898) and to Landau (1908), but shall concentrate on that of Bernstein (1912).

The proof that $(3.1) \equiv (3.2)$ is easy.   It is also easy to show that $(3.3) \equiv (3.1)$.

Lebesgue's Proof of Theorem 3.1

We note that, in virtue of uniform continuity, we can approximate $f(x)$ arbitrarily closely by a polygonal function, $g(x)$.   We can represent $g(x)$ as a linear combination of polynomials and distorted functions $|x|$.   The distortion consists in a change of origin and of scale: $a\,|x - b|$.   The problem is therefore reduced to that of approximating $|x|$ by polynomials.   This is done by noticing that, when $|x| \leq 1$,

$$|x| = \sqrt{1 - (1 - x^2)}$$

and expanding the right-hand side as a binomial series

$$1 - \tfrac{1}{2}(1 - x^2) - \tfrac{1}{8}(1 - x^2)^2 - \cdots.$$

There is some difficulty about the behavior of this at $x = 0$.   This can be overcome by a careful analysis of the convergence of the series at $x = 0$.   This can be done by examining the ratio of consecutive terms of the series or, preferably, by a direct discussion of the remainder in the Maclaurin series

$$(1 - t)^{1/2} = 1 - \tfrac{1}{2}t - \tfrac{1}{8}t^2 - \cdots - \frac{1 \cdot 3 \cdots (2n - 3)}{2 \cdot 4 \cdots 2n} t^n$$
$$+ \frac{t^{n+1}}{n!} \int_0^1 \left[\left(\frac{d}{d(tx)}\right)^{n+1} (1 - tx)^{1/2}\right] (1 - x)^n\, dx.$$

An alternative, more elementary (but more complicated) treatment has been given by Ostrowski [29].

Landau's Proof of Theorem 3.1

Landau's proof depends on the use of a singular integral (delta function). Consider, in the case $a = 0$, $b = 1$,

$$I_n(\delta) = \int_\delta^1 (1 - x^2)^n \, dx, \qquad 0 \le \delta \le 1.$$

It is plausible, from consideration of the graphs of $y = x^n$, that $I_n(\delta)$ is negligible with respect to $I_n(0)$; the area represented by $I_n(\delta)$ is concentrated near $\delta = 0$. It can indeed be shown that when $\delta > 0$

$$I_n(\delta)/I_n(0) \to 0 \qquad \text{as } n \to \infty.$$

This suggests that

$$[2I_n(0)]^{-1} \int_0^1 f(z)\{[1 - (z - x)^2]\}^n \, dz \to f(x).$$

This can be proved. Further, the left-hand side is a polynomial in x. This is essentially the result required.

This proof makes use of the integral calculus, but it is not difficult to avoid this (see Landau [30]).

de la Vallée Poussin's Proof of Theorem 3.3

The de la Vallée Poussin proof is similar to that of Landau. It is shown that, if

$$V_n(F,\theta) = \frac{(2n)!!}{2\pi(2n-1)!!} \int_{-\pi}^{+\pi} F(\phi) \cos^{2n} \tfrac{1}{2}(\phi - \theta) \, d\phi,$$

then

$$V_n(F,\theta) \to F(\theta)$$

uniformly.

Bernstein's Proof of Theorem 3.1

This proof is best motivated from elementary considerations of probability. The proof, however, does not depend on any probability ideas and, indeed, rather serves to justify these ideas.

Consider repeated, independent experiments with two possible outcomes: H or T, T or F, for which the probabilities are x, $(1 - x)$, respectively. It is reasonable to suppose that in a large number n of experiments there will be approximately xn successes, $(1 - x)n$ failures. Now, by elementary reasoning, we know that the probability of exactly

k successes is $p_{nk} = \binom{n}{k} x^k (1-x)^{n-k}$. This quantity, regarded as a function of k, with n, x fixed, should have a high peak where $k \doteq nx$ and should fall off rapidly on either side. This suggests that, although $\sum_{k=0}^{n} p_{nk} = 1$, *the sum over the k close to nx will be close to 1, and the sum of remaining p_{nk} will be near zero.*

With these thoughts in mind, we consider the Bernstein polynomials for $f(x)$:

$$B_n(f,x) = \sum p_{nk} f\left(\frac{k}{n}\right)$$

and, f being continuous, it follows that the right-hand side should be nearly $f(k/n) \doteq f(x)$, and the approximation should improve as n increases.

We shall now begin afresh and establish the following result rigorously.

Theorem 3.4. *If $f(x)$ is continuous in $[0,1]$, then*

$$B_n(f,x) = \sum p_{nk} f\left(\frac{k}{n}\right) \to f(x)$$

uniformly in $[0,1]$.

We need several lemmas. The first two can be obtained directly, or alternatively, by differentiating the identity

$$(p+q)^n = \sum \binom{n}{k} p^k q^{n-k}$$

with respect to p, treating p, q as independent variables.

Lemma 3.5:

$$\sum p_{nk}(k-nx) = 0.$$

Lemma 3.6:

$$\sum p_{nk}(k-nx)^2 = nx(1-x).$$

We shall now establish a third lemma, essentially the *Chebyshev inequality*.

Lemma 3.7. *If $\delta > 0$, then $\Sigma' p_{nk} < x(1-x)/n\delta^2$ if Σ' is the sum over those k for which $|(k/n) - x| \geq \delta$.*

Proof. Consider the summation in Lemma 3.6. Break it up into Σ' and a complementary Σ''. We have

$$nx(1-x) = \Sigma' p_{nk}(k-nx)^2 + \Sigma'' p_{nk}(k-nx)^2$$
$$\geq \Sigma' p_{nk}(k-nx)^2$$
$$\geq \Sigma' p_{nk} n^2 \delta^2.$$

The first inequality follows because each term in Σ and therefore in Σ'' is essentially nonnegative. The second inequality follows because, by definition of Σ', we have $|k - nx| \geq n\delta$. Hence

$$\Sigma' p_{nk} \leq \frac{x(1 - x)}{n\delta^2}.$$

Remembering that $0 \leq x(1 - x) \leq \frac{1}{4}$, we conclude that

$$\Sigma'' p_{nk} \geq 1 - (4n\delta^2)^{-1}, \qquad \Sigma' p_{nk} \leq (4n\delta^2)^{-1}. \tag{3.6}$$

(This is the precise form of the statement in italics on page 123.)

Since $\Sigma p_{nk} = 1$, in order to prove Theorem 3.4 it will be sufficient to show that

$$e_n(x) = B_n(f,x) - f(x) = \sum_{k=0}^{n} p_{nk}\left[f\left(\frac{k}{n}\right) - f(x) \right]$$

tends uniformly to zero. We do this by breaking up the sum into Σ' and Σ'' and showing that each part, separately, tends uniformly to zero. The first does so because $\Sigma' p_{nk}$ is small and $f(k/n) - f(x)$ is bounded, the second because although Σ'' is near unity, since f is continuous, $f(k/n)$ is near $f(x)$.

Take any $\epsilon > 0$. Then choose δ such that

$$|f(x') - f(x'')| < \frac{1}{2}\epsilon \qquad \text{if } |x' - x''| < \delta, 0 \leq x', x'' \leq 1.$$

Let $M = \max |f(x)|$. Then, using (3.6), we have

$$|e_n(x)| \leq \Sigma' p_{nk} |f\left(\frac{k}{n}\right) - f(x)| + \Sigma'' p_{nk} |f\left(\frac{k}{n}\right) - f(x)|$$

$$\leq 2M \Sigma' p_{nk} + \frac{1}{2}\epsilon \Sigma'' p_{nk}$$

$$\leq 2M(4n\delta^2)^{-1} + \frac{1}{2}\epsilon.$$

To get the last inequality, we have also used the fact that $\Sigma'' p_{nk} \leq \Sigma p_{nk} = 1$. If $n \geq M\epsilon^{-1}\delta^{-2}$, then the first term in the last inequality does not exceed $\frac{1}{2}\epsilon$, and we conclude that

$$|e_n(x)| \leq \epsilon, \qquad \text{all } x, \qquad n \geq M\epsilon^{-1}\delta^{-2}.$$

This completes the proof of Theorem 3.4.

It is clear that $(3.4) \Rightarrow (3.1)$. It is also true that $(3.1) \Rightarrow (3.4)$; this can be established along the following lines.

It is clear that $B_n(x)$ is a polynomial in x of degree n at most. We shall show that the coefficient of x^K in B_n is $\binom{n}{K} \Delta^K(0)$, where the differences are taken at interval n^{-1}.

We observe that x^K occurs only in the terms with $k = 0, 1, \ldots, K$ and that the contribution from the $(k + 1)$st term is

$$f\left(\frac{k}{n}\right)\binom{n}{k}(-1)^{K-k}\binom{n-k}{K-k}$$

$$= (-1)^{K-k}f\left(\frac{k}{n}\right)\frac{n!}{k!\,(n-k)!}\frac{(n-k)!}{(K-k)!\,(n-K)!}$$

$$= (-1)^{K-k}f\left(\frac{k}{n}\right)\binom{n}{K}\frac{K!}{k!\,(K-k)!}$$

$$= \binom{n}{K}\binom{K}{k}(-1)^{K-k}f\left(\frac{k}{n}\right),$$

and the result follows, since

$$(-1)^K\Delta^K f(0) = f(0) - \binom{K}{1}f\left(\frac{1}{n}\right) + \binom{K}{2}f\left(\frac{2}{n}\right) - \cdots + (-1)^K f\left(\frac{K}{n}\right).$$

Hence, if $f(x)$ is a polynomial of degree r, so is B_n, for $n \geq r$. Further, we can write

$$\binom{n}{k}\Delta^k f(0) = \frac{1}{k!}\left(1 - \frac{1}{n}\right)\left(1 - \frac{2}{n}\right)\cdots\left(1 - \frac{k-1}{n}\right)\frac{\Delta^k f(0)}{(\Delta x)^k},$$

and so, letting $n \to \infty$, keeping k fixed, and assuming that $f^{(k)}(0)$ exists, we see that

$$\binom{n}{k}\Delta^k f(0) \to \frac{f^{(k)}(0)}{k!},$$

the coefficient of x^k in the Maclaurin expansion of $f(x)$.   This idea can be developed into a proof of Bernstein's theorem.   Using the Weierstrass theorem, we get a polynomial approximating $f(x)$ uniformly, and the above argument shows that the Bernstein polynomials of a *polynomial* approximate it uniformly, thus establishing the implication (3.1) $\Rightarrow$ (3.4).

There are many generalizations of the Weierstrass theorems.   Axiomatic accounts have been given by M. H. Stone and N. Bourbaki.

It is easy to compute the $B_n(f)$ for $f = x^r$, $r = 0, 1, 2, \ldots$.   For instance, we have

$$B_n(1) \equiv 1$$
$$B_n(x) \equiv x$$
$$B_n(x^2) = x^2 + x(1 - x)/n$$
$$B_n(x^3) = x^3 + 3x^2(1 - x)/n + x(1 - x)(1 - 2x)/n^2.$$

It is evident that the $B_n(f)$ do not give the best approximation to f, among all polynomials of degree $\leq n$; for example, if $f(x) = x^2$, $n = 2$, the best approximation in any reasonable sense is $x^2 \neq B_n(x^2)$. The order of approximation in this special case is typical. Voronowskaja [42] has established the following result.

Theorem 3.8.   *Let $f(x)$ be continuous in $[0,1]$ and let $f''(x_0)$ be finite for some x_0, $0 \leq x_0 \leq 1$.   Then*

$$\lim n\,[B_n(x_0) - f(x_0)] = \tfrac{1}{2}f''(x_0)x_0(1 - x_0).$$

The weakness of the Bernstein polynomials as a means for approximation is discussed at the end of Sec. 3.3.

3.3   The Chebyshev Theory

We have just seen that, given any function $f(x)$, continuous in $[a,b]$, and any $\epsilon > 0$, there is a polynomial $p = p_\epsilon$ such that

$$|f(x) - p(x)| < \epsilon, \qquad a \leq x \leq b.$$

It is natural to ask, for any integer n, what is the polynomial of degree at most n which is the best approximation to a given $f(x)$. Indeed, we should ask, first, Is there a best approximation? and, secondly, Is it unique? A third question is then relevant: How can one determine the extremal polynomial?

We shall deal with a special case first: the approximation of $f(x) \equiv 0$ by a $p_n(x)$ or, what is the same thing, the approximation of x^n by a polynomial of lower degree. We shall establish the following result.

Theorem 3.9.

$$\text{Let } \tilde{p}_n(x) = x^n + a_1 x^{n-1} + \cdots + a_n. \quad \text{Let}$$

$$\mu(\tilde{p}_n) = \max_{-1 \leq x \leq 1} |\tilde{p}_n(x)|.$$

Then

$$\mu(\tilde{p}_n) \geq \mu_n = 2^{1-n}.$$

There is equality if and only if

$$\tilde{p}_n = \tilde{T}_n(x) = 2^{1-n} \cos(n \arccos x).$$

Proof.   We note that $\tilde{T}_n = \pm 2^{1-n}$ *alternately* at the points

$$x_\nu = \cos \nu\,\pi/n, \qquad \nu = 0, 1, \ldots, n.$$

Suppose there is a $\tilde{p}_n(x)$, say $\tilde{\pi}_n(x)$, such that

$$\mu(\tilde{\pi}_n) < \mu_n. \tag{3.7}$$

Consider

$$r = \tilde{\pi}_n - \tilde{T}_n.$$

This is a polynomial of degree $n - 1$ which does not vanish identically. [If it did, then $\mu(\tilde{\pi}_n) = \mu(\tilde{T}_n) = \mu_n$, contradicting (3.7).]   Now consider the values of r at the points x_ν.   Clearly r has alternate signs at these points.   (Since $|\tilde{\pi}_n| < \mu_n$, the sign of r is that of $\tilde{T}_n$.]   By Bolzano's theorem, r must vanish between consecutive x_ν, that is, n times in all— which implies, since it is a polynomial of degree $n - 1$, that it vanishes identically.   This is a contradiction.   Hence (3.7) is false.   Hence

$$\mu(\tilde{p}_n) \geq \mu_n = 2^{1-n}.$$

The proof of the equality results is left as an exercise.

We shall now show that $\tilde{T}_n(x)$ has some compensation for having the smallest deviation from zero within $[-1,1]$: it is the largest such polynomial outside $[-1,1]$.

Theorem 3.10.   *Let $p_n(x)$ be a polynomial of degree at most n.   Let $M = \max\limits_{-1 \leq x \leq 1} |p_n(x)|$.   Then, for any real $\xi, |\xi| > 1$, we have $|p_n(\xi)| \leq M T_n(\xi)$, where $T_n(x) = \cos(n \arccos x)$.*

Proof.   Suppose the conclusion is false and consider

$$r(x) = [p_n(\xi) T_n(x)/T_n(\xi)] - p_n(x).$$

This is a polynomial of degree at most n and $r(\xi) = 0$.   Further, since $|p_n(\xi)/T_n(\xi)| > M$ and since $T_n(\cos i\pi/n) = (-1)^i$, $i = 0, \ldots, n$, it follows that

$$r(\cos i\pi/n) = (-1)^i[p_n(\xi)/T_n(\xi)] - p_n(\cos i\pi/n)$$

has opposite signs for consecutive i, $|p_n(x)|$ being bounded by M in $[-1,1]$.   Hence r has n zeros inside $[-1,1]$ and another zero outside, at $x = \xi$.   Hence $r(x) = 0$.   Hence

$$p_n(x) = p_n(\xi) T_n(x)/T_n(\xi),$$

so that

$$p_n(1) - p(\xi)/T_n(\xi),$$

and so

$$|p_n(1)| > M$$

—a contradiction.

Chebyshev Polynomials

We insert here a collection of formulas concerning Chebyshev polynomials which will be required later.

Definitions.   There are several normalizations of these polynomials in current use, and care must be exercised.   We define the Chebyshev polynomials of the first and second kind by

$$T_n(x) = \cos(n \arccos x)$$

$$= x^n - \binom{n}{2} x^{n-2}(1 - x^2) + \binom{n}{4} x^{n-4}(1 - x^2)^2 - \cdots$$

$$= \frac{n}{2} \sum_{m=0}^{[n/2]} \frac{(-1)^m (n - m - 1)!}{m! (n - 2m)!} (2x)^{n-m}$$

$$= 2^{n-1}\left(x^n - \frac{n}{4} x^{n-2} + \cdots \right)$$

$$= 2^{n-1} \tilde{T}_n(x)$$

and $$U_n(x) = \frac{1}{n+1} T'_{n+1}(x) = \frac{\sin[(n+1)\arccos x]}{\sin(\arccos x)}$$

$$= \binom{n+1}{1} x^n - \binom{n+1}{3} x^{n-2}(1 - x^2)$$

$$+ \binom{n+1}{5} x^{n-4}(1 - x^2)^2 - \cdots$$

$$= \sum_{m=0}^{[n/2]} \frac{(-1)^m (n - m)!}{m! (n - 2m)!} (2x)^{n-2m}.$$

We therefore have

$T_0 = 1$	$\tilde{T}_0 = 1$	$U_0 = 1$
$T_1 = x$	$\tilde{T}_1 = x$	$U_1 = 2x$
$T_2 = 2x^2 - 1$	$\tilde{T}_2 = x^2 - \frac{1}{2}$	$U_2 = 4x^2 - 1$
$T_3 = 4x^3 - 3x$	$\tilde{T}_3 = x^3 - \frac{3}{4}x$	$U_3 = 8x^3 - 4x$
$T_4 = 8x^4 - 8x^2 + 1$	$\tilde{T}_4 = x^4 - x^2 + \frac{1}{8}$	$U_4 = 16x^4 - 12x^2 + 1.$

We shall use the following notation for the Chebyshev polynomials appropriate to the interval $[0, 1]$:

$$T_n^*(x) = T_n(2x - 1).$$

Recurrence Relation.   Both T_n and U_n satisfy the recurrence relation

$$p_n(x) = 2x p_{n-1}(x) - p_{n-2}(x)$$

with appropriate initial conditions.

Zeros. $T_n(x) = 0$ for $x = x_\nu = \cos[(2\nu - 1)\pi/2n]$, $\nu = 1, 2, \ldots, n$, so that $x_1 = -x_n$, $x_2 = -x_{n-1}, \ldots$.

Inequalities. $|T_n(x)| \leq 1$ with equality if and only if $x = \cos \nu\pi/n$, $\nu = 0, 1, 2, \ldots, n$, and $|U_n(x)| \leq n + 1$ with equality if and only if $x = \pm 1$.

Values at Endpoints. $T'_n(\pm 1) = n^2$.

Lagrangian Interpolation at the Chebyshev Abscissas. When, in the notation of Sec. 2.6, the nodes are the zeros x_i of $T_n(x)$, we have

$$l_i(x) = T_n(x)/(x - x_i)\, T'_n(x_i).$$

Now
$$T'_n(x_i) = nU_{n-1}(x_i) = \frac{n \sin (n \arccos x_i)}{\sin (\arccos x_i)}$$

and with
$$x_i = \cos \left[(2i - 1)\pi/2n\right]$$

we have
$$\sin (n \arccos x_i) = (-1)^{i-1}, \qquad \sin (\arccos x_i) = \sqrt{1 - x_i^2}$$

so that
$$l_i(x) = \frac{T_n(x)/(x - x_i)}{n(-1)^{i-1}/\sqrt{1 - x_i^2}}.$$

Existence of Polynomial of Best Approximation

We now take up the general question of the existence for each n, of a polynomial of degree at most n, of best approximation to a given continuous function.   This is best handled from the point of view of elementary functional analysis.

The following general problem of approximation has a meaning in a real normed linear vector space X:

Given an $f \in X$ and a set of linearly independent elements b_1, b_2, . . . , b_n, all in X, to find the linear combination $\Sigma\, \lambda_i b_i$ which is the best approximation (in the sense of the given norm) to f; that is, determine

$$\min_{\{\lambda_i\}} \| f - \Sigma\, \lambda_i b_i \|.$$

We shall show that this problem always has a solution.   By taking $X = C$, the set of functions $f(x)$ continuous on $[a,b]$, with

$$\| f(x) \| = \max_{a \le x \le b} | f(x)|,$$

and $b_i = x^{i-1}$, we obtain the result required. It is not possible to show that the solution to the general problem is unique.   However, we can establish uniqueness if we insist on our space being *strongly normed*, that is, if

$$\| x + y \| = \| x \| + \| y \|, \qquad x \ne 0, y \ne 0,$$

only if $y = \alpha x$ ($\alpha \ge 0$).   Observe that this result does not give us uniqueness in the Chebyshev case, for C is not strongly normed; the latter fact follows from the remark that, if

$$f(x_0) = \max | f(x)| \qquad and \qquad g(x_0) = \max |g(x)|,$$

then $\|f + g\| = \|f\| + \|g\|$, and we can certainly choose $f \neq \alpha g$. Uniqueness is established later (Theorem 3.14).

We begin by showing that $\phi(\lambda_1, \ldots, \lambda_n) = \|f - \Sigma \lambda_i b_i\|$ is a continuous function of its arguments.

$$|\phi(\Lambda) - \phi(\lambda)| = \left| \|f - \Sigma \Lambda_i b_i\| - \|f - \Sigma \lambda_i b_i\| \right|$$
$$\leq \|\Sigma (\Lambda_i - \lambda_i) b_i\|$$
$$\leq \Sigma |\Lambda_i - \lambda_i| \|b_i\|$$
$$\leq \max_{1 \leq i \leq n} |\Lambda_i - \lambda_i| \Sigma \|b_i\|.$$

The b_i's are fixed and so therefore is $\Sigma \|b_i\|$.

It follows, in particular, that

$$\Psi(\lambda) = \|\Sigma \lambda_i b_i\|$$

is a continuous function of λ. The shell

$$\lambda_1{}^2 + \lambda_2{}^2 + \cdots + \lambda_n{}^2 = 1$$

is a bounded, closed set in ordinary n-dimensional space, and on it the continuous function Ψ must assume its minimum, μ. Since $\Psi \geq 0$, $\mu \geq 0$. Since the b_i are linearly independent, $\mu \neq 0$. Hence $\mu > 0$. It follows, by the homogeneity of the norm, that for any $(\lambda_1, \ldots, \lambda_n)$,

$$\|\Sigma \lambda_i b_i\| \geq \mu \sqrt{(\lambda_1{}^2 + \lambda_2{}^2 + \cdots + \lambda_n{}^2)}. \tag{3.8}$$

Let ρ be the lower bound of $\phi(\lambda)$. Then $\rho \geq 0$, and we have to show that this bound is attained, that is, that there is a λ^* such that $\phi(\lambda^*) = \rho$. We shall show that $\phi(\lambda)$ *is large* (specifically $\phi(\lambda) > \rho + 1$) *when λ is large* (specifically, when $\sqrt{\Sigma \lambda_i{}^2} > R = (\rho + 1 + \|f\|)/\mu$). Hence the lower bound of $\phi(\lambda)$, for all λ, is the same as the lower bound when λ is restricted by $\sqrt{\Sigma \lambda_i{}^2} \leq R$, and we are now concerned with the lower bound of a continuous function on a *ball* (solid sphere). Since the ball is closed and bounded, the lower bound is attained, and the existence of λ^* is established. To establish the italicized statement above, we observe that when λ is restricted to $\sqrt{\Sigma \lambda_i{}^2} \geq R$ we have, by (3.8),

$$\phi(\lambda) \geq \|\Sigma \lambda_i b_i\| - \|f\|$$
$$\geq \mu \cdot (\rho + 1 + \|f\|)/\mu - \|f\| = \rho + 1.$$

Note that we have made two appeals to the fact that a continuous function defined on a bounded, closed subset of an ordinary n-dimensional space attains its lower bound.

We have now established, in particular, the following result, due to Borel.

Theorem 3.11. *If $f(x)$ is continuous in $[a,b]$, then, for each n, there exists a polynomial (of degree $\leq n$) of best approximation.*

Characterization and Uniqueness

Our next task is the development of the qualitative Chebyshev criterion for the polynomials of best approximation; we shall also obtain the uniqueness. We let $\hat{p}(x)$ be *a* best approximation to $f(x)$ on $[a,b]$, among all polynomials of degree n at most. We write

$$E_n = E_n(f) = \max_x |f(x) - \hat{p}(x)| = \min_{p_n} \max_x |f(x) - p_n(x)|$$

We assume that $E_n > 0$—otherwise f is itself a polynomial of degree n at most. Consider

$$|f(x) - \hat{p}(x)|.$$

This is continuous in $[a,b]$ and so assumes its maximum E_n in at least one point in $[a,b]$. Such points are called e points (e = extremal). We classify the e points into $+$ points where the value of $f(x) - \hat{p}(x)$ is E_n and $-$ points where this value is $-E_n$.

Theorem 3.12. *There are always both $+$ points and $-$ points.*

Proof. From the general properties of continuous functions there is at least one e point. Suppose, for instance, that there were no $+$ points. This would mean that

$$\min \{\hat{p}(x) - f(x)\} = -E_n + 2h, \qquad h > 0.$$

Hence $$E_n \geq \hat{p}(x) - f(x) \geq -E_n + 2h,$$

which implies

$$E_n - h \geq [\hat{p}(x) - h] - f(x) \geq -E_n + h,$$

that is,

$$|(\hat{p}(x) - h) - f(x)| \leq E_n - h,$$

so that $\hat{p}(x)$ is not a polynomial of best approximation—a contradiction.

Theorem 3.13. *There is a sequence of $(n + 2)$ points in $[a,b]$ which are alternately $+$ and $-$ points.*

Proof in linear case, $E_1 > 0$. We now know that there is a $+$ point and a $-$ point. We shall show that there must be another e point in $[a,b]$ and that the signs of the e points alternate.

By uniform continuity of $\hat{p}(x) - f(x) = E(x)$, we can divide $[a,b]$ into a set of intervals $I_i = [x_i, x_{i+1}]$ by a set of points x_i with $a = x_0 < x_1 < \cdots < x_n = b$ with the following property for each $i = 0, 1, 2, \ldots, n - 1$:

If $$x' \in I_i, \qquad x'' \in I_i, \qquad then \qquad |E(x') - E(x'')| < \tfrac{1}{2}E_1.$$

Consider any x' in the interval I_+ in which the $+$ point, say x_+, lies. Then

$$E(x_+) = E_1 \qquad \text{and} \qquad |E(x') - E_1| < \tfrac{1}{2}E_1,$$

so that $E(x') \geq \tfrac{1}{2}E_1 > 0$.   Similarly, for x'' in the interval I_- in which the $-$ point lies, we have $E(x'') \leq -\tfrac{1}{2}E_1 < 0$.   These two intervals. therefore, cannot overlap, or even abut, and so we can choose a point z_1 between them.   Suppose that the $+$ point is to the left.   Then $(z_1 - x)$ has the same sign in the intervals $I_\pm$ as $E(x)$ has.   Let $R = \max\limits_{a \leq x \leq b} |z_1 - x|$.

Consider the "remaining" intervals I_i.   We have, in these,

$$\max |E(x)| < E_1$$

and, there being a finite number of them, we have

$$\max \{\max |E(x)|\} = E^* < E_1.$$

We observe that $E^* \geq \tfrac{1}{2}E_1$.   For the end points of the intervals $I_\pm$ are also end points of the remaining intervals, and we have seen that the values there satisfy $E(x') \geq \tfrac{1}{2}E_1, E(x'') \leq -\tfrac{1}{2}E_1$.   Hence certainly $E^* \geq \tfrac{1}{2}E_1$.

We consider, for $\epsilon > 0$,

$$p(x) = \hat{p}(x) - \epsilon(z_1 - x),$$

which is linear.   If we choose ϵ so small that

$$\epsilon R < E_1 - E^*,$$

which implies $\epsilon R < \tfrac{1}{2}E_1$, we see that the deviation of $p(x)$ from $f(x)$ is less than that of $\hat{p}(x)$.   For in I_+, since $(z_1 - x) > 0$, and in I_1, since $(z_1 - x) < 0$, and since $\epsilon R < \tfrac{1}{2}E_1$, the values of $p(x) - f(x)$ have the same signs as those of $\hat{p}(x) - f(x)$ but are reduced in absolute value.   In the remaining intervals, the absolute values may be increased, but they cannot exceed

$$E^+ + \epsilon R < E^+ + E_1 - E^* = E_1.$$

Hence $\hat{p}$ is not a polynomial of best approximation.   It follows that there must be more than two e points.   These cannot be disposed in the order $++-$ or $+--$ by essentially the same argument as above: z_1 is chosen between the $+$ point and the next $-$ point; it follows that we must have an alternation $+-+$.   [We cannot get a similar contradiction in this case because we would have to take a quadratic $(z_1 - x)(z_2 - x)$, which is illegal, to get a perturbation of the correct sign pattern.]

No essentially new ideas are needed to deal with the general case.

Theorem 3.14.   *The polynomial of best approximation (of degree $\leq n$) is unique.*

Proof.   Suppose there were two p', p''.   We then would have

$$-E_n \leq f - p' \leq E_n,$$
$$-E_n \leq f - p'' \leq E_n.$$

Then $p''' = \frac{1}{2}(p' + p'')$ would also be a polynomial of best approximation.   We can therefore construct, by Theorem 3.13, a series of $(n + 2)$ points, alternately $+$ and $-$, for p'''.

Take a $+$ point, x_+, for p'''.   Then at x_+,

$$p''' - f = -E_n, \qquad \text{that is,} \qquad (p'' - f) + (p' - f) = -2E_n.$$

Since $|p' - f| \leq E_n$, $|p'' - f| \leq E_n$, it follows that $f - p' = f - p'' = E_n$; that is, p', p'' coincide at any $+$ point.   Similarly, p', p'' coincide at any $-$ point.   But there are $(n + 2)$ $\pm$ points.   Hence $p' = p''$.

Theorem 3.15. $p(x)$ *is the polynomial of best approximation (of degree $\leq n$) to $f(x)$ if there exists a set of $(n + 2)$ points, alternately $+$ and $-$ points.*

Proof.   Suppose $\max\limits_{a \leq x \leq b} |f(x) - p(x)| = \mu$.   Then $\mu \geq E_n$.   We shall show that $\mu = E_n$.   Suppose not; that is, suppose $\mu > E_n$.   Let $q(x)$ be *the* polynomial of best approximation and unique, by Theorems 3.11 and 3.14.   Then, since

$$q(x) - p(x) = q(x) - f(x) + f(x) - p(x),$$

the signs of $q(x)$ and $p(x)$ coincide at the $(n + 2)$ extrema, because

$$|q - f| \leq E_n, \qquad |f - p| = \mu > E_n.$$

Hence the polynomial $(q - p)$, of degree $\leq n$, has $(n + 2)$ changes of sign in $[a,b]$ and so $(n + 1)$ zeros; it therefore vanishes identically.   This gives $\mu = \max |f - p| = \max |f - q| = E_n$, in contradiction with our assumption that $\mu > E_n$.   Hence $\mu = E_n$.

Alternative Treatment for the Prototype

Notice that in the proofs of Theorems 3.11 to 3.15 we have not made use of Theorem 3.9.   It is therefore appropriate to outline here an account of Theorem 3.9, which is more motivated than that given earlier.   We use Theorem 3.15 in the case $f = x^n$, $a = -1$, $b = 1$, and when we are approximating by polynomials of degree $\leq n - 1$.   Then the polynomial $p_{n-1}(x)$ we require is characterized by having

$$P(x) = \pm \mu, \qquad \text{where } P = x^n - p_{n-1}(x),$$

alternately, at $n + 1 = [(n - 1) + 2]$ points in $[-1,1]$, where

$$\mu = \max\limits_{-1 \leq x \leq 1} |P(x)|.$$

Now at each interior extrema, of which there are at least $n - 1$, we must have $P' = 0$. But P is a polynomial of degree n. Hence all the zeros of P' are simple. Consider

$$g = y^2 - \mu^2.$$

Since $g' = 2yy'$ vanishes when $y' = 0$, all the interior extrema of y (and all zeros of y') are double zeros of $y^2 - \mu^2$. Hence $y^2 - \mu^2$ is divisible by y'^2, and the residual factor is a quadratic. This quadratic must be $M(1 - x^2)$ since we must have $|y(\pm 1)| = \mu$. Hence

$$y^2 - \mu^2 = M(1 - x^2)y'^2,$$

and if we compare the leading coefficients, we find $M = n^{-2}$. If we write $\eta = y/\mu$, we obtain

$$\frac{n \, dx}{\sqrt{1 - x^2}} = \pm \frac{d\eta}{\sqrt{1 - \eta^2}}$$

Integrating this relation *carefully*, we find

$$\eta = \cos{(n \arccos x)}.$$

The basic ideas in this chapter can be applied in much more general situations—for example, to the case in which we consider weighted approximations to continuous functions by rational functions of assigned degree, where the weight function is an arbitrary positive continuous function. On the other hand, we can consider approximations by families of functions which share with the polynomials the properties we need to draw the conclusion.

Extrema under Different Constraints

The problem of determining polynomials of minimum deviation where a coefficient, not the leading one, is fixed was studied by W. A. Markoff. Here again the Chebyshev polynomials turned out to be the critical ones. The result obtained is the following.

Theorem 3.16. *If the coefficient of x^r, $r \leq n$ in $p_n(x)$ is unity, then, according to whether r, n have the same or different parity, we have*

$$\max_{-1 \leq x \leq 1} |p_n(x)| \geq 1/\tau_r^{(n)} \qquad or \qquad \max_{-1 \leq x \leq 1} |p_n(x)| \geq 1/\tau_r^{(n-1)},$$

where $\tau_r^{(n)}$ is the coefficient of x^r in $T_n(x)$. There is strict inequality in the first unless $p_n(x)$ is a multiple of $T_n(x)$ and in the second unless $p_n(x)$ is a multiple of $T_{n-1}(x)$, with the following exceptions: $r = 0$ in both cases and $r = 1$, $n = 2$ in the second.

This problem suggests a series of problems solved by Zolotareff which cannot be discussed by elementary methods. We quote one:

Among all polynomials of degree n, with leading coefficients unity and with their second coefficient fixed, determine that with minimum deviation from zero in [−1,1].

The solution of this and the related problems depends on the theory of elliptic functions and has important technical applications (see Piloty [41]).

Inconsistent Linear Systems

We note here the recent studies on the construction of the Chebyshev approximation to the solution of an inconsistent system of linear equations (see, e.g., Stiefel [39]).

Given, say, m equations

$$\sum a_{ij}x_j + b_i = 0$$

in the $n < m$ unknowns $x_1, \ldots, x_n$, we consider the m residuals

$$\eta_i = \sum a_{ij}x_j + b_i$$

and ask for the set of x which minimizes

$$\max |\eta_i|.$$

It has been shown that this problem is not essentially different from that of solving a system of linear equations by the Gaussian elimination process or of solving a "linear program," in the sense of Dantzig, by the simplex method.

Construction of Polynomials of Best Approximation

It is convenient to state our present position. We have now established the existence and uniqueness of polynomials $\hat{p}_n(x)$ of best approximation to functions $f(x)$ continuous in an interval $[a,b]$. We have exhibited the $\hat{p}_n(x)$ in the case $f(x) \equiv 0$ in $[−1,1]$. So far no finite algorithm for the construction of the extremal polynomials in a general case has been discovered. Indeed the extent of the special cases in which this has been done is remarkably small. We shall discuss some of these briefly.

a. Formulas can be given for the cases $n = 0$ and $n = 1$ when $f(x)$ is a twice-differentiable convex (or concave) function.

When $n = 0$, if m, M are the lower and upper bounds of $f(x)$ in $[a,b]$, it is clear that

$$\hat{p}_0(x) = \tfrac{1}{2}(m + M).$$

When $n = 1$, suppose f is twice-differentiable and convex, so that $f''(x) > 0$. By the fundamental criterion, $p(x) = Ax + B$ is the best approximation if there are three points $x_1 < x_2 < x_3$ in $[a,b]$ for which

$f(x) - p(x)$ attains its extreme values alternately.   Hence x_2 is definitely inside $[a,b]$, and we can use the differential calculus to conclude that

$$f'(x_2) = A.$$

Now, since $f''(x) > 0$, $f'(x)$ is strictly increasing, so that $f'(x)$ can only assume the value A once; this means that the derivative of $f - p$ cannot vanish at x_1 or at x_3, and so these extreme points must be end points: $a = x_1$, $b = x_3$.   Put $x_2 = c$.   Then, using the equality of the extreme values, we must have

$$f(a) - p(a) = f(b) - p(b) = -[f(c) - p(c)],$$

which are equations for A, B which give

$$A = [f(b) - f(a)]/(b - a),$$

$$B = \tfrac{1}{2}[f(a) + f(c)] - \tfrac{1}{2}(a + c)[f(b) - f(a)]/(b - a).$$

The value of c is given by

$$f'(c) = [f(b) - f(a)]/(b - a).$$

b.   We discuss in some detail the case of $1/(1 + x)$ in $[0,1]$.   This is essentially due to Chebyshev (1892) (see Hornecker [36]).

If we write $\theta = \arccos(2x - 1)$ and $c = 3 - 2\sqrt{2}$, then we find, by elementary trigonometry, that

$$\sqrt{2}[\tfrac{1}{2} - cT_1^*(x) + c^2 T_2^*(x) - c^3 T_3^*(x) + \cdots]$$
$$= (1 + x)^{-1} = 2(3 + \cos\theta)^{-1}. \quad (3.9)$$

With the same notation, we can show that

$$\pi_n(x) = \sqrt{2}\Big\{[\tfrac{1}{2} - cT_1^*(x) + \cdots + (-1)^{n-1}c^{n-1}T_{n-1}^*(x)]$$
$$+ (-1)^n \frac{c^n}{1 - c^2} T_n^*(x)\Big\}$$
$$= \sqrt{2}\Big[\frac{\tfrac{1}{2}(1 - c^2) - (-1)^n c^n(\cos n\theta + \cos(n - 1)\theta)}{1 + 2c\cos\theta + c^2}$$
$$+ (-1)^n \frac{c^n \cos n\theta}{1 - c^2}\Big]$$

and then that

$$\frac{1}{1 + x} - \pi_n(x) = \frac{(-1)^{n-1}c^n}{4}\left\{\frac{\cos(n + 1)\theta + 2c\cos n\theta + c^2\cos(n - 1)\theta}{1 + 2c\cos\theta + c^2}\right\}.$$

We next verify that the term in braces on the right of the last equation can be written as

$$\{\cdots\} = \cos(n\theta + \phi)$$

where $\qquad \cos\phi = \dfrac{3\cos\theta + 1}{3 + \cos\theta}, \qquad \sin\phi = \dfrac{2\sqrt{2}\sin\theta}{3 + \cos\theta}.$

We observe that ϕ is a function of θ. As x goes from 0 to 1, $2x - 1$ goes from -1 to 1, θ goes from π to 0, ϕ goes from π to θ. Hence, as x goes from 0 to 1, $\cos(n\theta + \phi)$ goes from $\cos(n + 1)\pi$ to $\cos\theta$ and so has $(n + 2)$ extrema, alternately ± 1. It follows from the Chebyshev criterion that $\pi_n(x)$ must be the best approximation to $(1 + x)^{-1}$, and the error is $\frac{1}{4}c^n$.

The approximation to $(1 + x)^{-1}$ given by truncating the expansion (3.9) has been discussed numerically by Lanczos [37]; it is very close to the optimal $\pi_n(x)$. We shall pursue this question a little further. For $n = 1$, the best possible polynomial is

$$\frac{1}{4} + \frac{1}{\sqrt{2}} - \frac{1}{2}x, \qquad \text{that is,} \qquad .9571 - .5x,$$

whereas that given by truncating the Chebyshev expansion is

$$\tfrac{1}{2}(7\sqrt{2} - 8) - (6\sqrt{2} - 8)x, \qquad \text{that is,} \qquad .9497 - .4853x.$$

The corresponding errors are $\frac{1}{4}c = .0439$ and $.0503$. Take $n = 6$; then $E_n = \frac{1}{4}c^n \doteq 6.4 \times 10^{-6}$. A rough estimate gives

$$|(1 + x)^{-1} - \sqrt{2}[\tfrac{1}{2} - c_1 T_1^*(x) + \cdots + c^6 T_6^*(x)]| \leq 7.5 \times 10^{-6}.$$

Let us next consider the approximation given to $(1 + x)^{-1}$ by truncating the power series $1 - x + x^2 - \cdots$. The remainder $x^{n+1}(1 + x)^{-1}$ depends on x, and the numbers of terms needed to get errors less than 10^{-5} are

$|x| \leq .1, \quad 5; \qquad |x| \leq .5, \quad 17; \qquad |x| \leq .8, \quad 49; \qquad |x| \leq .9, \quad 104.$

Finally, consider the approximation given by the Bernstein polynomials. From Theorem 3.8, it follows that we would need to take a Bernstein polynomial of order about 10^5 to get a comparable error.

    $c.$ We return briefly to the three sequences in Eqs. (3.3) to (3.5). The first gives the best mean-square approximation (see Sec. 3.5 below), and the third gives the actual polynomials of best approximation. Specifically, for instance, $x^2 + \frac{1}{8}$ is the best *cubic* approximation, for

$$x^2 + \tfrac{1}{8} - |x|$$

takes on the values

$$\tfrac{1}{8}, \quad -\tfrac{1}{8}, \quad \tfrac{1}{8}, \quad -\tfrac{1}{8}, \quad \tfrac{1}{8}$$

at the points

$$-1, \quad -\tfrac{1}{2}, \quad 0, \quad \tfrac{1}{2}, \quad 1.$$

Current Developments

There has been a recent revival of interest in the construction of algorithms for the determination of polynomials of best approximation (see, e.g., Hastings [33], Remez [32]).   In practice it has been found that the truncation of an expansion in Chebyshev polynomials gives nearly optimal results.

The question of determining the most efficient methods of interpolation has been taken up recently, and the relations between the Chebyshev ideas and the Comrie throwback have been investigated (see, e.g., Fox [24]).   The use of "economized" polynomials has also been studied.

3.4   The Theorems of the Markoffs

Let $p_n(x)$ be a polynomial of degree n, such that

$$|p_n(x)| \le 1, \qquad -1 \le x \le 1.$$

Does this imply any restriction on the bounds of the derivatives of $p_n(x)$ for $-1 \le x \le 1$?   This question was raised by the chemist Mendeleev for the case of $p_n'(x)$ and was answered by A. A. Markoff in 1890.

Theorem 3.17.   *If $|p_n(x)| \le 1$ for $-1 \le x \le 1$, then*

$$|p_n'(x)| \le n^2, \qquad -1 \le x \le 1.$$

This result is a best possible one: there is equality if and only if

$$p_n(x) = \epsilon T_n(x), \qquad |\epsilon| = 1, \qquad x = \pm 1.$$

Repeated applications of this theorem give the following result.

Theorem 3.18.   *If $|p_n(x)| \le 1$ for $-1 \le x \le 1$, then*

$$|p_n^{(k)}(x)| \le n^2(n-1)^2 \cdots (n-k+1)^2, \qquad -1 \le x \le 1$$

for $k = 1, 2, \ldots, n$.

This result is not best possible if $k > 1$.   The best possible result is the following, which is due to W. A. Markoff.

Theorem 3.19.   *If $|p_n(x)| \le 1$ for $-1 \le x \le 1$, then*

$$|p_n^{(k)}(x)| \le \frac{n^2(n^2 - 1^2) \cdots [n^2 - (k-1)^2]}{1 \cdot 3 \cdots (2k-1)}, \qquad -1 \le x \le 1.$$

The critical polynomial is again $T_n(x)$.   The original proof of this theorem was rather complicated.   A simple proof of a somewhat weaker result has been given by W. W. Rogosinski.   A comparatively simple proof, based on Lagrange interpolation, and using some complex variable ideas, has been given by Duffin and Schaeffer [43]. They show that it is even sufficient to assume

$$|p_n(x)| \leq 1 \text{ at } x = \cos(v\pi/n), \quad v = 0, 1, 2, \ldots, n.$$

To compare these two theorems consider the case of $T_4(x)$, for which $T_4''(x) = 96x^2 - 16$. The exact bound of T_4'' is therefore 80, as given by Theorem 3.19; the weaker Theorem 3.18 gives a bound of 144.

We shall now outline a proof of the result of A. A. Markoff. We begin with the following result.

Theorem 3.20. *If $p_{n-1}(x)$ satisfies the inequality*

$$(1 - x^2)^{1/2} |p_{n-1}(x)| \leq 1, \qquad -1 \leq x \leq 1,$$

then

$$|p_{n-1}(x)| \leq n, \qquad -1 \leq x \leq 1.$$

Proof. We use Lagrangian interpolation at the Chebyshev abscissas. We have, identically,

$$p_{n-1}(x) = \sum_{i=1}^{n} \frac{T_n(x)}{x - x_i} \frac{\sqrt{1 - x_i^2}(-1)^{i-1}}{n} p_{n-1}(x_i).$$

We consider separately the behavior of p_{n-1} in the three subintervals

$$[-1, x_n], \quad [x_n, x_1], \quad [x_1, 1].$$

In the middle interval, since $x_1 = -x_n = \cos(\pi/2n)$, we have

$$(1 - x^2)^{1/2} \geq \sin\frac{\pi}{2n} > \frac{2}{\pi}\frac{\pi}{2n} = n^{-1}.$$

Hence, the hypothesis implies the conclusion immediately.

The two end intervals are treated similarly; we deal with $[x_1, 1]$ only. In this interval, $T_n(x) = \cos(n \arccos x)$ increases from 0 to 1, and each $x - x_i \geq 0$. Hence, using our hypothesis,

$$|p_{n-1}(x)| \leq \frac{1}{n} \sum \frac{T_n(x)}{x - x_i} = \frac{1}{n} T_n'(x) = U_{n-1}(x) \leq n.$$

The result can be shown to be the best possible: there is equality if and only if $p_{n-1}(x) = rU_{n-1}(x)$, $|r| = 1$, $x = \pm 1$.

A trigonometrical consequence of (3.4) is the following.

Theorem 3.21. *Let $s(\phi) = a_1 \sin \phi + \cdots + a_n \sin n\phi$ satisfy*

$$|s(\phi)| \leq 1.$$

Then

$$|s(\phi)/\sin \phi| \leq n.$$

Proof. Apply the preceding result to $p_{n-1}(x)$, where

$$p_{n-1}(\cos \theta) = s(\phi)/\sin \phi.$$

This result is the best possible: there is equality if and only if

$$s(\phi) \equiv \pm\sin n\phi.$$

We next establish the second of the following two equivalent results.

Theorem 3.22. *If $t_n(\phi)$ is a trigonometrical sum of order n and* $\max |t_n'(\phi)| = 1$, *then* $\max |t_n(\phi)| \geq n^{-1}$.

Theorem 3.23. *If $t_n(\theta)$ is a trigonometrical sum of order n, then* $|t_n'(\theta)| \leq$ $n \max |t_n(\theta)|$.

Proof. We may assume $\max |t_n(\theta)| = 1$. Consider

$$s(\theta,\phi) = \tfrac{1}{2}[t_n(\theta + \phi) - t_n(\theta - \phi)].$$

Since

$$\sin [r(\theta + \phi)] - \sin [r(\theta - \phi)] = 2 \cos r\theta \sin r\phi,$$

$$\cos [r(\theta + \phi)] - \cos [r(\theta - \phi)] = -2 \sin r\theta \sin r\phi,$$

the hypothesis of Theorem 3.21 is satisfied for any value of the parameter θ. It follows that

$$\left|\frac{s(\theta,\phi)}{\sin \phi}\right| \leq n.$$

But

$$\frac{s(\theta,\phi)}{\sin \phi} = \frac{t_n(\theta + \phi) - t_n(\theta - \phi)}{2\phi} \frac{\phi}{\sin \phi},$$

and letting $\phi \to 0$, we find

$$|t_n'(\theta)| \leq n$$

for any fixed θ.

An immediate consequence is the following inequality, valid in the interior of $(-1,1)$.

Theorem 3.24. *If $p_n(x)$ satisfies $|p_n(x)| \leq 1$ for $-1 \leq x \leq 1$, then*

$$|p_n'(x)| \leq n/(1 - x^2)^{1/2}, \qquad -1 < x < 1.$$

We are now able to deal with the theorem of A. A. Markoff. The inequality established in Theorem 3.24 can be written as

$$|n^{-1}p_n'(x)(1 - x^2)^{1/2}| \leq 1,$$

and we can apply Theorem 3.20 to deduce

$$|n^{-1}p_n'(x)| \leq n,$$

that is,

$$|p_n'(x)| \leq n^2.$$

The inequality cases can be traced by going over the argument carefully.

3.5 Orthogonal Polynomials

The purpose of this section is to indicate some of the properties of orthogonal polynomials relevant in the present context.   Accounts of the general theory are available, for example, in Szegö [14], Erdélyi [34], and Sansone [31].

The basic fact is that, given any "reasonable" weight function $w(x)$ which is nonnegative in an interval $[a,b]$ (which may be finite or infinite) and whose integral over any subinterval of $[a,b]$ is positive, we can construct from the sequence of powers $1, x, x^2, \ldots$ a sequence of polynomials $\pi_n(x)$, of exact degree n, which are normalized and orthogonal with respect to $w(x)$ in $[a,b]$.   That is,

$$(\pi_m(x),\pi_n(x)) = \int_a^b \pi_m(x)\pi_n(x)w(x) \; dx = \delta(m,n). \qquad (3.10)$$

Here we use the inner product notation

$$(f(x), \; g(x)) = \int_a^b f(x)g(x)w(x) \; dx.$$

We may assume that the coefficient of x^n in $\pi_n(x)$ is positive.   This orthogonalization can be carried out explicitly by the Gram-Schmidt process, provided all the moments

$$\mu_n = \int_a^b x^n w(x) \; dx, \qquad n = 0, 1, 2, \ldots$$

exist and are finite—this is the meaning of the word "reasonable" above.

The proof of the existence of $\{\pi_n(x)\}$ is by induction.   We take $\pi_0' = 1$ and then normalize this by taking $\pi_0 = \pi_0'/\sqrt{(\pi_0',\pi_0')}$.   Assume, therefore, that $\pi_0, \pi_1, \ldots, \pi_n$ have been constructed and satisfy (3.10).   Then take

$$\pi_{n+1}' = x^{n+1} - \sum_{r=1}^{n} (x^{n+1},\pi_r)\pi_r.$$

Since $1, x, \ldots, x^{n+1}$ are linearly independent, π_{n+1}' cannot be zero.   It is easy to see that, for $s = 0, 1, \ldots, n$,

$$(\pi_{n+1}',\pi_s) = (x^{n+1},\pi_s) - \sum_{r=1}^{n} (x^{n+1},\pi_r)(\pi_r,\pi_s) = 0.$$

Also, π_{n+1}' is of exact degree $n + 1$.   Hence we may take

$$\pi_{n+1} = \pi_{n+1}'/\sqrt{(\pi_{n+1}',\pi_{n+1}')}.$$

This completes the proof.

To establish the uniqueness we require the following lemma.

Lemma 3.25. *If $f(x)$ is continuous and nonnegative in $[a,b]$ and if*

$$\int_a^b f(x)w(x)\,dx = 0, \qquad then \qquad f(x) \equiv 0 \qquad in\ [a,b].$$

Proof.   If this is false, then there is a c, $a \le c \le b$ such that $f(c) \ne 0$. Hence, by continuity and nonnegativity, there is an interval $[d,e]$, including c, throughout which $f(x) \ge \frac{1}{2}f(c) > 0$.   Hence

$$0 = \int_a^b f(x)w(x)\,dx \ge \int_d^e f(x)w(x)\,dx \ge \frac{1}{2}f(c)\int_d^e w(x)\,dx > 0$$

—a contradiction.

We shall now show that the sequence $\{\pi_n(x)\}$ is unique.

We note first that, if the $\pi_n(x) = k_n x^n + \cdots$ satisfy (3.10), then, since

$$1 = \int_a^b \pi_n{}^2(x)w(x)\,dx = \int_a^b \pi_n(x)k_n x^n w(x)\,dx,$$

we have

$$\int_a^b \pi_n(x)x^n w(x)\,dx = 1/k_n.$$

Suppose that $\pi_n'(x) = k_n' x^n + \cdots$, $\pi_n''(x) = k_n'' x^n + \cdots$ both satisfy (3.10).   Then

$$\int_a^b \pi_n'(x)\pi_n''(x)w(x)\,dx = k_n''/k_n' = k_n'/k_n'',$$

so that $k_n'' = \pm k_n'$.   Since both are positive, we have $k_n' = k_n''$, and so

$$\int_a^b \pi_n'(x)\pi_n''(x)w(x)\,dx = 1.$$

We now note that

$$\int_a^b [\pi_n'(x) - \pi_n''(x)]^2 w(x)\,dx = 1 - 2 + 1 = 0.$$

Hence, by our lemma,

$$\pi_n'(x) = \pi_n''(x).$$

We next establish the following result.

Theorem 3.26.   *All the zeros of $\pi_n(x)$ are real and distinct and lie in the interval $[a,b]$.*

Proof.   Consider the zeros of $\pi_n(x)$.   Since all the coefficients are real, complex zeros occur in conjugate pairs, $\alpha \pm i\beta$.   The corresponding factors of $\pi_n(x)$ can be combined as $(x - \alpha)^2 + \beta^2$, and this is positive for all x.   If there are any (real) zeros of even multiplicity, the corresponding factor $(x - \alpha_r)^{2n_r}$ is nonnegative for all x.   The residual, real zeros are of odd multiplicity; denote by $b_1, \ldots b_k$ those which lie in $[a,b]$.   Clearly $k \le n$, and our result follows if $k = n$.

Observe now that

$$(x - b_1)(x - b_2) \cdots (x - b_k)\pi_n(x)$$

is of constant sign in $[a,b]$. It follows from Lemma 3.25 that

$$\int_a^b (x - b_1)(x - b_2) \cdots (x - b_k)\pi_n(x)w(x) \, dx \neq 0.$$

This can happen only if $k = n$, for if $k < n$, the integral vanishes by orthogonality.

We now quote without proof two further properties of orthogonal polynomials.

Theorem 3.27. *Any three consecutive orthogonal polynomials are connected by a linear relation of the form*

$$\pi_{n+1}(x) = (A_n x + B_n)\pi_n(x) - C_n \pi_{n-1}(x), \qquad n = 1, 2, \ldots.$$

Theorem 3.28 (interlacing). *If $z_1 < z_2 < \cdots < z_n$ are the zeros of $\pi_n(x)$, and if $Z_1 < Z_2 < \cdots < Z_{n+1}$ are the zeros of $\pi_{n+1}(x)$, then*

$$a < Z_1 < z_1 < Z_2 < z_2 < \cdots < Z_n < z_n < Z_{n+1} < b.$$

We now want to discuss some extremal properties of orthogonal expansions. It is convenient to discuss this in a somewhat general setting.* Suppose given a set (or space) of functions provided with an inner product $(\, , \,)$. Two functions, f, g, of this space are said to be orthogonal if $(f,g) = 0$. A sequence of functions $\{\phi_n\}$ is said to be an orthogonal system if $(\phi_n,\phi_m) = 0$, $n \neq m$; it is said to be a normal orthogonal system if, in addition, $(\phi_n,\phi_n) = 1$. Given such a normal orthogonal system, we can ask whether it is possible to represent an arbitrary function f as a linear combination of the ϕ_n:

$$f = \Sigma \, a_n \phi_n.$$

Proceeding formally, on this assumption, it is easy to calculate the a_n. Indeed,

$$(f,\phi_n) = (\Sigma \, a_r \phi_r, \phi_n) = \Sigma \, a_r (\phi_r,\phi_n) = \Sigma \, a_r \, \delta(r,n) = a_n.$$

These a_n are called the *Fourier coefficients* of f with respect to $\{\phi_n\}$. The fact that we can calculate the Fourier coefficients in a special case gives us no guarantee about the convergence of $\Sigma \, a_n \phi_n$ or that its sum is f, should it be convergent.

It is clear that, if there were nontrivial functions f such that

$$(f,\phi_n) \equiv 0,$$

---

* A natural setting for this theory is the space L^2. It is not our purpose here to develop the appropriate theory rigorously and the proofs we give are formal.

then different functions could have the same Fourier coefficients. We call a sequence $\{\phi_n\}$ *complete* if this cannot happen. For instance, the sequence sin x, sin $2x$, . . . is not complete in $(0,2\pi)$, for all the Fourier coefficients of cos x with respect to this sequence vanish. [It is, however, complete in $(0,\pi)$.]

The *formal* series $\Sigma\, a_r\phi_r$ is called the *Fourier series* of f with respect to $\{\phi_n\}$. The partial sums, $f_n = \sum_{r=0}^{n} a_r\phi_r$, of this are called the *Fourier polynomials* of f with respect to $\{\phi_n\}$; we call any finite sum $\sum_{r=0}^{n} c_r\phi_r$ a *trigonometrical* polynomial of degree n.

Theorem 3.29. *Among all the trigonometrical polynomials of degree n, that which gives the best mean-square approximation to $f(x)$ is the Fourier polynomial.*

Proof. We want to minimize, with respect to the c_r,

$$\int_a^b \left[f(x) - \sum_{r=0}^{n} c_r\phi_r(x) \right]^2 dx.$$

(We have taken a simple, weightless case!)   We have

$$\int_a^b \left[f(x) - \sum_{r=0}^{n} c_r\phi_r(x) \right]^2 dx = \int_a^b f^2(x)\, dx - 2\, \Sigma\, c_r \int_a^b f(x)\phi_r(x)\, dx$$
$$+ \sum_{r,s=0}^{n} c_r c_s \int_a^b \phi_r(x)\phi_s(x)\, dx$$
$$= \int_a^b f^2(x)\, dx - 2\, \Sigma\, a_r c_r + \Sigma\, c_r^2$$
$$= \int_a^b f^2(x)\, dx + \Sigma\, (c_r - a_r)^2 - \Sigma\, a_r^2.$$

The right-hand side is not less than

$$\int_a^b f^2(x)\, dx - \sum_{r=0}^{n} a_r^2 = \int_a^b \left[f(x) - \sum_{r=0}^{n} a_r\phi_r(x) \right]^2 dx$$

no matter what the c_r are, and there is equality if (and only if) $c_r = a_r$. This is the result required.   The same argument applies in the general context to show that the Fourier polynomial is the best approximation in the sense of the norm induced by the inner product.

Theorem 3.30. *Among all polynomials $\tilde{p}_n(x)$ of degree n and leading coefficient unity, that which minimizes $\int_a^b \tilde{p}_n(x)^2 w(x)\, dx$ is the $\tilde{\pi}_n(x)$, where the $\{\pi_n(x)\}$ are orthogonal with respect to $w(x)$ over $[a,b]$.*

Proof. We can write

$$\tilde{p}_n(x) = \tilde{\pi}_n(x) + \sum_{r=0}^{n-1} \alpha_r \tilde{\pi}_r(x)$$

Hence

$$\int_a^b \tilde{p}_n{}^2(x)w(x)\,dx = \int_a^b \tilde{\pi}_n{}^2(x)w(x)\,dx + 2\sum_{r=0}^{n-1}\alpha_r\int_a^b \tilde{\pi}_n(x)\tilde{\pi}_r(x)w(x)\,dx$$

$$+ \sum_{r,s=0}^{n-1}\alpha_r\alpha_s\int_a^b \tilde{\pi}_r(x)\tilde{\pi}_s(x)w(x)\,dx$$

$$= \int_a^b \tilde{\pi}_n{}^2(x)w(x)\,dx + \sum_{r=0}^{n-1}\alpha_r{}^2.$$

In words, this theorem says that $\pi_n(x)$ is the best mean-square approximation to zero by polynomials of degree n and leading coefficient unity.

We shall now discuss a little further the concept of completeness introduced earlier.

Theorem 3.31. *If the range $[a,b]$ is finite, the corresponding sequence $\{\pi_n(x)\}$ is complete (for continuous functions).*

Proof. Suppose $f(x)$ is continuous in $[a,b]$. Take any $\epsilon > 0$. Then, by the Weierstrass theorem, there is a polynomial $p(x) = p_\epsilon(x)$ such that

$$|f(x) - p(x)| < \epsilon, \qquad a \le x \le b.$$

Now, if we take n larger than the degree of $p_\epsilon(x)$, we have, by Theorem 3.29,

$$\int_a^b [f(x) - f_n(x)]^2 w(x)\,dx \le \int_a^b [f(x) - p(x)]^2 w(x)\,dx,$$

and so

$$\int_a^b [f(x) - f_n(x)]^2 w(x)\,dx = \int_a^b f^2(x)w(x)\,dx - \sum_{r=0}^n a_r{}^2 \le u_1\epsilon^2.$$

Hence $\qquad 0 \le \int_a^b f^2(x)w(x)\,dx - \sum_{r=0}^\infty a_r{}^2 \le \mu_1\epsilon^2.$

This means, ϵ being arbitrary, that

$$\int_a^b f^2(x)w(x)\,dx = \sum_{r=0}^\infty a_r{}^2. \qquad (3.11)$$

This equality is Parseval's theorem.

To show that $\{\pi_n(x)\}$ is complete for continuous functions, we have to show that, if all the Fourier coefficients of any continuous $f(x)$ vanish, then so does f. But this is now evident from (3.11) and Lemma 3.25.

Theorem 3.32. *If $f(x)$ is continuous in a finite interval $[a,b]$ and if all its moments*

$$\mu_n = \int_a^b x^n f(x)w(x)\,dx = 0, \qquad n = 0, 1, 2, \ldots,$$

then $f(x)$ is identically zero.

This "finite-moment theorem" is equivalent to Theorem 3.31. It is important to note that we cannot extend this to an infinite integral. This is shown, for example, by the following example, due to T. J. Stieltjes:

$$f(x) = \exp(-x^{\frac{1}{4}}) \sin x^{\frac{1}{4}}.$$

3.6 Interpolation and Interpolation Schemes

The bases of the theory of polynomial interpolation are presented in Chap. 2. We now discuss some extremal problems which arise in that theory and which are now accessible.

The classical error estimates for n-point Lagrangian and hermitian interpolation are*

$$f(x) - L_{n-1}(f,x) = \frac{f^{(n)}(\xi)}{n!} (x - x_1)(x - x_2) \cdots (x - x_n),$$

$$f(x) - H_{2n-1}(f,x) = \frac{f^{(2n)}(\xi)}{(2n)!} (x - x_1)^2 (x - x_2)^2 \cdots (x - x_n)^2,$$

where it is assumed that the derivatives which occur exist in an interval including the nodes $x_1, x_2, \ldots, x_n$ and the current point x and where ξ, which depends on x, lies in this interval.

(a) Suppose we are going to interpolate in $[-1,1]$, using an n-point Lagrangian formula, for a function $f(x)$, whose nth derivative is bounded in $[-1,1]$. What is the best choice of $x_1, x_2, \ldots, x_n$? From the above representation of the error, it follows that this choice is that which minimizes the maximum of

$$|(x - x_1)(x - x_2) \cdots (x - x_n)|, \qquad -1 \le x \le 1.$$

This means that the x_i should be taken as the zeros of $T_n(x)$, that is,

$$x_i = \cos[(2i - 1)\pi/2n], \qquad i = 1, 2, \ldots, n.$$

(b) Suppose that we are going to interpolate in $[-1,1]$, using an n-point Hermite formula, for a function $f(x)$ whose $2n$th derivative is bounded in $[-1,1]$. What is the best choice of $x_1, x_2, \ldots, x_n$ if we measure the error in the M_1 norm? That is, we want to minimize

$$\left[\max_{-1 \le x \le 1} |f^{(2n)}(x)|/(2n)!\right] \int_{-1}^{+1} (x - x_1)^2 \cdots (x - x_n)^2 \, dx.$$

It follows from Theorem 3.30 that the x_i should be taken as the zeros of the Legendre polynomial $P_n(x)$.

---

* Note that the notation here differs slightly from that in Chap. 2. The nodes there denoted by $x_0, x_1, \ldots, x_{n-1}$ are here denoted by $x_1, x_2, \ldots, x_n$.

The way in which we try $(n + 1)$-point interpolation if n-point interpolation is not satisfactory suggests a study of a sequence of (Lagrangian) interpolation schemes defined by a sequence of nodes:

$$x_1^{(1)}; \quad x_1^{(2)}, x_2^{(2)}; \quad x_1^{(3)}, x_2^{(3)}, x_3^{(3)}; \quad \ldots,$$

all in a fixed interval $[a,b]$. Suppose we pick on a special function $f(x)$, defined in $[a,b]$, and we consider for $n = 1, 2, \ldots$ the Lagrangian interpolant of degree $n - 1$, $L_{n-1}(f,x)$, with nodes $x_1^{(n)}, x_2^{(n)}, \ldots, x_n^{(n)}$. We can ask whether

$$L_n(f,x) \to f(x) \qquad \text{as } n \to \infty \tag{3.12}$$

for any or all of the points $x \in [a,b]$. There are many questions and some solutions to problems of this kind. We prove two positive results.

Theorem 3.33. *If $f(x)$ is a polynomial, (3.12) is true for all x.*

Proof. If $f(x)$ has degree N, then for $n \geq N$, $L_n(f,x) \equiv f(x)$, and the sequence $\{L_n(f,x)\}$ is stationary and therefore convergent.

Theorem 3.34. *If $f(x)$ is any continuous function, we can choose the $x_n^{(m)}$ so that (3.12) will be true for any $x \in [a,b]$.*

Proof. By the fundamental existence theorem 3.11, for each n, there is a polynomial $\pi_n(x)$ of best approximation to $f(x)$. We know that the difference $\pi_n(x) - f(x)$ vanishes $n + 1$ times in $[a,b]$; these zeros we take to be the $x_m^{(n+1)}$. This means that the corresponding $L_n(f,x)$ is forced to be $\pi_n(x)$. But we know that $\{\pi_n(x)\}$ converges uniformly to $f(x)$.

Another application of the fundamental theorem is to the proof of the following result of Erdös and Turán (1937), concerning interpolation at the zeros of the orthogonal polynomials $\pi_n(x)$, where orthogonality is with respect to $w(x)$ in $[a,b]$. Denote by $L_{\pi_n}(f,x)$ the corresponding Lagrangian interpolant.

Theorem 3.35. *For every continuous $f(x)$, we have*

$$\lim_{n \to \infty} \int_a^b w(x)[L_{\pi_n}(f,x) - f(x)]^2 \, dx = 0.$$

This can be interpreted to mean that (3.12) is true in a mean-square sense.

We now discuss some negative results. First of all, it is tempting to suppose that, when the nodes are equally spaced, we should have

$$L_n(f,x) \to f(x)$$

uniformly in $[a,b]$ and so have another proof of the Weierstrass theorem. This is false even for very simple functions.

For instance, Bernstein, using real variable methods, established the following result.

Theorem 3.36. *If $f(x) = |x|$ and the $x_n^{(m)}$ are equally spaced in $[-1,1]$, there is convergence only at $0, \pm 1$.*

The following result is due to Runge.

Theorem 3.37. *If $f(x) = (1 + x^2)^{-1}$ and the $x_n^{(m)}$ are equally and symmetrically spaced in $[-5,5]$, then the sequence $\{L_n(f,x)\}$ is divergent if $|x| > 3.6334\ldots$.*

We shall outline a proof of this, using complex variable theory.

We rely on the following relation (cf. Sec. 2.6):

$$\frac{1}{2\pi i}\int_{\mathscr{C}}\frac{f(z)w_n(x)}{(z-x)w_n(z)}\,dz = f(x) - L_{n-1}(f,x) - \sum_i \frac{R_i w_n(x)}{(x-p_i)w_n(p_i)}$$

where $f(z)$ is regular in and on a closed curve $\mathscr{C}$ except at a finite set of poles p_i, where it has residues R_i, where the distinct nodes $a_1, \ldots, a_n$ lie in the interior of $\mathscr{C}$, where $x \neq a_r$ $(r = 1, 2, \ldots, n)$, and where $w_n(x) = (x - a_1)(x - a_2)\cdots(x - a_n)$.

Let us apply this to the case $f(x) = (1 + x^2)^{-1}$. Then, if $\mathscr{C}$ includes $\pm i$, the integral is zero, for we can deform $\mathscr{C}$ to an arbitrary large circle $|z| = R$ on which $|f(z)| = O(R^{-2})$, which implies that the integral is $o(1)$ and therefore zero. Combining the terms corresponding to the poles $\pm i$, we find, the nodes being assumed symmetrical with respect to the origin,

$$f(x) - L_{n-1}(f,x) = \frac{1}{1+x^2}\frac{w_n(x)}{w_n(i)}.$$

Convergence, therefore, depends on the behavior of $w_n(x)/w_n(i)$. We observe that, if $r_i = |x - a_i|$, then

$$\log|w_n(x)|^{1/n} = \frac{1}{n}(\log r_1 + \cdots + \log r_n).$$

Suppose further that $a_r = -5 + 10(r - \frac{1}{2})(n - 1)^{-1}$ for $r = 1, 2, \ldots, n$. Then the above expression is a Riemann sum for

$$I(x) = \frac{1}{10}\int_{-5}^{+5}\log|x - \xi|\,d\xi,$$

which can be integrated explicitly.

The curves $I(x) = k$ are equipotentials for the logarithmic potential of a uniform mass distribution on $[-5,5]$ and are ovals expanding from the segment $[-5,5]$ as k increases. If x and i lie on different equipotentials k_1, k_2 with $k_1 > k_2$, so that $I(x) > I(i)$, then for sufficiently large n we have

$$\log|w_n(x)|^{1/n} - \log|w_n(i)|^{1/n} \geq \tfrac{1}{2}(k_1 - k_2).$$

This means that

$$\frac{|w_n(x)|}{|w_n(i)|} \geq \exp\tfrac{1}{2}n(k_1 - k_2) \to \infty.$$

If we evaluate $I(x)$ and solve the transcendental equation

$$I(x) = I(i),$$

we find $x = 3.6334 \ldots$.

We conclude by listing, without proof, two further negative results.

Theorem 3.38. *No matter what the $x_n{}^{(m)}$ are, there are continuous functions $f(x)$ for which (3.12) is not true uniformly in $[a,b]$.*

Theorem 3.39. *If the $x_n{}^{(m)}$ are the Chebyshev abscissas, there are continuous functions for which (3.12) is always false.*

3.7 Approximate Quadratures and Quadrature Schemes

The idea of an approximate quadrature of the form

$$I = \int_a^b f(x) \, dx \doteq Q = \sum \lambda_i f(x_i)$$

is a very ancient one, and various practical aspects of it are covered in Chap. 2. Here we concentrate on some of the more theoretical aspects.

An obvious approach to this problem is the following: an approximation to the integral of a function is the integral of an approximation to the function. Application of this idea leads to Lagrangian quadratures. If

$$f(x) \doteq L_n(f,x) = \sum f(x_i) l_i(x)$$

then

$$I \doteq Q = \int_a^b \sum f(x_i) l_i(x) \, dx = \sum f(x_i) \int_a^b l_i(x) \, dx = \sum \lambda_i f(x_i).$$

The error estimate given earlier is

$$|I - Q| \leq \frac{\max |f^{(n+1)}(x)|}{(n+1)!} \int_a^b |(x - x_0)(x - x_1) \cdots (x - x_n)| \, dx.$$

This result implies that any $(n + 1)$-point Lagrangian quadrature for a polynomial of degree n is exact. This is also true in the weighted case.

As in Sec. 3.6, we can ask what is the best choice of the nodes $x_1, x_2, \ldots, x_n$? One answer to this was given by Korkine and Zolotareff in 1873, based on the above estimate: the Lagrangian quadrature based on the zeros of $U_n(x)$ is a best possible one. This follows from the following theorem.

Theorem 3.40. *The minimum value of $\int_{-1}^{+1} |\tilde{p}_n(x)| \, dx$, over all polynomials of degree n, with leading coefficient unity, is 2^{1-n}, and this is attained only by $\tilde{p}_n(x) = \tilde{U}_n(x)$.*

Proof. It will be enough to show that

$$\int_{-1}^{+1} x^r \operatorname{sign} \tilde{U}_n(x) \, dx = 0, \qquad \text{if } r = 0, 1, 2, \ldots, n - 1$$

$$= 2^{1-n}, \qquad \text{if } r = n. \tag{3.13}$$

This will imply that

$$\int_{-1}^{+1} \tilde{p}_n(x) \text{ sign } \tilde{U}_n(x) \, dx = 2^{1-n}$$

and therefore, invariably, that

$$\int_{-1}^{+1} |\tilde{p}_n(x)| \, dx \geq 2^{1-n},$$

and also that

$$\int_{-1}^{+1} |\tilde{U}_n(x)| \, dx = 2^{1-n}.$$

It follows that, if $\int_{-1}^{+1} |\tilde{p}_n(x)| \, dx = 2^{1-n}$, we would have

$$\int_{-1}^{+1} |\tilde{p}_n(x)| \, [1 - \text{sign } \tilde{p}_n(x) \text{ sign } \tilde{U}_n(x)] \, dx = 0.$$

This implies that

$$\text{sign } \tilde{p}_n(x) \text{ sign } \tilde{U}_n(x) \equiv 1,$$

so that the zeros of $\tilde{p}_n(x)$, $\tilde{U}_n(x)$ must coincide; however, each has leading coefficient unity, and we must have $\tilde{p}_n(x) \equiv \tilde{U}_n(x)$, establishing the uniqueness of the extremal polynomial.

We establish (3.13) as follows. Putting $\theta = \arccos x$, we have to evaluate

$$I_r = \int_0^\pi \cos^r \theta \text{ sign } (\sin \overline{n+1} \, \theta / \sin \theta) \sin \theta \, d\theta.$$

We can omit the $\sin \theta$ in the argument of sign.   Now

$$\text{sign } (\sin \overline{n+1} \, \theta) = (-1)^k \qquad \text{if } k\pi < (n+1)\theta < (k+1)\pi.$$

Hence

$$I_r = \sum (-1)^k \int_{k\phi}^{(k+1)\phi} \cos^r \theta \sin \theta \, d\theta,$$

where the summation is for $k = 0, 1, \ldots, n$ and where $\phi = \pi/(n+1)$. Thus

$$(r + 1)I_r = \sum (-1)^{k+1}[\cos^{r+1}(k+1)\phi - \cos^{r+1}k\phi].$$

The evaluation of $I_r = 2^{1-n} \delta(r,n)$ now follows by elementary trigonometry.

A reasonable question is whether we can get better quadrature formulas if we do not insist on their being Lagrangian.   In a Lagrangian quadrature, assigning the nodes determines the multipliers $\lambda_i = \int_a^b l_i(x) \, dx$.   It is plausible that we can choose the $2n$ quantities λ_i, x_i in such a way as to satisfy the $2n$ equations

$$\int_a^b x^r \, dx = \sum \lambda_i x_i^r, \qquad r = 0, 1, \ldots, 2n - 1,$$

which would imply that the quadrature is exact, that is,

$$\int_a^b p_{2n-1}(x) \, dx = \sum \lambda_i p_{2n-1}(x_i)$$

for any polynomial of degree $2n - 1$ at most.   This is indeed the case; moreover, we can find such quadratures for any fixed positive weight function $w(x)$.   In fact, we have the following result.

Theorem 3.41.   *Let $\{\pi_n(x)\}$ denote the polynomials orthogonal with respect to $w(x)$ on $[a,b]$.   Then, if x_i are the zeros of $\pi_n(x)$, we have*

$$\int_a^b p_{2n-1}(x)w(x) \, dx = \sum \lambda_i p_{2n-1}(x_i)$$

for any polynomial $p_{2n-1}(x)$ of degree $2n - 1$, where

$$\lambda_i = \int_a^b w(x) l_i(x) \, dx, \qquad l_i(x) = \frac{\pi_n(x)}{\pi_n'(x_i)(x - x_i)}.$$

This result has been established in Chap. 2.   We note here, additionally, that the following converse is true.

Theorem 3.42.   *If $x_1, \ldots, x_n$ are distinct points in $[a,b]$ such that*

$$\int_a^b p_{2n-1}(x)w(x) \, dx = \sum \lambda_i p_{2n-1}(x_i)$$

for certain numbers λ_i and for all polynomials $p_{2n-1}(x)$ of degree $2n - 1$ at most, then $x_1, \ldots, x_n$ are the zeros of a polynomial of degree n, orthogonal with respect to $1, x, \ldots, x^{n-1}$ over the interval $[a,b]$ with weight function $w(x)$.

We note an alternative representation of the multipliers of Christoffel numbers λ_i, using the notation of Sec. 3.5:

$$\lambda_i = \frac{k_{n+1}}{k_n} \frac{-1}{\pi_{n+1}(x_i) \pi_n'(x_i)}.$$

Theorem 3.43.   *The Christoffel numbers λ_i are always positive.*

Proof.   The quadrature formula in Theorem 3.41 is necessarily exact for

$$f(x) = f_i(x) = \pi_n^2(x)/(x - x_i)^2,$$

since this is a polynomial of degree $2n - 2$.   It is clear that

$$f_i(x_j) = 0, \qquad j = 1, 2, \ldots, n; j \neq i$$
$$f_i(x_i) = \pi_n'^2(x_i).$$

Hence
$$\int_a^b [\pi_n{}^2(x)/(x - x_i)^2] w(x)\, dx = \lambda_i \pi_n'{}^2(x_i),$$

that is,
$$\lambda_i = \int_a^b l_i{}^2(x) w(x)\, dx, \qquad l_i = \frac{\pi_n(x)}{\pi_n'(x_i)(x - x_i)},$$

so that $\lambda_i > 0$, $i = 1, 2, \ldots, n$.

Theorem 3.44. *If $f^{(2n)}(x)$ exists in $[a,b]$, then we have*

$$I - Q = [f^{(2n)}(\xi)/(2n!)] \int_a^b \tilde{\pi}_n{}^2(x) w(x)\, dx$$

for some ξ in $[a,b]$.

Proof. Let $x_1, x_2, \ldots, x_n$ be the zeros of $\pi_n(x)$. Consider the Hermite interpolant $H(x)$, introduced in Chap. 2, which satisfies

$$H(x_i) = f(x_i), \qquad H'(x_i) = f'(x_i), \qquad i = 1, 2, \ldots, n.$$

We have noted that

$$f(x) - H(x) = \frac{f^{(2n)}[\xi(x)]}{(2n)!} (x - x_1)^2 \cdots (x - x_n)^2.$$

If we multiply across by $w(x)$ and integrate between (a,b), we find

$$\int_a^b f(x) w(x)\, dx = \int_a^b H(x) w(x)\, dx$$
$$+ \int_a^b \frac{f^{(2n)}[\xi(x)]}{(2n)!} (x - x_1)^2 \cdots (x - x_n)^2 w(x)\, dx.$$

Now, since $H(x)$ is of degree $2n - 1$, we have, exactly,

$$\int_a^b H(x) w(x)\, dx = \sum \lambda_i H(x_i) = \sum \lambda_i f(x_i).$$

Hence
$$\int_a^b f(x) w(x)\, dx = \sum \lambda_i f(x_i) + R_n$$

where
$$R_n = \int_a^b \frac{f^{(2n)}[\xi(x)]}{(2n)!} (x - x_1)^2 \cdots (x - x_n)^2 w(x)\, dx.$$

But
$$(x - x_1)^2 \cdots (x - x_n)^2 w(x)/(2n)!$$

is positive in $[a,b]$, and so the mean-value theorem gives us the result we require.

The integral in Theorem 3.44 can be calculated for any particular set of orthogonal polynomials; the results in the classical cases are given below.

Our last topic is that of quadrature schemes (see the discussion of interpolation schemes of Sec. 3.6). We now consider two triangular arrays, one of nodes and one of multipliers:

$$
\begin{array}{ccc}
x_1^{(1)} & & \\
x_1^{(2)} & x_2^{(2)} & \\
x_1^{(3)} & x_2^{(3)} & x_3^{(3)} \\
\cdots\cdots\cdots\cdots\cdots & &
\end{array}
\qquad
\begin{array}{ccc}
A_1^{(1)} & & \\
A_1^{(2)} & A_2^{(2)} & \\
A_1^{(3)} & A_2^{(3)} & A_3^{(3)} \\
\cdots\cdots\cdots\cdots\cdots & &
\end{array}
$$

A special case is that of a Gaussian scheme, where the $x_k^{(n)}$ are the zeros of the orthogonal polynomials associated with a weight function $w(x)$ and where the $A_k^{(n)}$ are the corresponding Christoffel numbers.

We consider the truth of the relation

$$
Q_n(f) = \sum A_i^{(n)} f(x_i^{(n)}) \to \int_a^b f(x)\, dx. \tag{3.14}
$$

The following result is due to Pólya (1933) and Stekloff (1916).

Theorem 3.45. *In order for (3.14) to hold for every continuous function $f(x)$, it is necessary and sufficient that*

(i) *(3.14) hold for every polynomial $f(x)$.*

(ii) $\displaystyle\sum_{k=1}^{n} |A_k^{(n)}|$ *be bounded.*

The most appealing proof of this is by methods of functional analysis.

We note that (i) is satisfied for any Lagrangian quadrature. We note also that in the case when the $A_k^{(n)}$ are nonnegative, (i) $\Rightarrow$ (ii); for if we take $f(x) \equiv 1$, $Q_n(f) \to (b - a)$, so that $Q_n(f)$ is certainly bounded but $Q_n(f) = \sum A_k^{(n)} = \sum |A_k^{(n)}|$. Combining these two observations, we deduce from Theorem 3.45 the following result.

Theorem 3.46. *A Lagrangian quadrature scheme with nonnegative multipliers is convergent for any continuous function.*

It can be proved that the multipliers are positive in the cases in which the nodes are the zeros of $T_n(x)$, or of $U_n(x)$. This result is to be distinguished from the corresponding special case of Theorem 3.43.

Theorem 3.47 [*Stieltjes* (1884)]. *The general Gaussian quadrature scheme, for any weight function $w(x)$ on an interval $[a,b]$, is convergent for any continuous function $f(x)$.*

Proof. By the Weierstrass theorem, given any $\epsilon > 0$, there is a polynomial $p(x) = p_\epsilon(x)$ of degree N, say, such that $|p(x) - f(x)| < \epsilon$, $a \leq x \leq b$.

$$
|I - Q_n(f)| \leq \left| \int_a^b f(x) w(x)\, dx - \int_a^b p(x) w(x)\, dx \right|
$$
$$
+ \left| \int_a^b p(x) w(x)\, dx - Q_n(p) \right| + |Q_n(p) - Q_n(f)|.
$$

The first term on the right does not exceed $\epsilon \int_a^b w(x)\ dx$ by our choice of $p(x)$. The third term similarly does not exceed $\epsilon\ \Sigma\ A_k^{(n)} = \epsilon \int_a^b w(x)\ dx$ [the last equality follows by taking $f(x) = 1$]. All this is true for any n. If we take n so that $2n - 1 \geq N$, the middle term vanishes, since the quadrature is exact. Hence we have

$$|I - Q_n(f)| \leq 2\epsilon \int_a^b w(x)\ dx, \qquad 2n - 1 \geq N$$

and so, ϵ being arbitrary,

$$I = \lim Q_n(f).$$

We conclude with the following negative result, of which we do not give the proof.

Theorem 3.48. *A Lagrangian quadrature scheme with equally spaced nodes is not convergent for every continuous function.*

Results for the Classical Cases

Chebyshev, T_n: $a = -1$, $b = 1$, $w(x) = (1 - x^2)^{-\frac{1}{2}}$.
   Nodes: $\cos\ [(2k - 1)\pi/2n]$, $k = 1, 2, \ldots, n$.
   Christoffel numbers: π/n, $k = 1, 2, \ldots, n$.
   Coefficient of $f^{(2n)}(\xi)$ in error estimate: $\pi/[2^{2n-1}(2n)!]$.
Chebyshev, U_n: $a = -1$, $b = 1$, $w(x) = (1 - x^2)^{\frac{1}{2}}$.
   Nodes: $\cos\ k\pi/(n + 1)$, $k = 1, 2, \ldots, n$.
   Christoffel numbers: $\{\pi \sin^2\ [k\pi/(n + 1)]\}/(n + 1)$, $k = 1, 2, \ldots, n$.
   Coefficient of $f^{(2n)}(\xi)$ in error estimate: $\pi/[(2n)!\ 2^{2n+1}]$.
Legendre, P_n: $a = -1$, $b = 1$, $w(x) = 1$.
   Coefficient of $f^{(2n)}(\xi)$ in error estimate: $2^{2n+1}(n!)^4/[(2n)!]^3(2n + 1)$.
Laguerre, $L_n^{(\alpha)}$: $a = 0$, $b = \infty$, $w(x) = x^\alpha \exp\ (-x)$.
   Coefficient of $f^{(2n)}(\xi)$ in error estimate: $n!\ \Gamma(n + 1 + \alpha)/(2n)!$
Hermite, H_n: $a = -\infty$, $b = \infty$, $w(x) = \exp\ (-x^2)$.
   Coefficient of $f^{(2n)}(\xi)$ in error estimate: $\sqrt{\pi}(n!)/[(2n)!\ 2^n]$.

The numerical values of the nodes and the Christoffel numbers in the cases where they are not known explicitly have been tabulated in various forms. Among the standard tables are the following:

Legendre:
   A. N. Lowan, N. Davids, and A. Levenson, *Bull. Amer. Math. Soc.,* vol. 48, pp. 739–743, 1942.
   P. Davis and P. Rabinowitz, *J. Res. Nat. Bur. Standards,* vol. 56, pp. 35–37, 1956.
Laguerre:
   H. E. Salzer and R. Zucker, *Bull. Amer. Math. Soc.,* vol. 55, pp. 1004–1012, 1949.

Hermite:

H. E. Salzer, R. Zucker, and R. Capuano, *J. Res. Nat. Bur. Standards*, vol. 48, pp. 111–116, 1952.

We note that in the Hermite case it is sometimes convenient to tabulate, instead of the Christoffel numbers λ_i themselves, the numbers $\alpha_i = \lambda_i \exp x_i^2$, for then we can write the Hermite quadrature formula as

$$I = \int_{-\infty}^{\infty} f(x)\ dx = \int_{-\infty}^{+\infty} f(x)e^{+x^2}e^{-x^2}\ dx \doteq \sum \alpha_i f(x_i),$$

and similarly for the Laguerre case. This device seems to be due to A. Reiz and has been adopted in some of the tables cited above.

PROBLEMS

3.1. If $S_m(p) = \sum_{k=0}^{n} \binom{n}{k} p^k q^{n-k}(k - np)^m$, obtain a three-term recurrence relation for $S_m(p)$ and use it, and Lemmas 3.5–3.6, to evaluate $S_3(p)$, $S_4(p)$ (see Lorentz [12]).

3.2. Evaluate the de la Vallée Poussin integrals

$$V_n(F,\theta) = \frac{(2n)!!}{(2n-1)!!\,2\pi} \int_{-\pi}^{+\pi} F(\phi)\cos^{2n}\tfrac{1}{2}(\phi - \theta)\ d\phi$$

for some simple periodic functions $F(\theta)$—for example, $F(\theta) = |\cos\theta|$.

3.3. Express the de la Vallée Poussin integral

$$V_n(F,\theta) = \frac{(2n)!!}{(2n-1)!!\,2\pi} \int_{-\pi}^{+\pi} F(\phi)\cos^{2n}\tfrac{1}{2}(\phi - \theta)\ d\phi$$

explicitly as a trigonometrical polynomial

$$V_n = \tfrac{1}{2}A_0 + \sum_{r=1}^{n}(A_r\cos r\theta + B_r\sin r\theta)$$

and show that the ratios of A_r, B_r to the corresponding Fourier coefficients of $F(\phi)$ are $(n!)^2/(n+r)!\,(n-r)!$. {Express $\cos^{2n}\tfrac{1}{2}(\phi - \theta)$ first as a sum of cosines of multiples of $(\phi - \theta)$, then use $\cos[r(\phi - \theta)] = \cos r\phi\cos r\theta + \sin r\phi\sin r\theta$, and then integrate.}

3.4. Evaluate $B_n(e^x,x)$ and establish the convergence and rate of convergence directly.

3.5. If $m \le f(x) \le M$, $0 \le x \le 1$, show that $m \le B_n(f,x) \le M$.

3.6. Show that given any function $f(x)$ continuous in $[a,b]$, $0 < a < b < 1$, it is possible to find a sequence of polynomials $\{p_n(x)\}$ with integral coefficients such that

$$p_n(x) \to f(x)$$

uniformly in $[a,b]$ (see Lorentz, [12]).

3.7. Show that $\int_{-1}^{+1} T_n^2(x)\,dx = 1 - (4n^2 - 1)^{-1}$.

3.8. Find the polynomial $ax^2 + bx + 1$ which has least deviation from zero in $[-1,1]$, a, b being arbitrary.

3.9. Repeat Prob. 3.8 for $ax^2 + x + b$.

3.10. Establish the minimum deviation of $T_2(x)$, using elementary arguments.

3.11. Find the polynomial of degree n and leading coefficient unity which vanishes at $x = 0$, $x = 1$ and which deviates least from zero in the interval $0 \leq x \leq 1$. {Consider $\check{T}_n[(2x - 1)\cos \pi/2n]$.}

3.12. Let P_k be the class of all polynomials $p(x)$ of degree at most k of the form $p(x) = 1 + x + a_2 x^2 + \cdots + a_k x^k$. For each $p(x)$, there is a greatest $\tau = \tau(p) > 0$ such that $-\tau \leq x \leq 0$ implies $|p(x)| \leq 1$. Find the polynomial $E_k(x)$ in P_k for which $\tau = \tau_k$ is maximum. What is the value of τ_k? Write down $E_k(x)$ for $k = 2, 3, 4$ (see Franklin [40]).

3.13. Find (a) the best constant and (b) the best linear approximation in the Chebyshev sense to arctan x, in $0 \leq x \leq 1$. Draw a rough graph of the error in the linear approximation. [(a) $\pi/8$, (b) .7854x + .0355.]

3.14. Find (a) the best constant and (b) the best linear approximation in the Chebyshev sense and in the mean-square sense to x^{-1} in $1 \leq x \leq 2$. Find the corresponding errors. [(a) $\frac{3}{4}$, $\log 2$; (b) $-\frac{1}{2}x + \frac{3}{4} + \sqrt{1/2}$, $(12 - 18 \log 2)x + (28 \log 2 - 18)$.]

3.15. Repeat Prob. 3.14 for 10^x in $0 \leq x \leq 1$. [(a) $11\frac{1}{2}$, $9M = 3.9086$. (b) $9x + (1 + 9M - \frac{9}{2}\log 9M)$, i.e., $9x + 2.5946$; $(66M - 108M^2)x - 24M + 54M^2$, i.e., $8.2934x - .2380$. We have written $M = \log e = .4343$.]

3.16. We have seen that, among the polynomials $\tilde{p}_n(x) = x^n + \cdots$, that which is the best approximation to zero in the Chebyshev sense is $\check{T}_n(x)$ and that which is the best approximation to zero in the mean-square sense is $\check{P}_n(x)$. Compare, for general and for large n, the efficiencies of $\check{T}_n(x)$ and $\check{P}_n(x)$, as approximations to zero, in both norms (see Oberhettinger and Magnus [35]).

3.17. Obtain the expansions of $|x|$ given in (3.1) and (3.2). Obtain also the expansion in terms of Chebyshev polynomials of the second kind.

3.18. Expand arctan x and $\log [(a + x)/(a - x)]$, where $a > 1$, in a series of Chebyshev polynomials of the first kind in $[-1,1]$ (see Murnaghan and Wrench [38]).

3.19. Expand ln $(1 + x)$ in a series of Chebyshev polynomials of the first kind in $[0,1]$ (see Murnaghan and Wrench [38]).

3.20. Suppose $\{\pi_n(x)\}$ are the polynomials orthogonal with respect to $w(x)$ in the interval $[a,b]$ and write

$$l_i(x) = \pi_n(x)/\pi_n'(x_i)(x - x_i).$$

a. Prove that l_i and l_j are orthogonal with respect to $w(x)$ in $[a,b]$.

b. Prove that

$$\sum_{i=1}^{n} \int_a^b w(x)[l_i(x)]^2\,dx = \int_a^b w(x)\,dx.$$

3.21. Write down an expression for the error $f(x) - L_n(f,x)$ in the Lagrangian interpolation for a function $f(x)$, for which $f^{(11)}(x)$ exists, at the points which are the zeros of $T_{10}(x)$. Assuming that $|f^{(11)}(x)| \leq 1$, find an estimate for the numerical value of this error at a point x_1, $-1 \leq x_1 \leq 1$. What are the corresponding numerical values when the nodes are (a) the zeros of $U_{10}(x)$, (b) the zeros of $P_{10}(x)$, and (c) the points ± 1, $\pm\frac{7}{9}$, $\pm\frac{5}{9}$, $\pm\frac{3}{9}$, $\pm\frac{1}{9}$.

3.22. Show that the quadrature

$$\int_1^3 f(x)\,dx = \tfrac{5}{9}f(2 - \sqrt{\tfrac{3}{5}}) + \tfrac{8}{9}f(2) + \tfrac{5}{9}f(2 + \sqrt{\tfrac{3}{5}})$$

is exact when f is a polynomial of degree at most 5.

Indicate how you would obtain a similar result which would be exact when f is a polynomial of degree at most 7 and the integration is over an arbitrary interval $[a,b]$.

3.23. $P_n(x)$ being the Legendre polynomial, show that for $-1 \leq x \leq 1$ we have

$$|P_n(x)| \leq 1, \quad |P_n'(x)| \leq \tfrac{1}{2}n(n + 1).$$

3.24. Find the least upper bound of $|U_n'(x)|$ for $-1 \leq x \leq 1$.

3.25. Show that $|T_n(x + iy)| \leq |T_n(1 + iy)|$ when $-1 \leq x \leq 1$, $-\infty < y < \infty$ (see Duffin and Schaeffer [43]).

3.26. Show that the transcendental equation $I(x) = I(i)$ of Theorem 3.37 is

$$(1 + \tfrac{1}{5}x)\log(1 + \tfrac{1}{5}x) + (1 - \tfrac{1}{5}x)\log(1 - \tfrac{1}{5}x) = \log 1.04 + \tfrac{2}{5}\arctan 5$$

and verify that $x = 3.6334\ldots$ is a root.

REFERENCES

The standard work in this field is the treatise of I. P. Natanson, published in Russian in 1951, but now available in a German translation by K. Bügel.

1. I. P. Natanson, "Konstruktive Funktionentheorie," Akademie-Verlag G.m.b.H., Berlin, 1955.

A collection of essays on related topics is:

2. R. E. Langer, ed., "On Numerical Approximation," University of Wisconsin Press, Madison, Wis., 1959.

This collection includes two expository articles:

3. R. C. Buck, Linear Spaces and Approximation Theory, pp. 11–23.

4. J. Todd, Special Polynomials in Numerical Analysis, pp. 423–446.

An introduction to the theory is presented in lecture notes:

5. J. Todd, Introduction to the Constructive Theory of Functions, California Institute of Technology, Pasadena, Calif., 1960, 1961.

Other standard sources include the following:

6. N. I. Achieser, "Vorlesungen über Approximationstheorie," Akademie-Verlag G.m.b.H., Berlin, 1955; "Theory of Approximation," F. Ungar Publishing Company, New York, 1956.

7. S. Bernstein, "Leçons sur les propriétés extrémales et la meilleure approximation des fonctions analytiques d'une variable réelle," Gauthier-Villars, Paris, 1926.

8. E. Borel, "Leçons sur les fonctions de variables réelles et les développements en séries de polynomes," Gauthier-Villars, Paris, 1928.

9. E. Feldheim, "Théorie de la convergence des procédés d'interpolation et de quadrature mécanique," Gauthier-Villars, Paris, 1939.

10. V. L. Goncarov, "Theory of Interpolation and Approximation of Functions," Gosudarstvennoe Izdatel'stvo Tekhniko-Teoreticheskoi Literatury, Moscow, 1954 (in Russian).

11. D. Jackson, "The Theory of Approximation," American Mathematical Society, Providence, R.I., 1930.

12. G. G. Lorentz, "Bernstein Polynomials," University of Toronto Press, Toronto, 1953.

13. G. Pólya and G. Szegö, "Aufgaben und Lehrsätze aus der Analysis," I, II, Springer-Verlag, Berlin, 1925.

14. G. Szegö, "Orthogonal Polynomials," American Mathematical Society, Providence, R.I., 1959.

15. C. J. de la Vallée Poussin, "Leçons sur l'approximation des fonctions d'une variable réelle," Gauthier-Villars, Paris, 1919.

16. J. L. Walsh, "Interpolation and Approximation in the Complex Domain," American Mathematical Society, Providence, R.I., 1955.

In addition to the standard sources listed above, there are several mimeographed lecture notes or reports, some not generally available, including:

17. E. K. Blum, Polynomial Approximation, U.S. Naval Ordnance Laboratory Report 3740, 1956.

18. J. C. Burkill, Approximations by Polynomials, Tata Institute, Bombay, 1959.

19. C. Lanczos, Approximations by Orthogonal Polynomials, University of California, Los Angeles, 1952.

20. T. S. Motzkin, Chebyshev Polynomials and Extremum Problems, University of California, Los Angeles, 1955.

21. I. J. Schoenberg, Approximations: Theory and Practice, Stanford University, Stanford, California, 1955.

There is also relevant material in various books of tables, notably:

22. "Tables of Lagrangian Interpolation Coefficients," National Bureau of Standards Columbia University Press Series, vol. 4, 1944.

23. "Tables of Chebyshev Polynomials," National Bureau of Standards Applied Mathematics Series, vol. 9, 1952.

24. L. Fox, "The Use and Construction of Mathematical Tables," National Physical Laboratory, Mathematical Tables, vol. I, 1956.

Some of the material is to be found in textbooks on calculus, on numerical analysis, and on finite differences. These include:

25. F. B. Hildebrand, "Introduction to Numerical Analysis," McGraw-Hill Book Company, Inc., New York, 1956.

26. Z. Kopal, "Numerical Analysis," John Wiley & Sons, Inc., New York, 1955.

27. C. Lanczos, "Applied Analysis," Prentice-Hall, Inc., Englewood Cliffs, N.J., 1956.

28. L. M. Milne-Thomson, "Calculus of Finite Differences," Macmillan & Co., Ltd., London, 1933.

29. A. M. Ostrowski, "Vorlesungen über Differential- und Integralrechnung," vol. 2, p. 168, Birkhauser, Basel, 1951.

30. E. Landau, "Differential and Integral Calculus," Chelsea Publishing Company, New York, 1950.

31. G. Sansone, "Orthogonal Functions," A. H. Diamond, tr., Interscience Publishers, Inc., New York, 1959.

32. E. Ya. Remez, "General Computation Methods for Chebyshev Approximation: Problems with Real Parameters Entering Linearly," Izdatel'stvo Akademii Nauk Ukrainskoi SSR, Kiev, 1957 (in Russian).

33. C. Hastings, Jr., "Approximations for Digital Computers," Princeton University Press, Princeton, N.J., 1955.

34. A. Erdélyi, W. Magnus, F. Oberhettinger, F. G. Tricomi, "Higher Transcendental Functions," vol. 2, McGraw-Hill Book Company, Inc., New York, 1953.

35. F. Oberhettinger and W. Magnus, "Anwendung der elliptischen Funktionen in Physik and Technik," Springer-Verlag, Berlin, 1949.

The following papers are explicitly referred to in the text:

36. G. Hornecker, Evaluation approché de la meilleure approximation polynomiale d'ordre n de $f(x)$ sur un segment fini (a,b), *Chiffres*, vol. 1, pp. 157–169, 1958.

37. C. Lanczos, Trigonometric Interpolation of Empirical and Analytical Functions, *J. Math. Phys.*, vol. 17, pp. 123–199, 1938.

38. F. D. Murnaghan and J. W. Wrench, Jr., The Determination of the Chebyshev Approximating Polynomial for a Differentiable Function, *Math. Tables Aids Comput.*, vol. 13, pp. 185–193, 1959.

39. E. Stiefel, Note on Jordan Elimination, Linear Programming and Tchebycheff Approximation, *Numer. Math.*, vol. 2, pp. 1–17, 1960.

40. J. N. Franklin, Numerical Stability in Digital and Analog Computation for Diffusion Problem, *J. Math. Phys.*, vol. 37, pp. 305–315, 1959.

41. H. Piloty, Zolotareffsche rationale Funktionen, *Z. Angew. Math. Mech.*, vol. 34, pp. 175–189, 1956.

42. E. W. Voronowskaja, Détermination de la forme asymptotique d'approximation des fonctions par les polynomes de M. Bernstein, *Comptes Rendus Acad. Sci. URSS*, pp. 79–85, 1932.

43. R. J. Duffin and A. C. Schaeffer, A Refinement of an Inequality of the Brothers Markoff, *Trans. Amer. Math. Soc.*, vol. 50, pp. 517–528, 1941.

4

Automatic Computers

MORRIS NEWMAN

NATIONAL BUREAU OF STANDARDS

JOHN TODD

PROFESSOR OF MATHEMATICS

CALIFORNIA INSTITUTE OF TECHNOLOGY

4.1 General Introduction

It is desirable at this point to restate the terms of reference for the present chapter. Its original aim was to introduce experienced mathematicians to the actual use of automatic computers and, at the same time, to give them material from which they could build courses for class use. It has been the authors' experience that many mathematicians begin programming courses, that some even complete the courses and write programs, but that few ever take them to the machine. The authors have had considerable experience in these matters and have a corresponding sympathy for both the instructor and the student. A suggested solution to the problem just stated is presented below.

In the first place, programming courses should be highly concentrated, the student should have no other commitments, and the instructor should be always available. Secondly, plenty of time for actual use of the machine should be available. The latter may be difficult to justify when only an upper-class machine is available, but the authors consider it worthwhile to delay for an hour or so the results of a calculation of doubtful accuracy on a problem of uncertain value in order to allow one new mathematician to get familiar with the machine. Such machines as the SEAC, UNIVAC, and the Datatron 220 have been found quite suitable for beginners.

In order to maintain the interest of the students, the material used should have some novelty and mathematical content; worked examples in number theory and Monte Carlo, for example, are preferred to those of the form, "Fill every cell with a stop command."

160

It is recommended that the initial words be written in the machine language and not in any pseudo codes. Only when the student has himself realized the possibility of pseudo codes, should he be allowed to use them.

The frightening complication of the actual subroutines, compilers, etc., at any particular working organization makes them unsuitable for a beginner; the worked examples should begin with programs which do not involve subroutines, and then a few subroutines and some elementary processing routines for them should be written by the student before he is allowed to graduate into current practice.

The authors are fully aware of the enormous duplication of effort in the programming field and appreciate the efforts directed toward uniformization, but these efforts have not yet produced anything definitive enough to present to beginners. Perhaps a more systematic presentation will soon be available to replace the following naïve approach.

For a general introduction to the subject of automatic computers, see Alt [13], and for an informal account of the logic of computer usage see Chap. 5.

BASIC TRAINING ON A HYPOTHETICAL COMPUTER

4.2 Introduction

In this chapter we construct a hypothetical automatic computer and learn how to program for it. Although no such computer exists, the ability to write programs for it will be transferable immediately to any existing automatic computer. The differences are only in machine characteristics, not in what is referred to as programming logic.

We begin with an entirely abstract situation, which we later make concrete. Imagine an unlimited number of compartments, or cells, numbered 0, 1, 2, . . . in each of which a real number, or an *instruction*, can be stored ("instruction" is defined below). The numbers 0, 1, . . . are the *addresses* of the cells. We make the convention that, if α is the address of a cell, then (α) denotes the contents of the cell. Similarly, if x is a real number which is stored in a cell, then $[x]$ denotes the address of such a cell. Notice that (α) is uniquely defined but that $[x]$ is not, since more than one cell may contain the real number x. Always, however, $([x]) = x$. We use the symbol $\rightarrow$ ambiguously to mean "goes into," "replaces," or "go to." An instruction is any of the following expressions:

$$(\alpha) + (\beta) \rightarrow \gamma$$
$$(\alpha) - (\beta) \rightarrow \gamma$$
$$(\alpha) \cdot (\beta) \rightarrow \gamma$$
$$(\alpha) \div (\beta) \rightarrow \gamma$$
$$(\alpha) < (\beta) \rightarrow \gamma.$$

All except the final instruction are *arithmetic* instructions, the first, for example, being understood to mean that the contents of cells α and β are added together, and the result stored in compartment γ. Similar interpretations are given to the next three instructions. It is further assumed that once any of these instructions has been performed, the next instruction performed is the one following immediately in sequence.

The last instruction, however, is of a different nature and is a *logical* instruction. Here the contents of cells α and β are compared, and if $(\alpha) < (\beta)$, the next instruction performed is the one in cell γ, whereas if $(\alpha) \geq (\beta)$, then the next instruction performed is the one that follows immediately in sequence.

We pay no attention at this point to stopping, starting, input, or output. These matters are considered later.

We are now in a position to write simple programs. These must perforce be limited severely, since we have made no provisions for modifying instructions, but the basic idea of a *loop* can be made plain.

Instructions are written with the address to the left and an explanation on the right.

Example 1. *Compute x^p, where x is a real number, p a positive integer, and $p = (1)$, $x = (2)$, $1 = (3)$.*

10	$(4) - (4) \to 4$	Set $(4) = 0$	$(r = 0)$
11	$(3) \cdot (3) \to 5$	Set $(5) = 1$	$(x^r = 1)$
12	$(3) + (4) \to 4$	$1 + r$ replaces r	
13	$(2) \cdot (5) \to 5$	$x \cdot x^r = x^{1+r}$ replaces x^r	
14	$(4) < (1) \to 12$	If $r < p$, go to 12; otherwise go to 15.	

Instructions 10 and 11 are "setting" instructions, which are necessary because we assume nothing about the contents of a cell. Instruction 12 is a "tally" instruction, which records the power r to which x has been raised. Instruction 13 is the "work" instruction, and instruction 14 is the "comparison" instruction which produces the loop. Notice that instruction 15, which we have not specified, would presumably be a command to print (5) or to halt.

Example 2. *Let $\epsilon > 0$, $1 \geq x \geq 0$ be given. Compute e^x with an error not exceeding ϵ.*

We set $T_0 = 1$, $T_n = (x/n) T_{n-1}$, $n \geq 1$; $S_0 = 1$, $S_n = S_{n-1} + T_n$, $n \geq 1$. Then for every $n \geq 1$, $e^x = S_{n-1} + t_n$, where $0 \leq t_n \leq T_n e$. Thus, if $T_n < \epsilon/e$, then $0 \leq e^x - S_{n-1} < \epsilon$.

The program follows, with storage assignments to the left:

1	n		10	$(7) + (8) \to 1$	Set $n = 1$.	
2	$T_0, T_1, \ldots$		11	$(7) + (8) \to 2$	Set $T_0 = 1$	$(T_{n-1}, n = 1)$.
3	$S_0, S_1, \ldots$		12	$(7) + (8) \to 3$	Set $S_0 = 1$	$(S_{n-1}, n = 1)$.

4	Temporary storage	13	$(5) \div (1) \to 4$

$\dfrac{x}{n} \to 4.$

5	x	14	$(4) \cdot (2) \to 2$

$\dfrac{x}{n} T_{n-1} = T_n$ replaces T_{n-1}.

6   ϵ/e 15 $(2) < (6) \to 19$ If $T_n < \epsilon/e$ go to 19; otherwise go to 16.

7   1   16 $(3) + (2) \to 3$ $S_{n-1} + T_n = S_n$ replaces S_{n-1}.

8   0   17 $(1) + (7) \to 1$ $n + 1$ replaces n.

           18   $(8) < (7) \to 13$ Go to 13.

Instructions 10 to 12 are setting instructions.   Instructions 13 and 14 compute T_n from T_{n-1}.   Instruction 15 decides whether or not the computation has gone far enough.   Instruction 16 computes S_n from S_{n-1} and T_n.   Instruction 17 "resets" n, and instruction 18 is a transfer instruction.   Although instruction 19 has not been specified, it would presumably be a print command or a halt command, as in Example 1.

Examples 1 and 2 illustrate different methods of controlling the length of a loop.   In example 1, we counted until a specified number of multiplications had been performed.   In example 2, we computed until a number produced by the computation was made smaller than a specified quantity.

Example 3.   *Compute (a,b), the greatest common divisor of the nonnegative integers a, b.*

We use the properties $(a,b) = (b,a) = (a, b - a)$ and $(0,b) = b$.   We assume $a = (1), b = (2), 0 = (3), 1 = (4)$.

10	$(2) < (1) \to 14$	If $b < a$, go to 14; otherwise go to 11.
11	$(1) < (4) \to 18$	If $a < 1$, go to 18; otherwise go to 12.
12	$(2) - (1) \to 2$	$b - a$ replaces b.
13	$(3) < (4) \to 10$	Go to 10.
14	$(1) + (3) \to 5$	
15	$(2) + (3) \to 1$	Interchange a and b.
16	$(5) + (3) \to 2$	
17	$(3) < (4) \to 11$	Go to 11.

The instruction 13 is an "unconditional transfer" built out of the comparison instruction.   Actual machines will usually have such an instruction in their repertoire, and it will be faster than this artificial one.

Once again the unspecified instruction in cell 18 would be a halt command or a print command.

It must be understood that this is a most impractical algorithm to compute (a,b).

It is instructive to follow the course of a computation in detail.   Suppose that, in Example 3, $a = 9$, $b = 30$.   The instructions would be executed as follows:

(1) (2)
10
  9 30
	11	(1) (2)
		12
		  3 6
			13

11	(1) (2) 12 9 3	13	10

(1) (2)
12
  9 21
	13	10	(1) (2) (5)
			14
			  3 0 3

13	10	11	(1) (2) (5) 15 0 0 3

10	(1) (2) (5)
	14
	  9 3 9
		(1) (2)
		12
		  3 3
			(1) (2) (5)
			16
			  0 3 3

11	(1) (2) (5) 15 3 3 9	13	17

(1) (2)
12
  9 12
	(1) (2) (5)
	16
	  3 9 9
		10	11

13	17	11	18
10	11	(1) (2) 12 3 0	

On the right, in each column, we have indicated the contents of the active cells. It is interesting to observe, in this simple example, how little computing is being done.

4.3 Specification of HAC

We go on now to the construction of our hypothetical automatic computer (HAC). HAC's "memory" consists of 100 cells numbered from 00 to 99. Each cell is capable of retaining a "word," which may be interpreted as a number or as an instruction. Each word is made up of seven decimal digits followed by a sign, and if the word is to be understood as a number, then the decimal point is at the left. Thus

$$1000000+ = 10^{-1}$$
$$5000000- = -2^{-1}$$
$$0000000+ = 0$$
$$0000000- = -0$$
$$0000001+ = 10^{-7}$$
$$9999999- = -1 + 10^{-7},$$

etc. If the word is to be understood as an instruction, then the first two digits are the α digits, the next two the β digits, the next two the γ digits, and the final one is the δ, or operation, digit, as follows:

$$00 \quad 00 \quad 00 \quad 0 \quad \pm$$
$$\alpha \quad \beta \quad \gamma \quad \delta \ \text{sign.}$$

The actual instructions follow:

Input-output instructions

$\alpha \beta \gamma \, 0+$	Read into $\alpha, \alpha + 1, \ldots, \beta$ (γ irrelevant).
$\alpha \beta \gamma \, 1+$	Print from $\alpha, \alpha + 1, \ldots, \beta$ (γ irrelevant).

Arithmetic instructions

$\alpha \beta \gamma \, 2+$	$(\alpha) + (\beta) \rightarrow \gamma$.
$\alpha \beta \gamma \, 3+$	$(\alpha) - (\beta) \rightarrow \gamma$.
$\alpha \beta \gamma \, 4+$	$(\alpha) \cdot (\beta) \rightarrow \gamma$ (low-order product).
$\alpha \beta \gamma \, 5+$	$(\alpha) \cdot (\beta) \rightarrow \gamma$ (unrounded high-order product).
$\alpha \beta \gamma \, 6+$	$(\alpha) \div (\beta) \rightarrow \gamma$ (unrounded quotient).

Logical instructions

$\alpha \beta \gamma \, 7+$	$(\alpha) < (\beta) \rightarrow \gamma$.
$\alpha \beta \gamma \, 8+$	$|(\alpha)| < |(\beta)| \rightarrow \gamma$.

If $x = (\alpha), y = (\beta)$, then operations 2 and 3 actually produce $\{x + y\}$, $\{x - y\}$, respectively ($\{x\}$ stands for the fractional part of x). Thus, for example, if $(01) = 5000000+, (02) = 8000000-$, then the instructions

$$01 \quad 02 \quad 03 \quad 2+$$
$$01 \quad 01 \quad 04 \quad 3+$$

produce $3000000-, 0000000+$ in cells 03, 04, respectively, and the instructions

$$01 \quad 01 \quad 03 \quad 2+$$
$$01 \quad 02 \quad 04 \quad 3+$$

produce $0000000+, 3000000+$ in cells 03, 04, respectively. This loss of digits on the left is termed *overflow*. No such loss is possible with operations 4 and 5. Thus, for example, if $(01) = 5000000+$, $(02) = 9999999+$, then the instructions

$$01 \quad 01 \quad 03 \quad 5+$$
$$02 \quad 02 \quad 04 \quad 4+$$
$$02 \quad 02 \quad 05 \quad 5+$$

produce $2500000+, 0000001+, 9999998+$, respectively, in cells 03, 04, and 05. The low-order product is the one to use for computing with whole numbers, which are thought of as stored with a scale factor $10^{-7} = \epsilon$.

In operation 6, HAC halts if $(\alpha) \geq (\beta)$ and does not perform the instruction. If $(01) = 0100000+$, $(02) = 0600000-$, then the instruction

$$01 \quad 02 \quad 03 \quad 6+$$

produces $1666666-$ in cell 03.

The logical operations 7 and 8 are straightforward and need no comment.

The input operation 0 and the output operation 1 have no counterparts in our earlier discussion. Here we provide for moving data into and out from HAC's memory. Notice that the γ digits are irrelevant. If $\beta < \alpha$, then HAC will read or print one word into or from cell α. If $\beta \geq \alpha$, then HAC will read or print into or from cells $\alpha, \alpha + 1, \ldots, \beta$ in this order.

We make the convention that an instruction with a minus sign halts HAC, after the instruction is performed.

We assume that HAC has a "start switch." When this switch is on, HAC reads a word into cell 00 and *goes there*, so that (00) will be interpreted as an instruction and performed. Thus, suppose that we wish to read a program into HAC's memory that begins in 10 and ends in 40, the first instruction performed by the program being the one in 20. The actual program should be preceded by the instructions

$$01 \quad 02 \quad 00 \quad 0+$$
$$10 \quad 40 \quad 00 \quad 0+$$
$$00 \quad 01 \quad 20 \quad 7+.$$

We return to this point later.

HAC treats 0 and -0 as identical numbers.

In planning our programs, we follow the convention that 00 will be used only as a "starter," 01 to 09 will be used for temporary storage, and 10 to 19 will be used for "standard constants," which we list below:

$$
\begin{array}{lll}
10 & 0000000+ & = 0 \\
11 & 0000001+ & = 10^{-7} = \epsilon \\
12 & 0000010+ & = 10^{-6} \\
13 & 0000100+ & = 10^{-5} \\
14 & 0001000+ & = 10^{-4} \\
15 & 0010000+ & = 10^{-3} \\
16 & 0100000+ & = 10^{-2} \\
17 & 1000000+ & = 10^{-1} \\
18 & 5000000+ & = 2^{-1} \\
19 & 9999999+ & = 1 - 10^{-7} = 1 - \epsilon.
\end{array}
$$

4.4   Worked Example: Cyclotomic Numbers

We are going to construct a program for HAC which will compute and print the n cyclotomic numbers, for a series of values of n,

$$\zeta^r, \qquad 1 \leq r \leq n, \qquad \zeta = \exp \frac{2\pi i}{n}.$$

The simplest scheme to follow would be to employ the recurrence formula

$$\zeta^{r+1} = \zeta \cdot \zeta^r,$$

so that the only significant computation involved would be that of ζ. This, however, has the disadvantage that the round-off error incurred by the multiplications tends to accumulate and could be serious enough to ruin ζ^r for values of r near n.   Instead, we adopt a procedure which makes the computation of the rth number independent of the preceding ones.   We must also remember that HAC rejects numbers ≥ 1 in absolute value.   The steps (in broad outline) follow.

Step 1.   Read in word.   If the word is a legitimate number n, go to step 2; otherwise halt.

Step 2.   Print n.

Step 3.   Compute $\theta = \pi/4n$.

Step 4.   Set $r = 1$, $\theta_r = \theta$, where $\theta_r = r\theta$.

Step 5.   Compute $\cos \theta_r$, $\sin \theta_r$.

Step 6.   Compute $\cos 8\theta_r$, $\sin 8\theta_r$ by repeated use of the identities $\cos 2x = \cos^2 x - \sin^2 x$, $\sin 2x = 2 \sin x \cos x$.

Step 7.   Print r, $\cos 8\theta_r$, $\sin 8\theta_r$.

Step 8.   If $r < n$, go to step 9; otherwise go to step 1.

Step 9.   Replace r by $r + 1$, θ_r by θ_{r+1}, and go to step 5.

An examination of this schedule reveals that step 5 is the only one involving serious computation, and accordingly we concentrate our attention here.   We need routines for $\cos x$, $\sin x$ where x is a HAC number. Put

$$C_0 = 1, \qquad C_k = -\frac{x^2}{2k(2k - 1)} C_{k-1}, \qquad k \geq 1,$$

$$S_0 = x, \qquad S_k = -\frac{x^2}{2k(2k + 1)} S_{k-1}, \qquad k \geq 1,$$

$$A_k = C_0 + C_1 + \cdots + C_k, \qquad k \geq 0,$$

$$B_k = S_0 + S_1 + \cdots + S_k, \qquad k \geq 0.$$

Then
$$\cos x = A_{k-1} + c_k, \qquad k \geq 1,$$

$$\sin x = B_{k-1} + s_k, \qquad k \geq 1$$

where $|c_k| \leq |C_k|$, $|s_k| \leq |S_k|$.   Also,

$$S_k = \frac{x}{2k+1} C_k,$$

and so $|S_k| \leq |C_k|$.   To compute cos x, sin x to a given precision E, it is necessary only that $|C_k| < E$.

We write this as a subroutine, anticipating the possibility that we may want such a routine elsewhere.

We now write out step 5 in somewhat more detail.   Instead of θ_r, we write x.

Step 5.1.   Set $k = 1$, $C_{k-1} = C_0 = 1$, $S_{k-1} = S_0 = x$, $A_{k-1} = A_0 = 1$, $B_{k-1} = B_0 = x$.

Step 5.2. $C_k = -\{x^2/[2k(2k-1)]\}C_{k-1}$ replaces C_{k-1}.

Step 5.3.   If $|C_k| < E$, go to exit; otherwise go to step 5.4.

Step 5.4. $S_k = -\{x^2/[2k(2k+1)]\}S_{k-1}$ replaces S_{k-1}.

Step 5.5. $A_{k-1} + C_k = A_k$ replaces A_{k-1}.

Step 5.6. $B_{k-1} + S_k = B_k$ replaces B_{k-1}.

Step 5.7. $k + 1$ replaces k, and go to step 5.2.

For the detailed code for step 5, we assume that x has been put into 09 and that the starting point is 20.

20	41	10	05	2+	Set $2k\epsilon = 2\epsilon$ in 05.
21	19	10	01	2+	Set $C_{k-1} = C_0 = 1 - \epsilon$ in 01.
22	09	10	02	2+	Set $S_{k-1} = S_0 = x$ in 02.
23	19	10	03	2+	Set $A_{k-1} = A_0 = 1 - \epsilon$ in 03.
24	09	10	04	2+	Set $B_{k-1} = B_0 = x$ in 04.
25	09	09	09	5+	$-x^2$ replaces x in 09.
26	10	09	09	3+	
27	05	05	06	4+	$(2k)^2\epsilon \to 06.$
28	06	05	07	3+	$2k(2k-1)\epsilon \to 07.$
29	06	05	08	2+	$2k(2k+1)\epsilon \to 08.$
30	11	07	07	6+	
31	07	09	07	5+	$C_k = -\dfrac{x^2}{2k(2k-1)} C_{k-1}$ replaces C_{k-1}.
32	07	01	01	5+	
33	01	42	00	8+	If $|C_k| < E$, go to exit; otherwise go on.
34	11	08	08	6+	
35	08	09	08	5+	$S_k = -\dfrac{x^2}{2k(2k+1)} S_{k-1}$ replaces S_{k-1}.
36	08	02	02	5+	
37	03	01	03	2+	$A_{k-1} + C_k = A_k$ replaces A_{k-1}.
38	04	02	04	2+	$B_{k-1} + S_k = B_k$ replaces B_{k-1}.
39	05	41	05	2+	$k + 1$ replaces k.
40	10	11	27	7+	Go to 27.
41	00	00	00	2+	2ϵ.
42	00	00	00	5+	$E = 5 \cdot 10^{-7}$.

One or two points should be noted.   The original value of x has been destroyed, 09 containing $-x^2$ after the subroutine has run its course. Instruction 33 is an "exit" instruction and must be set up before the subroutine is entered.   (This will be clumsy, since HAC lacks an "extract" order.)   The nonstandard constants 2ϵ and E (which was taken to be 5ϵ) are part of the subroutine.   The cell 03 contains $\cos x$ and 04 contains $\sin x$ at the end of the subroutine.

It is generally better to write subroutines as if they originated in 00 and then to "incorporate" them, but we disregard this refinement here. We return to this point in Sec. 4.21.

The next part of the program which should be examined is step 6, since the identities are applied three times.   There is a simple loop involved here, and step 6 in more detail follows (once again we write x instead of θ_r).

Step 6.1.   Set $k = 1$.

Step 6.2. $\cos 2x = \cos^2 x - \sin^2 x$, $\sin 2x = 2 \sin x \cos x$; replace $\cos x$, $\sin x$, respectively.

Step 6.3.   If $k < 3$, go to step 6.4; otherwise go to exit.

Step 6.4.   Replace k by $k + 1$, and go to step 6.2.

Remembering that $\cos x$, $\sin x$ are in 03, 04, respectively, the detailed code would be as follows:

43	11	10	01	2+	Set $k\epsilon = 1 \cdot \epsilon$ in 01.
44	03	03	09	5+	
45	04	04	08	5+	$\cos 2x = \cos^2 x - \sin^2 x \rightarrow 09$.
46	09	08	09	3+	
47	03	04	04	5+	$\sin 2x = 2 \sin x \cos x$ replaces $\sin x$.
48	04	04	04	2+	
49	09	10	03	2	$\cos 2x$ replaces $\cos x$.
50	41	01	00	7+	If $2 < k$, go to exit; otherwise go on.
51	01	11	01	2+	$k + 1$ replaces k.
52	10	11	44	7+	Go to 44.

We have now written out all the difficult bits, and we can prepare the final HAC program with little difficulty.   The question of inputting the program should be discussed somewhat more fully, however.   A realistic approach to this question involves the knowledge that any computer can make an error, and provision must be made for checking any data read into the computer.   A simple way to do this with a program which will be read in more than once is to compute and print a "memory sum."   Thus a program which occupies cells A through C and has its first instruction in B should be preceded by the following instructions:

00	01	08	00	0+	Read in 01 to 08.
01	A	C	00	0+	Read in program.
02	C	00	00	2+	
03	02	01	06	7+	
04	02	08	02	3+	Form memory sum in 00.
05	03	04	02	7+	
06	00	00	00	1+	Print memory sum.
07	03	04	B	7+	Go to B.
08	01	00	00	0+	1 in α position.

Notice that nothing is set up, since the instructions will be performed just once and will be destroyed when the program begins. The fact that the summing cell 00 is not initially clear (empty) is irrelevant, since we are interested only in the *constancy* of the memory sum, not in any given value; and 00 contains the same number initially each time the program is read into HAC.

The actual HAC program follows. Since we are comparing to zero to determine when no more sets of cyclotomic numbers are to be computed, the input for the computation of the numbers of orders 5, 7, 12 might be

$$0000005+$$
$$0000007+$$
$$0000012+$$
$$1234567-.$$

The last word is completely arbitrary, so long as it is negative. Notice that the halt order 76 prints out this word at the end of the run.

A good problem is to examine the program on page 171 for possible errors by "clocking it through" with a numerical example.

Note that the "empty" cells 53, 54, 55, and 56 will contain n, r, e, and e_r, respectively.

4.5   Worked Example: Minors of Triple-diagonal Matrix

We go on now to another example. Let M be the triple-diagonal matrix

$$M = \begin{pmatrix} b_1 & c_1 & & & \\ a_1 & b_2 & c_2 & & \\ \cdots & \cdots & \cdots & \cdots & \cdots \\ & & a_{n-2} & b_{n-1} & c_{n-1} \\ & & & a_{n-1} & b_n \end{pmatrix}$$

with whole-number entries. We are going to compute and print the

00	01	08	00	0+	20	41	10	05	2+
01	10	76	00	0+	21	19	10	01	2+
02	76	00	00	2+	22	09	10	02	2+
03	02	01	06	7+	23	19	10	03	2+
04	02	08	02	3+	24	09	10	04	2+
05	03	04	02	7+	25	09	09	09	5+
06	00	00	00	1+	26	10	09	09	3+
07	03	04	60	7+	27	05	05	06	4+
08	01	00	00	0+	28	06	05	07	3+
					29	06	05	08	2+
10	00	00	00	0+	30	11	07	07	6+
11	00	00	00	1+	31	07	09	07	5+
12	00	00	01	0+	32	07	01	01	5+
13	00	00	10	0+	33	01	42	43	8+
14	00	01	00	0+	34	11	08	08	6+
15	00	10	00	0+	35	08	09	08	5+
16	01	00	00	0+	36	08	02	02	5+
17	10	00	00	0+	37	03	01	03	2+
18	50	00	00	0+	38	04	02	04	2+
19	99	99	99	9+	39	05	41	05	2+
40	10	11	27	7+	60	53	53	00	0+
41	00	00	00	2+	61	53	10	76	7+
42	00	00	00	5+	62	53	53	00	1+
43	11	10	01	2+	63	11	53	55	6+
44	03	03	09	5+	64	55	59	55	5+
45	04	04	08	5+	65	11	10	54	2+
46	09	08	09	3+	66	55	10	56	2+
47	03	04	04	5+	67	56	10	09	2+
48	04	04	04	2+	68	10	11	20	7+
49	09	10	03	2+	69	54	10	02	2+
50	41	01	69	7+	70	02	04	00	1+
51	01	11	01	2+	71	54	53	73	7+
52	10	11	44	7+	72	10	11	60	7+
53	00	00	00	0+	73	54	11	54	2+
54	00	00	00	0+	74	56	55	56	2+
55	00	00	00	0+	75	10	11	67	7+
56	00	00	00	0+	76	53	53	00	1-
57	00	00	00	0+					
58	00	00	00	0+					
59	78	53	98	2+					

running minors of M, which are given by the recurrence formula

$$D_0 = 1, \qquad D_1 = b_1, \qquad D_k = b_k D_{k-1} - a_{k-1} c_{k-1} D_{k-2}, \qquad 2 \leq k \leq n.$$

The steps (in broad outline) follow:

Step 1.   Set $D_0 = 1$, $D_1 = b_1$, $k = 2$.
Step 2.   If $n < k$, go to step 5; otherwise go to step 3.
Step 3.   Compute and store $D_k = b_k D_{k-1} - a_{k-1} c_{k-1} D_{k-2}$.
Step 4.   Replace k by $k + 1$ and go to step 2.
Step 5.   Print $D_0, D_1, \ldots, D_n$.

The significant computation occurs in step 3, and when we write this out in detail, it has something of the following appearance:

$$
\begin{array}{cccc}
[a_{k-1}] & [c_{k-1}] & 01 & 4+ \\
[D_{k-2}] & 01 & 01 & 4+ \\
[b_k] & [D_{k-1}] & 02 & 4+ \\
02 & 01 & [D_k] & 3+
\end{array}
\left.\begin{array}{l}
\\
\\
\\
\end{array}\right.
\begin{array}{l}
a_{k-1} c_{k-1} D_{k-2} \rightarrow 01. \\[4pt]
b_k D_{k-1} \rightarrow 02. \\[4pt]
D_k \rightarrow \text{storage}.
\end{array}
$$

We see that a new feature emerges.   Just as in forming a memory sum, the orders performing the computation are subject to change and will have to be set up and modified during the course of the computation. We have introduced here a common convention: enclosing instructions (or parts of them) which are subject to modification, in brackets [ ]. Since the computation starts with $k = 2$, the initial form of the orders is

$$
\begin{array}{cccc}
[a_1] & [c_1] & 01 & 4+ \\
[D_0] & 01 & 01 & 4+ \\
[b_2] & [D_1] & 02 & 4+ \\
02 & 01 & [D_2] & 3+.
\end{array}
$$

Assuming that

$$
\begin{array}{lll}
a_k \text{ is in } a + k, & 1 \leq k \leq n - 1 \\
b_k \text{ is in } b + k, & 1 \leq k \leq n \\
c_k \text{ is in } c + k, & 1 \leq k \leq n - 1 \\
D_k \text{ is in } D + k, & 0 \leq k \leq n,
\end{array}
$$

the orders become

$$
\begin{array}{cccc}
a + k - 1 & c + k - 1 & 01 & 4+ \\
D + k - 2 & 01 & 01 & 4+ \\
b + k & D + k - 1 & 02 & 4+ \\
02 & 01 & D + k & 3+,
\end{array}
$$

and this initial form becomes

$$
\begin{array}{cccc}
a + 1 & c + 1 & 01 & 4+ \\
D & 01 & 01 & 4+ \\
b + 2 & D + 1 & 02 & 4+ \\
02 & 01 & D + 2 & 3+.
\end{array}
$$

We can now write out the program.   We assume that n is in cell N.

20	11	10	D	2+	Set $D_0 = 1$.
21	$b + 1$	10	$D + 1$	2+	Set $D_1 = b_1$.
22	11	11	09	2+	Set $k = 2$ in 09.
23	41	10	28	2+	
24	42	10	29	2+	Set up 28, 29, 30, 31.
25	43	10	30	2+	
26	44	10	31	2+	
27	N	09	38	7+	If $n < k$, go to 38; otherwise go on.
28	$a + k - 1$	$c + k - 1$	01	4+	
29	$D + k - 2$	01	01	4+	Compute and store D_k.
30	$b + k$	$D + k - 1$	02	4+	
31	02	01	$D + k$	3+	
32	09	11	09	2+	$k + 1$ replaces k.
33	45	28	28	2+	
34	16	29	29	2+	Reset 28, 29, 30, 31.
35	45	30	30	2+	
36	12	31	31	2+	
37	10	11	27	7+	Go to 27.
38	N	15	08	6+	Set up 40.
39	46	08	40	3+	
40	D	$D + n$	00	1−	Print $D_0, D_1, \ldots,$ D_n and halt.
41	$a + 1$	$c + 1$	01	4+	
42	D	01	01	4+	
43	$b + 2$	$D + 1$	02	4+	Constants.
44	02	01	$D + 2$	3+	
45	01	01	00	0+	
46	D	D	00	1	

We do not bother to assign actual numerical values to a, b, c, D, N or to write a complete program. It should be noted that the actual contents of cells 28, 29, 30, 31, and 40 are irrelevant.

In 38 we use a division to "shift" a number. More sophisticated machines do this with a special operation. We could have accomplished the same thing by low-order multiplying by 1000ϵ.

4.6 Problems: Generation of Partitions and Permutations

The reader is invited to prepare the detailed HAC program for the generation of all the partitions of a positive integer n into precisely k parts. We denote the parts occurring in such a partition by $x_1, x_2, \ldots, x_k$ and assume that $x_1 \geq x_2 \geq \cdots \geq x_k \geq 1$. Then $n = x_1 + x_2 + \cdots + x_k$, and so $kx_k \leq n$. The outline for the program follows:

Step 1. Set $r = 2$.

Step 2.   Set $x_1 = x_2 = \cdots = x_k = 1$.

Step 3.   Compute $S = x_1 + x_2 + \cdots + x_k$.

Step 4.   If $n < S$, go to step 9; otherwise go to step 5.

Step 5.   Replace x_1 by $x_1 + n - S$.

Step 6.   Print $x_1, x_2, \ldots, x_k$.

Step 7.   Set $r = 2$.

Step 8.   Replace each of $x_1, x_2, \ldots, x_r$ by $1 + x_r$ and go to step 3.

Step 9.   If $n < kx_k$, halt; otherwise go to step 10.

Step 10.   Replace r by $r + 1$ and go to step 8.

This outline should be clocked through with specific numbers for k and n, say $k = 4, n = 10$. The programming logic here is much more subtle than in any of our previous examples, and the reader should convince himself that the routine is correct.

As a final "challenge problem," the reader is invited to prepare a program to compute the $n!$ permutations of the integers $1, 2, \ldots, n$ where $n \leq 7$. The permutations must be run through once and once only.*

4.7 Conclusion

In conclusion, we remark that HAC is actually a modified three-address machine. Most present-day computers are one-address machines with accumulators. The programming logic, however, is independent of the machine, although the detailed code very much depends on the machine. In fact, to become a skillful programmer and coder, one must know a particular machine intimately.

SEQUENCE OF CODING PROBLEMS

4.8 Introduction

We now assume a familiarity with the basic concepts of programming and coding. We sketch a sequence of problems for programming on any general-purpose computer, which will develop some basic elementary knowledge. The approach is almost historical. The instructor will have to clothe the skeleton we provide according to the equipment he has available and to emphasize or deemphasize sections according to his audience.

4.9 Memory Summation

The most naïve program to compute $\sum\limits_{\alpha=n}^{m} (\alpha)$, disregarding overflow, will include a tally which counts from 1 to $m - n + 1$, in some units:

0. Clear counter for partial sum, clear tally.
1. [Add a new term to the partial sum.]
2. Compare tally with limit: if less, carry on; if equal, go to 6.

* See, for a solution, D. H. Lehmer [41].

3. Advance tally.
4. Advance variable instruction (i.e., 1).
5. Go to 1.
6. Print total and stop.

A little thought shows that the variable instruction is changing with the tally and that the variable instruction can be used as a tally, being compared with its ultimate form.   Our program can be revised as follows:

0. Clear counter for partial sum.
1. [Add a new term to the partial sum.]
2. Compare variable instruction with its final form: if less; carry on, if equal go to 5.
3. Advance variable instruction.
4. Go to 1.
5. Print total and stop.

Comparison of these two programs will show that the latter is more compact and that it saves one addition per cycle; instead of the cycle $1 \to 2 \to 3 \to 4 \to 5 \to 1$, we have $1 \to 2 \to 3 \to 4 \to 1$.

It is instructive to make time estimates for problems as early as possible and to check these whenever the problems are run.   In this way a body of knowledge will be accumulated which can be applied directly in new situations, or used as a basis for extrapolation to them.   We do not return to this point explicitly again, but it is relevant in practically all the problems of our sequence.

The sequence of instructions "obey, compare, advance" is one which is always occurring; it is usually safer to prefix this sequence by another one, setting the variable instruction to its initial state.   Our program would then read:

0. Clear counter for partial sum.

"Set   1. Set variable instruction to its initial state.

obey   2. [Add a new term to the partial sum.]

compare   3. Compare variable instruction with its final form; if less, carry on; if equal, go to 6.

advance"   4. Advance variable instruction.

     5. Go to 2.

     6. Print total and stop.

We can elaborate this into an equipment test program of a form which was very necessary in the early days, when deterioration of the storage presented problems.   We imagine the following situation: most of the storage $\alpha \le n \le \beta$ is filled in any manner, and the rest is to contain a test program with the following characteristics.   Compute and record the sum $\sum_{n=\alpha}^{\beta} (n)$; compute again and compare with the recorded sum; if there is a discrepancy, print out both sums and stop; if there is agreement, recompute, recompare, etc.   If the machine is functioning perfectly, no print-out will be observed—the same may be true if the machine is functioning very imperfectly. It is therefore desirable to modify our specification by requiring a periodic print-out of, for instance, the latest computed sum and the number of summations carried out. The actual frequency of print-out will be determined by the speed of the machine,

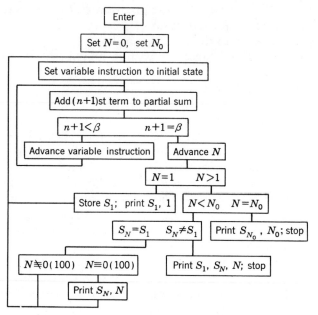

FIG. 4.1   Memory sum test program.
(The variable instruction is "Add $(n + 1)$st term to partial sum"; the setting of this to its initial state, i.e., "Add (α) to partial sum," should be accompanied by the clearing of the cell reserved for the partial sum).

and the duration of the test will be specified by the total number of summations to be carried out. Suppose that we require N_0 summations altogether and that s_N is printed out each time N is a multiple of 100.

Instead of the linear arrangement used for earlier programs, we now indicate the program by a "flow diagram."

Many elaborate schemes for flow diagrams, bristling with conventions, are in use. In the present account we use only the most obvious conventions and do not attempt to give any formal description. We note that a flow diagram is largely independent of the machine contemplated for the solution of the problem. Further, the preparation of a flow diagram, or something equivalent, is an essential preliminary to the programming of problems of significant size; such diagrams can be used for subcontracting the work and especially for the detailed checking of programs prepared by others (see Burks, Goldstine, and von Neumann [38]).

The usefulness of memory summation is underlined by the fact that machines have been built which have such a summation as a basic instruction. This fact raises the general question of the economics of simplifying programming by complicating equipment. It is not feasible to discuss this question here.

Let us return, for simplicity, to the naïve inductive program. It is certainly compact, but it is much more time-consuming than a simple linear program of the form:

0. Clear register for partial sum.
1. Add (n).
2. Add $(n + 1)$.
   $. . . . .$
$(m - n + 1)$. Add (m).
$(m - n)$. Print total and stop.

The heartbreaking sequence of "compare, advance, obey" can be avoided at the expense of more complicated equipment. One way is to use an "index register," or "B register," a simple form of which will now be described. This is a special register in which the number of iterations required is set initially and is then decreased after each iteration is carried out. The equipment is arranged so that, as long as the index register is positive, one action is taken, whereas if it becomes zero, another action is taken. This avoids the repeated comparison order, at the expense of a single setting of the index register. The structure of the program in this context would be of the form:

0. Clear register for partial sum.
1. Set index register.
2. [Add a new term to the partial sum.]
3. Decrease index register: if positive, carry on; if zero, go to 6.
4. Advance variable instruction (i.e., 2).
5. Go to 2.
6. Print total and stop.

Note that here the summation is carried out backwards.
Other uses of the index register are discussed in Sec. 4.21.

4.10   Square Root

We now discuss the evaluation of square roots. Some machines have a single instruction which produces the square root; this is rather unusual, as this facility requires additional equipment. We therefore consider the determination of square roots by programming. Several

algorithms can be considered. For instance, the elementary-school
method, indicated below, can be readily mechanized.

		.	7	0	7	1	0	6
			.50	00	00	00	00	00
7			49					
140			1	00	00			
1407				98	49			
14141				1	51	00		
				1	41	41		
141420					9	59	00	00
1414206								

A little thought will show that this is a comparatively slow process and
that the iterative processes discussed in Chap. 2 are to be preferred. We
recall the results of the analysis of the scheme

$$x_0 = 1, \qquad x_{n+1} = \tfrac{1}{2}(x_n + Nx_n^{-1}).$$

The sequence $\{x_n\}$ decreases steadily to $\sqrt{N}$ for any N, $0 < N < 1$, and
the convergence is quadratic.

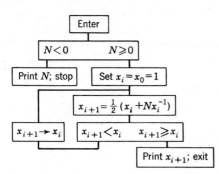

FIG. 4.2   Square-root program.

Some of the points which require
consideration have already been discussed.   A possible program is indicated by the flow diagram alongside.

The check that $N \geq 0$ is to prevent nonsense from developing.

Note that, if we have a machine
which recognizes only numbers
strictly between -1 and $+1$, then
we cannot set $x_0 = 1$ but must use
$x_0 = 1 - \epsilon$, where ϵ is the smallest
positive number recognized by the
machine. Again, in order to avoid
overflow, we must compute

$$x_{i+1} = \tfrac{1}{2}x_i + (\tfrac{1}{2}N)x_i^{-1},$$

and even then we must be sure that in case, for example, $N = 1 - \epsilon$
we do not get an overflow on the addition; moreover, we must be sure
that the division is invariably proper, that is, that $0 < x_i > \tfrac{1}{2}N$.   The
detailed analysis of this process is quite complicated and depends vitally
on the detailed behavior of the arithmetic unit.   For the discussion of
special cases, we refer to the work of Householder and Rumsey cited
earlier.   We note that, although the recurrence relation is theoretically

stationary only if $x_0 = \sqrt{N}$, an efficient practical version of the algorithm can give the exact result when N is a perfect square.

We conclude with these remarks.   If one does not make a complete analysis of the program, a rough estimate of the error can be made, and after the alleged square root is obtained, the difference $|x_{i+1}^2 - N|$ can be compared with a specified tolerance and the calculation can be stopped if the error is excessive.

It is clear that a program of the kind described is a finite one; it is important that its length be estimated.   In view of what happens for $N = 0$, it might be worthwhile to separate out this case.

It is also appropriate to discuss what is a reasonable precision for $\sqrt{N}$, it being assumed that $\sqrt{N}$ is a rounded number.   The schoolroom algorithm indicated that $\sqrt{N}$ is determined to about half the number of significant figures of N; this is confirmed by noting that, if $f(x) = \sqrt{x}$, then

$$\delta f \doteq \tfrac{1}{2} x^{-\frac{1}{2}}\, \delta x.$$

4.11   arctan d, $|d| < 1$

We discuss the calculation of arctan d, as representative of the calculation of the elementary transcendental functions.   Among the competing algorithms are the following:

1. The Gregory series

$$\arctan x = x - \tfrac{1}{3}x^3 + \tfrac{1}{5}x^5 - \cdots. \tag{4.1}$$

2. The continued fraction

$$\arctan x = \frac{x}{1+} \frac{x^2}{3+} \frac{(2x)^2}{5+} \frac{(3x)^2}{7+} \cdots$$

(see Teichroew [39]).

3. If $a_0 = 1$, $b_0 = \sqrt{1 + x^2}$ and if for $n = 0, 1, 2, \cdots$,

$$a_{n+1} = \tfrac{1}{2}(a_n + b_n), \qquad b_{n+1} = \sqrt{b_n a_{n+1}},$$

we have

$$\lim a_n = \lim b_n = x/\arctan x.$$

4. Chebyshev expansion (see Chap. 3, Hastings [40], Clenshaw [12], NPL 5).

We shall not make a comparative evaluation of these but shall discuss the simple Gregory series method in some detail.   It is known that the series (4.1) converges for $|x| \leq 1$, but very slowly when $|x|$ is near unity. One method of improving this is to choose a central value ρ of $\theta = \arctan x$ and compute

$$\theta = \rho + \arctan z, \qquad z = \frac{x - \tan \rho}{1 + x \tan \rho}.$$

We shall assume $0 \leq x \leq 1$. Then z varies from $-\tan \rho$ to $(1 - \tan \rho)/$ $(1 + \tan \rho)$, and it would appear advantageous to choose ρ so that the z interval is symmetrical about the origin. This means that $\tau = \tan \rho$ must satisfy the quadratic equation $\tau^2 + 2\tau - 1 = 0$, which gives

$$\tau = \sqrt{2} - 1 \doteq .41421\,35624, \qquad \rho = \arctan \tau \doteq .39269\,90817.$$

An unsophisticated program will have the following form:
1. Compute $x = |d|$, z, $-z^2$; put $\Sigma_0 = z = \tau_0$.
2. Compute $\tau_{i+1} = -z^2(2i + 1)\tau_i/(2i + 3)$.
3. If $\tau_{i+1} = 0$, go to 7; if $\tau_{i+1} \neq 0$, go to 4.
4. Compute the partial sum $\Sigma_{i+1} = \Sigma_i + \tau_i$.
5. Advance index, $2i + 3 \to 2i + 1$.
6. Go to 2.
7. Compute $\theta = \rho + \Sigma_i$.
8. Compute $\arctan d = (\mathrm{sign}\ d)\ \theta$

4.12   The Monte Carlo Method—Motivation

When the exact answer to a statistical or physical or mathematical problem appears inaccessible, a statistical answer may be acceptable. Such an answer, ideally, is qualified by some such statement as that the probability of its being in error by an amount ϵ is less than δ; very often this qualification is missing or vague, and the poser is content with the fact that an apparently satisfactory model of his problem is being used.

Let us consider, for orientation, a problem which can be readily solved analytically. Two gamblers begin with z and $(a - z)$ dollars; they toss a coin repeatedly, each time for a stake of 1 dollar, and we assume that the first player has a probability p of winning and that the second has a probability q of winning, where $p + q = 1$. We want to know the probability that the first player will be ruined (i.e., lose all his capital), and the expected number of tosses before this happens. The results are:

Condition	Probability of ruin	Duration
$p = q = \frac{1}{2}$	$1 - z/a$	$z(a - z)$
$p \neq q$	$\dfrac{(q/p)^a - (q/p)^z}{(q/p)^a - 1}$	$\dfrac{z}{q - p} - \dfrac{a}{q - p}\dfrac{1 - (q/p)^z}{1 - (q/p)^a}$

For a discussion of this, see Feller [11]. We call a game a sequence of tosses which leads to the ruin of one or the other player. We consider playing a large number of games, noting the relative frequency P of wins by the first player and the average number of tosses in a game. These provide approximations to the quantities desired in virtue of the law of large numbers for Bernoulli trials.   It is clear that these approximations can be obtained conveniently on a computer, provided we have some sort of "chance device" in our computer: an instruction which can cause one action with probability p and another with probability q.   Machines have been constructed with such instructions, but the use of genuine chance elements is not entirely satisfactory (e.g., we cannot repeat calculations for checking purposes).   The construction of deterministic arithmetic processes which have a suitable behavior has been studied experimentally with considerable success.

In the present context it will be enough if we can produce "pseudo-random numbers" which are "uniformly distributed" in [0,1] and make our discrimination according to whether the current pseudo-random number is $<p$ or $\geq p$.   What we want is a sequence of numbers r_n, $0 \leq r_n \leq 1$ such that, if N_n is the number of $r_1, r_2, \ldots, r_n$ contained in any interval of length α included in [0,1], then N_n/n is approximately α. In the next section we discuss one way of generating and testing such a sequence.

It is appropriate to quote here the definition given by D. H. Lehmer [Harvard 26] of a pseudo-random sequence.   It is "a vague notion embodying the idea of a sequence in which each term is unpredictable to the uninitiated and whose digits pass a certain number of tests, traditional with statisticians and depending somewhat on the uses to which the sequence is to be put."

For a survey of this subject, with an extensive bibliography, up to 1954, see Meyer [52]; see also NBSAMS 12.   Among the more recent papers are Bauer [15], Davis and Rabinowitz [16], and Hammersley [51].   A report on applications in nuclear physics has been written by Fortet [56]; considerable work in this area has been carried out by Richtmyer.

4.13   Generation and Testing of Pseudo-random Numbers

We begin with a scheme suitable for a decimal machine, with 10D. We write

$$\bar{r}_0 = 1, \qquad \bar{r}_{n+1} \equiv \bar{\rho}\bar{r}_n(\mathrm{mod}\ 10^{10}), \qquad \bar{\rho} = 7^9 - 0040353607$$

and then take

$$r_n = 10^{-10}\bar{r}_n.$$

The barred quantities are integers, and $\bar{r}_{n+1}$ is got by taking the last 10 digits of $\bar{\rho}\bar{r}_{n}$, that is, disregarding multiples of 10^{10}.   It can be shown that the sequences $\{r_n\}$, $\{\bar{r}_n\}$ each have period exactly $5 \cdot 10^7$.

The actual generation of the sequence r_n is trivial on a machine.   We take r_{n+1} as the less significant half of the double-length product of r_n and $\rho = 10^{-10}\bar{\rho}$.

The determination of the period in the decimal cases is rather involved. We digress to give the discussion in a binary case. We shall show that the sequence defined by $x_0 = 1$, $x_{n+1} = 5x_n \pmod{2^N}$ has period 2^{N-2}. The question is, What is the least integer M for which $5^M \equiv 1(2^N)$? Suppose we have $5^M \equiv 1$ and that we have, say, $M = r \cdot 2^S$, where r is odd. Then we can show that $5^{2^S} \equiv 1(2^N)$. For

$$5^{r \cdot 2^S} - 1 = [5^{(r-1)2^S} + \cdots + 5^{2^S} + 1](5^{2^S} - 1)$$

In the first factor, there is an odd number of terms, and each one of them is odd; so 2^N must divide the second factor.

We now restrict ourselves to the case $M = 2^S$ and show that $5^{2^S} - 1$ is divisible by 2^{S+2} and by no higher power of 2. We observe that

$$
\begin{aligned}
5^{2^S} - 1 &= (5^{2^{S-1}} - 1)(5^{2^{S-1}} + 1) \\
&= (5^{2^{S-2}} - 1)(5^{2^{S-2}} + 1)(5^{2^{S-1}} + 1) \\
&= \cdots \\
&= (5^{2^0} - 1)(5^{2^0} + 1)(5^{2^1} + 1)(5^{2^2} + 1) \cdots (5^{2^{S-1}} + 1).
\end{aligned}
$$

The first factor is 2^2, and the highest power of 2 that divides each of the remaining S factors is the first.

Thus, the least M for which $5^M \equiv 1(2^N)$ is 2^{N-2}.

In the case of current machines the word length is some 30 to 40 bits; this means that period is of the order of 10^8 to 10^{11}.

We now discuss a simple frequency test for these pseudo-random numbers. We propose to generate the first thousand of these and to record the number which lie in each of the intervals $[0,.1]$, $[.1,.2]$, $\ldots$, $[.9,1]$. We generate the next thousand and record the frequencies, and so on. The significance of the lack of uniformity in the distribution can be evaluated, for instance, by using the χ^2 test.

A convenient way of handling this is to record the count in the ith interval in cell $m + i$ and then to modify a dummy instruction, "Advance the count in cell m," by adding to it the first digit (suitably shifted) of the current pseudo-random number to get the appropriate instruction.

In a test the observed frequencies were 111, 95, 95, 101, 96, 94, 105, 109, 106, 88. This result gives a value of $\chi^2 = 5.10$, whereas for 9 degrees of freedom a significant departure from the expectation, at the 5 per cent level of significance, occurs if $\chi^2 > 16.9$ or if $\chi^2 < 3.3$.

For a more detailed account of this method and others, and their testing, together with detailed references, see Taussky and Todd [8].

4.14   Gambler's-ruin Problem

We now sketch a program for the "solution" of the gambler's-ruin problem by the Monte Carlo method. We consider playing sequences of 1000 games, up to a total of N^*; we denote by N the number of games played, by S the current total number of tosses, and by L the number of times the first player has been ruined. We shall print out N, L/N, S/N, and r, the current pseudo-random number, after each 1000 games.

0. Clear counters N, L, S.
1. Set data N^*, r_0, p, a.
2. Set datum z.
3. Generate a random number.
4. Advance S.
5. If $r_n < p$, go to 6; if $r_n \geq p$, go to 13.
6. Advance z.
7. If $z = a$, go to 8; if $z \neq a$, go to 3.
8. Advance N.
9. If $N \equiv 0(1000)$, go to 10; if $N \not\equiv 0(1000)$, go to 2.
10. Print N, L/N, S/N, r.
11. If $N = N^*$, go to 12; if $N \neq N^*$, go to 2.
12. Stop.
13. Decrease z.
14. If $z = 0$, go to 15; if $z \neq 0$, go to 3.
15. Advance N and L.
16. Go to 9.

The following are the results of some experiments:

$$p = .5, \quad a = 10, \quad z = 5, \quad N = 1000, \quad L/N = .515, \quad S/N = 24.$$
$$p = .5, \quad a = 10, \quad z = 6, \quad N = 1000, \quad L/N = .422, \quad S/N = 25.$$
$$p = .55, \quad a = 10, \quad z = 5, \quad N = 1000, \quad L/N = .272, \quad S/N = 25.$$

Comparison of these results with the theoretical results gives us additional confidence in the quality of our pseudo-random numbers.

4.15 Normal Deviates

In some problems it may be necessary to have available random numbers from a normal distribution, rather than from a uniform one. A practically convenient method for doing this makes use of the central-limit theorem: if $x_1, x_2, \ldots, x_k$ are chosen independently from a standard uniform distribution, then the distribution of the mean $\bar{x} = (x_1 + \cdots + x_k)/k$ approaches the normal distribution as $k \to \infty$. In practice, it is found that the approximation given when $k = 10$ is sufficient for many purposes. For other schemes, see, for example, Votaw and Rafferty [19].

It is suggested that this scheme be tested by generating 1000 pseudo-normal deviates by adding pseudo-random numbers in groups of 10 and obtaining their frequency distribution.

Two such tests gave the following counts:

$$0, 0, 13, 117, 360, 380, 117, 13, 0, 0$$
$$0, 0, 12, 127, 355, 368, 125, 13, 0, 0.$$

4.16   Youden's Problem

The following problem was proposed by W. J. Youden.   A sample of n numbers $x_1, x_2, \ldots, x_n$ is drawn from a normal distribution—in practice, the cases $n = 4, 5, \ldots, 10$ are of interest.   Suppose the numbers have been labeled so that $x_1 \leq x_2 \leq \cdots \leq x_n$.   Let $\bar{x} = (x_1 + x_2 + \cdots + x_n)/n$.   It is required to find the probabilities.

$$p_i{}^n = Pr\{x_i \leq \bar{x} < x_{i+1}\}, \qquad i = 1, 2, \ldots, n - 1.$$

Since the problem was raised, an explicit solution was found by H. T. Davis in the case $n = 4$:

$$p_2{}^4 = 6[\arccos(-\tfrac{1}{3}) - \tfrac{1}{2}\pi]/\pi = .649, \qquad p_1{}^4 = p_3{}^4 = \tfrac{1}{2}(1 - p_2{}^4).$$

The devices which we now possess enable these probabilities to be estimated experimentally.   Take the case $n = 4$.   We generate groups of four normal deviates by averaging sets of 40 pseudo-random numbers. We arrange the sets of four in order and observe whether the mean lies in the center or in the outer intervals.   We repeat this process and observe the relative frequencies of the three events.

The following estimates were obtained by I. A. Stegun.

No. of samples	n	$p_1{}^n$	$p_2{}^n$	$p_3{}^n$	$p_4{}^n$	$p_5{}^n$	$p_6{}^n$
7000	4	.17	.65	.17			
7000	5	.048	.448	.457	.048		
7000	6	.012	.220	.535	.223	.011	
5000	7	.0028	.087	.408	.406	.092	.0036

For a discussion of another, similar, problem, see Scheid [37].

4.17   The Dirichlet Problem

The two problems discussed so far—the gambler's-ruin problem and the Youden problem—have been statistical, and the Monte Carlo treatment was evident.   It is, however, possible to embed a mathematical problem in a statistical framework and then solve it by a Monte Carlo method.   We discuss a simple case of the classical Dirichlet problem.

Find $V = V(x,y)$, given that $V_{xx} + V_{yy} = 0$ for $0 \leq x \leq 1, 0 \leq y \leq 1$ and

$$V(x,1) = \sin \pi x, \qquad V(x,0) = 0, \qquad 0 < x < 1,$$
$$V(0,y) = 0, \qquad V(1,y) = 0, \qquad 0 < y < 1.$$

We shall obtain an estimate, not of V, but of the solution u to a corresponding discrete problem. Consider a lattice on the unit square with sides $h = (l + 1)^{-1}$, for some integer l. We replace the differential equation for V by a partial difference equation for $u(m,n) = u(mh,nh)$:

$$u(m - 1, n) + u(m, n - 1) - 4u(m,n) + u(m, n + 1) + u(m + 1, n) = 0$$
$$m, n = 1, 2, \ldots, l,$$

$$u(m, l + 1) = \sin \pi m h, \qquad u(m,0) = 0, \qquad m = 0, 1, \ldots, l + 1,$$

$$u(0,n) = 0, \qquad u(l + 1, n) = 0, \qquad n = 0, 1, \ldots, l + 1.$$

In this simple case, both u and V are known explicitly:

$$V(x,y) = \sin \pi x \sinh \pi y / \sinh \pi,$$
$$u(m,n) = \sin \pi m h \sinh \lambda \pi n h / \sin \sinh \lambda \pi,$$

where λ is given by

$$\sinh \tfrac{1}{2}\lambda \pi h = \sin \tfrac{1}{2}\pi h,$$

which gives $\lambda = .9968$ for $l = 15$.

An estimate for $u(P_0)$, where P_0 is an interior lattice point, can be obtained as follows. Imagine a particle beginning at $P = P_0$ of the lattice and continuing in the following way. If at any time it is at $P(\alpha,\beta)$, then it moves at the next instant to $(\alpha, \beta - h), (\alpha - h, \beta), (\alpha + h, \beta), (\alpha, \beta + h)$, each with probability $\tfrac{1}{4}$. When it reaches a boundary point Q, a score $u(Q)$ is made. The process is then repeated, starting at P_0. The problem is, What is the expected value of the score? It can be shown that the expected value of the score is $u(P_0)$.

In practice, this is estimated as the arithmetic mean of the score after N walks, as $N \to \infty$. The dispersion of this mean has been examined; in order to get m decimal places correct, about 4×10^{2m} walks are needed (see Curtiss [18]).

Granted a source of pseudo-random numbers from a uniform distribution, the above process can be readily carried out on a computer. It is not essentially different from the gambler's-ruin problem discussed earlier. The choice of the direction of a step is determined by finding in which of the intervals

$$[0,\tfrac{1}{4}), \quad [\tfrac{1}{4},\tfrac{1}{2}), \quad [\tfrac{1}{2},\tfrac{3}{4}), \quad [\tfrac{3}{4},1]$$

the current random number lies. The appropriate counter (one for the x coordinate and one for the y coordinate) is adjusted, and it is determined whether a boundary has been reached.

The construction of a flow diagram is left to the reader. There follows a summary of results of some experiments, carried out on a binary machine, with walks on a 16×16 lattice (see Todd [3]).

$x = \frac{1}{2}$,	$y = \frac{1}{2}$	Differential equation	.1993
		Difference equation	.2002
		Monte Carlo, 6592 walks	.2014
$x = \frac{3}{4}$,	$y = \frac{3}{4}$	Differential equation	.3201
		Difference equation	.3209
		Monte Carlo, 2176 walks	.3001
$x = \frac{3}{4}$,	$y = \frac{1}{4}$	Differential equation	.0532
		Difference equation	.0534
		Monte Carlo, 13440 walks	.0530
$x = \frac{7}{8}$,	$y = \frac{1}{2}$	Differential equation	.0763
		Difference equation	.0766
		Monte Carlo, 10368 walks	.0807

Among the theoretical studies of this problem, we note those of Wasow [53–55].

4.18 Polynomials and Polynomial Interpolation

(*a*) We have already indicated (Chap. 1) that a simple, efficient method of evaluating a polynomial

$$f(x) = a_n x^n + a_{n-1} x^{n-1} + \cdots + a_1 x + a_0$$

is by the recurrence relation

$$y_0 = a_n; \qquad y_{i+1} = a_{n-i+1} + xy_i, \qquad i = 0, 1, \ldots, n - 1,$$

which gives

$$y_n = f(x).$$

The construction of a subroutine to evaluate $f(x)$ where f is a polynomial of fixed degree or of arbitrary degree is formally easy. In the latter case the degree can be set as a parameter to stop the induction, or a special flag can be put at the end of the list of the a_i's to serve the same purpose. In general, however, overflows can occur, and this must not be allowed. Either we check at each stage to see whether the addition produces an overflow and make appropriate arrangements if it does, or we make a preliminary analysis of the problem and make appropriate changes of scale at the beginning. For instance, if we want to compute $f(x)$ for x in the range $(-10,10)$ on a machine recognizing numbers in $(-1,1)$ only, we can proceed as follows. We note that

$$F(X) = \alpha_n X^n + \alpha_{n-1} X^{n-1} + \cdots + \alpha_1 X + \alpha_0 = f(x)/\bar{n} \cdot 10^n$$

if
$$x = 10X; \qquad \alpha_i = 10^{i-n} a_i/\bar{n}, \qquad i = 0, 1, \ldots, n; \ \bar{n} \geq n.$$

It can be shown that no overflow can take place in the evaluation of $F(X)$. If we choose $\bar{n}$ to be a power of 10, then $f(x)$ can be read off by an adjustment of the decimal point; otherwise we have to multiply (by a scaled $\bar{n}$) and then adjust the decimal point.

(b) We have noted the possibility of polynomial (Lagrangian) interpolation as a method for approximation of functions given by a table. Probably the most convenient method of handling this is by use of the Aitken algorithm. This is left as an exercise. The subroutine should have as a parameter the order of interpolation to be used and the address of the first of the given arguments and of the given values, each of which may be supposed stored in consecutive cells.

(c) A subroutine for the manipulation of differences has many uses. It should, in the first place, compute and list the early differences of a table of values $f(a_0 + nh)$, $n = 0, 1, 2, \ldots$, stored in consecutive cells. This listing would be used for a preliminary study of the behavior of the function. After this study, it should become clear what is a reasonable number of decimals to retain, what is a reasonable number of differences to give, and whether or not they should be modified (Chap. 2). The subroutine should have an optional entrance to produce a final copy of the table, in standard format.

4.19   Special Devices

(a) We have noted the power of the Euler process (Chap. 2). It is useful to have a subroutine which carries out this process on a series, the terms of which are either stored in a specific place or generated by a specific recurrence relation (see Rosser [34]).

(b) We have noted the power of the Aitken δ^2 process and also its dangers (Chaps. 1, 2). It is useful to have a subroutine which carries out this process (see, e.g., Todd and Warschawski [35], Henrici [43]).

(c) The dangers of using recurrence relations for the generation of functions are considerable. We have discussed their use in the generation of Bessel functions in detail in Chap. 2. A practical study of this scheme will be found rewarding. See Stegun and Abramowitz [32,33] and Gautschi [49,50].

4.20   Sorting

We discuss, as an elementary type of combinatorial and data-processing problem, the rearranging of a given set of numbers a_1, a_2, $\ldots$, a_N, arranged in consecutive cells, in ascending order in the same cells, that is, as b_1, b_2, $\ldots$, b_N where $b_1 \leq b_2 \leq \cdots \leq b_N$.

One solution to this problem is the following. Assume that the first n have been arranged in order. Remove a_{n+1} to a temporary position t_1. We determine whether $a_{n+1} \geq b_n$. If $a_{n+1} \geq b_n$, we replace a_{n+1} as b_{n+1}, and we have now the first $n + 1$ in order.   However, if $a_{n+1} < b_n$, we have to determine the position of a_{n+1} in the sequence $b_1, b_2, \ldots, b_n$. To do this, we move b_n to the cell occupied by a_{n+1} and rename it b_{n+1}. We then determine whether $a_{n+1} \leq b_{n-1}$.   If $a_{n+1} \geq b_{n-1}$, we put a_{n+1} in the nth cell and call it b_n, and we then have the first $n + 1$ in order. However, if $a_{n+1} < b_{n-1}$, we have to carry on; that is, we have to move b_{n-1} to the nth cell, call it b_n, etc.   This backing up will end with a_{n+1} as b_1 if $a_{n-1} < a_1$ or with a_{n-1} occupying some intermediate position.   This completes the discussion of the inductive step.

In translating this into an actual program, it may be found convenient to assign fictitious elements $\pm \infty$ after and before the a_i.   The successive stages in the process are indicated in the following example:

$-\infty$	3	0	-2	5	1	∞
$-\infty$	0	3	-2	5	1	∞
$-\infty$	0	-2	3	5	1	∞
$-\infty$	-2	0	3	5	1	∞
$-\infty$	-2	0	3	1	5	∞
$-\infty$	-2	0	1	3	5	∞

The time to carry out such a sort depends on the disorder of the data, and a maximum time can easily be calculated.   With an efficient code, the maximum time for $N = 500$, on a millisecond machine, will be a few minutes.

4.21   Construction of a Program

The programs that we have discussed are far from typical, but some are likely to be of use in building up more representative programs. Consider the following two problems:

1. Obtain the numerical solution of the differential equation

$$y' = \sqrt{x} + \sqrt{y}, \qquad y(0) = 0,$$

for x satisfying $0 \leq x \leq 1$.

2. Prepare a table for conversion from rectangular coordinates to polar coordinates.   Specifically, find $r = \sqrt{x^2 + y^2}$, $\theta = \arctan(y/x)$ for $x = 1(1)y, y = 1(1)100$.

Disregarding for the time being the precise method of solution, we observe that the square-root and arctan routines prepared earlier can be reused.   However, it is most likely that the original locations in storage will be unsuitable.   It is, of course, possible to rewrite the routines in the location desired; this will only require adding a constant to various addresses in the instructions.   To do this clerical operation manually provides an opportunity for error which should and can be avoided by arranging for the computer itself to do the relocation. We propose to describe how this can be done.

We imagine a program built up as follows. On the input medium (paper tape, magnetic tape or wire, or punched cards) we write the new parts of the program and copy mechanically the required subroutines from the masters. We arrange for the new program to get into storage with the subroutines in the desired places but with wrong addresses.

What we have to do is to design a program which relocates the subroutines, adding constants to certain instruction words to correct the addresses and leaving other and, in particular, "arithmetic" words untouched. This will be possible only if the words to be altered can be distinguished in some way. How this is done depends greatly on the fine structure of the machine, and from now on we shall be necessarily rather vague in order to be general.

It can happen that certain digits in instruction words are superfluous. (For instance, original plans for a 10000 word storage may have been changed to 1000 words, so that, say, a decimal digit is left free. Inserting a digit in this position in the words which are to be altered is a satisfactory distinction. Again, the sign in an instruction word may not be sensed by the control, and the signs can be used to distinguish between two classes of instructions.) Let us suppose that all our subroutines are written with markers in the instruction words which have to be altered.

For simplicity, let us assume that the subroutines to be relocated are placed in the memory starting at cells M_i and that they are written as if they started in 0000, so that M_1 has to be added to the addresses of the marked instructions in the first case, M_2 in the second case, and so on. We can call the list $M_1, M_2, \ldots$ the "directory." With each M_i there will be listed the number of instructions in the ith subroutine which have to be processed. An outline of a relocating program follows.

1. Set up variable instruction 2.
2. [Obtain the next word in the directory.]
3. If all subroutines have been relocated, go to 4; if not, go to 5.
4. Stop. (We can then start on the main program!)
5. Isolate the constant M_i and construct (6), a variable instruction to bring in the fictitious instruction and (8), a variable instruction to put out the adjusted instructions. Also, make appropriate preparations in (7) and (9).
6. [Bring in the fictitious instruction.]
7. Process the fictitious instruction.
8. [Replace the adjusted instruction.]

9. If all instructions in the ith subroutine have been processed, go to 12; if not, go to 10.

10. Advance addresses in 6 and 8.

11. Go to 6.

12. Advance address in 2.

13. Go to 2.

The construction of a program of this character should be compulsory. For from this have developed massive programs called assemblers or compilers. For example, such programs can be organized to search a library tape for a specified subroutine, find a space in the main program for it, copy it there, and then relocate it in the sense just described. There is hardly any limit to the complexity of compilers, but there is certainly a point of diminishing returns from investment in their construction.

We now take up the question of the use of subroutines, now assumed in storage, properly addressed. If a subroutine is to be used in only one part of the main program, though repeatedly, then there is little trouble. The structure of the square-root subroutine is as follows: if the control is sent to the entry, with the argument x in a standard position (the accumulator, for instance), then the operation is carried out, finishing with $\sqrt{x}$ in the accumulator and the control at the exit. In the present circumstances we can direct the entry and set up the exit, once for all, in the main program.

However, if we want to use the same subroutine several times, in different places on the main program, more elaborate arrangements are necessary. These depend greatly on the facilities of the machine. We discuss an unsophisticated case first. For clarity, consider a square-root subroutine which produces $\sqrt{x}$ in β_2 with the control in m_2 if the control is sent to m_1 with x in β_1. Suppose that we want to use this subroutine in two places in the program, after instructions c_1 and c_2. We may then use the scheme

$c_1 + 1$	Put x in β_1.
$c_1 + 2$	Put "Go to $c_1 + 4$" in the accumulator.
$c_1 + 3$	Go to m_1.

.

.

.

$c_2 + 1$	Put x in β_1.
$c_2 + 2$	Put "Go to $c_2 + 4$" in the accumulator.
$c_2 + 3$	Go to m_1.

provided the subroutine begins by setting up its exit in the following way:

Entrance m_1 Put the instruction in the accumulator in m_2.

.

.

.

Exit m_2 Go to $c_i + 4$—set by m_1.

It is clear that we need to store an instruction of the form "Go to $c_i + 4$" for each i, for use in $c_i + 2$.

A more compact method of handling this problem—at the expense of equipment, of course—is the use of a "record" instruction.   Such an instruction in cell c has the form

c Record "Go to $c + 2$" in m_2.

If this is followed by

$c + 1$ Go to m_1.

we have accomplished our task.

To show the compactness of this, we indicate the programming for $x^{1/8}$, with x being given:

1. Put x in β_1.
2. Record "Go to 4" in m_2.
3. Go to m_1.
4. Put $x^{1/2}$ (now in β_2) in β_1.
5. Record "Go to 7" in m_2.
6. Go to m_1.
7. Put $x^{1/4}$ (now in β_2) in β_1.
8. Record "Go to 10" in m_2.
9. Go to m_1.
10. Exit; $x^{1/8}$ is in β_2.

We conclude this section by returning to the consideration of the relocation or incorporation of subroutines.   We have indicated how this can be done by a special program.   In some computers equipment is available to do this.   The subroutine always stays in the storage with fictitious addresses, but those instructions which require a constant to be added to the address are distinguished in some innocuous way—for example, by the use of a negative sign, where regular instructions have a positive sign.   Then the equipment is so arranged that the assigned constant is added to the address in the control unit during the decoding of the instruction and before its execution.

This feature can often be combined with the one discussed earlier, whereby a change in the sign of the B register triggers a change of path in the program, to give an elegant program.   We illustrate this by returning to the memory summation.   We use * to indicate B modification.

0. Clear register for partial sums.
1. Set $B = \beta - \alpha$.
2.*Clear and add (α).
3. Add partial sum.
4. Store partial sum.
5. Decrease B.   If B goes negative, go to 6; otherwise to 2.
6. Stop.

4.22   Ordinary Differential Equation

We now take up problem 1 of the preceding section.   We consider using the Heun method for $y' = f(x,y)$.   This consists in determining $y_n = y(x_n)$, $x_n = nh$, for $n = 0, 1, 2, \ldots$, by

$$y_{n+1} = \tfrac{1}{2}(y_n^* + y_n^{**}),$$

where $y_n^* = y_n + hf(x_n,y_n)$, $y_n^{**} = y_n + hf(x_{n+1},y_n^*)$.   Assuming the validity of Taylor expansions, it is easy to see that the local error is $O(h^3)$ and that the total error (assuming no magnification) is $O(h^2)$, since the number of steps is $O(h^{-1})$.   In the case under consideration, an *expansion in power series at the origin is not valid, and the errors will be larger.*   An interval $h = .001$ seems appropriate if we are to have results correct to about 6D. Rough calculations indicate that y will exceed unity somewhat, and in order to avoid overflows, in a fixed-point machine, using numbers in the range $(-1,1)$, a scaling by a factor of $\tfrac{1}{4}$ of each variable seems convenient.   We therefore consider the solution of

$$y' = \tfrac{1}{2}\sqrt{x} + \tfrac{1}{2}\sqrt{y}, \qquad y(0) = 0$$

for $x = 0(h).25$ (see Richter [10]).   It is instructive to keep h variable and to arrange to print out, not after every step, but only at an interval of .0125 in x.   The details of the program are omitted.

The results of the calculations on a UNIVAC for $h = .0125$, .0025, .00125, and .00025 are shown in the table on the facing page.

4.23   Rectangular-Polar Conversion Table

This is to be regarded as an exercise in using the output equipment. The task is to produce a table which, initially, is a list of the form

00002	00001	0022360680	4636476090
00003	00001	0031622777	3217505544
00003	00002	0036055513	5880026035
00004	00001	0041231056	2449786631
. . .	. . .	. . .	. . .
00100	00099	1407160261	7803730801

x	$h = .00025$	$h = .00125$	$h = .0025$	$h = .0125$
0	00000000000	00000000000	00000000000	00000000000
.0125	00054793700	00054084766	00052730731	00034938562
.0250	00159912174	00159108463	00157549032	00135795112
.0375	00299888889	00299020417	00297323965	00273099005
.0500	00469064935	00468145066	00466341119	00440237794
.0625	00664121481	00663158054	00661263636	00633609674
.0750	00882794453	00881792703	00879819092	00850825638
.0875	01123406696	01122370425	01120325726	01090141626
.1000	01384648727	01383580841	01381471217	01350207833
.1125	01665459906	01664362708	01662193028	01629937288
.1250	01964957501	01963832876	01961607102	01928429044
.1375	02282391333	02281240853	02278962286	02244919744
.1500	02617113183	02615938188	02613609625	02578751306
.1625	02968555308	02967356957	02964980810	02929348394
.1750	03336214844	03334994148	03332572516	03296202153
.1875	03719642145	03718399993	03715934729	03678858123
.2000	04118431874	04117169062	04114661815	04076907044
.2125	04532216083	04530933327	04528385574	04489977709
.2250	04960658706	04959356649	04956769724	04917731319
.2375	05403451139	05402130364	05399505479	05359856951
.2500	05860308623	05858969672	05856307932	05816067873

Then this should be edited by the suppression of initial zeros, insertion or suppression of decimal points, labeling of pages, separation of entries into groups of five, spacing between the groups of five, and double-spacing after completing a value of m.   The final arrangement should be comparable with the tables of Neville [31] or Todd [30].   The effort required to produce it will depend on the equipment available.

4.24   Sievert's Integral

Consider the evaluation of

$$S(x,y) = \int_0^x \exp\left(-y \sec t\right) dt$$

for a single argument pair.   We choose $x = .5, y = .5$ since in this case no scaling difficulties are encountered.   A rough calculation shows that using Simpson's rule with $h = .01$ will give an accuracy of about 10D. We suggest three methods.

(a) If we assume that we have available subroutines for the evaluation of exp x, sec x and for the application of Simpson's rule, the problem is an easy exercise in the combination of subroutines.   [The Simpson's rule subroutine would have the following structure: h, a, b would be parameters which required setting, and there would be an exit to the $f(x)$ subroutine from which the control would return with $f(x)$ in an assigned position.]

(b) We observe that it will probably be quicker to generate the secants from the cosines using the addition formula

$$\cos t_{r+1} = \cos t_r \cos h - \sin t_r \sin h$$

$$\sin t_{r+1} = \sin t_r \cos h + \cos t_r \sin h$$

than by an independent evaluation of the cosine from the power series for each t_r.

(c) Various orthogonal quadratures can be used (see Chaps. 2 and 3). The value obtained by the second method was

$$S(.5,.5) = .29665\ 75005;$$

the value obtained by interpolation in a standard table [9] is

$$S(.5,.5) = .29665\ 7503.$$

4.25   Matrix and Vector Operations

The construction of codes for the basic matrix problems of inversion and decomposition is considered beyond the scope of an elementary course.   We enumerate here a selection of auxiliary codes which are useful and the construction of which is instructive and not too involved.

(a) *The Component of Maximum Modulus of a Vector*

We note that in some machines the determination of the component of maximum modulus of a vector has been incorporated as a basic instruction.

(b) *Normalization of a Vector*

The normalization of a vector involves the replacement of $V = (v_1, v_2, \ldots, v_n)$ by $U = (u_1, u_2, \ldots, u_n)$ where $U = kV$, k being a constant such that $\Sigma u_i^2 = |U|^2$ has an assigned value.

Let us discuss scaling in this problem.   Suppose that we assume that always $n \leq 99$.   Then, if we assume $|v_i| \leq .1$, we have $\Sigma v_i^2 < 1$.   If we take

$$u_i = .1 v_i / (\Sigma v_i^2)^{\frac{1}{2}},$$

we observe that $|U| = .1$ and each $|u_i| \leq .1$.   No overflows will take place.

(c) Scalar Product of Two Vectors

It is often desirable to have the subroutine for the scalar product of two vectors written so that the partial sums are kept in double precision and the final result is presented as a single precision number.

(d) Various Norms of Matrices

Consider, in particular, the computation of

$$M_0 = \max_{i,j} |a_{ij}|, \qquad M_1 = n^{-2} \sum_{i,j} |a_{ij}|, \qquad M_2 = n^{-1} \Big(\sum_{i,j} a_{ij}^2 \Big)^{\frac{1}{2}}.$$

(e) Generation of Special Matrices

For instance, consider the storage by rows of the $n \times n$ matrix $A = (a_{ij})$, where $a_{ij} = a_{ji} = i/j$ if $i \leq j$, in storage beginning at m. That is, we want to put

$$a_{11}, a_{12}, \ldots, a_{1n} \quad \text{in} \quad m, m+1, \ldots, m+n-1$$
$$a_{21}, a_{22}, \ldots, a_{2n} \quad \text{in} \quad m+n, m+n+1, \ldots, m+2n-1$$
$$\cdots\cdots\cdots\cdots\cdots\cdots\cdots\cdots\cdots\cdots\cdots\cdots\cdots\cdots\cdots$$
$$a_{n1}, a_{n2}, \ldots, a_{nn} \quad \text{in} \quad m+n^2-n, m+n^2-n+1, \ldots, m+n^2-1.$$

Other examples of special matrices are given by Newman and Todd [2] (see also Chap. 6 and Marcus [42]).

(f) Matrix Multiplication

If we disregard all questions of overflow, matrix multiplication involves a straightforward triple induction. We give on p.196 a flow diagram for one arrangement in which the product $C = AB$ is computed by rows and the rows are printed out one at a time. We assume that each matrix is an $n \times n$ one.

(g) Evaluation of Efficiency of Inversion Programs

We assume given a program for the inversion of a matrix, and we want to apply it to special matrices and to observe norms of inversion errors. This involves the use of (e) above in generating the matrix, then the inversion program under examination, and then (f) to compute error matrices

$$XA - I, \qquad AX - I, \qquad \mathfrak{X} - A,$$

where X is the reputed inverse of A and $\mathfrak{X}$ that of X. If A^{-1} is known explicitly, we can also compute

$$X - A^{-1}.$$

Finally, we have to apply (d) to the error matrices. Typical results are given by Newman and Todd [2] (see also Chap. 6).

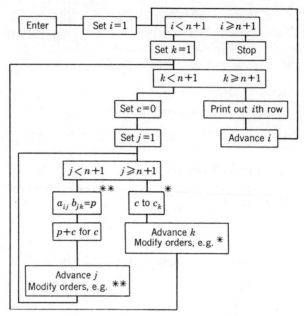

FIG 4.3.   Matrix multiplication program.

(h) *Determinations of Dominant Eigenvalue and Eigenvector by the Power Method*

We outline a simple method which is often quite efficient.   Suppose A is an $n \times n$ matrix with eigenvalues $\alpha_1, \alpha_2, \ldots, \alpha_n$, where $|\alpha_1| > |\alpha_2| \geq |\alpha_3| \geq \cdots \geq |\alpha_n|$.   For simplicity, suppose that the eigenvectors c_1, $c_2, \ldots, c_n$ span the whole space.   Take a vector $v^{(0)}$ and represent it in terms of the c_i:

$$v^{(0)} = \sum_i a_i c_i.$$

Since $Ac_i = \alpha_i c_i$ for $i = 1, 2, \ldots, n$, we have for any integer r, and for $i = 1, 2, \ldots, n,$

$$A^r c_i = \alpha_i{}^r c_i.$$

Hence, provided $a_1 \neq 0$, we have

$$v^{(r)} = A^r v^{(0)} = \sum_i a_i \alpha_i{}^r c_i \doteq a_1 \alpha_1{}^r c_1,$$

provided r is large enough, since our assumption that α_1 is the dominant eigenvalue means that the succeeding terms become negligible.   Thus we have shown that $v^{(r)}$ is approximately a multiple of c_1 and that the ratio of the components in $v^{(r+1)}$ to those of $v^{(r)}$ is approximately α_1.

This process is applied as follows.   An arbitrary normalized vector $v^{(0)}$ is chosen.   Then normalized vectors $v^{(i)}$ and constants $\mu^{(i)}$ are chosen so that

$$Av^{(i)} = \mu^{(i+1)}v^{(i+1)}.$$

Then $\mu^{(i)}$ will tend to α_1 and $v^{(i)}$ to the normalized c_1.   The normalization may be chosen in the sense of (b) above, or a fixed component of the $v^{(i)}$ may be forced to assume a fixed value.   The condition $a_1 \neq 0$, that is, that the initial vector should not be orthogonal to the dominant eigenvector c_1, is not a critical one; for the orthogonality will probably be destroyed by round-off, and the dominant vector will be obtained after some delay.

The following example, which presents no difficulties, is discussed by Taussky and Todd [4]:

$$A = \begin{pmatrix} .2 & .9 & 1.32 \\ -11.2 & 22.28 & -10.72 \\ -5.8 & 9.45 & -1.94 \end{pmatrix},$$

with $v^{(0)} = (1,0,0)$.   The following example has been discussed by Bodewig [7] and Wilkinson [5] and is troublesome:

$$A = \begin{pmatrix} 2 & 1 & 3 & 4 \\ 1 & -3 & 1 & 5 \\ 3 & 1 & 6 & -2 \\ 4 & 5 & -2 & -1 \end{pmatrix}.$$

Various refinements of this method have been discussed—in particular, the use of acceleration schemes such as the Aitken δ^2 method (see, e.g., Wilkinson [6] and Osborne [24])

4.26   Floating, Double-precision, and Complex Arithmetic

In many problems it is found that a straightforward use of the machine arithmetic is insufficient.   The quantities involved may have a large range, be required to higher precision, or be complex.   In order to cope with such problems it is essential to have subroutines to carry out the arithmetic operations in these cases.   Although these are, in principle, relatively easy to construct, they are slow in operation, and pressure has been brought on the machine designers to provide, in particular, machines with floating-point arithmetic.   The convenience of such equipment is notable, but it is dangerous in uncritical hands.   Perhaps the proper use of the added facilities is in exploratory calculations which will indicate when and where scaling will be needed in the main, faster fixed-point program.

(a) Floating-point Arithmetic

The usual arrangement on decimal machines with, say, a sign and 10 digits is the following. We consider numbers $A \neq 0$ which can be represented in the form $\pm 10^\beta \cdot a$, where $-50 \leq \beta \leq 49$ and where $.1 \leq a < 1$ and where a is represented by an 8-decimal-digit number. Then $\alpha = \beta + 50$ satisfies $0 \leq \beta \leq 99$, and A is represented by its sign, by the 2 digits of α, and by the 8 digits of a. Certain conventions about the handling of zero must be introduced.

We have to develop an arithmetic for the ordered pairs (α, a)—the unpacking of these is accomplished by extraction or shift operations. Let us discuss the addition of $A_1 = (\alpha_1, a_1)$ and $A_2 = (\alpha_2, a_2)$. Suppose that the numbers are labeled so that $\alpha_2 - \alpha_1 = \delta > 0$.

1. If $\delta > 8$ (in our case), then A_1 is negligible.

2. If $\delta = 0$, we can add $a_1 + a_2 = a$; and if there is no overflow, then $A_1 + A_2 = (\alpha_1, a)$. If there is overflow, we have to round the last digit but one, shift right one place, and insert a unit in the first place to get a. (Observe that, since the sign of $a_1 + a_2$ is not known, the rounding and the adjustment of the first digit must be done with care.) Then we have to advance the exponent and combine the α, a in one word. There is one further point to be considered: it is possible that $a_1 + a_2$ may not be in normal form. (An extreme case would be adding A and $-A$.) We have therefore to determine whether left shifts and adjustments of the exponent are necessary and, if so, to make them. (We note that the terminal zeros introduced here are not significant.)

3. If $1 \leq \delta \leq 8$, we have to shift a_1 to the right δ places before carrying out the addition, rounding off appropriately. We are then essentially in the case already discussed.

The schemes for multiplication and division are somewhat less complicated.

(b) Double-precision Arithmetic

Addition in this mode is comparatively simple, but multiplication and division are more troublesome. It is recommended that some double-length arithmetic on desk machines be carried out before undertaking the programming.

The case of the product $X_1 X_2$ is indicated in the following diagram, where $X_i = (x_i, y_i)$:

The rounding in the less significant part of y_1y_2 will usually be accomplished by a special rounding instruction or a special multiplication instruction.   We have now to add the less significant parts of x_1y_2, x_2y_1 to the (now rounded) more significant part of y_1y_2.   We observe the overflow, if any, and then observe whether the sum satisfies $|s| \geq \frac{1}{2}$, in which case, on rounding, it will contribute to the last digit in the less significant part of the product x_1x_2; the total contribution of this sum there will be 0, ± 1, ± 2, ± 3.

The next step in obtaining the less significant part of X_1X_2 is the addition of the more significant parts of x_1y_2 and x_2y_1, and the less significant part of x_1x_2 to the contribution just obtained.   Any overflow in this addition is carried to the more significant part of x_1x_2 to give the more significant part of X_1X_2.

(c) Complex Arithmetic

The handling of complex numbers in the form $x + iy$ or $re^{i\theta}$—where the pair of real numbers (x,y) or (r,θ) is stored in two cells, or in one—introduces no new complications.

(d) Subroutine Structure

The following remarks are relevant when the machine under consideration has no built-in operations of the kind contemplated.

In general, all the arithmetic operations will be needed—addition, subtraction, multiplication, and division—and it is convenient and economical to have a single subroutine to handle them, if entry to it is made at an appropriate point.   (It may also be convenient to have appropriate conversion routines included—e.g., to "float" or to "unfloat" a number, to convert from cartesian to polar form and inversely.)   It may also be convenient to place the whole subroutine in a fixed position in the memory, so that the addresses for the arguments will be fixed.

4.27   The Heat Equation $u_{xx} = u_t$

Some important considerations arise in the study of the numerical solutions of the partial differential equation $u_{xx} = u_t$.   We suppose that we are asked to solve this for $t \geq 0$, $0 \leq x \leq 1$, subject to the boundary conditions

$$u(x,0) = f(x), \qquad f(x) \text{ given for } 0 \leq x \leq 1;$$
$$u(0,t) = u(1,t) = 0, \qquad \text{all } t \geq 0.$$

The exact solution can be written down if we can expand $f(x)$ as an absolutely convergent Fourier series

$$f(x) = \sum a_i \sin i\pi x, \qquad a_i = 2\int_0^1 u(y,0) \sin i\pi y \, dy.$$

In this case,

$$u(x,t) = \sum a_i \sin i\pi x \exp(-i^2\pi^2 t).$$

A simple discretization of this problem, in which we replace the space derivative by $h^{-2}[u(x+h,y) - 2u(x,y) + u(x-h,y)]$ and the time derivative by $k^{-1}[u(x,y+k) - u(x,y)]$, where $kh^{-2} = r$, is

$$U(m, n+1) = rU(m-1, n) + (1-2r)U(m,n) + rU(m+1, n),$$
$$U(m,0) = f(mh), \qquad\qquad m = 0, 1, \ldots, M+1,$$
$$U(0,nk) = U(M+1, n) = 0, \qquad n = 0, 1, 2, \ldots.$$

Here $U(m,n)$ is to be thought of as an approximation to $u(mh,nk)$.

This partial difference equation can be solved explicitly, and it can be shown that $U \to u$ as $h \to 0$, provided the ratio $kh^{-2} = r$ satisfies $r \le \frac{1}{2}$. This question is fully discussed in Chap. 11 (see also Richtmyer [29]).

Let us discuss the case in which $f(x) = 2x$, $0 \le x \le \frac{1}{2}$, $f(x) = 2(1-x)$, $\frac{1}{2} < x \le 1$. Consider the evaluation of $u(\frac{1}{2}, \frac{3}{64})$ and various approximations $U_{h,k}(\frac{1}{2}, \frac{3}{64})$. This example was devised for a binary computer, but a little thought will show that it is equally suitable for a decimal one.

We find

$$u(x,t) = 8\pi^{-2}[\sin \pi x \exp(-\pi^2 t) - \tfrac{1}{9} \sin 3\pi x \exp(-9\pi^2 t)$$
$$+ \tfrac{1}{25} \sin 5\pi x \exp(-25\pi^2 t) - \cdots],$$

which gives

$$u(\tfrac{1}{2}, \tfrac{3}{64}) = .51175\ 20442.$$

We can obtain $U(m,n)$ explicitly as

$$U(m,n) = \sum_{i=1}^{M} c_i \sin 2mi\theta (1 - 4r \sin^2 i\theta)^n,$$

where $\quad \theta = \dfrac{1}{2}\dfrac{\pi}{M+1} \quad$ and $\quad c_i = \dfrac{2}{M+1}\sum_{s=1}^{M} U(sh,0) \sin 2is\theta.$

In the present case we find

$$c_i = 0, \quad i \text{ even}, \quad c_i = 2(-1)^{\frac{1}{2}(i-1)}(M+1)^{-2}\operatorname{cosec}^2 i\theta, \quad i \text{ odd}.$$

We now fix $r = \frac{1}{4}$ and obtain, where the summation is over odd i, $1 \le i \le M$,

$$U(m,n) = 2(M+1)^{-2} \sum (-1)^{\frac{1}{2}(i-1)} \operatorname{cosec}^2 i\theta \cos^{2n} i\theta \sin 2mi\theta.$$

If we now take M odd and put $m = \frac{1}{2}(M+1)$, so as to observe only the central point, we find

$$U(\tfrac{1}{2}(M+1), n) = 2(M+1)^{-2} \sum \operatorname{cosec}^2 i\theta \cos^{2n} i\theta. \qquad (4.2)$$

It is trivial to find directly for $M = 3$, $n = 3$ that

$$U_3(\tfrac{1}{2},\tfrac{3}{64}) = {}^{17}\!/_{32} = .53125.$$

An exact calculation by hand, or by machine, for $M = 7$, $n = 12$ gives

$$U_7(\tfrac{1}{2},\tfrac{3}{64}) = .51661\ 72981.$$

A hand calculation, using (4.2), gives for $M = 15$, $n = 48$,

$$U_{15}(\tfrac{1}{2},\tfrac{3}{64}) = .51296\ 84502$$

whereas for $M = 31$, $n = 192$, we find

$$U_{31}(\tfrac{1}{2},\tfrac{3}{64}) = .51205\ 61854.$$

The last 3 digits in U_{15} and U_{31} are doubtful.   The convergence to

$$u(\tfrac{1}{2},\tfrac{3}{64}) = U_\infty(\tfrac{1}{2},\tfrac{3}{64}) = .51175\ 20442$$

is evident.   If we round these values to five decimals and take the differences $U_M - u$, we find

$$1950, \quad 487, \quad 122, \quad 31,$$

indicating that the error is $O(h^2)$.

The programming of the solution of the partial difference equation is trivial.   The results given above should be reproduced if we choose any $r \leq \tfrac{1}{2}$.   However, if $r > \tfrac{1}{2}$, say $r = \tfrac{3}{4}$, the phenomenon of numerical instability appears: if some rounding error is introduced, it gets amplified exponentially, and no sensible results are obtained.   To make sure that a disturbance is introduced, it may be desirable to use, for example, $(\pi/64)f(x)$ in place of $f(x)$: the factor π ensures that rounding will take place, and the factor $\tfrac{1}{64}$ gives room to show the large oscillations which develop (see, e.g., Richtmyer [29], pp. 6–9).

4.28   Number Theoretical Problems

In number theoretical problems we have to imagine the decimal (or preferably, binary) point placed at the extreme right of the word, rather than at the extreme left.

(a) A basic subroutine is one for the factorization of a number N. This can be constructed by trying all possible divisors $d \leq N^{1/2}$.   A simpler version would be to try 2 and then all odd numbers.   A more sophisticated one would be to use a sieve technique—for example, trying the numbers congruent to 2, 3, 5, 7, 11, 13, 17, 19, 23, 29, 31 (mod 30).

It is, of course, only necessary to try prime numbers as divisors, but the storage of a table of primes in the memory might not be convenient.   We mention here an elegant device used by E. Lehmer [20] for a compact storage of primes on a binary machine: a zero or one is stored in consecutive positions of a word, according as the corresponding odd number is prime or composite.   Thus

$$0001 \quad 0010 \quad 0101 \quad 1001 \quad 1010 \quad 0101 \quad 1011 \quad 0011 \quad 0$$

corresponds to the odd numbers 3, 5, 7, 9, ...

(b) Another fundamental subroutine is one for the euclidean algorithm, that is, finding the highest common factor of two integers or solving linear diophantine equations of the form $ax + by = d$.

Various applications of this are possible.   It is convenient to have the early terms of various power series related to a given one—its various powers, its reciprocal, the inverse function, the logarithm, etc.   It is desirable to have the new coefficients exactly (as rational numbers), and since complicated manipulations with power series are fraught with error, it is natural to think of doing these manipulations mechanically.   Programs for this have been constructed by Henrici [25,27], and in them the euclidean algorithm in some form is essential, so that rational coefficients can be reduced to their lowest terms.

A euclidean algorithm can be used to exhibit any unimodular 2×2 matrix $\begin{pmatrix} a & b \\ c & d \end{pmatrix}$ with integral elements, $ad - bc = 1$, as a product of the two generators

$$S = \begin{pmatrix} 1 & 1 \\ 0 & 1 \end{pmatrix}, \qquad T = \begin{pmatrix} 0 & -1 \\ 1 & 0 \end{pmatrix}.$$

For instance,

$$\begin{pmatrix} 1 & 0 \\ 2 & 1 \end{pmatrix} = S\,TS^2\,TS.$$

If the algorithm subroutine is written for *complex* integers, then it is possible to carry out the corresponding decomposition for matrices $\begin{pmatrix} a & b \\ c & d \end{pmatrix}$, where a, b, c, d are complex integers with $ad - bc = 1$.   Any such matrix can be expressed as a product of powers of

$$\begin{pmatrix} 1 & 1 \\ 0 & 1 \end{pmatrix}, \quad \begin{pmatrix} 0 & 1 \\ -1 & 0 \end{pmatrix}, \quad \begin{pmatrix} 1 & i \\ 0 & 1 \end{pmatrix}.$$

(c) The theory of quadratic forms is a fertile source of problems.

(d) There are many other problems in this area, some of which place great demands on the computing equipment (see, e.g., Chaps. 15, 16; E. Lehmer [20]; Taussky [22]; Tompkins [23]; D. H. Lehmer [41]; Taussky and Todd [48]).

4.29 Game Theory and Linear Programming

The basic idea of a two-person zero-sum game and the Brown–Robinson method for its solution have been described in Sec. 1.7. This is easily programmed.

The most satisfactory solution of linear-programming problems is often by the simplex method. The programming of this method, which is essentially equivalent to the Gaussian elimination method for the solution of a system of linear equations, or the inversion of a matrix, is not a task for a novice. Nevertheless, the use of any simplex-method programs on special cases is a valuable exercise. Some results have been given by Hoffman, Mannos, Sokolowsky, and Wiegmann [28].

4.30 Service, Checking, and Engineering Subroutines

(a) Anyone who does a lot of programming, and any efficient organization, will see the desirability of a battery of service routines to do certain recurring, more or less clerical jobs. For instance, it is convenient to have a subroutine which examines two tapes T_1, T_2 containing supposedly identical programs word by word and prepares a third tape T_3 identical with T_1 and T_2 should these coincide. If at any stage the words in T_1 and T_2 differ, then both are printed out, and the machine does not proceed until the operator has decided which, if either, is correct. An even simpler subroutine is one which copies an assigned part of one tape onto another or which both copies and inserts specified corrections. The details of these service subroutines depend greatly on the equipment, and we shall not discuss them further.

(b) The process of checking a program is one which deserves a thorough study. It is clear that many isolated parts of the program—essentially "subroutines"—should be checked by themselves. Then the checking of the major program is reduced essentially to that of logic, the interconnections of the subprograms.

Many schemes have been devised to use the computer itself to help in this process. If, for example, the machine has special actions on overflow, it may be desirable to list all instructions in the program which can cause overflow and then to check visually that the appropriate actions are arranged. Such a listing is easy to obtain mechanically. Note, however, that this is not easily made foolproof. For we would probably only examine the static program, and during the course of running it, instructions might be built up which could cause overflow.

Again, a very naïve check (and, one would hope, a last resort) would be to work through the program, instruction by instruction, examining the contents of critical registers. Such information can be obtained and printed by the machine for contemplation by the programmer. Some machines have equipment which does this monitoring by use of a simple switch. Somewhat more sophisticated would be the monitoring, not of all instructions, but only of specified ones—often those causing transfers of control—which could be indicated by break points.

The path of a computation can be followed by printing, for instance, symbols indicating the instructions used, with a new line at each transfer of control. A useful exercise would be to carry this out for a simple subroutine, like that for the square root.

It is also possible to design a subroutine which compares the program as it was when inserted with what it was when trouble developed and lists any changes.

(c) Various phases of the work of computer engineers can be facilitated by the use of a computer. For instance, a series of diagnostic subroutines can be used to pinpoint trouble when it develops and also to aid in preventive maintenance. The memory-summation process discussed earlier is a simple example.

It is possible to use the machine to find out where time is spent in running problems. The number of times each type of instruction is carried out during the running of a problem can be counted. This information can indicate areas where effort could be directed to improve the design of the equipment (see Herbst, Metropolis, and Wells [36]).

Finally, machines can be used to prepare the wiring diagrams for their successors.

4.31   Current Developments

At this stage the reader should have become aware of the extraordinary obedience, reliability, and speed of current computers. He will probably have experienced, in this context, some human weaknesses. He will have rightly concluded that efficiency will be increased by the use of the computer to assist in programming.

The cost of the selection of an algorithm for the solution of a general problem (for instance, the determination of all the eigenvalues of a symmetric matrix), the analysis of its realization on an actual computer, and the programming and the comparison of the theoretical error estimates with the observed ones in a series of representative cases is enormous. When such a program is needed on a different computer, it may be worthwhile to simulate the first one on the second, rather than to recode the algorithm. This sort of operation is often used by organizations when they get new machines and are not able to decide whether recoding, taking advantage of the facilities of the new equipment and the accumulated experience on the older, is desirable.

Considerations of this kind lead to the concept of a universal language for the algorithms; each computer would have a translator program which produces from a program written in the algorithmic language the program appropriate for its own use. One of the more elaborate international experiments in this direction is the use of the Algol language (see, e.g., Backus et al. [46]).

It is not appropriate for us to elaborate on these ideas here. For an account of the ideas of the Russian schools, we refer to Liapunov [44]; the British point of view is put forward by Gill [45] and an American by Carr [1].

Our present position on the use of advanced programming techniques is that, although they are essential for the expert, the use of "simplified" pseudo codes by the novice is dangerous, for he will produce too many solutions, by improper methods, to incorrect problems. The additional time spent by the novice in handling his problems by traditional methods will force him to think through his problems again and improve their formulation and analysis.

REFERENCES

A comprehensive bibliography is available in:

1. J. W. Carr, III, Digital Computer Programming, "Handbook of Automation, Computation and Control," E. M. Grabbe, S. Ramo, D. E. Wooldridge, eds., vol. 2, chap. 2, John Wiley & Sons, Inc., New York, 1959.

Additional material is available in the periodical literature and in the literature issued by the manufacturers and various technical groups at universities and research organizations. The following material is explicitly referred to in the text.

2. M. Newman and J. Todd, The Evaluation of Matrix Inversion Programs, *J. Soc. Indust. Appl. Math.*, vol. 6, pp. 466–476, 1958.

3. J. Todd, Experiments in the Solution of a Differential Equation by Monte Carlo Methods, *J. Washington Acad. Sci.*, vol. 44, pp. 377–381, 1954.

4. O. Taussky and J. Todd, Systems of Equations, Matrices and Determinants, *Math. Mag.*, pp. 9–20, 71–88, 1952; reprinted in G. James, ed., "The Tree of Mathematics," pp. 305-337, The Digest Press, Pacoima, Calif., 1957.

5. J. H. Wilkinson, The Use of Iterative Methods for Finding the Latent Roots and Vectors of Matrices, *Math. Tables Aids Comput.*, vol. 9, pp. 184–191, 1955.

6. J. H. Wilkinson, The Calculation of the Latent Roots and Vectors of Matrices on the Pilot Model of the A.C.E., *Proc. Cambridge Philos. Soc.*, vol. 50, pp. 536–566, 1954.

7. E. Bodewig, A Practical Refutation of the Iteration Method for the Algebraic Eigenvalue Problem, *Math. Tables Aids Comput.*, vol. 8, pp. 237–239, 1954.

8. O. Taussky and J. Todd, Generation and Testing of Pseudo-random Numbers, pp. 15–28 in [52].

9. "Tables of Sievert's Integral," National Bureau of Standards Applied Mathematics Series, to appear.

10. W. Richter, Estimation de l'erreur commise dans la méthode de M. W. E. Milne pour l'intégration d'un système de *n* equations différentielles du premier ordre, *Bull. Soc. Neuchateloise Sci. Nat.*, vol. 75, pp. 1–43, 1952.

11. W. Feller, "An Introduction to Probability Theory and Its Application," vol. 1, chap. 14, John Wiley & Sons, Inc., New York, 1950.

12. C. W. Clenshaw, Polynomial Approximations to Elementary Functions, *Math. Tables Aids Comput.*, vol. 8, pp. 143–147, 1954.

13. F. L. Alt, "Electronic Digital Computers," Academic Press, Inc., New York, 1958.

14. G. E. Forsythe, Contemporary State of Numerical Analysis, in "Surveys in Applied Mathematics," vol. 5, pp. 1–42, John Wiley & Sons, Inc., New York, 1958.

15. W. F. Bauer, The Monte Carlo Method, *J. Soc. Indust. Appl. Math.*, vol. 6, pp. 438–451, 1958.

16. P. Davis and P. Rabinowitz, Some Monte Carlo Experiments in Computing Multiple Integrals, *Math. Tables Aids Comput.*, vol. 10, pp. 1–7, 1956.

17. J. M. Hammersley and K. W. Morton, Poor Man's Monte Carlo, *J. Roy. Statist. Soc. Ser. B*, vol. 16, pp. 23–38, 1954.

18. J. H. Curtiss, Sampling Methods Applied to Differential and Integral Equations, in "Proceedings, Seminar on Scientific Computation," IBM Corporation, New York, 1949.

19. D. F. Votaw and J. A. Rafferty, High Speed Sampling, *Math. Tables Aids Comput.*, vol. 5, pp. 1–8, 1951.

20. E. Lehmer, Number Theory on the SWAC, in [21], pp. 103–108.

21. J. H. Curtiss, ed., "Numerical Analysis: Proceedings of Symposia in Applied Mathematics—Volume 6," McGraw-Hill Book Company, Inc., New York, 1956.

22. O. Taussky, Some Computational Problems in Algebraic Number Theory, in [21], pp. 187–194; Some Computational Problems Involving Integral Matrices, *J. Res. Nat. Bur. Standards*, vol. 65B, pp. 15–17, 1961.

23. C. B. Tompkins, Machine Attack on Problems Whose Variables Are Permutation, in [21], pp. 195–212.

24. E. E. Osborne, On Acceleration and Matrix Deflation Processes Used with the Power Method, *J. Soc. Indust. Appl. Math.*, vol. 6, pp. 279–287, 1958.

25. P. Henrici, A Subroutine for Computations with Rational Numbers, *J. Assoc. Comput. Mach.*, vol. 3, pp. 6–9, 1956.

26. K. D. Tocher, The Application of Automatic Computers to Sampling Experiments, *J. Roy. Statist. Soc. Ser. B*, vol. 16, pp. 39–75, 1954.

27. P. Henrici, Automatic Computations with Power Series, *J. Assoc. Comput. Mach.*, vol. 3, pp. 10–15, 1956.

28. A. J. Hoffman, M. Mannos, D. Sokolowsky, and N. Wiegmann, Computational Experience in Solving Linear Programs, *J. Soc. Indust. Appl. Math.*, vol. 1, pp. 17–34, 1953.

29. R. D. Richtmyer, "Difference Methods for Initial-value Problems," Interscience Publishers, Inc., New York, 1957.

30. J. Todd, "Table of Arctangents of Rational Numbers," National Bureau of Standards Applied Mathematics Series, vol. 11, 1951.

31. E. H. Neville, "Rectangular-Polar Conversion Tables," Royal Society Mathematical Tables Series, vol. 2, Cambridge University Press, London, 1956.

32. I. A. Stegun and M. Abramowitz, Generation of Bessel Functions on High Speed Computers, *Math. Tables Aids Comput.*, vol. 11, pp. 255–257, 1957.

33. I. A. Stegun and M. Abramowitz, Generation of Coulomb Wave Functions by Means of Recurrence Relations, *Phys. Rev.*, vol. 98, pp. 1851–1852, 1955.

34. J. Barkley Rosser, Transformations to Speed the Convergence of Series, *J. Res. Nat. Bur. Standards*, vol. 47, pp. 56–64, 1951.

35. J. Todd and S. E. Warschawski, On the Solution of the Lichtenstein-Gershgorin Integral Equation in Conformal Mapping, II: Computational Experiments, in "Experiments in the Computation of Conformal Maps," National Bureau of Standards Applied Mathematics Series, vol. 42, pp. 31–44, 1955.

36. E. Herbst, N. Metropolis, and M. B. Wells, Analysis of Problem Codes on the Manaic, *Math. Tables Aids Comput.*, vol. 9, pp. 14–20, 1958.

37. F. Scheid, Radial Distribution of the Center of Gravity of Random Points on a Unit Circle, *J. Res. Nat. Bur. Standards*, vol. 60, pp. 307–308, 1958.

38a. A. W. Burks, H. H. Goldstine, and J. von Neumann, "Preliminary Discussion of the Logical Design of an Electronic Computing Instrument," mimeographed report, Institute for Advanced Study, Princeton, N.J., 1946.

38b,c,d. H. H. Goldstine and J. von Neumann, "Planning and Coding of Problems for an Electronic Computing Instrument," 3 vols., mimeographed report, Institute for Advanced Study, Princeton, N.J., 1947–1948.

39. D. Teichroew, Use of Continued Fractions in High Speed Computing, *Math. Tables Aids Comput.*, vol. 6, pp. 127–133, 1952.

40. C. Hastings, Jr., assisted by J. T. Hayward and J. P. Wong, Jr., "Approximations for Digital Computers," Princeton University Press, Princeton, N.J., 1955.

41. D. H. Lehmer, Teaching Combinatorial Tricks to a Computer, in [47], pp. 179–193.

42. M. Marcus, "Basic Theorems in Matrix Theory," National Bureau of Standards Applied Mathematics Series, vol. 57, 1960.

43. P. Henrici, Application of Two Methods of Numerical Analysis to the Computation of the Reflected Radiation of a Point Source, *J. Washington Acad. Sci.*, vol. 45, pp. 38–45, 1955.

44. A. A. Liapunov, Mathematical Investigations Related to the Use of Electronic Computing Machines, M. D. Friedman, tr., *Comm. Assoc. Comput. Mach.*, vol. 3, pp. 107–118, 1960.

45. S. Gill, Current Theory and Practice of Automatic Programming, *Comput. J.*, vol. 2, pp. 110–114, 1959.

46. J. W. Backus et al., Report on the Algorithmic Language ALGOL 60, *Numer. Math.*, vol. 2, pp. 106–136, 1960; or *Comm. Assoc. Comput. Mach.*, vol. 3, pp. 299–314, 1960.

47. R. Bellmann and M. Hall, Jr., eds., "Combinatorial Analysis: Proceedings of Symposia in Applied Mathematics—Volume 10," American Mathematical Society, Providence, R.I., 1960.

48. O. Taussky and J. Todd, Some Discrete Variable Computations, in [47], pp. 201–209.

49. W. Gautschi, Recursive Computation of the Repeated Integrals of the Error Function, *Math. Comp.*, vol. 15, pp. 227–232, 1961.

50. W. Gautschi, Recursive Computation of Certain Integrals, *J. Assoc. Comput. Mach.*, vol. 8, pp. 21–40, 1961.

51. J. M. Hammersley, Monte Carlo Methods for Solving Multivariable Problems, *Ann. New York Acad. Sci.*, vol. 86, pp. 844–874, 1960.

52. H. A. Meyer, ed., "Symposium on Monte Carlo Method," John Wiley & Sons, Inc., New York, 1956.

53. W. Wasow, On the Duration of Random Walks, *Ann. Math. Stat.*, vol. 22, pp. 199–216, 1951.

54. W. Wasow, On the Mean Duration of Random Walks, *J. Res. Nat. Bur. Standards*, vol. 46, pp. 462–471, 1951.

55. W. Wasow, Random Walks and the Eigenvalues of Elliptic Differential Equation, *J. Res. Nat. Bur. Standards*, vol. 46, pp. 65–73, 1951.

56. R. Fortet, "Applications de la statistique à la physique nucléaire," Monografias de ciencia moderna, vol. 40, Consejo superior de investigaciones cientificas, Departmento de Estadistica, Madrid, 1953.

5

Use and Limitation of Computers

HARVEY COHN

PROFESSOR OF MATHEMATICS
UNIVERSITY OF ARIZONA

5.1 Introduction

The numerical analyst can rightfully claim credit for motivating the development of the high-speed computer. With the development of the computer, however, a very conscious development of design logic occurred which was largely irrelevant to the analyst's interest. Then another type of logic, computability logic (which had been developed long before the computer), suddenly found relevance "in principle," without helping the analyst get specific answers!

Perhaps computer logic will not long remain remote from practical numerical analysis. Right now the newer machines seem to be beyond the speed and storage requirements of the problems that were their motivation, and the newer machines still can be made to seem inadequate only when confronted with problems of a new type (in programming, pattern recognition, etc.).

The purpose of this chapter is not futuristic. It is to describe the logic of computer usage briefly and informally, requiring some basic familiarity with programming but no familiarity of any sort with formal mathematical logic. The state of the literature [1] is too dynamic to make a comprehensive bibliography feasible, and the references cited are mostly cursory in nature.

5.2 Computer Requirements

The electronic computer was designed to imitate both the straight numerical work and the routinized thinking of the numerical analyst.

The straight numerical work consists of an ordered list of instructions defining new quantities on the basis of calculations of the type

$$A \otimes B = C. \tag{5.1}$$

Here a variety of arithmetic calculations are called forth, such as addition, subtraction, multiplication, and division, as well as extended operations such as $A - |B| = C$ and $-AB = C$.   In fact, operations with only one variable, such as $-|A| = C$, are still written in the form (5.1) (i.e., B is ignored).   The letters, of course, stand for numerical values (and not formal polynomials, for instance).   Still, calculations of type (5.1) do not make manifest certain widely accepted techniques, such as *comparisons*, *data layout*, and the merging of different *subroutines*.

We might start by considering *comparisons*, as required by that well-known flow chart for solving $A = f(A)$ to accuracy ϵ in Fig. 5.1.   Certainly we do not know beforehand how many iterations are needed, nor

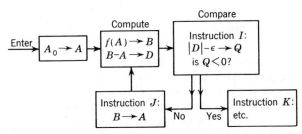

Fig. 5.1   Flow chart for iterated solution to $A = f(A)$.

is it practical or even correct (considering round-off) always to use the same number of iterations.   Hence the loop in the flow chart spares us the writing of instructions in the running program.   It also spares us the writing of data-iteration symbols of the type $C = f(B)$, $D = f(C)$, etc. (Note, even here, the parallelism involved in saving writing of data and instructions.)   For that reason we generalize the "$=$" to "$\rightarrow$," meaning that, if C has already been computed, the new value replaces the old.   In effect then, $A, B, D, Q, \ldots$ become not only names but *locations* into which the variables are to be written.   In corresponding fashion, the instructions are denoted by symbols which refer to the location where the instructions are written out.

Our general instruction now is described by saying that the value of the instruction at location I is given by

$$I = \boxed{A \otimes B \rightarrow C \qquad \text{and} \qquad \begin{cases} J \text{ follows if } C \geq 0 \\ K \text{ follows if } C < 0, \end{cases}} \qquad (5.2a)$$

or, symbolically,

$$I = (A, B, C; J, K; \otimes). \qquad (5.2)$$

There are five addresses (locations A, B, C, J, K) and one operation $\otimes$. Certainly many of the addresses can be coincident or superfluous.

The idea of *data layout* is probably best exemplified by matrix methods. The spacesaving feature does not apply to data but to instructions, since only one instruction need be given to apply to a whole column (e.g., "Subtract 5 times column one from column two"). The column operation can be performed by using the same instruction over again by changing the data locations in adding a constant. Hence, defining $A(I), B(I)$, $C(I)$ to be the data *locations* used within instruction I (not the data values) and letting A', B', C' be locations at which new locations (not data) are to be found, we must be able to extract into the instructions at I the value of the location found at location A', by means of the statement

$$E_A = \boxed{A' \to A(I) \qquad \text{and} \qquad J \text{ follows,}} \tag{5.3}$$

and likewise for E_B, E_C. Parenthetically, such an instruction has meaning only if the appropriate arithmetic can be performed on the data *locations A, B, C* as well as on the data values.

One would expect an instruction-location analogue to the data-location operations (5.3). One would expect that, defining $J(I)$, $K(I)$ as the J and K locations in instruction (5.2), one would have the extraction instruction for inserting the address at J' or K' into an arbitrary instruction at I, namely,

$$F_J = \boxed{J' \to J(I) \qquad \text{and} \qquad L \text{ follows,}} \tag{5.4}$$

and likewise for F_K. This type of instruction actually comes about when we are digressing from a main calculation to an auxiliary calculation or *subroutine*. For instance, we may wish to calculate C and then proceed to the instruction at J' if $C \geq 0$ or K' if $C < 0$. If I in (5.1) is the *last* (or "exit") calculation, yielding C, we perform extractions of the type F_J, F_K [see (5.4)] into instruction I before entering the subroutine producing C.

Thus we see that operations (5.2) to (5.4), made inevitable by the needs of numerical analysis, are a kind of irreducible minimum [2] for a numerical analyst. We might well ask whether the minimum can become greater with the advent of more skillful numerical analysts. Although the answer seems to be negative, such an eventuality can be considered only by reducing the machine to several equivalent forms.

5.3   The Stored-program Computer

A computer can meet the requirements of the previous section simply by treating instructions in the same fashion as data [3]. Then the arithmetic operations, augmented by extractions, are applied to data and to instructions.   Now instructions and data are composed in digital fashion (with the A, B, C, J, K locations expressed and distinguished digitally, together with a digital representation of the operation $\otimes$).   What characterizes an instruction is the fact that it becomes executed.   The instructions that become executed, however, need not all appear in the program; some instructions are composed when needed and then destroyed.

In effect, the five-address system (5.2) is not necessary.   Many high-speed machines are one-address; that is, only one address appears in the instructions.   This system is set up by first sequencing a natural order of instructions so that, say, $I + 1$ is the next location after I and then by singling out a special storage location R to serve as a so-called "accumulator."   Then the instruction I reduces to the following set of instructions in natural sequence:

$$
\begin{array}{lll}
I & \text{(load)} & A \rightarrow R. \\
I + 1 & \text{(calculate)} & R \otimes B \rightarrow R. \\
I + 2 & \text{(store)} & R \rightarrow C. \hspace{2em} (5.5) \\
I + 3 & \text{(branch)} & \text{Follow by } K \text{ if } R < 0. \\
I + 4 & \text{(transfer)} & \text{Follow by } J \text{ unconditionally.}
\end{array}
$$

Note that in each case there is only one address in reference: A, B, C, K, or J.

Obviously a great variety of machines are feasible.   Only one other point is worth mentioning here.   An instruction is usually fetched to a separate "instruction register" for execution (and, as it is performed, the values of the data are loaded and stored; then the value of the succeeding instruction, at J or K, replaces I in the instruction register).

This setup has the advantage that the particular extraction operations (5.3) and (5.4) can be separated from the rest of the arithmetic (5.2). For instance, the machine can have three "indexing registers" at fixed locations A_0, B_0, C_0 such that in the executed form (rather than in the stored form) of I the effective A address is incremented by the contents of location A_0, etc., thus taking care of (5.3), whereas the machine can have in its so-called "instruction counter" I_1 the successor of the current instruction location I.   Hence, in using a subroutine, the machine need only file the instruction counter in the J or K portion of the exit instruction I.   Fortunately, science is so much the richer for the fact that indiscriminate mixing of instructions and data occurred before machines were developed for avoiding the mixing.

We have made no mention of how the arithmetic is to be performed, or essentially how many $\otimes$ operations are to be permitted, and how much of the extraction, indexing, and filing facility is to be permitted.   Clearly these operations are highly interdependent in the sense of Boolean algebra, which we give a wide berth in this discussion.   In fact, without mentioning it, we showed that (5.2) to (5.4) constitute a machine *equivalent* in some way to (5.5) (provided the proper digital structure and extractions are assumed).   Certainly a standard machine would be helpful, as well as an equivalence theory.

5.4   Turing Machines

Turing, in 1937 (before the age of advanced electronics), conceptualized a machine [4] to describe the human-decision problem.   The outcome of his work was that his machine could not make certain methodological decisions which human beings generally regard themselves as being capable of making.   We come to this phase of machine theory later, but for the present we consider just Turing's machine.

The Turing machine has only a *finite* number of *states* (or instructions) $I_1, \ldots, I_N$, but the machine has a semi-infinite tape.   The tape is divided into squares which are either marked (1) or blank (0).   The machine has a scanning head which can read and write only one square at a time.   The basic operation is as follows.   The machine starts in state I.   Then the scanning head reads a square.   Next the machine has two alternatives, depending on whether the head has read a mark or a blank.   Once the alternative is decided, the scanning head follows a predetermined course of action, marking or erasing the scanned square.   The machine finally goes into another predetermined state, while the scanning head makes a predetermined motion on the tape, right or left, by one square (or with no motion at all).   The finiteness of the human physical structure is presumably reflected in the finiteness of the number of states, and the infinite variety of physical data is represented by the semi-infinite tape.   In practical terms, Turing considers the initial and final data to be given on, say, odd-numbered squares, and the calculation is known to be at an end when the reading head reaches the finite end of the tape.

There are unfortunately very few problems which are *conveniently* programmed on the Turing machine just described.   We mention one simply to show how the Turing machine, like the stored-program computer, uses accessories as flow charts [5].

Consider the following problem concerning a tape marked as shown:

$$(\text{End}) \quad 00100101000110010\ldots.$$

We wish to have a general program in which the reading head, starting at the leftmost symbol (presumed to be zero), will progress and erase all isolated 1s, up to the first nonisolated 1s and then return.   Thus the final tape will be, for example,

$$(\text{End}) \quad 00000000000110010\ldots$$

and the reading head will return to the original zero.

The program is shown in Fig. 5.2.   Actually, programs (or flow charts) are called "special-purpose" machines, whereas the Turing machine (which simulates any flow chart step by step) is called a "general-purpose" or "universal" machine.   The idea of the equivalence of two

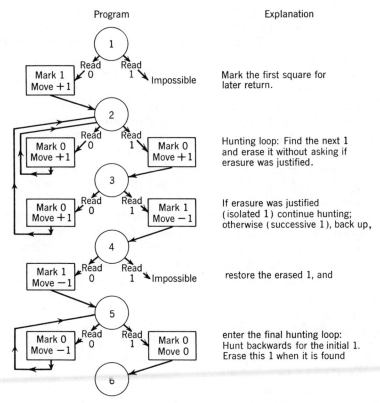

Program   Explanation

Mark the first square for
later return.

Hunting loop: Find the next 1
and erase it without asking if
erasure was justified.

If erasure was justified
(isolated 1) continue hunting;
otherwise (successive 1), back up,

restore the erased 1, and

enter the final hunting loop:
Hunt backwards for the initial 1.
Erase this 1 when it is found

FIG. 5.2   Illustrative special Turing machine.

machines implies the ability of each machine to simulate the other.   A rigorous definition of equivalence will not be attempted, since it would involve a system of recognition of data and states between two machines and is possible only within the framework of formal logic [6].

What we shall show, intuitively, however, is that the Turing machine is equivalent to the more sophisticated stored-program computer.   Not the least of the difficulties is the fact that the former has only a finite number of states, whereas the latter has an infinite number of possible instructions, owing to the infinitude of data locations.   As a consequence, the word length for instructions will be indefinite (as well as for data if no round-off is desired).

5.5   Equivalence Theory

We first of all note that the behavior of any Turing machine can easily be simulated by a stored-program computer (of sufficient storage) with a finite program.   The semi-infinite tape can correspond to a semi-infinite portion of storage, and the program can be put into a separate portion containing two special registers S and L, indicating, respectively, the location of the state of the Turing machine and the location of the simulated position of the scanning head.   The finite matrix of N states with alternative actions can be put into a finite part of storage.   It is now an elementary programming problem to see how the stored-program computer looks up the contents at L, looks up the alternative in S, executes the action required, and then changes the indicators S and L.   The branching property (5.2) and the data location (5.3) are the only properties required; that is, the property of altering an instruction address (5.4) need not be brought into play.   We can seem to get away with less of a machine, since we can find the right address by successive choices, without extracting any instruction locations into an instruction directly [7].

The converse equivalence is more difficult, namely, the designing of a Turing machine with a sufficiently large number of states to simulate a stored-program computer.   The literature fails to show any estimate of how many states are needed, nor shall we try to find such an estimate here.   We merely outline a procedure for seeing the equivalence intuitively in several states:

1. The Turing machine is improved to the extent that the scanning head reads and writes any finite number of symbols.   Thus a symbol on a square can be marked (e.g., by a star) for later reference and will be readable.   Thus the $A, B, C, J, K, \otimes$ components of (5.1) can be separated and distinguished.

2. The Turing machine of item 1 is further improved so that it reads and writes a finite number of tapes at once.   Specifically, we have six (register) tapes to store the A, B, C, I, J, K locations and contents, one tape to serve as the general storage, containing *locations and contents* of words suitably marked.

3. By a comparison operation, the machine can match locations and fetch any (data or instruction) item by location and then store any item at a new blank spot on the tape.   (Since the word length is generally unlimited, the fetched item may have to be destroyed in storage if a new item goes with the same location but is too long to insert.)

4. The arithmetic is performed serially; so the problem is independent of the size of the numbers.   This process is described in most books on computer design [8] (and may require another utility tape or two in item 2).

To give an example of the austerity of such proofs as are called forth here, we might just consider item 1.   The symbols are all put in binary representation, so that the basic induction operation is a proof that a (modified) Turing machine that can read and write M symbols $a, b, \ldots$ is equivalent to one that can read and write M^2 symbols $aa, ab, ba, bb, \ldots$. This is shown in Fig. 5.3 (where the states, as usual, are encircled, and superfluous steps are omitted).

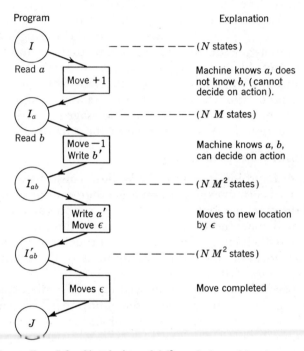

FIG. 5.3   Simulation of M^2 symbol machine by
an M symbol machine.

We start with a machine with N states that can read M^2 symbols (symbolically) ab in state I and can write M^2 symbols (symbolically) $a'b'$ moving 2ϵ units ($\epsilon = 0, \pm1$) and going into state J.   When these steps are accomplished, the number of intermediate states augment the total to $N(2M^2 + M + 1)$ states for a machine that reads only M symbols and does the "same" operations.

The reader may wish to construct the flow chart for item 2, indicating how the following double tape,

$$abc^1d \ldots$$

$$mnop^2 \ldots,$$

with [1] and [2] denoting the scanning heads, can be replaced by the single tape *$ambnc^1odp^2$ . . . , where the scanning head is on some reserved symbol * between moves.

5.6 Duality of Instructions and Data

One principle that can be abstracted from the preceding description is some duality of instructions and data.   Certain evidences may be cited. First of all, the extraction operations in Sec. 5.2 arise naturally for each. Therefore, instructions and data are both treated in the same arithmetic fashion by the stored-program computer.   In the Turing machine, the number of symbols goes down at the same time that the number of states goes up.   In fact, Shannon [9] describes a two-state Turing machine with very many symbols and asks for the machine which has a minimum value for the product of the numbers of states and symbols.

One way of finding new areas in machine usage is to ask for instances in which instructions have not yet received the same treatment as data.

5.7 Automatic Programming

The idea of handling instructions like data constitutes *automatic programming*.   To a certain extent, automatic programming is built into the circuitry of the machine, but usually the term denotes activity *preparatory* to conventional machine computation.   As techniques become more advanced, such distinctions should vanish (through built-in features).

The earliest form of automatic programming seems to have been the *floating-address system* [10] due to Wilkes (1951).   The purpose of this system is to permit subroutines to be written with symbolic addresses so that the symbols may be translated by machine into permanent addresses (avoiding those portions of storage that might have been preempted by an earlier subroutine).

A later development was the *interpretative system*, or "pseudo code."   In this system one programs for a hypothetical machine, and the actual machine translates the program step by step and executes each program step between translations.   Thus the one-address analogue (5.5) of the stored-program computer (of Sec. 5.2) is an interpretative system (although usually the one-address code possesses a multiaddress interpretative system).   The interpretative system has the disadvantage, in regard to time, that the translation process is used every time the instruction is executed (very much oftener than the number of times the instruction was *written* in the original program).   The floating-address translation occurs only once, however, for each time the instruction is written. Hence the pseudo code is an equivalent machine.

Here it might be mentioned that one form of interpretative system would be of inestimable value to numerical analysts for the automatic monitoring of round-off errors.   Symbolically each A, B, . . . has an associated error ΔA, ΔB.   Therefore, of considerably more value than $A \otimes B \to C$, would be the pair of calculations

$$A \otimes B \to C \tag{5.6}$$

$$\max |A \otimes B - A' \otimes B'| \to \Delta C, \tag{5.7}$$

where A', B' are subject to $|A - A'| \leq \Delta A, |B - B'| \leq \Delta B$.   This refine-ment would double the data-storage requirement to include the ΔA, ΔB, . . . and triple the running time (at least).   Unfortunately the program would have to interpret $A \otimes B$ by a subroutine each time it occurred.   (The same could be done for truncation error if the general term of a series was given.)   If, after suitable trials, the numerical analyst decided to ignore round-off analysis or change to a simple scaling or floating-point method, he should be able to make the new interpretation of his code in whole or part, entirely by machine.

An interpretative system that is translated *before* use is called a *compiler* [11].   It is usually much more elaborate than a mere floating-address system, and it requires an amazing degree of complexity in the translation of even simple phrases of pidgin English.   The details of such systems go far beyond the scope of this chapter, and probably the manuals of lead-ing computer manufacturers are the best source of information.   Two points, however, are of interest to users of computers and to numerical analysts in particular.

First of all, experiments in *machine learning* actually point in the direc-tion of helping the customer get answers.   Machine learning (or con-ditioning) is the process whereby the machine performs a subroutine in a manner dependent on the previous "experience" of the machine, with-out the user's being in attentive control.   This might require a large file of previous (similar) problems to be called upon by the machine without the specific knowledge of the user.   It might, however, just involve fairly current calculations.   This learning process would be a valuable pro-cedure when it takes too long to decide each case ahead of time, for the machine could then sample, say, every dozen usages, or else it could apply to the next case information available only after the subroutine is completed each time.   A more daring procedure [12] is to extend the learning process from data to instructions and have the machine write a sequence of instructions by trial and error.   A prohibitive factor, in-cidentally, could be the machine time involved in translating English syntax or using trial and error.   It seems that automatic programming, rather than larger reactors, is the more creative justification for faster machines.

A final point is a rather gloomy one.   A human being can decide better than a machine whether a statement is translatable into machine language. This is a form of a mathematical theorem (not a mere humanistic sentiment), and it is presently discussed further.

5.8 Undecidability: Gödel's and Turing's Problems

A good starting point for seeing limitations of a computing machine is some kind of paradox [13]. Then the process of putting the paradox into machine language must have a weak spot, which must turn out to be machine decidability. For instance, consider the famous paradox concerning phrases of English that represent integers. We consider the connotations of all phrases of 11 or fewer words. Most of them represent gibberish, or at least they represent no integer. Those that represent an integer can be enumerated lexicographically, and the largest integer, say M, can be selected. We then consider the phrase, "One plus the largest integer representable by eleven or fewer words." If we count the number of words, we find that in 11 words we have represented $M + 1$, producing a contradiction to the definition of M. From the machine point of view, we need not worry about the paradox, since it only proves that no program can enable a computing machine to examine a phrase of English and decide (with the help of however many encoded rules of syntax, grammar, etc.) whether or not the phrase connotes an integer.

The limitations of a machine, put succinctly, are that *no program exists which enables a machine to examine any program and to decide in a finite number of steps on a property that effects visualization of the infinitely many possible steps of the program.* We display this limitation by two different arguments, which, however informal, are more palpable than representation by "phrases of English."

To do this, we first imagine all programs written out as instructions and data (with locations), console settings, etc. Thus any program is a finite sequence of ordered *integers only* (considering alphabetics to be treated numerically, namely, $a_1, a_2, \ldots, a_m$). The number $k = 2^{a_1}3^{a_2} \cdots p_m{}^{a_m}$ (where p_m is the mth prime) corresponds uniquely to the program. It is called the *Gödel number* of the program.

Adapting Gödel's procedure [14] to machines, we define a program as *deciding on a property* if and only if it is so constituted that the program starts with a variable number n in a special register and stops with $+1$ or -1 in that same register, depending on whether or not n has the property of the program. Clearly very few programs will do this, but we assert that there is no machine program for deciding whether an arbitrary number is the Gödel number of a property-deciding program in particular.

For if so, the machine program could be modified slightly to enumerate all property-deciding programs, and the machine could consequently enumerate all integers (in numerical order) that represent property-deciding programs. Hence the machine could, by a finite program, decide the truth or falsity (± 1) for any n of the property that "n is *not* satisfied by the nth property-deciding program."   But this property would have a Gödel number in this numerical sequence of programs, say q, and the question of whether q satisfies the qth property-deciding program leads to a paradox.   Hence no finite program can identify a property-deciding program.

Turing's form of the paradox [15] is quite similar, except that it can be adapted to fit a machine more closely.   We consider some attribute relative to the indefinite running of a program—for instance, the question of whether error stops ever occur in the running of the program.   *There does not exist a program which enables the machine to examine an arbitrary program to decide in a finite number of steps whether error stops occur.*

To prove this statement, let us suppose the contrary.   Then a program $\mathscr{M}$ exists, such that an arbitrary program $\mathscr{A}$ could be examined in finite time to decide, by just running the combination ($\mathscr{M}, \mathscr{A}$) ($\mathscr{M}$ as a program followed by $\mathscr{A}$ as data), whether or not $\mathscr{A}$ produces error stops. We can then modify the procedure by saying that, since we assume we can test the running of $\mathscr{A}$, we can also test the running of program $\mathscr{A}$ followed by data $\mathscr{A}$, or the combination ($\mathscr{A}, \mathscr{A}$).   This combination involves a procedure for reading a program into the machine, having the machine acknowledge the end of the program, and then having the machine read data to do what it will (which even may include the error-stop rejection of data $\mathscr{A}$ following program $\mathscr{A}$).   Thus, most often ($\mathscr{A}, \mathscr{A}$) will be meaningless; but regardless of this fact, on our assumption that $\mathscr{M}$ exists, the machine could then tell whether ($\mathscr{A}, \mathscr{A}$) will produce an error stop.   Let the machine announce the *effect* of ($\mathscr{A}, \mathscr{A}$), by the *running* of ($\mathscr{M}, \mathscr{A}$), as follows: if ($\mathscr{A}, \mathscr{A}$) becomes known to produce an error stop, let ($\mathscr{M}, \mathscr{A}$) run to a normal stop; if ($\mathscr{A}, \mathscr{A}$) produces no error stop, let ($\mathscr{M}, \mathscr{A}$) run to an (artificially produced) error stop. Then the running of ($\mathscr{M}, \mathscr{M}$) leads to a paradox (seemingly neither producing nor failing to produce an error stop).

Note that the programs that have been shown to be nonexistent are programs that do things which the average programmer can very often decide (in fact is expected to decide).   The programmer still has no right to say he has a "method"; he is safer when he attributes his decision to an inspired guess or to good fortune.   True randomness, if it exists, acquires an even greater role by defeating the undecidability argument [16].

5.9   Concluding Remarks

We have gone through a rather rapid description of the logical basis for computer usage.   Actually numerical analysts have not yet carried their programming anywhere near the limits of computer capacities.

They can do this only by further ventures into automation in directions that may not be clear today. Yet even so, their achievements are circumscribed by the machine's inability to predict the running of its program, and these restrictions can be lifted only by new types of randomization.

NOTES AND REFERENCES

1. The author must acknowledge that his earliest major source of information has been through personal contact with Prof. Saul Gorn, of the University of Pennsylvania.

The literature has recently mushroomed. The two most significant works are probably: M. Davis, "Computability and Unsolvability," McGraw-Hill Book Company, Inc., New York, 1958, and R. M. Smullyan, "Theory of Formal Systems," Annals of Mathematics Studies, vol. 47, Princeton University Press, Princeton, N.J., 1961.

2. The operations are not independent; that is, operations (2.3) and (2.4), as it will turn out, each imply the other (see [7]).

3. The revolutionary idea of treating instructions electronically, like data, has been variously attributed to J. P. Eckert and J. von Neumann. See H. H. Goldstine and J. von Neumann, Planning and Coding of Problems for an Electronic Computing Instrument, mimeographed reports, Institute for Advanced Study, Princeton, N.J., 1946.

4. See A. M. Turing, On Computable Numbers, with an Application to the Entscheidungsproblem, *Proc. London Math. Soc.*, vol. 42, pp. 230–265, 1937.

5. Another such problem appears in H. Freudenthal, Les Possibilités des Machines à Calculer, *Bull. Soc. Math. Belg.*, vol. 6, pp. 14–22, 1953.

6. The best single reference is probably S. C. Kleene, "Introduction to Metamathematics," chap. XIII, D. Van Nostrand Company, Inc., Princeton, N.J., 1952.

7. We could similarly avoid altering data addresses within an instruction, although the difference is that the number of data locations can be unlimited (see [2]).

8. See M. Phister, Jr., "Logical Design of Digital Computers," John Wiley & Sons, Inc., New York, 1958.

9. See C. E. Shannon, A Universal Turing Machine with Two Internal States, in "Automata Studies," C. E. Shannon and J. McCarthy, eds., Annals of Mathematics Studies, vol. 34, pp. 157–166, Princeton University Press, Princeton, N.J., 1956.

10. See M. V. Wilkes, The Use of a Floating Address System for Orders in an Automatic Digital Computer, *Proc. Cambridge Philos. Soc.*, vol. 49, pp. 84–89, 1953.

11. An excellent source of historical information is G. M. Hopper, "Automatic Coding for Digital Computers," Remington Rand Corporation, 1955.

12. For an account of the problem involved in teaching a machine, by trial and error, to reproduce a quantity unaltered, see R. M. Friedberg, A Learning Machine, I, *IBM J. Res. Development*, vol. 2, pp. 1–13, 1958.

13. See S. C. Kleene, "Introduction to Metamathematics," chap. III, D. Van Nostrand Company, Inc., Princeton, N.J., 1952.

14. See the Introduction of A. Mostowski, "Sentences Undecidable in Formalized Arithmetic," North Holland Publishing Company, Amsterdam, 1957.

15. See A. M. Turing, Solvable and Unsolvable Problems, *Sci. News*, vol. 31, pp. 7–23, 1953.

16. Random discovery of formulas (not programs) is envisioned in W. R. Ashby, Design for an Intelligence Amplifier, in "Automata Studies," C. E. Shannon and

J. McCarthy, eds., Annals of Mathematics Studies, vol. 34, pp. 215–234, Princeton University Press, Princeton, N.J., 1956 (see also [12]). The automatic randomization of data (rather than instructions or even formulas) is the well-known Monte Carlo procedure of J. von Neumann and S. Ulam, discussed, for example, in Chap. 4. Also see A. S. Householder, G. E. Forsythe, and H. H. Germond, eds., "Monte Carlo Methods," National Bureau of Standards Applied Mathematics Series, vol. 12 1951.

⑥

Matrix Computations

MORRIS NEWMAN

NATIONAL BUREAU OF STANDARDS

6.1   General Introduction

The study of matrix computations—in which we include the evaluation of determinants, the solution of simultaneous systems of linear equations and linear inequalities, the inversion of matrices, the determination of characteristic values and vectors of a matrix, and the solution of the general characteristic-value problem $Ax = \lambda Bx$—has been most intense in the last two decades.   We cannot attempt to cover this field, but we shall discuss some representative methods.

For an account of some of these problems from the point of view of desk computation, we refer to Fox [1]; the books of Crandall [2] and Frazer, Duncan, and Collar [11] are valuable accounts of the use of these methods in actual practice, as are various accounts of "relaxation" methods (see Forsythe [6]).   Expository accounts, with worked examples, are available, for instance, in Taussky and Todd [8], in [9], and at greater length in Faddeeva [10].

Among the more elaborate texts are those of Bodewig, Dwyer, Zurmühl, and Householder, for which detailed references are given in Sec. 2.43.   See also Wilkinson [37].

Four volumes of the National Bureau of Standards Applied Mathematics Series [3, 4, 5, 13] are devoted to various aspects of matrix calculations.   A symposium on the subject was held at Wayne University in 1957, but the papers are rather scattered (see [18] for abstracts).

From the current point of view on high-speed automatic computers, there are four classical papers: Turing [14], von Neumann and Goldstine [15], Givens [16], and Goldstine, Murray, and von Neumann [17].

Among those who have made notable contributions, in addition to these cited above, are Aitken, Bauer, Hestenes, Rutishauser, Stiefel, Varga, Wilkinson, Young, Forsythe, Householder, Lanczos, and Ostrowski.

222

THE SOLUTION OF LINEAR EQUATIONS
AND THE INVERSION OF MATRICES

6.2   Introduction

It is convenient to distinguish between direct methods and indirect, or iterative methods, as exemplified by the (direct) Gaussian elimination method and the (indirect) Seidel method.   It is dangerous to make definite statements about their relative merits, but it would appear that the Gaussian methods are preferable in the case of general matrices, whereas the Seidel method and its developments (see Chap. 11) are successful with "sparse" matrices, such as those which arise from the numerical solution of differential equations.

The classification of methods has been studied by Forsythe and Householder in various papers.

6.3   Indirect Methods

The following method for computing the reciprocal of a number is in common use.   Let a be a nonzero number.   Let x_0 be arbitrary and define the sequence

$$x_{r+1} = x_r(2 - ax_r), \qquad r \geq 0. \tag{6.1}$$

Then, in appropriate circumstances, $x_r \to 1/a$ as $r \to \infty$.   To see what these circumstances are, set $y_r = 1 - ax_r$.   Then, upon multiplication by a, (6.1) implies that

$$y_{r+1} = y_r^2, \qquad r \geq 0, \tag{6.2}$$

so that

$$y_r = y_0^{2^r}, \qquad r \geq 0. \tag{6.3}$$

Thus, if x_0 is chosen so that the modulus of $y_0 = 1 - ax_0$ is less than 1, then $y_r \to 0$ as $r \to \infty$, and consequently $x_r \to 1/a$ as $r \to \infty$.   Similarly, if $x_r \to 1/a$ as $r \to \infty$, then $y_r \to 0$ as $r \to \infty$, and y_0 must be of modulus less than 1.   That is, *the process defined by* (6.1) *produces the reciprocal of a if and only if the initial approximant x_0 is chosen so that* $|1 - ax_0| < 1$.   This simple remark finds application later in an analogous matrix problem.

A measure of the error engendered by (6.1) is y_r, and (6.2) shows that this error becomes squared at each step—a computationally pleasant fact.

Example.   Let us take $a = 7$, $x_0 = .1$. Then $1 - ax_0 = .3$, so that the conditions for the convergence of (6.1) are satisfied.   We have $x_1 = .13$, $x_2 = .1417$, $x_3 = .142\ 84777$, $x_4 = .14205\ 71422 \ldots$, so that x_4 agrees with $\frac{1}{7}$ to 9 places of decimals.

If instead of $x_0 = .1$ we took $x_0 = .5$, say, then $1 - ax_0 = -2.5$, and process (6.1) would fail.   Thus $x_1 = -.75$, $x_2 = -5.4375$ and $x_r \to -\infty$ as $r \to \infty$.

If a is a number, it is easy to decide when $a^r \to 0$ as $r \to \infty$. This happens if and only if $|a| < 1$. The corresponding question for matrices, however, is not so trivial, and we develop the necessary and sufficient condition that a square matrix A with complex entries satisfy $\lim_{r \to \infty} A^r = 0$.

Let E be the $n \times n$ matrix which has 1 in positions $(1,2)$, $(2,3)$, ..., $(n-1, n)$ and 0 elsewhere. Then $E^k, 0 \leq k \leq n - 1$ is the matrix which has 1 in positions $(1, k+1), (2, k+2), \ldots, (n-k, n)$ and 0 elsewhere. Furthermore, $E^n = 0$. We put

$$B = \lambda I + cE.$$

Then
$$B^r = (\lambda I + cE)^r = \sum_{k=0}^{r} \binom{r}{k} \lambda^{r-k} c^k E^k.$$

Thus, if $r \geq n - 1$,

$$B^r = \sum_{k=0}^{n-1} \binom{r}{k} \lambda^{r-k} c^k E^k. \tag{6.4}$$

Since $\binom{r}{k} \lambda^{r-k} \to 0$ as $r \to \infty$ if and only if $|\lambda| < 1$, we can make the following statement.

Lemma 6.1. $B^r \to 0$ as $r \to \infty$ if and only if $|\lambda| < 1$.

Suppose now that A is an $n \times n$ matrix with complex entries. From the Jordan decomposition theorem we know that there is a matrix S and a matrix C such that $A = S^{-1}CS$ and C is a direct sum of B matrices:

$$C = B_1 + B_2 + \cdots + B_t$$

where $B_k = \lambda_k I^{(n_k)} + c_k E^{(n_k)}, 1 \leq k \leq t$. Here $I^{(n_k)}$ and $E^{(n_k)}$ denote I and E matrices, respectively, of orders n_k with $\sum_{k=1}^{t} n_k = n$. Since $A^r = S^{-1}C^rS$, we conclude that $A^r \to 0$ as $r \to \infty$ if and only if $C^r \to 0$ as $r \to \infty$. But this happens if and only if $B_k{}^r \to 0$ as $r \to \infty, 1 \leq k \leq t$. If we notice now that the λ_k's are just the eigenvalues of C (and so of A, since A and C are similar), Lemma 6.1 implies our first important result.

Theorem 6.2. $A^r \to 0$ as $r \to \infty$ if and only if each eigenvalue of A is of modulus less than 1.

This observation underlies many iteration schemes in computation with matrices. Here we adapt scheme (6.1), which produces the reciprocal of a number, to the computation of the inverse of a matrix. Suppose that A is a nonsingular matrix and X_0 an arbitrary matrix. We define

$$X_{r+1} = X_r(2I - AX_r), \qquad r \geq 0, \tag{6.5}$$

and we put $Y_r = I - AX_r$. Then, as with (6.1), we have

$$Y_{r+1} = Y_r^2, \tag{6.6}$$

$$Y_r = Y_0^{2^r}. \tag{6.7}$$

Thus $X_r \to A^{-1}$ as $r \to \infty$ if and only if $Y_r \to 0$ as $r \to \infty$; and $Y_r \to 0$ as $r \to \infty$ if and only if the eigenvalues of $Y_0 = I - AX_0$ are all of modulus less than 1, by Theorem 6.2.   Thus we have the following result.

Theorem 6.3.   *A necessary and sufficient condition for the process* (6.5) *to produce A^{-1} is that X_0, the initial approximant, be chosen so that each eigenvalue of $I - AX_0$ is of modulus less than* 1.

Example.   We take

$$A = \begin{bmatrix} 1 & 1 \\ 1 & 2 \end{bmatrix},$$

so that

$$A^{-1} = \begin{bmatrix} 2 & -1 \\ -1 & 1 \end{bmatrix}.$$

We take

$$X_0 = \begin{bmatrix} 1.9 & -.9 \\ -.9 & .9 \end{bmatrix}.$$

Then

$$I - AX_0 = \begin{bmatrix} 0 & 0 \\ -.1 & .1 \end{bmatrix}$$

has eigenvalues 0, .1 which are both of modulus less than 1.   The conditions for the convergence of (6.5) are satisfied, and we have

$$X_1 = \begin{bmatrix} 1.99 & -.99 \\ -.99 & .99 \end{bmatrix},$$

$$X_2 = \begin{bmatrix} 1.9999 & -.9999 \\ -.9999 & .9999 \end{bmatrix},$$

so that X_2 is in good agreement with A^{-1}.

The process suffers from certain defects, the most serious one being that in practice the choice of X_0 is difficult, if not impossible.   If, however, an approximate inverse of A has been determined by some other method, then (6.5) finds its proper role as an *improvement scheme*, and this is how it is generally used.   Another defect is that a large number of figures must be carried to obtain any improvement at all, principally because two matrix multiplications must be performed.

As another example, consider the recurrence

$$X_{r+1} = B + (I - BA)X_r, \qquad r \geq 0, \tag{6.8}$$

with $X_0 = 0$ and A nonsingular.   Setting $Y_r = I - AX_r$ as before, we find from (6.8) that

$$Y_r = (I - AB)Y_{r-1}, \tag{6.9}$$

$$Y_r = (I - AB)^r. \tag{6.10}$$

From (6.10) we can conclude that $X_r \to A^{-1}$ as $r \to \infty$ if and only if each eigenvalue of $I - AB$ (or of $I - BA$) is of modulus less than 1.   Contrary to the previous process, the error matrix is not squared at each step but is multiplied by a constant matrix, as shown by (6.9).   The convergence therefore cannot be as rapid as that of (6.5).   Scheme (6.8) has the advantage, however, that each step requires just one matrix multiplication instead of two, and this is occasionally an important consideration.

Example.   As before, we take

$$A = \begin{bmatrix} 1 & 1 \\ 1 & 2 \end{bmatrix},$$

so that

$$A^{-1} = \begin{bmatrix} 2 & -1 \\ -1 & 1 \end{bmatrix}.$$

We take

$$B = \begin{bmatrix} 1.9 & -.9 \\ -.9 & .9 \end{bmatrix},$$

so that

$$I - AB = \begin{bmatrix} 0 & 0 \\ -.1 & .1 \end{bmatrix}$$

has eigenvalues 0, .1.   Process (6.8) will therefore succeed, and we find $X_1 = B$,

$$X_2 = \begin{bmatrix} 1.99 & -.99 \\ -.99 & .99 \end{bmatrix}.$$

The improvement, roughly speaking, is one digit at a time.

Choosing $B = I$ and setting $I - A = C$ in (6.8), we see that $X_r = I + C + \cdots + C^{r-1}$.   From the preceding discussion we obtain the following useful corollary.

Corollary 6.4.   *The identity*

$$(I - C)^{-1} = I + C + C^2 + \cdots$$

is valid if and only if each eigenvalue of C is of modulus less than 1.

The preceding discussion shows that it is of interest to possess some simple criterion for deciding whether or not the eigenvalues of a matrix are inside the unit circle.   Let λ be an eigenvalue of $A = (a_{ij})$ and $x = (x_1, x_2, \ldots, x_n)'$ a corresponding eigenvector, so that $Ax = \lambda x$.   Let m be a subscript for which x_m is a maximum (and so certainly not zero).   Then

$$\sum_{j=1}^{n} a_{mj}x_j = \lambda x_m,$$

$$\lambda - a_{mm} = \sum_{j \neq m} a_{mj} \frac{x_j}{x_m},$$

$$|\lambda - a_{mm}| \leq \sum_{j \neq m} |a_{mj}|.$$

Thus λ is contained in the circle in the complex plane with center a_{mm} and radius $\sum\limits_{j \neq m} |a_{mj}|$. Thus we have the following result.

Theorem 6.5. *The eigenvalues of A lie in the union of the circles*

$$|z - a_{ii}| \leq \sum_{j \neq i} |a_{ij}|, \qquad 1 \leq i \leq n. \tag{6.11}$$

This theorem is known as the Geršgorin circle theorem and (6.11) as the Geršgorin circles.

For developments of this and related results, see Chap. 8.

Example. The matrix

$$\begin{bmatrix} 0 & 0 \\ -.1 & .1 \end{bmatrix}$$

which occurred previously has eigenvalues 0, .1. Theorem 6.5 shows that these eigenvalues lie in the union of the two circles $|z| \leq 0$, $|z - .1| \leq .1$ and so certainly are inside the unit circle. It happens quite frequently that this theorem obviates the need of computing the eigenvalues.

Corollary 6.6. *If the sums*

$$\sum_{j=1}^{n} |a_{ij}|, \qquad 1 \leq i \leq n,$$

are all less than 1, or if

$$\sum_{i=1}^{n} |a_{ij}|, \qquad 1 \leq j \leq n,$$

are all less than 1, then all the eigenvalues of A are inside the unit circle.

We want to associate with a matrix A a number which will measure its "distance" from the zero matrix or, more generally, will measure the distance between two matrices A, B. More precisely, we require a real-valued function N having the following properties:

$$N(A) \geq 0 \qquad \text{and} \qquad N(A) = 0 \qquad \text{if and only if } A = 0, \tag{6.12}$$

$$N(cA) = |c|\, N(A), \qquad c \text{ a complex number,} \tag{6.13}$$

$$N(A + B) \leq N(A) + N(B), \tag{6.14}$$

$$N(AB) \leq N(A)N(B). \tag{6.15}$$

There have been recent studies of norms by Faddeeva [10] and Ostrowski [29].

Properties (6.12) and (6.14) are the usual properties of a distance function in a metric space. Property (6.13) is familiar also, but (6.15) is peculiar to matrices. It is not evident that such functions exist, and we define

$$F(A) = \left(\sum_{i,j} |a_{ij}|^2 \right)^{1/2} \qquad \text{(the \textit{Frobenius norm}),} \tag{6.16}$$

$$M(A) = n \max_{i,j} |a_{ij}|. \tag{6.17}$$

Properties (6.12) to (6.15) are tolerably obvious for M, whereas (6.12) to (6.14) are also clear for F, if A is regarded as a vector in euclidean n^2-dimensional space and $F(A)$ as its length. As for (6.15), if A and B are conformal (that is, if it is possible to form AB), then

$$F(AB)^2 = \sum_{i,j} \left| \sum_k a_{ik}b_{kj} \right|^2$$

$$\leq \sum_{i,j} \left(\sum_k |a_{ik}b_{kj}| \right)^2$$

$$= \sum_{i,j,r,s} |a_{ir}b_{rj}a_{is}b_{sj}|$$

$$= \sum_{i,j,r,s} |a_{ir}b_{sj}| \, |a_{is}b_{rj}|$$

$$\leq \sum_{i,j,r,s} \tfrac{1}{2}(|a_{ir}b_{sj}|^2 + |a_{is}b_{rj}|^2)$$

$$= \sum_{i,j,r,s} |a_{ir}b_{sj}|^2$$

$$= \sum_{i,r} |a_{ir}|^2 \sum_{s,j} |b_{sj}|^2$$

$$= F(A)^2 F(B)^2.$$

We note some additional properties of the Frobenius norm. Let A^* denote $\bar{A}'$. Then

$$F(A)^2 = \operatorname{tr}(AA^*) \tag{6.18}$$

where $\operatorname{tr} A$ denotes the trace of A. Let U and V be unitary matrices; that is, $UU^* = VV^* = I$. Then also

$$F(UAV) = F(A). \tag{6.19}$$

This holds because

$$F(UAV)^2 = \operatorname{tr}(UAVV^*A^*U^*)$$

$$= \operatorname{tr}(UAA^*U^*)$$

$$= \operatorname{tr}(AA^*) \quad \text{(since } AA^* \text{ and } UAA^*U^* \text{ are similar)}$$

$$= F(A)^2.$$

Using (6.19) and a result of Schur, we can derive a significant inequality for the eigenvalues of a matrix A. Schur's result is that an arbitrary complex matrix A can be transformed into triangular form by a unitary matrix U. Now, for a triangular matrix $T = (t_{ij})$, we have

$$\sum_{i=1}^n |t_{ii}|^2 \leq F(T)^2$$

with equality if and only if T is diagonal. We obtain, therefore, the following theorem.

Theorem 6.7.   *Let A have eigenvalues $\lambda_1, \lambda_2, \ldots, \lambda_n$.   Then*

$$|\lambda_1|^2 + \cdots + |\lambda_n|^2 \leq F(A)^2 \qquad (6.20)$$

with equality if and only if A is unitarily equivalent to a diagonal matrix.

It is worth noting that a necessary and sufficient condition for A to be unitarily equivalent to a diagonal matrix is that A be normal, that is, that A satisfy $AA^* = A^*A$.

Clearly we always have

$$F(A) \leq M(A). \qquad (6.21)$$

In terms of a norm N, we can now say that *a sufficient condition for the process* (6.5), *or* (6.8), *to produce the inverse of A is that $N(I - AX_0)$, or $N(I - AB)$, respectively, be less than* 1.

Example.   The Frobenius norm of the matrix

$$\begin{bmatrix} 0 & 0 \\ -.1 & .1 \end{bmatrix}$$

occurring previously is $\frac{1}{10}\sqrt{2}$, so once again we are in a position to infer that processes (6.5), or (6.8), will converge with X_0, or B, as chosen.

From (6.6), (6.7), and (6.15), we obtain the quantitative estimates for process (6.5):

$$N(Y_{r+1}) \leq N(Y_r)^2, \qquad (6.22)$$

$$N(Y_r) \leq N(Y_0)^{2^r}, \qquad (6.23)$$

where N is any norm.   Quite often it is better to have directly an estimate for $N(A^{-1} - X_r)$ than for $N(Y_r)$.   Let us suppose that a state in the computation has been reached such that

$$N(Y_r) < 1.$$

Then we have

$$AX_r = I - Y_r,$$

$$X_r^{-1}A^{-1} = (I - Y_r)^{-1}.$$

By Corollary 6.4 and (6.20), we have

$$X_r^{-1}A^{-1} = I + Y_r + Y_r^2 + \cdots,$$

$$A^{-1} - X_r = X_r(Y_r + Y_r^2 + \cdots),$$

and using the properties of a norm we find easily that

$$N(A^{-1} - X_r) \leq \frac{N(X_r)N(Y_r)}{1 - N(Y_r)}. \qquad (6.24)$$

This estimate is useful computationally, since the matrices X_r are available at each iteration. For the process (6.5), we have as a consequence of (6.23) and (6.24) that

$$N(A^{-1} - X_r) \leq \frac{N(X_r) N(Y_0)^{2^r}}{1 - N(Y_0)^{2^r}}. \tag{6.25}$$

The next process we describe, the Gauss-Seidel process, is a practical iterative scheme for finding the solution of a set of linear equations in certain circumstances. We let $A = (a_{ij})$, $b = (b_1, b_2, \ldots, b_n)'$, and define a sequence of vectors

$$x_r = [x_1^{(r)}, x_2^{(r)}, \ldots, x_n^{(r)}]', \qquad r \geq 0,$$

as follows: x_0 is arbitrary, and x_{r+1} is obtained from x_r by finding the solution of the triangular system

$$
\begin{aligned}
a_{11}x_1^{(r+1)} + a_{12}x_2^{(r)} \quad &+ \cdots + a_{1n}x_n^{(r)} = b_1 \\
a_{21}x_1^{(r+1)} + a_{22}x_2^{(r+1)} &+ \cdots + a_{2n}x_n^{(r)} = b_2 \\
&\cdots\cdots\cdots\cdots\cdots\cdots\cdots\cdots \\
a_{n1}x_1^{(r+1)} + a_{n2}x_2^{(r+1)} &+ \cdots + a_{nn}x_n^{(r+1)} = b_n.
\end{aligned}
\tag{6.26}
$$

The matrix equivalent of this process is as follows. Write $A = L + U$, where L is the lower triangular part of A and where U is the part of A above the main diagonal. Then we have

$$Lx_{r+1} + Ux_r = b. \tag{6.27}$$

We assume now that L is nonsingular, and we put $a = L^{-1}b$, $C = -L^{-1}U$: Then

$$x_{r+1} = a + Cx_r,$$

from which it is easy to show that

$$x_r = (I + C + \cdots + C^{r-1})a + C^r x_0. \tag{6.28}$$

Taking into account Corollary 6.4, we see that the sequence of vectors x_r converges for any vector b if and only if each eigenvalue of C is of modulus less than 1. For the limit of the sequence (when it converges) we have, from (6.28),

$$x = \lim_{r \to \infty} x_r = (I - C)^{-1}a = A^{-1}b,$$

which is the solution of the system $Ax = b$. We have, then, the following result.

Theorem 6.8. *The Gauss-Seidel process defined by* (6.26) *produces the solution of the system* $Ax = b$ *for arbitrary* b *if and only if each eigenvalue of the matrix* C *defined above is of modulus less than 1.*

Other schemes in terms of different decompositions of A are possible.

Example. Take

$$A = \begin{bmatrix} 1 & 1 \\ 1 & 2 \end{bmatrix},$$

so that

$$L = \begin{bmatrix} 1 & 0 \\ 1 & 2 \end{bmatrix}, \qquad U = \begin{bmatrix} 0 & 1 \\ 0 & 0 \end{bmatrix}.$$

Then

$$C = -L^{-1}U = \begin{bmatrix} 0 & -1 \\ 0 & .5 \end{bmatrix}$$

has eigenvalues 0, .5, so the process will succeed for arbitrary b. Choosing $b = (1,1)'$ and $x_0 = 0$, we have the system

$$x_1^{(r+1)} + x_2^{(r)} = 1$$
$$x_1^{(r+1)} + 2x_2^{(r+1)} = 1,$$

from which we obtain

$$x_r = (1 - 2^{-r+1}, 2^{-r})' \qquad r \geq 1,$$

so that $x_r \to (1,0)'$ as $r \to \infty$. This is the solution of the system

$$x_1 + x_2 = 1$$
$$x_1 + 2x_2 = 1.$$

The criterion of Theorem 6.8 is rather obscure, and it is of interest to look for sufficient conditions which will guarantee the success of the process. In this connection we prove the following.

Theorem 6.9. *Let F, G be matrices such that F is nonsingular and $F + G$ and $F - G^*$ hermitian positive definite. Then the eigenvalues of $F^{-1}G$ are all inside the unit circle.*

Proof. Let λ, x be an eigenvalue and eigenvector, respectively, of $F^{-1}G$: $F^{-1}Gx = \lambda x$. Then $Gx = \lambda Fx$, $x^*Gx = \lambda x^*Fx$. Adding x^*Fx to both sides of the latter equation, we obtain

$$x^*(F + G)x = (1 + \lambda)x^*Fx. \tag{6.29}$$

Now (6.29) shows that $\lambda \neq -1$, since otherwise $x^*(F + G)x = 0$, which cannot happen, $F + G$ being positive definite.

Since $F + G$ is hermitian, we obtain from (6.29)

$$(1 + \lambda)x^*F^*x = (1 + \lambda)x^*Fx$$
$$= (1 + \lambda)[x^*(F - G^*)x + x^*G^*x]$$
$$= (1 + \lambda)[x^*(F - G^*)x + \bar{\lambda}x^*F^*x],$$
$$(1 - |\lambda|^2)x^*F^*x = (1 + \lambda)x^*(F - G^*)x.$$

Making use of (6.29) again and the fact that $F + G$ is hermitian, we have

$$(1 - |\lambda|^2)x^*(F + G)x = |1 + \lambda|^2x^*(F - G^*)x.$$

But both $F + G$ and $F - G^*$ are positive definite, and $\lambda \neq -1$. Thus

$$1 - |\lambda|^2 > 0,$$

and the proof is complete.

Suppose now that A is hermitian positive definite. Then A may be written as $K + D + K^*$, where K is the part of A below the diagonal and D is the diagonal of A. Setting $F = K + D$, $G = K^*$ and noting that D is also hermitian positive definite, we have $A = F + G$, $D = F - G^*$. Theorem 6.9 applies, and we obtain the following result.

Theorem 6.10.   *The Gauss-Seidel process will converge if A is hermitian positive definite.*

We now observe that Theorem 6.10 is actually of universal application, since the system $Ax = b$ may be replaced by the system $A^*Ax = A^*b$, and A^*A is hermitian positive definite when A is nonsingular. This multiplication is of dubious value, however, and is *not recommended*. See the Rutishauser example below and Taussky [32].

6.4   Direct Methods

Among the simplest systems are the triangular ones:

$$
\begin{aligned}
a_{11}x_1 & & & = b_1 \\
a_{21}x_1 + a_{22}x_2 & & & = b_2 \\
a_{31}x_1 + a_{32}x_2 + a_{33}x_3 & & & = b_3 \\
& \cdots \\
a_{n1}x_1 + a_{n2}x_2 + a_{n3}x_3 + \cdots + a_{nn}x_n & & & = b_n.
\end{aligned}
\tag{6.30}
$$

Provided that $a_{11}a_{22} \cdots a_{nn} \neq 0$, the system (6.30) can be solved recursively as follows:

$$
\begin{aligned}
x_1 &= b_1/a_{11} \\
x_2 &= (b_2 - a_{21}x_1)/a_{22} \\
x_3 &= (b_3 - a_{31}x_1 - a_{32}x_2)/a_{33} \\
& \cdots \\
x_n &= (b_n - a_{n1}x_1 - a_{n2}x_2 - \cdots - a_{nn-1}x_{n-1})/a_{nn}.
\end{aligned}
$$

We may therefore consider the solution of a triangular system as completely settled. There is some advantage, then, in attempting to reduce an arbitrary system to a triangular system. This can be done in a variety of ways. Thus if A is an arbitrary matrix, we try to find a lower triangular matrix L and an upper triangular matrix U such that

$$A = LU.$$

If $A = (a_{ij})$, $L = (l_{ij})$, $U = (u_{ij})$, this is equivalent to the system of n^2 equations in $(n^2 + n)$ unknowns:

$$a_{ij} = \sum_{k=1}^{\min(i,j)} l_{ik} u_{kj}.$$

Our latitude lies in the specification of the diagonal coefficients.   Let us regard the diagonal elements of L as known.   Then the remaining elements of L and the elements of U may be determined stepwise in the order

$$u_{11}, u_{12}, u_{13}, \ldots, u_{1n}$$
$$l_{21}, u_{22}, u_{23}, \ldots, u_{2n}$$
$$l_{31}, l_{32}, u_{33}, \ldots, u_{3n}$$
$$\cdots \cdots \cdots \cdots \cdots \cdots$$
$$l_{n1}, l_{n2}, l_{n3}, \cdots, u_{nn}.$$

It is important to notice that not every matrix A can be written as $A = LU$.   For example, the 2×2 matrix $A = (a_{ij})$ where $a_{11} = a_{22} = 0$, $a_{12} = a_{21} = 1$ cannot be put into this form.

Once A has been expressed in this manner, the system $Ax = b$ becomes $LUx = b$ so that x is obtainable by solving two triangular systems:

$$x = U^{-1}(L^{-1}b).$$

An important instance not covered by this process occurs when A is hermitian positive definite.   In this case we look for an upper triangular matrix T such that

$$A = T^*T.$$

It is worthwhile remarking that probably the simplest way to determine whether or not a given hermitian matrix A *is* positive definite is to try to express it as T^*T; the attempt will succeed if and only if A is positive definite.   In addition, the determinant of A is the square of the product of the diagonal elements of T.

The actual algorithm which produces T is quite simple.   If $T = (t_{ij})$, we have

$$a_{ij} = \sum_{k=1}^{\min(i,j)} \bar{t}_{ki} t_{kj}.$$

Thus
$$|t_{11}| = \sqrt{a_{11}}, \ldots, t_{1n} = a_{1n}/t_{11}$$
$$|t_{22}| = \sqrt{a_{22} - |t_{12}|^2}, \ldots, t_{2n} = (a_{2n} - \bar{t}_{12}t_{1n})/t_{22}$$
$$\cdots \cdots \cdots \cdots \cdots \cdots \cdots \cdots \cdots \cdots$$
$$|t_{nn}| = \sqrt{a_{nn} - |t_{1n}|^2 - \cdots - |t_{n-1n}|^2}.$$

The quantities $|t_{ii}|^2$ are just the quotients of the consecutive principal minors [that is, a_{11}, $(a_{11}a_{22} - |a_{12}|^2)/a_{11}$, etc.], and in practice we would usually choose t_{ii} to be real and positive.   Because of the presence of the square roots, this is known as the *square-root method*.

Example.   The matrix of the system

$$x_1 + x_2 = 1$$
$$x_1 + 2x_2 = 1$$

(6.31)

is

$$\begin{bmatrix} 1 & 1 \\ 1 & 2 \end{bmatrix},$$

which is symmetric positive definite.   Thus we can write

$$\begin{bmatrix} 1 & 1 \\ 1 & 2 \end{bmatrix} = \begin{bmatrix} t_{11} & 0 \\ t_{12} & t_{22} \end{bmatrix} \begin{bmatrix} t_{11} & t_{12} \\ 0 & t_{22} \end{bmatrix},$$

from which $t_{11} = 1$, $t_{12} = 1$, $t_{22} = 1$ in order.   Thus

$$\begin{bmatrix} 1 & 1 \\ 1 & 2 \end{bmatrix} = \begin{bmatrix} 1 & 0 \\ 1 & 1 \end{bmatrix} \begin{bmatrix} 1 & 1 \\ 0 & 1 \end{bmatrix},$$

and the system (6.31) becomes

$$\begin{bmatrix} 1 & 0 \\ 1 & 1 \end{bmatrix} \begin{bmatrix} 1 & 1 \\ 0 & 1 \end{bmatrix} \begin{pmatrix} x_1 \\ x_2 \end{pmatrix} = \begin{pmatrix} 1 \\ 1 \end{pmatrix},$$

so that

$$\begin{pmatrix} x_1 \\ x_2 \end{pmatrix} = \left\{ \begin{bmatrix} 1 & 0 \\ 1 & 1 \end{bmatrix}^{-1} \right\}' \begin{bmatrix} 1 & 0 \\ 1 & 1 \end{bmatrix}^{-1} \begin{pmatrix} 1 \\ 1 \end{pmatrix}$$

$$= \begin{bmatrix} 1 & 0 \\ -1 & 1 \end{bmatrix}' \begin{bmatrix} 1 & 0 \\ -1 & 1 \end{bmatrix} \begin{pmatrix} 1 \\ 1 \end{pmatrix}$$

$$= \begin{pmatrix} 1 \\ 0 \end{pmatrix}.$$

The evident advantage of the square-root method over general decomposition is that only one triangular system need be solved, since

$$(T^*)^{-1} = (T^{-1})^*.$$

The next method we consider, the elimination method, is by far the best general method available for solving a system or inverting a matrix. Let A be an arbitrary $n \times n$ matrix, B an arbitrary $n \times k$ matrix.   The method consists of performing elementary transformations (adding a multiple of a row to some other row, interchanging two rows, multiplying a row by a constant) on the $n \times n + k$ matrix $[A,B]$ until A has been reduced to the identity, when B will have become $A^{-1}B$.   Some care must be exercised here, and it is a good idea to choose the so-called pivotal elements to be the largest columnwise.

Example. Consider the following system:

$$\begin{aligned} x_1 + 2x_2 + 3x_3 &= 1 \\ 3x_1 + x_2 + x_3 &= 0 \\ 2x_1 + x_2 + x_3 &= 0. \end{aligned} \qquad (6.32)$$

The steps involved in finding the solution are as follows:

$$\begin{bmatrix} 1 & 2 & 3 & 1 \\ \underline{3} & 1 & 1 & 0 \\ 2 & 1 & 1 & 0 \end{bmatrix}$$
Original matrix.
First pivot.

$$\begin{bmatrix} 3 & 1 & 1 & 0 \\ 1 & 2 & 3 & 1 \\ 2 & 1 & 1 & 0 \end{bmatrix}$$
Rows 1 and 2 interchanged.

$$\begin{bmatrix} 1 & \tfrac{1}{3} & \tfrac{1}{3} & 0 \\ 0 & \tfrac{5}{3} & \tfrac{8}{3} & 1 \\ 0 & \underline{\tfrac{1}{3}} & \tfrac{1}{3} & 0 \end{bmatrix}$$
Row 1 divided by first pivot.
Rows 2 and 3 modified by row 1.
Second pivot.

$$\begin{bmatrix} 1 & 0 & -\tfrac{1}{5} & -\tfrac{1}{5} \\ 0 & 1 & \tfrac{8}{5} & \tfrac{3}{5} \\ 0 & 0 & \underline{-\tfrac{1}{5}} & -\tfrac{1}{5} \end{bmatrix}$$
Row 2 divided by second pivot.
Rows 1 and 3 modified by row 2.
Third pivot.

$$\begin{bmatrix} 1 & 0 & 0 & 0 \\ 0 & 1 & 0 & -1 \\ 0 & 0 & 1 & 1 \end{bmatrix}$$
Row 3 divided by third pivot.
Rows 1 and 2 modified by row 3.

The solution is thus

$$x_1 = 0, \qquad x_2 = -1, \qquad x_3 = 1.$$

A word about checking. Let δ_k be the $k \times 1$ vector $(1,1,\ldots,1)'$. Then $A\delta_n + B\delta_k$ consists just of the row sums of $[A,B]$ and so is easily computed. If the previous process is applied to the $n \times n + k + 1$ matrix

$$C = [A, B, -A\delta_n - B\delta_k],$$

then each row sum of C is initially 0, and this fact will remain true throughout the computation. Thus, if at any stage some row sum differs from 0 significantly, an error has been introduced. At the end of the computation, the largest row sum produced is a good measure of the error in the solution $A^{-1}B$.

Example (*with checking*).   For the system

$$7x_1 - x_2 = 3$$
$$3x_1 + 5x_2 = 2$$

the solution is as follows:

$$\begin{bmatrix} \underline{7} & -1 & 3 & -9 \\ 3 & 5 & 2 & -10 \end{bmatrix}$$

Original matrix.
First pivot.

$$\begin{bmatrix} 1 & -\tfrac{1}{7} & \tfrac{3}{7} & -\tfrac{9}{7} \\ 0 & \tfrac{38}{7} & \tfrac{5}{7} & -\tfrac{43}{7} \end{bmatrix}$$

Row 1 divided by first pivot.
Row 2 modified by row 1.
Second pivot.

$$\begin{bmatrix} 1 & 0 & \tfrac{17}{38} & -\tfrac{55}{38} \\ 0 & 1 & \tfrac{5}{38} & -\tfrac{43}{38} \end{bmatrix}$$

Row 2 divided by second pivot.
Row 1 modified by row 2.

Thus $x_1 = \tfrac{17}{38}$, $x_2 = \tfrac{5}{38}$, and the row sums are both 0.

It is worth noting that the product of the pivotal elements is the determinant of A.

If we are interested primarily in matrix inversion, rather than in the solution of equations, there are several possible approaches.   We can solve the n systems

$$Ax_i = \delta_i, \qquad 1 \le i \le n,$$

where the δ_i are the n unit vectors.   The inverse of A is then $[x_1, x_2, \ldots, x_n]$.   Or we can do this at one blow by choosing B as the identity matrix, in the previous discussion.   Quite often it is desirable to avoid carrying the identity matrix (to save space) or to solve n systems (to save time), and the following scheme is especially suitable for these purposes and is easily programmed for high-speed computers.

Disregarding check vectors, our matrix initially is the $n \times n + 1$ matrix $[A, 0]$.   At step i, $1 \le i \le n$, the first column of the matrix is scanned to determine the element of largest absolute value which has not previously been used as a pivotal element in steps $1, 2, \ldots, i - 1$.   When this element has been determined, the number of the row in which it occurs, say k_i, is recorded in a "permutation store."   The element so determined is 0 if and only if A is singular.   If the element is not 0, the k_ith unit vector is put into the $(n + 1)$st column of the matrix.   The k_ith row of this matrix is now divided by the pivotal element, and appropriate multiples of the k_ith row are added to the remaining rows to make all first-column elements, other than the k_ith element, 0.   The entire matrix is now shifted left one column and the procedure repeated until n such steps have been accomplished.   At this point, A has been replaced by its permuted inverse, and this is unscrambled as follows by means of the permutation

$$\begin{pmatrix} 1 & 2 & \cdots & n \\ k_1 & k_2 & \cdots & k_n \end{pmatrix}.$$

Rearrange the columns so that column 1 becomes column k_1, column 2 becomes column $k_2, \ldots$, column n becomes column k_n. Now rearrange the rows so that row k_1 becomes row 1, row k_2 becomes row 2, ..., row k_n becomes row n.

In practice, the unscrambling would be part of the print routine.

The justification for this process is quite simple. Let P be the permutation matrix which has 1 in the k_ith row and ith column. Then the process determines a matrix M such that

$$M[A,P] = [MA,MP] = [P,MP].$$

Hence

$$MA = P, \qquad MP = PA^{-1}P, \qquad A^{-1} = P'(MP)P'.$$

Example (*without checking*). We choose

$$A = \begin{bmatrix} 1 & 10 & 1 \\ 2 & 0 & 1 \\ 3 & 3 & 2 \end{bmatrix}.$$

The computation is as follows:

$$\begin{bmatrix} 1 & 10 & 1 & 0 \\ 2 & 0 & 1 & 0 \\ \underline{3} & 3 & 2 & 1 \end{bmatrix} \quad \begin{matrix} 3 \\ {} \\ {} \end{matrix} \quad \begin{matrix} \text{Original matrix.} \\ \text{First pivot.} \\ \text{Third unit vector in last column.} \end{matrix}$$

$$\begin{bmatrix} 0 & \underline{9} & \tfrac{1}{3} & -\tfrac{1}{3} \\ 0 & -2 & -\tfrac{1}{3} & -\tfrac{2}{3} \\ 1 & 1 & \tfrac{2}{3} & \tfrac{1}{3} \end{bmatrix} \quad \begin{matrix} 3 \\ 1 \\ {} \end{matrix} \quad \begin{matrix} \text{Step 1 performed.} \\ \text{Second pivot.} \\ {} \end{matrix}$$

$$\begin{bmatrix} 9 & \tfrac{1}{3} & -\tfrac{1}{3} & 1 \\ -2 & -\tfrac{1}{3} & -\tfrac{2}{3} & 0 \\ 1 & \tfrac{2}{3} & \tfrac{1}{3} & 0 \end{bmatrix} \quad \begin{matrix} 3 \\ 1 \\ {} \end{matrix} \quad \begin{matrix} \text{First column deleted.} \\ \text{First unit vector in last column.} \\ {} \end{matrix}$$

$$\begin{bmatrix} 1 & \tfrac{1}{27} & -\tfrac{1}{27} & \tfrac{1}{9} \\ 0 & -\tfrac{7}{27} & -\tfrac{20}{27} & \tfrac{2}{9} \\ 0 & \tfrac{17}{27} & \tfrac{10}{27} & -\tfrac{1}{9} \end{bmatrix} \quad \begin{matrix} 3 \\ 1 \\ 2 \end{matrix} \quad \begin{matrix} \text{Step 2 performed.} \\ \text{Third pivot.} \\ {} \end{matrix}$$

$$\begin{bmatrix} \tfrac{1}{27} & -\tfrac{1}{27} & \tfrac{1}{9} & 0 \\ -\tfrac{7}{27} & -\tfrac{20}{27} & \tfrac{2}{9} & 1 \\ \tfrac{17}{27} & \tfrac{10}{27} & -\tfrac{1}{9} & 0 \end{bmatrix} \quad \begin{matrix} 3 \\ 1 \\ 2 \end{matrix} \quad \begin{matrix} \text{First column deleted.} \\ \text{Second unit vector in last column.} \\ {} \end{matrix}$$

$$\begin{bmatrix} 0 & -\tfrac{1}{7} & \tfrac{1}{7} & \tfrac{1}{7} \\ 1 & \tfrac{20}{7} & -\tfrac{6}{7} & -\tfrac{27}{7} \\ 0 & -\tfrac{10}{7} & \tfrac{3}{7} & \tfrac{17}{7} \end{bmatrix} \quad \begin{matrix} 3 \\ 1 \\ 2 \end{matrix} \quad \begin{matrix} {} \\ \text{Step 3 performed.} \\ {} \end{matrix}$$

The matrix

$$\begin{bmatrix} -\tfrac{1}{7} & \tfrac{1}{7} & \tfrac{1}{7} \\ 20\tfrac{2}{7} & -6\tfrac{6}{7} & -27\tfrac{3}{7} \\ -10\tfrac{4}{7} & 3\tfrac{3}{7} & 17\tfrac{1}{7} \end{bmatrix}$$

must now be unscrambled according to the permutation

$$\begin{pmatrix} 1 & 2 & 3 \\ 3 & 1 & 2 \end{pmatrix}$$

as follows.   Column 1 becomes column 3, column 2 becomes column 1, column 3 becomes column 2, to give

$$\begin{bmatrix} \tfrac{1}{7} & \tfrac{1}{7} & -\tfrac{1}{7} \\ -6\tfrac{6}{7} & -27\tfrac{3}{7} & 20\tfrac{2}{7} \\ 3\tfrac{3}{7} & 17\tfrac{1}{7} & -10\tfrac{4}{7} \end{bmatrix}.$$

Now row 3 becomes row 1, row 1 becomes row 2, row 2 becomes row 3, to give

$$\begin{bmatrix} 3\tfrac{3}{7} & 17\tfrac{1}{7} & -10\tfrac{4}{7} \\ \tfrac{1}{7} & \tfrac{1}{7} & -\tfrac{1}{7} \\ -6\tfrac{6}{7} & -27\tfrac{3}{7} & 20\tfrac{2}{7} \end{bmatrix}.$$

This is the inverse of the original matrix, as may be verified by direct multiplication.

We note that one of the more efficient ways of evaluating determinants is by the triangularization of the matrix.   This can be done at the expense of about $\tfrac{1}{3}n^3$ multiplications.   Since the value of the determinant gives some information about the "condition" of a matrix or system, it is desirable that programs for matrix inversion or the solution of equations include computation of the determinant, which can be secured with negligible expense.

Another method which is sometimes useful is inversion by partitioning.   Let us suppose that A is a nonsingular $n \times n$ matrix and write

$$A = \begin{bmatrix} a & b \\ c & d \end{bmatrix},$$

where a is an $r \times r$ matrix, b an $r \times s$ matrix, c an $s \times r$ matrix, and d an $s \times s$ matrix.   Here r and s are positive integers with sum n.   We assume A^{-1} partitioned similarly:

$$A^{-1} = \begin{bmatrix} \alpha & \beta \\ \gamma & \delta \end{bmatrix}.$$

Then the relationship $AA^{-1} = I$ leads to the following system of equations for the unknown matrices α, β, γ, δ:

$$a\alpha + b\gamma = 1^{(r \times r)}, \qquad a\beta + b\delta = 0^{(r \times s)},$$
$$c\alpha + d\gamma = 0^{(s \times r)}, \qquad c\beta + d\delta = 1^{(s \times s)},$$

from which we can deduce in general that

$$\alpha = a^{-1} + a^{-1}b\delta ca^{-1}, \qquad \beta = -a^{-1}b\delta,$$
$$\gamma = -\delta ca^{-1}, \qquad \delta = (d - ca^{-1}b)^{-1}.$$

This of course necessitates that both a and $d - ca^{-1}b$ be nonsingular.

Partitioning does not save time, but it makes possible the inversion of matrices too large for storage in the "fast" memory of a high-speed computer.

We note here that it is possible to invert matrices with complex elements by real operations only. If

$$A = X + iY, \qquad X \text{ and } Y \text{ real,}$$

then the inverse of

$$\begin{bmatrix} X & Y \\ -Y & X \end{bmatrix}$$

is of the same form, and if

$$\begin{bmatrix} X & Y \\ -Y & X \end{bmatrix}^{-1} = \begin{bmatrix} Z & W \\ -W & Z \end{bmatrix},$$

then

$$A^{-1} = Z + iW.$$

6.5 Evaluation of Methods

In the examples discussed, the matrices whose inverses were computed had integral elements and were of low order, the computations being carried through exactly. In practice this is not possible, and computations must be carried out to a fixed number of places, thus introducing round-off errors. These are more critical in the direct methods and are serious enough to prevent completion of the algorithm and often to invalidate the results obtained. It is important to have some numerical estimate for this error in terms of the matrix. Such an estimate for a variant of the elimination method above has been given by von Neumann and Goldstine [15]. In their method, fixed-point arithmetic with scaling is used, and the matrix A to be inverted is always real and symmetric. The inverse produced is forced to be symmetric by identifying upper and lower triangular parts. For another treatment see Wilkinson [36].

We define the P-condition number of an arbitrary nonsingular matrix A by

$$P = P(A) = \left| \frac{\lambda}{\mu} \right|$$

where λ is a root of largest modulus of A and μ a root of least modulus of A. A is assumed real, symmetric, and positive definite. Then, if the algorithm of von Neumann and Goldstine actually produces an inverse X, it is shown that

$$|\lambda_0| \leq 14.24 P(A) n^2 \epsilon,$$

where λ_0 is a root of largest modulus of $I - AX$, n is the order of matrix A, and ϵ is the smallest number recognized by the algorithm (which in practice might be 2^{-35}, or 10^{-12}). If, however, the algorithm fails to produce an inverse, then it is shown that A is nearly singular, and

$$|\mu| \leq 10 n^2 \epsilon.$$

In the case when A is not positive definite, the algorithm is applied instead to AA', and

$$A^{-1} = A'(AA')^{-1}$$

is used to show that, if the algorithm produces an inverse X, then

$$|\lambda_0| \leq 36.58 P(AA') n^2 \epsilon.$$

It is known that $P(AA') \geq P(A)^2$. Thus matrices A for which $P(A)$ is large can be expected to be troublesome, and it is reasonable to use this number as a measure of the "ill condition" of A, even when A is not of the class considered by von Neumann and Goldstine.

We consider a significant example suggested by Rutishauser. We put

$$B = \begin{bmatrix} 1 & & & & \\ 1 & -1 & & 0 & \\ 1 & -2 & 1 & & \\ 1 & -3 & 3 & -1 & \\ 1 & -4 & 6 & -4 & 1 \\ \cdots & \cdots & \cdots & \cdots & \cdots \end{bmatrix}.$$

Then the eigenvalues of B are either 1 or -1, so that $P(B) = 1$. We put

$$A = BB' = \left(\binom{i+j}{i} \right), \qquad 0 \leq i, j \leq n - 1.$$

Then A is symmetric positive definite. We note that $B^2 = I$, so that $A^{-1} = B'B$. Thus

$$A = BA^{-1}B^{-1},$$

which implies that the eigenvalues of A and the eigenvalues of A^{-1} coincide. From this we conclude that $P(A)$ is just the square of the largest eigenvalue of A. Now, if λ is the largest eigenvalue of A, we have

$$\lambda \leq \operatorname{tr} A \leq n\lambda.$$

It is easy to show that positive constants α, β exist such that

$$\alpha \cdot \frac{4^n}{n} \leq \operatorname{tr} A \leq \beta \cdot 4^n,$$

and this allows the estimate

$$\log \lambda \sim n \log 4$$

implying that

$$\log P(A) \sim 4n \log 2.$$

Thus A is exponentially ill-conditioned.

Another difficult example is the Hilbert matrix

$$H = ((i + j + 1)^{-1}), \qquad 0 \leq i, j \leq n - 1.$$

It can be shown that H is exponentially ill-conditioned. The results of attempts to invert H for small n are given by Todd [31].

The question of evaluating methods for inverting matrices, in particular the Gaussian method, has been discussed by Newman and Todd [30]. They give a set of test matrices and include representative numerical results from various machines.

The time involved in the two processes discussed can be estimated roughly in terms of the multiplications they require, working with fixed-point arithmetic. With floating-point arithmetic a more thorough discussion is required, since the time spent in performing the additions may not be negligible. The Gauss-Seidel process requires about n^2 multiplications per iteration for a "full" matrix; it is difficult to make any general statement about the number of iterations required, except in the case in which the matrix has a dominant diagonal.

The solution of a system of equations by the Gauss process requires about $\frac{1}{3}n^3$ multiplications. The inversion of a matrix by this process requires about n^3 multiplications: $\frac{1}{3}n^3$ for the triangulation, $\frac{1}{6}n^3$ to handle the right-hand sides, and $\frac{1}{2}n^3$ for the back substitutions. If we used the Jordan variant of the process in which we diagonalize our matrix completely, so that no back substitution is required, we would still need n^3 multiplications: $\frac{1}{2}n^3$ for the diagonalization and $\frac{1}{2}n^3$ for the manipulation of the right-hand side.

We conclude this section by discussing the solution of the system (due to T. S. Wilson)

$$
\begin{aligned}
10x_1 + 7x_2 + 8x_3 + 7x_4 &= 32 \\
7x_1 + 5x_2 + 6x_3 + 5x_4 &= 23 \\
8x_1 + 6x_2 + 10x_3 + 9x_4 &= 33 \\
7x_1 + 5x_2 + 9x_3 + 10x_4 &= 31.
\end{aligned}
\tag{6.33}
$$

If

$$
A = \begin{bmatrix}
10 & 7 & 8 & 7 \\
7 & 5 & 6 & 5 \\
8 & 6 & 10 & 9 \\
7 & 5 & 9 & 10
\end{bmatrix}
$$

is the matrix of the system, then A is nonsingular and

$$
A^{-1} = \begin{bmatrix}
25 & -41 & 10 & -6 \\
-41 & 68 & -17 & 10 \\
10 & -17 & 5 & -3 \\
-6 & 10 & -3 & 2
\end{bmatrix}.
\tag{6.34}
$$

The solution of the system (6.33) is thus $x_1 = x_2 = x_3 = x_4 = 1$. If we ask for a vector

$$
x(\epsilon) = [x_1(\epsilon), x_2(\epsilon), x_3(\epsilon), x_4(\epsilon)]'
$$

satisfying

$$
Ax(\epsilon) = (32 + \epsilon, 23 - \epsilon, 33 + \epsilon, 31 - \epsilon)',
$$

then it is easily determined from (6.34) that

$$
x(\epsilon) = (1 + 82\epsilon, 1 - 136\epsilon, 1 + 35\epsilon, 1 - 21\epsilon)'.
$$

Thus, for example, the vector

$$
(9.2, -12.6, 4.5, -1.1)'
$$

satisfies the system (6.33) with an error of $\pm.1$ in each equation, but in no sense can it be considered an approximation to the true solution

$$
(1,1,1,1)'.
$$

This indicates that, if the solution of (6.33) is computed with no more than 2 or 3 figures retained after the decimal point, trouble is likely to arise; and this indeed is the case. The matrix A is ill-conditioned, with condition number

$$
P(A) \doteq 3000.
$$

It is important to note that the solution of this system by the Gauss-Seidel method is awkward.   Starting with the zero vector, we obtain the sequence

$$(3.20, .12, .67, .20)',$$
$$(2.44, .18, 1.06, .35)',$$
$$(1.98, .21, 1.28, .46)',$$
$$(1.55, .21, 1.44, .61)',$$
$$\dots\dots\dots\dots\dots\dots$$

This slow convergence should be compared with that obtained from such a system as

$$\begin{aligned} -2x_1 + x_2 \qquad\qquad &= -1 \\ x_1 - 2x_2 + x_3 \qquad &= 0 \\ x_2 - 2x_3 + x_4 &= 0 \\ x_3 - 2x_4 &= -1. \end{aligned}$$

A related example is furnished by the pair of matrices

$$A = \begin{bmatrix} 1 & 1 \\ 1 & 1 - \dfrac{1}{n^2} \end{bmatrix}, \qquad B = \begin{bmatrix} 1 + n - n^2 & n^2 \\ n^2 - n & -n^2 \end{bmatrix}.$$

Here $\qquad F(AB - I) = \dfrac{1}{n}, \qquad F(BA - I) = 2n.$

THE DETERMINATION OF EIGENVALUES AND EIGENVECTORS

6.6   Introduction

In this context a direct method might be the determination of the characteristic polynomial, the solution of the characteristic equation, followed by the solution of the (singular) linear systems.   Elementary theoretical considerations and the study of simple examples suggest that this method is not likely to be very satisfactory (see, e.g., Wilkinson [34], Goldstine, Murray, and von Neumann [17]).

There are two essentially different problems, according to whether we require the dominant (or a few dominant) characteristic values or *all* the characteristic values.   The solution to the first problem does not imply, in practice, a solution to the second.   For, in general, some loss of accuracy is incurred in determining the dominant root; and when the process of "deflation" is applied (the removal of the dominant root so that another one becomes dominant), there is a further loss of accuracy.

Repetition of this process involves "successive contamination," so that results without significance may be obtained.

We discuss first the Jacobi method of rotations, which was shown to be a practicable one by Goldstine, Murray, and von Neumann [17] and by Givens [16]. This method was first shown to be suitable for real symmetric matrices and later for normal matrices [25]. The situation in more general cases is still rather obscure.

There have been valuable studies of variants and developments of the Jacobi method by Forsythe and Henrici [19], Pope and Tompkins [20], Causey and Henrici [21], and Henrici [35], among others. The paper by Pope and Tompkins contains the results of various experimental computations.

A standard method of finding the dominant characteristic root and associated characteristic vector is the power method. This method applies to *any* matrix A with a dominant eigenvalue and converges if the initial vector has a nonzero component of the dominant eigenvector. An important case in which A has a dominant eigenvalue is that in which A is a positive matrix, that is, the case in which all the elements of A are positive. This follows from the Perron-Frobenius theory (see, e.g., [33]). This theory and its extensions cover many important practical cases (see, e.g., Varga [26]).

Another method for finding the characteristic roots of real symmetric matrices is the Rayleigh quotient method. This has been investigated thoroughly by Ostrowski [24], who has shown that it is applicable in general cases.

For a survey of methods for the solution of this problem, see White [22].

6.7 Rotations

The properties of the orthogonal group are quite important in the determination of eigenvalues and eigenvectors, and we develop some of these properties here.

The orthogonal group of order n, denoted by O_n, is the multiplicative group of real $n \times n$ matrices R such that

$$RR' = I.$$

The elements of O_n have determinant ± 1. The subgroup of O_n consisting of matrices R with determinant 1 will be denoted by $O_n{}^+$ and the complex of matrices R of O_n with determinant -1 by $O_n{}^-$. The elements of O_n are referred to as *orthogonal* matrices, and sometimes as *rotation* matrices. Evidently $O_n{}^+$ is of index 2 in O_n and

$$O_n = O_n{}^+ + KO_n{}^+ = O_n{}^+ + O_n{}^-$$

where $K = (-1) \dotplus I^{(n-1)}.$

A well-known subgroup of O_n is the group P_n of permutation matrices. A permutation matrix is one in which each row and column contains just one nonzero entry, which is a 1.

Suppose $1 \leq \alpha < \beta \leq n$. We define the matrices $R_{\alpha,\beta} = R_{\alpha,\beta}(c,s)$ as follows: $R_{\alpha,\beta}$ has $-s$ in the (α,β) position, s in the (β,α) position, c in the (α,α) and (β,β) positions, 1 elsewhere on the diagonal, and 0 in every other position. Thus, for some suitable permutation matrix P,

$$R_{\alpha,\beta} = P\left(\begin{bmatrix} c & -s \\ s & c \end{bmatrix} + I^{(n-2)}\right)P'.$$

We shall always require that c, s be real and

$$c^2 + s^2 = 1.$$

Then the matrices $R_{\alpha,\beta}$ are in $O_n{}^+$. We shall prove the following theorem.

Theorem 6.11. $O_n{}^+$ is generated by the matrices $R_{\alpha,\beta}$.

Proof. Let $R = (r_{ij})$ be in $O_n{}^+$. Suppose that $r_{13} = \cdots = r_{1\,k-1} = 0$, $r_{1k} \neq 0$, for some k satisfying $3 \leq k \leq n$. Then the first row of $RR_{2,k}$ is

$$(r_{11}, cr_{12} + sr_{1k}, 0, 0, \ldots, -sr_{12} + cr_{1k}, \ldots).$$

Since $r_{1k} \neq 0$, we can choose

$$c = r_{12}(r_{12}{}^2 + r_{1k}{}^2)^{-\frac{1}{2}},$$
$$s = r_{1k}(r_{12}{}^2 + r_{1k}{}^2)^{-\frac{1}{2}}.$$

Then $c^2 + s^2 = 1$ and $-sr_{12} + cr_{1k} = 0$. Thus we have shown that for suitable matrices $R_{2,k}$ with $3 \leq r \leq n$, the first row of

$$W = RR_{2,3}R_{2,4} \cdots R_{2,n}$$

is
$$(w_{11}, w_{12}, 0, 0, \ldots, 0).$$

Since W is orthogonal, we have $w_{11}{}^2 + w_{12}{}^2 = 1$. Now the first row of $WR_{1,2}$ is

$$(cw_{11} + sw_{12}, -sw_{11} + cw_{12}, 0, 0, \ldots, 0);$$

and choosing $c = w_{11}$, $s = w_{12}$, we find that this becomes

$$(1, 0, 0, \ldots, 0).$$

Thus
$$RR_{2,3}R_{2,4} \cdots R_{2,n}R_{1,2} = \begin{bmatrix} 1 & 0 \\ v & R_0 \end{bmatrix}.$$

But this matrix belongs to $O_n{}^+$. This implies that $v = 0$ and that R_0, which is of order $n - 1$, is also orthogonal. The conclusion now follows by induction, since the theorem is certainly true for $n = 2$.

6.8 Givens' Method for Real Symmetric Matrices

The procedure used in reducing the matrix R in the proof of Theorem 6.11 has the following important application.   Let A be a real symmetric matrix.   Then by transformations of the type $R'_{\alpha,\beta}AR_{\alpha,\beta}$ we can make the

$$(1,3),\ (1,4),\ (1,5),\ \ldots,\ (1,n)$$
$$(2,4),\ (2,5),\ \ldots,\ (2,n)$$
$$\cdots\cdots\cdots\cdots\cdots$$
$$(n-2,\ n)$$

elements of A zero *in this order* by appropriate rotations

$$R_{2,3},\ R_{2,4},\ R_{2,5},\ \ldots,\ R_{2,n}$$
$$R_{3,4},\ R_{3,5},\ \ldots,\ R_{3,n}$$
$$\cdots\cdots\cdots\cdots\cdots$$
$$R_{n-1,n}.$$

Set
$$B = R'_{n-1,n}\cdots R'_{2,3}AR_{2,3}\cdots R_{n-1,n}.$$

Then B can have nonzero elements only on the principal diagonal and on the two diagonals immediately above and below the principal diagonal and is referred to as a *triple-diagonal* matrix.   But A and B are similar, and so have the same eigenvalues.   Thus *the problem of determining the eigenvalues of a real symmetric matrix is entirely equivalent to that of determining the eigenvalues of a real symmetric triple-diagonal matrix.*   It is only necessary to apply the $\frac{1}{2}(n-1)(n-2)$ transformations $R_{\alpha,\beta}$ as outlined above.   Suppose then that we consider a triple-diagonal matrix

$$C_n = \begin{bmatrix} b_1 & c_1 & & & & & \\ c_1 & b_2 & c_2 & & & & \\ & c_2 & b_3 & c_3 & & & \\ & & & \ddots & & & \\ & & & & \ddots & & \\ & & & & & c_{n-2} & b_{n-1} & c_{n-1} \\ & & & & & & c_{n-1} & b_n \end{bmatrix}.$$

Expanding $f_n = \det(xI - C_n)$ by minors, we see that the sequence f_0, $f_1, \ldots, f_n$ satisfies $f_0 = 1, f_1 = x - b_1$,

$$f_r = (x - b_r)f_{r-1} - c^2_{r-1}f_{r-2}, \qquad r \geq 2. \tag{6.35}$$

It is well known [33] that the sequence

$$f_n, f_{n-1}, \ldots, f_0 \tag{6.36}$$

is a Sturm sequence, provided that no c_i vanishes.   That is, if $V(x)$ denotes the number of variations in sign in the sequence (6.36), zero terms being omitted, then the number of zeros of f_n in the interval $[a,b]$ is just $V(a) - V(b)$, provided that a and b are not zeros of f_n.   Thus, if no c_i vanishes, it follows that the characteristic roots of C_n are all real and simple, since f_n is the characteristic polynomial of C_n.   (If some c_i were to vanish, C_n would become a direct sum, and each summand could be treated separately.)   This can be developed into an effective method for computing the eigenvalues of C_n.   We illustrate this by examples.

Example 1.   Take

$$C_3 = \begin{bmatrix} 1 & 1 & 0 \\ 1 & 2 & 1 \\ 0 & 1 & 0 \end{bmatrix}.$$

Then $f_0 = 1, f_1 = x - 1, f_2 = x^2 - 3x + 1, f_3 = x^3 - 3x^2 + 1$.   We make a small table of signs:

x	f_3	f_2	f_1	f_0	$V(x)$
-1	$-$	$+$	$-$	$+$	3
0	$+$	$+$	$-$	$+$	2
1	$-$	$-$	0	$+$	1
2	$-$	$-$	$+$	$+$	1
3	$+$	$+$	$+$	$+$	0

This shows that f_3 has one root in $(-1,0)$, one root in $(0,1)$, and one root in $(2,3)$.   If we are interested in, say, the root between 0 and 1, we can proceed by successive bisection.

It should be noted that in computing $f_n(x)$ in general, the most economical way is by the recurrence (6.35).   There is therefore no "waste" in this method, and it is highly recommended.

Example 2.   We consider the application of this method to the matrix

$$\begin{bmatrix} 5 & 7 & 6 & 5 \\ 7 & 10 & 8 & 7 \\ 6 & 8 & 10 & 9 \\ 5 & 7 & 9 & 10 \end{bmatrix}.$$

Working to 6 decimals, we find the equivalent triple-diagonal matrix to be

$$\begin{bmatrix} 5 & 10.488089 & 0 & 0 \\ 10.488089 & 25.472729 & 3.521903 & 0 \\ 0 & 3.521898 & 3.680571 & -.185813 \\ 0 & 0 & -.185813 & .846701 \end{bmatrix}$$

The lack of symmetry in this matrix and the discrepancy between the traces give some indication of the errors incurred at this stage—a few units in the last place.

It is now possible to apply the Sturm process to locate the roots. They are, approximately,

$$.01015, \quad .8431, \quad 3.858, \quad 30.29.$$

We note that the reduction to triple-diagonal form involves about $\frac{4}{3}n^3$ multiplications. Thereafter each evaluation of the Sturm sequence involves n multiplications.

6.9 Jacobi's Method for Real Symmetric Matrices

Once again the elementary orthogonal matrices $R_{\alpha,\beta}$ are employed, this time in such fashion that A is brought nearer to diagonal form at each step.

We proved in (6.19) that the Frobenius norm is invariant with respect to unitary transformations, and since orthogonal transformations are just real unitary transformations, we have

$$F(R'AR) = F(A), \qquad R \text{ orthogonal.} \tag{6.37}$$

Suppose now that in the matrix A the largest off-diagonal element in modulus is $a \neq 0$. We lose no generality in assuming $a = a_{12}$. We choose c, s so that $c^2 + s^2 = 1$ and

$$\begin{bmatrix} c & s \\ -s & c \end{bmatrix}\begin{bmatrix} a_{11} & a_{12} \\ a_{12} & a_{22} \end{bmatrix}\begin{bmatrix} c & -s \\ s & c \end{bmatrix} = \begin{bmatrix} b_{11} & 0 \\ 0 & b_{22} \end{bmatrix}.$$

We put

$$R = \begin{bmatrix} c & -s \\ s & c \end{bmatrix} + I^{(n-2)}.$$

Then (6.37) implies that

$$a_{11}^2 + 2a_{12}^2 + a_{22}^2 = b_{11}^2 + b_{22}^2. \tag{6.38}$$

Let $J(A)$ denote the sum of the squares of the off-diagonal elements of A. Then, using (6.37) once again, we find that

$$J(R'AR) + b_{11}^2 + b_{22}^2 + a_{33}^2 + \cdots + a_{nn}^2 = J(A) + a_{11}^2 + a_{22}^2$$
$$+ \cdots + a_{nn}^2,$$
$$J(R'AR) + b_{11}^2 + b_{22}^2 = J(A) + a_{11}^2 + a_{22}^2.$$

This, with (6.38), implies that

$$J(R'AR) = J(A) - 2a_{12}^2.$$

Since $J(A) \leq (n^2 - n)a_{12}^2$, this implies that

$$J(R'AR) \leq \left(1 - \frac{2}{n^2 - n}\right)J(A). \tag{6.39}$$

Suppose that after k such transformations the matrix resulting is denoted by A_k. Then (6.39) implies that

$$J(A_k) \leq \left(1 - \frac{2}{n^2 - n}\right)^k J(A).$$

From this result we conclude that by choosing k sufficiently large, A_k can be made to differ from a diagonal matrix by as little as desired.

For example, suppose A normalized so that $J(A) = 1$. Then, to make $J(A_k) < \epsilon$, it is sufficient to choose

$$k \geq \frac{\log (1/\epsilon)}{\log [(n^2 - n)/(n^2 - n - 2)]} \sim \frac{n^2}{2} \log \frac{1}{\epsilon}.$$

Thus for a matrix of order 10 and $\epsilon = 10^{-6}$ we find that some 600 rotations may be required. The process in any case is an "n^2" process. Each rotation involves about $4n$ multiplications, so that we require $O(n^3)$ multiplications altogether.

It is possible to determine the eigenvectors also, if the rotation matrices are saved. For if

$$R'AR = D, \qquad D \text{ diagonal,}$$

then the columns of R are the eigenvectors of A.

Example. Consider the diagonalization of

$$A = \begin{bmatrix} 2.879 & -.841 & -.148 & .506 \\ -.841 & 3.369 & -.111 & .380 \\ -.148 & -.111 & 1.216 & -.740 \\ .506 & .380 & -.740 & 3.536 \end{bmatrix}.$$

The first stage is the annihilation of the (1,2) (2,1) elements. Working to 3 places, an appropriate rotation produces

$$\begin{bmatrix} 2.250 & .001 & -.186 & .636 \\ .001 & 4.000 & .002 & -.002 \\ -.186 & .002 & 1.216 & -.740 \\ .636 & -.002 & -.740 & 3.536 \end{bmatrix}.$$

A further rotation is applied to annihilate the (3,4) (4,3) elements and then another rotation to annihilate the new (1,4) (4,1) elements; thus the matrix becomes

$$\begin{bmatrix} 4.005 & -.002 & .000 & -.001 \\ -.002 & 4.000 & .001 & -.002 \\ .000 & .001 & 1.004 & .000 \\ -.001 & -.002 & .000 & 1.999 \end{bmatrix}.$$

For further details see Taussky and Todd [8]. It should be noted that the diagonalization has been accomplished more rapidly than might have been expected. The size of the off-diagonal elements and the change in the trace give some indication of the accuracy of the process.

6.10   The Power Method

The next method we consider will produce eigenvectors and eigenvalues simultaneously. In addition, it is sometimes applicable when the previous methods are not. There are certain disadvantages, however.

We choose an arbitrary vector $v^{(0)}$ normalized in some way—for example, to have one of its coordinates unity or to have the sums of the squares of the coordinates unity. We apply the matrix A repeatedly to the vector $v^{(0)}$, expressing each product vector as a scalar multiple of a vector in the chosen normalization. Specifically, if $v^{(i)}$ is normalized, then we define $\mu^{(i+1)}$ by the equation

$$Av^{(i)} = \mu^{(i+1)}v^{(i+1)}$$

where $v^{(i+1)}$ is normalized. It can be shown that, if A has a single dominant root, then these multipliers tend to this value, and the (normalized) vectors tend to the corresponding (normalized) characteristic vector.

The justification of this process is simple. It is known that, commonly, a matrix A has n different characteristic roots λ_i and n distinct characteristic vectors c_i which are linearly independent and which therefore span the whole space. An arbitrary vector $v^{(0)}$ can be expressed in the form

$$v^{(0)} = \sum \alpha_i c_i.$$

Since $Ac_i = \lambda_i c_i$ for $i = 1, 2, \ldots, n$, we have

$$v^{(n)} = A^n v^{(0)} = \sum \alpha_i \lambda_i^n c_i,$$

and from this, if $|\lambda_1| > |\lambda_2| \geq \cdots \geq |\lambda_n|$, we have, for sufficiently large n (depending on the separation of the λ's),

$$v^{(n)} = A^n v^{(0)} \doteq \alpha_1 \lambda_1^n c_1.$$

From this the statements made above follow: that $v^{(n)}$ is approximately a multiple of c_1 and that the ratio of corresponding components of $v^{(n)}$ and $v^{(n-1)}$ is approximately λ_1.

For a thorough discussion of this method see Wilkinson [23].

Example.   Let us consider the case

$$A = \begin{bmatrix} .2 & .9 & 1.32 \\ -11.2 & 22.28 & -10.72 \\ -5.8 & 9.45 & -1.94 \end{bmatrix}$$

and choose $v^{(0)} = (1,0,0)$ and normalize by making the first coordinate unity for simplicity.   We obtain the following results:

$$Av^{(0)} = (.2, -11.2, -5.8) = \mu^{(1)}v^{(1)} \qquad \text{where } \mu^{(1)} = .2,$$
$$v^{(1)} = (1, -56, -29)$$

$$Av^{(1)} = (-88.48, -948, -478.74) = \mu^{(2)}v^{(2)} \qquad \text{where } \mu^{(2)} = -88.48,$$
$$v^{(2)} = (1, 10.7143, 5.4107)$$

$$Av^{(2)} = (16.9850, 169.5119, 84.9534) = \mu^{(3)}v^{(3)} \qquad \text{where } \mu^{(3)} = 16.9850,$$
$$v^{(3)} = (1, 9.9801, 5.0017)$$

$$Av^{(3)} = (15.7843, 157.5384, 78.8086) = \mu^{(4)}v^{(4)} \qquad \text{where } \mu^{(4)} = 15.7843,$$
$$v^{(4)} = (1, 9.9807, 4.9928)$$

$$Av^{(4)} = (15.7731, 157.6472, 78.8316) = \mu^{(5)}v^{(5)} \qquad \text{where } \mu^{(5)} = 15.7731,$$
$$v^{(5)} = (1, 9.9947, 4.9979)$$

$$Av^{(5)} = (15.7925, 157.9044, 78.9540) = \mu^{(6)}v^{(6)} \qquad \text{where } \mu^{(6)} = 15.7925,$$
$$v^{(6)} = (1, 9.9987, 4.9995).$$

It can be verified that the exact results are $\lambda_1 = 15.8$ and $v_1 = (1,10,5)$.

6.11   The Rayleigh Quotient Method

The Rayleigh quotient method has some similarities with the power method, and the ideas in the two are often combined.

The basis of the method is the remark that near a maximum x_0 of $f(x)$, if $f'(x)$ exists, then

$$f(x) - f(x_0) = O(x - x_0)^2.$$

This is applied where x is an n-dimensional vector and $f(x) = R(x)$, the Rayleigh quotient for the matrix A in question, which initially is assumed to be real and symmetric and to have a dominant characteristic value λ_1. The Rayleigh quotient is defined by

$$R(x) = \frac{x'Ax}{x'x}.$$

If x is a characteristic vector corresponding to the characteristic value λ, then clearly $R(x) = \lambda$.

The method proceeds as follows.   Let ξ_0 be an initial approximation to a characteristic vector.   If

$$A\xi_0 - R(\xi_0)\xi_0$$

is small enough to be considered zero, ξ_0 is taken as the characteristic vector.   If not, we determine an *approximate solution* ξ_1 *to the nearly singular system*

$$A\xi = R(\xi_0)\,\xi,$$

and we repeat the process with ξ_1 replacing ξ_0.

A meaning for the phrase in italics which enables convergence to be established has been given by Ostrowski [24].

Example.   Let

$$A = \begin{bmatrix} 3.500 & .750 & 1.299 \\ .750 & 1.625 & 1.083 \\ 1.299 & 1.083 & 2.875 \end{bmatrix}.$$

We guess $\xi_0 = (1,1,1)$ and estimate the dominant characteristic value $R(\xi_0) = 4.755$.   A "solution" to $A\xi = 4.755\xi$ is $\xi_1 = (1,0.5,.9)$.   We find $R(\xi_1) = 4.999$, and a "solution" to $A\xi = 4.999\xi$ is $\xi_2 = (1,.5,.867)$.   Since this gives $R(\xi_2) = 4.999 = R(\xi_1)$, the process terminates here.

6.12   Deflation

The following remark is also worth noticing.   Let A_1 be the first row of A.   Let λ be an eigenvalue of A and let x be a corresponding eigenvector, normalized to have first component unity.   We define

$$\tilde{A} = A - xA_1.$$

Then $\tilde{A}$ and A have the same eigenvalues except for λ, which has become 0, and there is a simple relation between the eigenvectors of $\tilde{A}$ and of A. Thus, suppose that λ_1 is an eigenvalue of A and that x_1 is a corresponding eigenvector, normalized to have first component unity.   Then, if $\lambda \neq \lambda_1$,

$$\begin{aligned} \tilde{A}(x - x_1) &= (A - xA_1)(x - x_1) \\ &= A(x - x_1) - xA_1(x - x_1) \\ &= \lambda x - \lambda_1 x_1 - x(\lambda - \lambda_1) \\ &= \lambda_1(x - x_1), \end{aligned}$$

so that λ_1 is also an eigenvalue of $\tilde{A}$, and $x - x_1$ is a corresponding eigenvector; whereas if $\lambda = \lambda_1$,

$$\tilde{A}x = (A - xA_1)x = Ax - xA_1x = \lambda x - x\lambda = 0.$$

We note that the first row of $\tilde{A}$ is 0 and that each eigenvector $x - x_1$ of $\tilde{A}$ has first component zero.   It is only necessary, therefore, to work with the principal minor matrix of $\tilde{A}$ obtained by striking out its first row and column.   This process may be continued and is known as *deflation*, since the order of the matrix is reduced by unity as each pair λ, x is computed.

REFERENCES

1. L. Fox, Practical Solution of Linear Equations and the Inversion of Matrices, in [4], pp. 1–59.

2. S. H. Crandall, "Engineering Analysis," McGraw-Hill Book Company, Inc., New York, 1956.

3. L. J. Paige and O. Taussky, eds., "Simultaneous Linear Equations and the Determination of Eigenvalues," National Bureau of Standards Applied Mathematics Series, vol. 29, 1953.

4. O. Taussky, ed., "Contributions to the Solution of Systems of Linear Equations and the Determination of Eigenvalues," National Bureau of Standards Applied Mathematics Series, vol. 39, 1954.

5. E. L. Stiefel, P. Henrici, H. Rutishauser, "Further Contributions to the Solution of Simultaneous Linear Equations and the Determination of Eigenvalues," National Bureau of Standards Applied Mathematics Series, vol. 49, 1958.

6. G. E. Forsythe, What Are Relaxation Methods? in [12], pp. 428–447.

7. G. E. Forsythe, Solving Linear Algebraic Equations Can Be Interesting, *Bull. Amer. Math. Soc.*, vol. 59, pp. 299–329, 1953.

8. O. Taussky and J. Todd, Systems of Equations, Matrices and Determinants, *Math. Mag.*, pp. 9–20, 71–88, 1957; reprinted in G. James, ed., "The Tree of Mathematics," pp. 305–337, The Digest Press, Pacoima, Calif., 1957.

9. "Modern Computing Methods," H.M. Stationery Office, London, 1961.

10. V. N. Faddeeva, "Computational Methods of Linear Algebra," C. D. Benster, tr., Dover Publications, New York, 1959. There is a new Russian edition of this: D. K. Faddeev and V. N. Faddeeva, "Vyčislitel'nye metody lineĭnoĭ algebry," Gosudarst. Isdat. Fiz. Mat. Lit., Moscow, 1960.

11. R. A. Frazer, W. J. Duncan, and A. R. Collar, "Elementary Matrices," Cambridge University Press, London, 1947.

12. E. F. Beckenbach, ed., "Modern Mathematics for the Engineer," McGraw-Hill Book Company, Inc., New York, 1956.

13. M. Marcus, "Basic Theorems in Matrix Theory," National Bureau of Standards Applied Mathematics Series, vol. 57, 1960.

14. A. M. Turing, Rounding-off Errors in Matrix Processes, *Quart. J. Mech. Appl. Math.*, vol. 1, pp. 287–308, 1948.

15. J. von Neumann and H. H. Goldstine, Numerical Inverting of Matrices of High Order, *Bull. Amer. Math. Soc.*, vol. 53, pp. 1021–1097, 1947; *Proc. Amer. Math. Soc.*, vol. 2, pp. 188–202, 1951.

16. W. Givens, "Numerical Computation of the Characteristic Values of a Real Symmetric Matrix," Oak Ridge National Laboratory Report ORNL1574, 1954.

17. H. H. Goldstine, F. J. Murray, and J. von Neumann, The Jacobi Method for Real Symmetric Matrices, *J. Assoc. Comput. Mach.*, vol. 6, pp. 59–96, 1959.

18. Conference on Matrix Computations, *J. Assoc. Comput. Mach.*, vol. 4, pp. 100–115, 1958.

19. G. E. Forsythe and P. Henrici, The Cyclic Jacobi Method for Computing the Principal Values of a Complex Matrix, *Trans. Amer. Math. Soc.*, vol. 94, pp. 1–23, 1960.

20. D. A. Pope and C. B. Tompkins, Maximizing Functions of Rotations: Experiments Concerning the Speed of Diagonalization of Symmetric Matrices Using Jacobi's Method, *J. Assoc. Comput. Mach.*, vol. 4, pp. 459–466, 1957.

21. R. L. Causey and P. Henrici, Convergence of Approximate Eigenvectors in Jacobi Methods, *Numer. Math.*, vol. 2, pp. 67–78, 1960.

22. P. A. White, The Computation of Eigenvalues and Eigenvectors of a Matrix, *J. Soc. Indust. Appl. Math.*, vol. 6, pp. 393–437, 1958.

23. J. H. Wilkinson, The Calculations of the Latent Roots and Vectors of Matrices on the Pilot Model of the A.C.E., *Proc. Cambridge Philos. Soc.*, vol. 50, pp. 536–566, 1956.

24. A. M. Ostrowski, On the Convergence of the Rayleigh Quotient Iteration for the Computation of the Characteristic Roots and Vectors, I–VI, *Arch. Rational Mech. Anal.*, vol. 1, pp. 233–241, 1958; vol. 2, pp. 423–428, 1959; vol. 3, pp. 325–340, 341–367, 472–481, 1959; vol. 4, pp. 153–165, 1960.

25. H. H. Goldstine and L. P. Horwitz, A Procedure for the Diagonalization of Normal Matrices, *J. Assoc. Comput. Mach.*, vol. 6, pp. 176–195, 1959.

26. R. S. Varga, "Iterative Numerical Analysis," Prentice-Hall, Inc., Englewood Cliffs, N.J. (to appear).

27. A. M. Ostrowski, Über näherungsweise Auflösung von Systemen homogene linearer Gleichungen, *Z. Angew. Math. Phys.*, vol. 8, pp. 280–285, 1957.

28. E. E. Osborne, On Acceleration and Matrix Deflation Processes Used with the Power Method, *J. Soc. Indust. Appl. Math.*, vol. 6, pp. 179–287, 1958.

29. A. M. Ostrowski, Über Normen von Matrizen, *Math. Z.*, vol. 63, pp. 2–18, 1955.

30. M. Newman and J. Todd, The Evaluation of Matrix Inversion Programs, *J. Soc. Indust. Appl. Math.*, vol. 6, pp. 466–476, 1958.

31. J. Todd, The Condition of the Finite Segments of the Hilbert Matrix, in [4], pp. 109–116.

32. O. Taussky, Note on the Condition of Matrices, *Math. Tables Aids Comput.*, vol. 4, pp. 111–112, 1950.

33. F. R. Gantmakher, "Theory of Matrices," Moscow, 1954 (in Russian; two English translations are available).

34. J. H. Wilkinson, The Evaluation of the Zeros of Ill-conditioned Polynomials, *Numer. Math.*, vol. 1, pp. 150–180, 1959.

35. P. Henrici, On the Speed of Convergence of Cyclic and Quasicyclic Jacobi Methods for Computing Eigenvalues of Hermitian Matrices, *J. Soc. Indust. Appl. Math.*, vol. 6, pp. 144–162, 1958.

36. J. H. Wilkinson, Error Analysis of Direct Methods of Matrix Inversion, *J. Assoc. Comput. Mach.*, vol. 8, pp. 281–330, 1961.

37. J. H. Wilkinson, "The Algebraic Eigenvalue Problem," Clarendon Press, Oxford (to appear).

7

Numerical Methods for Finding Solutions of Nonlinear Equations

URS HOCHSTRASSER

SCIENTIFIC COUNSELOR
EMBASSY OF SWITZERLAND
WASHINGTON, D.C.

7.1 Introduction

The following problem is considered here: given an equation

$$f(z) = 0, \tag{7.1}$$

where $f(z)$ is a nonlinear function of z in the complex plane, find solutions z_i, which are sometimes also called roots of $f(z)$ satisfying this relation. If $f(z)$ is a transcendental function, there may exist an infinity of solutions, whereas in the case of algebraic functions the number is always finite.

In most cases it is not possible to give an expression in closed form for the solutions of this problem. Even in those instances where such expressions exist, they may not be very useful for numerical purposes. Therefore, they are not considered here. As is very frequently the case in numerical analysis, iterative methods which lead to approximations for the solutions will be the best tool for solving the stated problem. There already exist a large number of them, some better than others, but up to now there is no one method which is the best in all cases. The advantages and disadvantages of each method depend to a large extent on the particular nature of the problem at hand. In general, one can distinguish three categories of problems:

1. Determination of a single root whose approximate situation is known.

2. Determination of approximate values for all the roots.

3. Determination of the number of roots in a given region of the complex plane.

The methods which are most efficient in solving these problems are not the same for all three, although each of them can be used in all the mentioned cases. It is, for instance, quite obvious that a procedure which finds all the roots can be applied also in the first and third case; there, however, it may be very wasteful with respect to the computational work which has to be done.

For this reason, the three categories of problems are treated separately. In each case, some methods of solution are given which have proved to be effective and efficient in practical work. Because of the limited scope of this discussion, no attempt can be made to be complete in the exposition of available methods. For additional information on such methods, see the list of recent papers at the end of the chapter; for the older literature, the textbooks, in particular [1,2], can be consulted. An evaluation of the relative merits of the different methods is very difficult, since it depends much on the particular case at hand. For this reason, one should not infer that any method which is not considered here has no practical value. The selection here is based mainly on actual experience in numerical work with automatic digital computers. It is therefore mainly intended for the users of such machines.

The following discussion is restricted to the consideration of polynomials whenever this is convenient. This simplification is justified, since in digital computers any transcendental function has to be represented by rational approximations, so that the problem of finding zeros of such functions reduces, from a practical point of view, to finding zeros of polynomials.

When numerical methods, to be used with digital computers, for finding zeros of polynomials are considered, one fundamental question arises with respect to the meaningfulness of the results. Since in most practical cases the coefficients of the given polynomials can be introduced into the machine with only a limited accuracy, it is important to know whether, irrespective of the magnitude of the coefficients, a certain number of significant digits can be guaranteed for the roots. This problem has been considered by Ostrowski [32], who proved the following theorem*.

* Note, that this result is frequently not very practical. (The reader should determine the τ necessary to ensure a relative error of, say, 1 per cent, in the case $n = 10$.) On the other hand, the result is near the truth, e.g., if $f(z) \equiv (z - 1)^n$, $g(z) = f(z) - \epsilon$. On the whole, the stability of the roots as functions of the coefficients should be studied, usually experimentally, in any particular case. The paper of Wilkinson [33] includes discussions of many particular cases and points out that violent changes in the roots can be observed even in cases when the roots are well separated. The paper of Olver [38], although mainly addressed to desk computers, contains valuable worked examples.

Theorem 7.1. *Let*

$$f(z) = \sum_{j=0}^{n} a_j z^j, \qquad g(z) = \sum_{j=0}^{n} b_j z^j$$

be two polynomials whose corresponding coefficients differ only that much from each other that there exists a $\tau \neq 0$, with $4n\tau^{1/n} \leq 1$, for which

$$|b_j - a_j| \leq \tau |a_j|, \qquad j = 0, 1, 2, \ldots, n. \tag{7.2}$$

(It is assumed that $a_0, a_n \neq 0$.)   Then if we designate by $x_i (i = 1, 2, \ldots, n)$ the roots of $f(z)$ and by y_i the roots of $g(z)$, the y_i can be ordered such that

$$\left| \frac{y_i}{x_j} - 1 \right| < 8n\tau^{1/n}, \qquad j = 1, 2, \ldots, n. \tag{7.3}$$

This theorem gives assurance that, if a reasonable number of significant digits are used for the coefficients, one can expect also some meaningfulness in the results.   Obviously, the theorem does not take into account any errors introduced by the method of solution, which may still affect the results considerably.

After these introductory remarks, some numerical methods for each of the three stated problems are discussed in the following sections.

7.2 Determination of a Single Root Whose Approximate Situation Is Known

It has already been noted that for numerical purposes iterative methods are in general the only effective way of finding roots of non-linear equations.   It will be convenient here to reformulate the problem in the following form.

Find solutions of

$$z = g(z) \qquad \text{where } g(z) = z - h(z) \cdot f(z). \tag{7.4}$$

$h(z)$ is supposed to be an analytic function different from zero in the neighborhood of the considered root x.

For this problem, an iterative method of solution can easily be defined, starting from an initial guess z_0 and finding new approximations z_i for the root by the formula

$$z_i = g(z_{i-1}) \qquad i = 1, 2, 3, \ldots. \tag{7.5}$$

It remains to be shown that this process actually converges to a solution of the problem stated at the beginning.   It is easy to see that, if the sequence of the z_i converges, it must converge to a root of $f(z)$, since both the z_i and $g(z_{i-1})$ have the same limit.

In cases where $g(z)$ is an analytic function (e.g., a polynomial) in a neighborhood $N(x)$ of the considered root x, the convergence of the given iteration can be easily shown if $|g'(z)| < 1$ for all $z \in N(x)$. For then

$$g(z) - x = (z - x)g'(x) + \tfrac{1}{2}(z - x)^2 g''(x) + \cdots + \frac{1}{n!}(z - x)^n g^{(n)}(\xi),$$
(7.6)

where $\xi \in N(x)$ if $z \in N(x)$ or, if $g'(x) = g''(x) = \cdots = g^{(n-1)}(x) = 0$,

$$g(z) - x = \frac{1}{n!}(z - x)^n g^{(n)}(\xi).$$
(7.7)

Therefore $|g(z) - x| < k\,|z - x|^n$ for a suitably chosen constant k and z in $N(x)$.   From this it follows that $|z_1 - x| = |g(z_0) - x| < k\,|z_0 - x|^n$,

$$|z_m - x| < k^{(n^m - 1)/(n-1)}|\,z_0 - x|^{n^m} = (k^{1/(n-1)}\,|z_0 - x|\,)^{n^m}\,k^{1/(1-n)}$$
(7.8)

For $n \neq 1$, one sees immediately that the process converges if

$$k^{1/(n-1)}\,|z_0 - x| < 1;$$
(7.9)

this means that it converges always if the initial guess is sufficiently close to the desired root.

For $n = 1$,

$$|z_m - x| < k^m\,|z_0 - x|;$$
(7.10)

therefore, the method converges only if $k < 1$, which is the case if—as has been assumed—$|g'(z)| < 1$.

From this consideration it follows also that, for a given initial guess z_0, the iteration converges the better the more derivatives of $g(z)$ are zero.

Definition: The iteration $z_{i+1} = g(z_i)$ is of order m in a neighborhood of a root x if $g'(x) = g''(x) = \cdots = g^{(m-1)}(x) = 0$ and $g^{(m)}(x) \neq 0$.

Many of the well-known classical methods are special cases of these iteration methods.   A few of them, which have proved their value in numerical work, are discussed here.

(a) Rule of False Position

One of the simplest and still quite useful methods for determining real roots of a nonlinear function is the rule of false position.   The method uses, geometrically speaking, the chord between two points $[z_i, f(z_i)]$ and $[\bar{z}, f(\bar{z})]$ in order to find a better approximation z_{i+1} to the root x of $f(z)$. If $\bar{z}$ is kept fixed during the whole iteration, this corresponds to choosing

$$g(z) = \frac{\bar{z}f(z) - zf(\bar{z})}{f(z) - f(\bar{z})}.$$
(7.11)

The derivative of $g(z)$ at the root x is

$$g'(x) = \frac{f(\bar{z}) + (x - \bar{z})f'(x)}{f(\bar{z})} = \tfrac{1}{2}(\bar{z} - x)^2 \frac{f''(\xi)}{f(\bar{z})},$$
(7.12)

where ξ is a point in the interval between $\bar{z}$ and x.   This expression is in general not zero, but for $\bar{z}$ sufficiently close to x it will be smaller than one in absolute value; that is, the method is convergent.   The rule of false position is therefore a first-order iteration procedure.

Instead of keeping $\bar{z}$ fixed, one can move it during the computation— for example, by using always the latest two points given by the iteration. Ostrowski has shown that the speed of convergence is then somewhat better than in the considered case.

(b) Newton's Method

Newton's method works for real and complex roots.   In the case of real roots, it corresponds, geometrically speaking, to using the tangent to the curve $f(z)$ in the last-found point $[z_i, f(z_i)]$ to find a new approximation z_{i+1}.   Therefore,

$$g(z) = z - \frac{f(z)}{f'(z)}. \tag{7.13}$$

In order to determine the convergence of this method, the first two derivatives at the root x are determined: $g'(x) = 0$,

$$g''(x) = \frac{f''(x)}{f'(x)}. \tag{7.14}$$

The second derivative is therefore in general different from zero, so that the Newton method is always convergent (if the first guess is sufficiently close to a root) and is a second-order iteration method. However, the choice of the initial approximation is very important, since by a bad first guess the method may diverge [17].   It has also to be noted that for polynomials with real coefficients, a first approximation on the real axis can lead only to real roots, since the iteration formula gives only real values.

(c) Laguerre's Method

The Laguerre method is an iterative method for determining the zeros of polynomials.   If $f(z) = P_n(z)$ is a polynomial of nth degree, the Laguerre method is obtained by setting

$$g(z) = z - \frac{nf(z)}{f'(z) \pm \sqrt{(n-1)[(n-1)f'(z)^2 - nf(z)f''(z)]}}. \tag{7.15}$$

In its geometrical interpretation, this method amounts to approximating the polynomial by parabolas between two zeros.   Accordingly, there are two values of $g(z)$, depending on which root is to be approximated. For practical purposes, that sign is used which makes the denominator larger; that is, the solution closest to the first guess is approximated.

The first few derivatives at a root x are

$$g'(x) = 0, \quad g''(x) = 0, \quad g'''(x) = -\frac{f'''(x)}{f'(x)} - \frac{3}{4}\frac{n-2}{n-1}\left[\frac{f''(x)}{f'(x)}\right]^2, \quad (7.16)$$

so that in general the third derivative is the first different from zero; that is, the method is a third-order iteration procedure.

In comparison with the other methods so far discussed, the Laguerre method has the advantage that it converges faster and that it works also for the complex roots of polynomials with real coefficients, even if one starts out with a real guess. (The expression under the root in the denominator may become negative.) It has, however, the drawback that higher-order derivatives have to be computed. This can be done most conveniently by using synthetic division (Horner scheme); that is, if

$$f(z) = \sum_{j=0}^{n} a_{n-j}z^j$$

should be evaluated with its derivatives for $z = x$, then this can be done recursively by computing

$$a_{0,0} = a_0, \tag{7.17}$$

$$a_{i,0} = a_{i-1,0}x + a_i, \quad i = 1, 2, \ldots, n, \tag{7.18}$$

$$a_{0,j} = a_0,$$
$$a_{i,j} = a_{i-1,j}x + a_{i,j-1}, \quad i = 1, 2, \ldots, n-j, \tag{7.19}$$

and then

$$f(x) = a_{n,0}, \quad f'(x) = a_{n-1,1}, \quad f''(x) = 2!\, a_{n-2,2},$$
$$f^{(j)}(x) = j!\, a_{n-j,j}, \quad j = 1, 2, \ldots, n. \tag{7.20}$$

(d) Higher-order Processes by a Combination of Lower-order Processes

Higher-order processes can also be obtained by combining lower-order processes. The formula $z_{i+1} = g(z_i)$ generates a sequence of values z_i, which, as has been shown, converges if $|g'(z)| < 1$. Geometrically, this sequence corresponds to a sequence of points on the curve defined by $g(z)$. Any two successive points (z_{i-1}, z_i) and (z_i, z_{i+1}) can be used to obtain a new estimate by intersecting the straight line through them with the line $y = z$. In formulas,

$$\bar{z} = z_{i-1} - \frac{(z_i - z_{i-1})^2}{z_{i+1} - 2z_i + z_{i-1}}. \tag{7.21}$$

This can be interpreted as a new iterative procedure of the same type as before, but with another function, $G(z)$, in the place of $g(z)$:

$$G(z) = \frac{zg[g(z)] - g^2(z)}{z - 2g(z) + g[g(z)]}. \tag{7.22}$$

It is easy to show that the iteration

$$z_{i+1} = G(z_i) \tag{7.23}$$

has a higher order of convergence than the one with $g(z)$, if $g'(z) \neq 1$. In particular, if $g(z)$ is of order 1, then the $G(z)$ is at least of order 2; if $g(z)$ is of order r $(r > 1)$, then $G(z)$ is at least of order $2r - 1$.

Proof. In order to simplify the proof, x is assumed to be zero, which corresponds to a simple translation of the coordinate system. Therefore, if $g(z)$ is a convergent process of order r,

$$g(z) = \frac{1}{r!} g^{(r)}(0) z^r + \cdots , \tag{7.24}$$

$$g[g(z)] = \frac{1}{r!} g^{(r)}(0) \left[\frac{1}{r!} g^{(r)}(0) z^r + \cdots \right]^r . \tag{7.25}$$

For $r > 1$, the term of lowest degree in the numerator is therefore of degree $2r$ in z, in the denominator of degree 1; that is, $G(z)$ expanded in powers of z has no terms in z of degree lower than $2r - 1$, from which the second part of the assertion follows.

For $r = 1$,

$$zg[g(z)] = [g'(0)]^2 z^2 + \cdots , \tag{7.26}$$

$$g^2(z) = [g'(0)]^2 z^2 + \cdots , \tag{7.27}$$

$$z - 2g(z) + g[g(z)] = z\{1 - 2g'(0) + [g'(0)]^2\} + \cdots . \tag{7.28}$$

Therefore, in the denominator the coefficient of z is different from zero [because of the assumption $g'(0) \neq 1$]. So the expansion of $G(z)$ in powers of z has no term lower than the second degree; that is, $G(z)$ defines an iteration of order 2 at least. Since it has only to be assumed that $g'(0) \neq 1$, this iterative procedure converges even if the iteration defined by $g(z)$ does not converge [when $|g'(0)| > 1$].

Obviously, even higher-order iteration procedures can be defined by repeated application of this method. In practical applications, iteration procedures of lower order are preferred, because of the simplicity of their application. The advantage of the more rapid convergence of higher-order methods comes fully into play only when the approximation is sufficiently close to the solution. Therefore, if the entire amount of work is considered for finding one zero, an iteration procedure of low-order convergence (order 2 or 3) usually is most advantageous.

7.3 Determination of Approximate Values for All Roots

(a) Combined Methods

The methods already discussed can be easily adapted to the determination of approximate values for all roots. It is only necessary to combine them with a procedure which prevents the repeated evaluation of the same root. In the case of polynomials, such a procedure consists, for instance, in the elimination of the roots already obtained by synthetic division. This amounts to carrying through a complete Horner scheme, where the argument z is equal to the root determined. The coefficients $a_{n-j,j}$ $(j = 1, 2, \ldots, n)$, given by (7.20), define then a polynomial of $(n-1)$st degree, $P_{n-1}(z) = \sum_{j=1}^{n} a_{n-j,j} z^{j-1}$, which has as its roots those roots of the original polynomial which have not yet been determined (provided that the roots are simple).

In using synthetic division, care has to be taken to minimize the accumulation of round-off errors introduced each time because of the limited accuracy of the computed roots. It is advisable to start by computing the roots smallest in absolute value and to proceed in the order of their relative magnitude. Starting with the larger roots (in absolute value) may introduce such large errors into the coefficients of the polynomials derived from the original one by synthetic division that it is impossible to obtain the smaller roots with the desired accuracy. The use of synthetic division has the advantage that the work necessary to obtain a root decreases as more roots are obtained, since the degrees of the polynomials decrease.

Another procedure, which avoids to some extent the mentioned difficulty of the accumulation of round-off errors, is based on the following observation: if $P_n(z) = \sum_{j=0}^{n} a_{n-j} z^j$ and $x_1, x_2, \ldots, x_n$ are its roots, then also

$$P_n(z) = a_0(z - x_1)(z - x_2) \cdots (z - x_n). \tag{7.29}$$

Therefore

$$\frac{P_n'(z)}{P_n(z)} = \sum_{i=1}^{n} \frac{1}{z - x_i} = s_1(z) \tag{7.30}$$

$$\frac{P_n''(z)P_n(z) - [P_n'(z)]^2}{P_n{}^2(z)} = -\sum_{i=1}^{n} \frac{1}{(z - x_i)^2} = -s_2(z) \tag{7.31}$$

The formulas for the Newton and Laguerre methods can be expressed in terms of the quantities $s_1 = s_1(z)$, $s_2 = s_2(z)$:

Newton: $$g(z) = z - \frac{1}{s_1(z)} ; \tag{7.32}$$

Laguerre: $$g(z) = z - \frac{n}{s_1 \pm \sqrt{(n-1)(ns_2 - s_1{}^2)}} . \tag{7.33}$$

Therefore, for these methods the roots which already have been computed can be eliminated by subtracting the appropriate expressions from $s_1(z)$ and $s_2(z)$, that is, by substituting in the formulas $S_1(z)$ and $S_2(z)$, where

$$S_1(z) = s_1(z) - \sum_{i=1}^{j} \frac{1}{z - x_i} \qquad (7.34)$$

$$S_2(z) = s_2(z) - \sum_{i=1}^{j} \frac{1}{(z - x_i)^2} \qquad (7.35)$$

(j being the number of roots computed already.)

This procedure gives in many cases more accurate results than synthetic division. However, it requires appreciably more work for finding all the roots, since one works at all times with the original polynomial.

(b) Graeffe Method

Where accuracy is not so important, the so-called Graeffe method provides a fast way of computing all the roots of a polynomial. This iterative procedure finds approximate values for all the roots at the same time, whereas the methods discussed so far determine only one root at a time. It is based on the following relation between the roots x_i ($i = 1, 2, \ldots, n$) and the coefficients a_i ($i = 0, 1, 2, \ldots, n$) of a polynomial of nth degree,

$$P_n(z) = \sum_{j=0}^{n} a_{n-j} z^j = a_0 \prod_{i=1}^{n} (z - x_i):$$

$$\frac{a_1}{a_0} = -\sum_{i=1}^{n} x_i, \qquad \frac{a_2}{a_0} = \sum_{\substack{i,j=1 \\ i \neq j}}^{n} x_i x_j, \qquad \cdots, \qquad \frac{a_n}{a_0} = (-1)^n x_1 x_2 \cdots x_n.$$
$$(7.36)$$

So, if the x_i are all real and well separated, that is, if $|x_1| > |x_2| > \cdots > |x_n|$ then the following relations hold approximately:

$$x_1 \doteq -\frac{a_1}{a_0}, \qquad x_2 \doteq -\frac{a_2}{a_1}, \qquad \cdots, \qquad x_n \doteq -\frac{a_n}{a_{n-1}}. \qquad (7.37)$$

Since this situation does not exist for all polynomials, a method is needed which allows new polynomials to be derived whose roots are in a simple relation to the ones of the original polynomial and are well separated in order to take advantage of this observation. The Graeffe method allows such polynomials to be found. It makes use of the fact that, if

$$P_n(z) = \sum_{j=0}^{n} a_{n-j} z^j \text{ has the roots } x_i \ (i = 1, 2, \ldots, n), \text{ then}$$

$$P_n^*(z) = (-1)^n \sum_{j=0}^{n} a_{n-j}(-z)^j \qquad (7.38)$$

has the roots $-x_i$ $(i = 1, 2, \ldots, n)$. Therefore, the polynomial of nth degree in z^2 obtained by multiplying $P_n(z)$ and $P_n^*(z)$ together,

$$_1P_n(z^2) = P_n(z)P_n^*(z) = a_0^2 \prod_{i=1}^{n} (z + x_i)(z - x_i) = \sum_{j=0}^{n} {}_1a_{n-j}(z^2)^j, \quad (7.39)$$

has as its roots x_i^2 $(i = 1, 2, \ldots, n)$.

The coefficients $_1a_j$ of the new polynomial are computed from the a_j of the old polynomial by the following relations:

$$_1a_j = (-1)^j[a_j^2 + 2 \sum_{l=1}^{j} (-1)^l a_{j+l} a_{j-l}].$$

For practical reasons, the factor $(-1)^j$ is usually dropped; that is, one computes the polynomial with roots $-x_i^2$ instead:

$$_1a_j = a_j^2 + 2 \sum_{l=1}^{j} (-1)^l a_{j+l} a_{j-l}, \qquad j = 0, 1, 2, \ldots, n. \quad (7.40)$$

All these coefficients are positive for real roots. By repeated application of this squaring method, polynomials $_kP_n(z) = \sum_{j=0}^{n} {}_ka_{n-j}z^j$ can be obtained, the roots of which are equal to $-x_i^{2^k}$, and the coefficients are determined recursively by

$$_ka_j = {}_{k-1}a_j^2 + 2 \sum_{l=1}^{j} (-1)^l \; {}_{k-1}a_{j+l} \; {}_{k-1}a_{j-l}. \quad (7.41)$$

If all roots are real and simple, then for a sufficiently large k the roots of $_kP_n(z)$ will be well separated, so that the approximate relations given before can be used to compute the roots:

$$\log x_i \doteq \frac{1}{2^k} \log \frac{ka_i}{k_{i-1}^a}, \qquad i = 1, 2, \ldots, n. \quad (7.42)$$

This situation is realized if the sum of the cross products in the above formula for the coefficients is small with respect to $_{k-1}a_j^2$ $(j = 1, 2, \ldots, n)$. So the ratios

$$r_{kj} = \frac{\sum_{l=1}^{j} (-1)^l \; {}_ka_{j+l} \; {}_ka_{j-l}}{{}_ka_j^2}, \qquad j = 1, 2, \ldots, n, \quad (7.43)$$

indicate when the iterative procedure of computing polynomials has produced a polynomial with well-separated roots.

The roots are determined only up to the sign by the given logarithmic relation. The sign has to be determined by back substitution or other methods. In the case of complex or multiple roots, at least some of the successively computed coefficients fail to exhibit the described behavior. The Graeffe method can be modified so as to take care also of these cases.

(c) Lehmer Method

Instead of discussing these modifications in detail, consideration is given here to a method, due to Brodetsky, Smeal, and Lehmer, which allows the roots to be computed directly also in these special cases.   This method amounts to performing two Graeffe methods, one for the polynomial $P_n(z)$, the other for $P_n(z + h)$, where h is an infinitesimal shift in the origin.   The two processes can be combined at a considerable saving in labor and will produce the roots (real or complex) with proper sign.

The formulas for the Lehmer method can be easily derived from those for the Graeffe method, if one notes that $P_n(z + h)$ is again a polynomial in z, the coefficients of which depend on h:

$$P_n(z + h) = \sum_{j=0}^{n} a_{n-j}(h)\, z^j = P_n(z,h) \tag{7.44}$$

$P_n(z,h)$ has $x_i + h$ as roots.   Therefore, if the previous root-squaring procedure is carried out, coefficients $_k a_j(h)$ are obtained, which are functions of h.   Assuming h to be very small and developing all coefficients up to the first power in h, one obtains from (7.41)

$$_k a_j(h) \doteq {}_k a_j + h \cdot {}_k b_j = {}_{k-1} a_j{}^2 + 2 \sum_{l=1}^{j} (-1)^l \, {}_{k-1} a_{j+l}\, {}_{k-1} a_{j-l}$$

$$+ 2h \sum_{l=-j}^{j} (-1)^l \, {}_{k-1} a_{j+l}\, {}_{k-1} b_{j-l}, \tag{7.45}$$

where $_k b_j = \dfrac{d}{dh} [{}_k a_j(h)]_{h=0}$ can be computed recursively by the formula:

$$_k b_j = 2 \sum_{l=-j}^{j} (-1)^l \, {}_{k-1} a_{j+l}\, {}_{k-1} b_{j-l}, \qquad j = 1, 2, \ldots, n,\ k = 1, 2, 3, \ldots. \tag{7.46}$$

It follows immediately that

$$_k b_0 = 0 \qquad \text{for all } k, \tag{7.47}$$

since $_k a_0(h) = {}_k a_0$.   For $k = 0$, the coefficients $_0 b_j$ are determined from the relation

$$P_n(z,h) = P_n(z) + h \left. \frac{dP_n(z,h)}{dh} \right|_{h=0} + \cdots$$

and

$$\left. \frac{dP_n(z,h)}{dh} \right|_{h=0} = \left. \frac{d}{dh} P_n(z + h) \right|_{h=0} = \frac{d}{dz} P_n(z);$$

therefore

$$_0 b_j = (n - j + 1) a_{j-1}, \qquad j = 1, 2, \ldots, n. \tag{7.48}$$

The $_k a_j$ are computed by formula (7.41).   With the aid of the $_k b_j$, all the roots can be directly computed.   The following cases have to be distinguished:

1. All the roots are real and simple.   Then, for sufficiently large k, the relations (7.37) hold:

$$(x_i + h)^{2^k} \doteq \frac{{}_k a_i(h)}{{}_k a_{i-1}(h)}, \qquad i = 1, 2, \ldots, n,$$

or $(x_i + h)^{2^k} = x_i^{2^k} + h 2^k x_i^{2^k-1} + \cdots \doteq \dfrac{{}_k a_i}{{}_k a_{i-1}} + h \dfrac{{}_k b_i \, {}_k a_{i-1} - {}_k a_i \, {}_k b_{i-1}}{{}_k a_{i-1}^2};$

comparing terms, one obtains

$$x_i = 2^k \frac{1}{\dfrac{{}_k b_i}{{}_k a_i} - \dfrac{{}_k b_{i-1}}{{}_k a_{i-1}}}, \qquad i = 1, 2, \ldots, n.$$

From this expression one sees that, for numerical purposes, it is more convenient to define the coefficients by the following set of formulas:

$$_k a_j = {}_{k-1}a_j^{\,2} + 2 \sum_{l=1}^{j} (-1)^l \, {}_{k-1}a_{j+l} \, {}_{k-1}a_{j-l}, \tag{7.49}$$

$$_k b_j = \sum_{l-j}^{j} (-1)^l \, {}_{k-1}a_{j+l} \, {}_{k-1}b_{j-l}, \qquad j = 1, 2, \ldots, n, \tag{7.50}$$

$$_k b_0 = 0$$

and $_0 a_j = a_j, \qquad j = 0, 1, 2, \ldots, n,$

$_0 b_j = (n - j + 1) a_{j-1}, \qquad j = 1, 2, \ldots, n,$

$$x_i = \frac{1}{\dfrac{{}_k b_i}{{}_k a_i} - \dfrac{{}_k b_{i-1}}{{}_k a_{i-1}}}, \qquad i = 1, 2, \ldots, n. \tag{7.51}$$

2. The first root has multiplicity m; the others are real and simple. Then, for sufficiently large k, the relations (7.36) give

$$m(x_1 + h)^{2^k} \doteq \frac{{}_k a_1(h)}{{}_k a_0} \cdots (x_1 + h)^{2^k m} \doteq \frac{{}_k a_m(h)}{{}_k a_0},$$

$$(x_1 + h)^{2^k m}(x_{m+1} + h)^{2^k} = \frac{{}_k a_{m+1}(h)}{{}_k a_0},$$

so that only in $_k a_m, \ldots, {}_k a_n$ will the cross products in (7.49) vanish as described in the case of a simple root.

Applying the same methods as before, one obtains

$$x_1 = \frac{1}{\dfrac{{}_k b_1}{{}_k a_1} - \dfrac{{}_k b_0}{{}_k a_0}} = \frac{{}_k a_1}{{}_k b_1}, \qquad x_{m+1} = \frac{1}{\dfrac{{}_k b_{m+1}}{{}_k a_{m+1}} - \dfrac{{}_k b_m}{{}_k a_m}}, \qquad \ldots \tag{7.52}$$

Therefore, the formulas have not changed except for the omission of the expressions for $x_2, \ldots, x_m$.

3. The first two roots are conjugate complex; the others are real and simple; that is,

$$x_1 = \rho e^{i\varphi}, \qquad x_2 = \rho e^{-i\varphi}.$$

Then, for sufficiently large k, one obtains, if the terms of zero order in h are compared,

$$\frac{{}_k a_1}{{}_k a_0} = +2\rho^{2^k} \cos 2^k\varphi + x_3^{2^k} + \cdots + x_n^{2^k} \doteq 2\rho^{2^k} \cos 2^k\varphi$$

$$\text{if } 2^k\varphi \neq \text{multiple of } \frac{\pi}{2}, \qquad (7.53)$$

$$\frac{{}_k a_2}{{}_k a_0} \doteq \rho^{2k+1}. \qquad (7.54)$$

Therefore, the conjugate complex roots cause an oscillation in ${}_k a_1$, which will no longer stay necessarily positive.   The other coefficients ${}_k a_j$ behave as usual. The comparison of the terms of order h gives

$$\frac{{}_k b_2}{{}_k a_0} \doteq 2^{k+1} \rho^{2^{k+1}-1} \cos \varphi. \qquad (7.55)$$

From (7.54), ρ can be determined uniquely, since it is positive, and from (7.55), one can find φ, the two possible values of which give x_1 and x_2.

Other cases can be similarly discussed.   All have in common that, as soon as all the roots are no longer real and simple, then in some of the coefficients ${}_k a_j$ the cross products are not becoming negligible in comparison to the other term for increasing k.   Further, it can be shown that the ${}_k a_j$ and ${}_k b_j$ give sufficient information so that the roots can be computed without any back substitution into the original polynomial.

When writing a program for an electronic computer, one has to decide how many of these cases one wants to incorporate, the alternative being that ${}_k a_j$, ${}_k b_j$ are printed out if only part of them exhibit the desired behavior for large k and that the further processing is then done manually.   This decision depends somewhat on individual taste.   In general, experience shows that it is not worthwhile to build a lot of sophistication into a code, because this is usually done at a considerable expense in time.

From the practical point of view, it has also to be mentioned that the Graeffe methods are not self-correcting iteration procedures, so that the round-off errors accumulate   In some cases it may therefore be necessary to check the accuracy of the roots obtained by a substitution into the original polynomial.   From the derivation of the method, it is obvious that the roots with largest modulus are obtained with the best accuracy.

7.4   Determination of the Number of Roots in a Given Region of the Complex Plane

First the special case is considered where the number of roots in an interval of the real axis of a polynomial with real coefficients has to be determined.

(a) The Region Is an Interval on the Real Axis

An economic method to solve this problem makes use of the so-called Sturmian sequences and thus avoids the explicit computation of the roots.   Since the algorithm to compute the particular Sturmian sequence for this case can also be used to determine multiple roots and thus to reduce any problem of finding roots of a polynomial to finding simple roots, it is briefly discussed here.

First it has to be shown how Sturmian sequences can be used for solving the stated problem.   For this one has to recall the following definition.

Definition.   A Sturmian sequence is a sequence of functions $f_n(z), f_{n-1}(z), \ldots, f_0(z)$ which satisfy on a given interval $[a,b]$ of the real axis the following conditions:

1. $f_i(z)$ = continuous function $(i = n, n - 1, \ldots, 0)$.
2. Sign $f_0(z)$ = constant for $a \leq z \leq b$.
3. If $f_i(z) = 0, f_{i+1}(z)$ and $f_{i-1}(z) \neq 0$ for $a \leq z \leq b$ and all i.
4. If $f_i(z) = 0$, sign $f_{i+1}(z) = -\text{sign} f_{i-1}(z)$ $(i = n - 1, \ldots, 1)$.
5. If $z = x$ is a root of $f_n(z)$, then for h sufficiently small,

$$\text{sign} \frac{f_n(x - h)}{f_{n-1}(x - h)} = -1, \qquad \text{sign} \frac{f_n(x + h)}{f_{n-1}(x + h)} = 1.$$

From these properties, the following theorem can be deduced.

Theorem 7.2.   *The number m of roots of the function $f_n(z)$ on the interval $[a,b]$ is equal to the difference between the number of changes of sign in the sequences $f_n(a), f_{n-1}(a), \ldots, f_0(a)$ and $f_n(b), f_{n-1}(b), \ldots, f_0(b)$.*

This statement can be verified by following the number of changes in sign in the sequence as z increases from a to b.   This number can change only if one function or several functions go through zero with increasing z.   Because of the properties of the Sturmian functions, this number actually changes only if $f_n(z)$ goes through a zero.   This can be easily shown, since if $f_i(\bar{z}) = 0$ $(i \neq n, 0)$, the following situations are possible according to properties 1, 3, and 4 (h small):

$z =$	f_{i-1}	f_i	f_{i+1}	or	f_{i-1}	f_i	f_{i+1}
$\bar{z} - h$	$+$	$\pm$	$-$		$-$	$\pm$	$+$
$\bar{z}$	$+$	0	$-$		$-$	0	$+$
$\bar{z} + h$	$+$	$\mp$	$-$		$-$	$\mp$	$+$

In both cases, the number of changes in sign in the sequence remains the same. According to property 2, $f_0(z)$ cannot cause any such change. From property 5, however, it follows that this number changes at each root of $f_n(z)$, which proves the correctness of the given theorem.

Therefore, the number of roots of $f_n(z)$ on $[a,b]$ can be obtained simply by evaluating a Sturmian sequence $f_n(z), f_{n-1}(z), \ldots, f_0(z)$ for $z = a$ and $z = b$.

It remains to give a method for constructing such a sequence. If one sets $f_{n-1}(z) = (d/dz) f_n(z)$, then property 5 is satisfied. Using $f_n(z)$ and $f_{n-1}(z)$, one can generate the rest of the functions by the euclidean algorithm:

$$f_n(z) = f_{n-1}(z)g_{n-1}(z) - f_{n-2}(z), \qquad \begin{array}{l} \text{where the } g_i(z) \\ \text{are linear functions} \\ \text{of } z, \end{array} \quad (7.56)$$

$$f_i(z) = f_{i-1}(z)g_{i-1}(z) - f_{i-2}(z) \qquad i = n, n-1, \ldots, 2.$$

Properties 2, 3, and 4 are easily verified for this sequence, and property 1 follows from the continuity of $f_n(z)$ and $f_{n-1}(z)$ if $f_n(z)$ is a polynomial.

If $f_n(z) = P_n(z) = \sum_{j=0}^{n} a_{n-j}z^j$, the functions in the sequence are polynomials of decreasing degree:

$$f_i(z) = \sum_{j=0}^{i} a_{i,i-j}z^j \qquad (7.57)$$

The coefficients are recursively determined by the relations

$$a_{i-1,j} = b_i a_{i,j+2} + c_i a_{i,j+1} - a_{i+1,j+2}, \qquad \begin{cases} j = 0, 1, \ldots, i-1, \\ i = n-1, n-2, \ldots, 1, \end{cases} \quad (7.58)$$

with $\quad b_i = \dfrac{a_{i+1,0}}{a_{i,0}}, \qquad c_i = \dfrac{1}{a_{i,0}}(a_{i+1,1} - b_i a_{i,1}), \qquad a_{i,i+1} = 0,$

and $a_{n,j} = a_j, \qquad a_{n-1,j} = (n-j)a_j, \quad j = 0, 1, 2, \ldots, n.$

If $P_n(z)$ has multiple roots, then this algorithm does not produce a complete Sturmian sequence, since some $f_i(z)$ becomes zero, where the i depends on the multiplicity of the roots $[f_{i+1}(z)$ being the greatest common divisor of $P_n(z)$ and $P_n'(z)]$. So this case has to be treated separately.

Polynomials with Multiple Roots. If a polynomial has multiple roots, the problem of finding its roots can be reduced to finding the roots of some lower-degree polynomials which have only roots with multiplicity one by applying the euclidean algorithm.

Since the greatest common divisor of $P_n(z)$ and $P'_n(z)$ contains the roots which have multiplicity p in $P_n(z)$ with multiplicity $p - 1$, a repeated application of the algorithm described before will generate a sequence of polynomials which will contain the multiple roots with decreasing multiplicity. These polynomials will be designated here by $F_1(z), F_2(z), \ldots, F_k(z)$, where

$$F_1(z) = \text{greatest common divisor of } P_n(z), P'_n(z),$$
$$F_2(z) = \text{greatest common divisor of } F_1(z), F'_1(z),$$

.

.

.

$$F_k(z) = \text{greatest common divisor of } F_{k-1}(z), F'_{k-1}(z).$$

Here k is the largest multiplicity occurring among the roots of $P_n(z)$ and $F_j(z)$ contains those roots of $P_n(z)$ which have multiplicity $k, k - 1, \ldots, j + 1 (j = 1, 2, \ldots, k - 1)$. [They have in $F_j(z)$ the multiplicities $k - j, \ldots, 1$.] Therefore, $F_k(z)$ is a constant, and $F_{k-1}(z)$ is a polynomial which has as simple roots those roots of $P_n(z)$ which have multiplicity k.

$$\frac{F_{k-2}(z)}{F^2_{k-1}(z)} = q_{k-1}(z)$$

is a polynomial which has as simple roots those roots of $P_n(z)$ which have multiplicity $k - 1$.

In general, if $F_0(z) = P_n(z)$, then, for $j = k - 2, \ldots, 1$,

$$\frac{F_{j-1}(z)F_{j+1}(z)}{F_j^2(z)} = q_j(z) \tag{7.59}$$

is a polynomial which has as simple roots those roots of $P_n(z)$ which have multiplicity j. The computation of the $F_j(z)$ is defined by formula (7.58), completed by the additional rule that, if $a_{i,j} = 0$ for all $j = 0, 1, \ldots, i$, these values have to be replaced by

$$a_{i,j} = (i + 1 - j)a_{i+1,j}, \qquad j = 0, 1, \ldots, i.$$

The computation of the $q_j(z)$ can be arranged conveniently in the following way.

The quotients $F_{j-1}(z)/F_j(z)$ can be directly computed from the b_i, c_i of formula (7.58), since, by back substitution in the relations (7.56), it can be readily shown that they are sums of products of $g_i(z) = b_i z + c_i$. Here consideration is restricted to finding $F_0(z)/F_1(z)$, since the other computations follow the same pattern.

Assume that the euclidean algorithm has given $f_k(z)$ as the greatest common divisor of $P_n(z) = f_n(z)$ and $f_{n-1}(z) = P'_n(z)$. Then, from (7.56), one obtains

$$
\begin{aligned}
f_n(z) &= g_{n-1}(z)[g_{n-2}(z)f_{n-2}(z) - f_{n-3}(z)] - f_{n-2}(z) \\
&= p_2(z)f_{n-2}(z) - p_1(z)f_{n-3}(z) = p_2(z)[g_{n-3}(z)f_{n-3}(z) - f_{n-4}(z)] \\
&\qquad\qquad\qquad\qquad\qquad - p_1(z)f_{n-3}(z) \\
&= p_3(z)f_{n-3}(z) - p_2(z)f_{n-4}(z) \\
&\;\;\vdots \\
&= p_{n-k-1}(z)f_{k+1}(z) - p_{n-k-2}(z)f_k(z) \\
&= p_{n-k}(z)f_k(z),
\end{aligned}
$$

where $p_{i+1}(z) = p_i(z)g_{n-i-1}(z) - p_{i-1}(z)$; $p_1(z) = g_{n-1}(z)$, $p_0 = 1$, $i = 1, 2, \ldots, n - k - 1$.

If the coefficients of $p_i(z)$ are denoted in the following way,

$$
p_i(z) = \sum_{j=0}^{i} \beta_{i,j} z^j, \qquad i = 1, 2, \ldots, n - k, \tag{7.60}
$$

then they can be computed recursively at the same time as the $a_{i,j}$ of formula (7.58), using the relations

$$
\begin{aligned}
\beta_{i,j} &= c_{n-i-1}\beta_{i-1,j} + b_{n-i-1}\beta_{i-1,j-1} - \beta_{i-2,j}, \\
j &= 0, 1, 2, \ldots, i, \qquad i = 1, 2, \ldots, n - k, \tag{7.61} \\
\text{and} \quad \beta_{i,j} &= 0 \qquad \text{for } j > i \text{ or } j < 0.
\end{aligned}
$$

We then have $p_{n-k}(z) = F_0(z)/F_1(z)$.

The other quotients are obtained analogously. Once these quotients are known, the coefficients of the $q_j(z)$ can be computed recursively, starting with the coefficient of the highest power from the relations

$$
\frac{F_{j-1}(z)}{F_j(z)} = \frac{F_j(z)}{F_{j+1}(z)} q_j(z).
$$

This method can be used in general to pretreat polynomials which are suspected of possessing multiple roots, in order to obtain polynomials which have only simple roots. Thus difficulties can be avoided when using any of the previously given methods for finding the roots. At the same time, one has also all the information available for determining the number of roots on a given interval of the real axis.

(b) General Case

The general case where one has to determine the number of roots of $f(z)$ in a certain region of the complex plane is solved by using the well-known relation that, if $f(z)$ has no poles in the considered region with boundary B,

$$\frac{1}{2\pi i} \oint_B \frac{f'(z)}{f(z)} \, dz = N, \tag{7.62}$$

where N is the number of roots (counted according to their multiplicity) in the region.

Numerically, this relation can be evaluated in two different ways. The first is to use numerical integration. If the boundary B is a polygon, the integrals over each side can be evaluated by using a suitable numerical integration formula (e.g., Gauss integration formulas). All other cases can be solved by approximating the boundary by a polygon. In selecting the integration method, any poles of the integrand arising from the existence of simple roots of $f(z)$ on the boundary have to be taken into account; otherwise the accuracy of the numerical integration rules may not be satisfactory (see, e.g., [1] or [3]). If such roots exist, then the real and imaginary parts of $f(z)$, written as functions of the parameter t used for defining the boundary, must have common factors which can be found by the euclidean algorithm.

Another method is particularly useful if the number of roots in a half plane have to be computed. It is based on the following observations. If one chooses for B a large circle of radius r around the origin, then, with $z = re^{i\varphi}$,

$$f(z) = \sum_{j=0}^{n} a_{n-j}z^j = \sum_{j=0}^{n} a_{n-j}r^j e^{ij\varphi} \doteq a_0 r^n e^{in\varphi}, \tag{7.63}$$

$$f'(z) \doteq a_0 n r^{n-1} e^{i(n-1)\varphi},$$

and so (7.62) gives $N = n$. Thus all the roots of $f(z)$ have to lie within the circle of radius r. One can easily see that, for

$$r \geq \frac{1}{A_0} \sum_{j=1}^{n} A_j, \quad \text{where } a_j = A_j e^{i\alpha_j} \quad (j = 0, 1, \dots, n), \tag{7.64}$$

this is certainly true, since if $r \geq 1$,

$$A_0 r > \sum_{j=1}^{n} A_j \, |z^{1-j}| \quad \text{or} \quad A_0 r^n > \sum_{j=1}^{n} A_j \, |z^{n-j}|,$$

so that $|f(z)| > 0$ for $|z| \geq r > 1$.

Therefore, to determine the roots in a half plane bounded by a straight line s, it is sufficient to determine the roots in a region bounded by this line and a sufficiently large half circle, using the expression (7.62).

Setting $f(z) = Re^{i\psi}$, one can replace the integral in (7.62) by the expression

$$N = \frac{1}{2\pi} \oint_{\bar{B}} d\psi, \qquad (7.65)$$

where $\bar{B}$ is the image of B defined by $f(z)$.   From (7.63), one concludes that the value of the integral over the image of the half circle is πn.   The contribution from the straight line is equal to 2π times the number of turns of the image of the straight line around the origin.   The number of turns can be obtained by counting the number of zeros of the real or imaginary part of $f(z)$, as z varies on the given straight line.   If a zero occurs for increasing ψ, it has to be counted positively; in the other case, negatively.   The number of zeros can be determined by forming a Sturmian sequence either with $f_n(z) = \text{Re}[f(z)] = R \cos \psi$ and $f_{n-1}(z) = -\text{Im}[f(z)] = -R \sin \psi$ or with $f_n(z) = \text{Im}[f(z)] = R \sin \psi$ and $f_{n-1}(z) = \text{Re}[f(z)]$ (depending on which of the two is the higher-degree polynomial).   One can verify immediately that, if one considers the signs of the functions in these sequences, the sequences lose a change in sign if $f_n(z)$ goes through zero for increasing ψ and gain a change in sign if it goes through zero for decreasing ψ.   Therefore, the difference between the number N_i of changes in sign between the successive functions at the initial point of the path of integration and the number N_e of changes in sign at the other end of the path of integration is equal to twice the number of turns.   So

$$N = \frac{n}{2} + \frac{N_i - N_e}{2}. \qquad (7.66)$$

These considerations can easily be extended to the case where the number of roots have to be determined in a region bounded by straight lines.   The described method can also be used for determining approximate values of roots by combining it with a method of subdividing into smaller and smaller parts the region in which the number of roots have to be computed.

Solution of Systems of Nonlinear Equations.   In this case, the problem is to find solutions for a set of m nonlinear equations in m independent variables:

$$f_i(\zeta_1, \ldots, \zeta_m) = 0, \qquad i = 1, 2, \ldots, m, \qquad (7.67)$$

where the f_i are analytic functions of the ζ_j in the neighborhood of zeros. For convenience, the ζ_j will be assumed to be real-valued.

The notation used previously can be taken over, if one understands now by $f(z)$ a vector with m components f_i, depending on the vector $z = (\zeta_1, \ldots, \zeta_m)$ nonlinearly.   Two groups of methods of solution are considered here: functional iterations and minimizing methods.

Functional Iterations. As in condition 5, one introduces, under analogous assumptions,

$$z = g(z) = z - h(z)f(z), \tag{7.68}$$

which is now a relation between vectors and which splits up into m equations. The convergence of the iteration

$$z_i = g(z_{i-1}), \qquad i = 1, 2, 3, \ldots, \tag{7.69}$$

has to be examined for this new situation. The proof of the convergence is analogous to the one for just one nonlinear equation. It is convenient here to introduce as an assumption the Lipschitz condition

$$\max |g(z') - g(z'')| < k \max |z' - z''| \qquad \text{with } k < 1 \tag{7.70}$$

for z', z'' in a certain neighborhood $N(x)$ of a solution of (7.68). By "max," the largest component of the vectors in absolute value is to be understood. Then, if z_0 is the first vector approximating the solution x and if z_1 is the next approximation defined by (7.69), one has, assuming z_0 in $N(x)$,

$$\max |z_1 - x| = \max |g(z_0) - x| < k \max |z_0 - x|$$

and $\max |z_j - x| = k^j \max |z_0 - x|, \qquad j = 1, 2, 3, \ldots.$

Hence, the z_j converge with increasing j to x under the stated assumptions, which are only sufficient conditions to ascertain convergence.

An example of such an iteration method is the Newton method generalized for this case. The formulas are easily derived if $f(x) = 0$ is developed into Taylor series around the approximation $z = (\zeta_1, \ldots, \zeta_m)$ $[x = (x_1, \ldots, x_m)]$:

$$0 = f(z) + \sum_{j=1}^{m} (x_j - \zeta_j) \frac{\partial}{\partial \zeta_j} f(z) + \cdots.$$

If the inverse of the Jacobian $J(z) = [\partial f_i(z)/\partial \zeta_j]$ exists, then $x \doteq z - J^{-1}(z)f(z)$. So, in this case

$$g(z) = z - J^{-1}(z)f(z), \tag{7.71}$$

and the iteration is

$$z_{i+1} = z_i - J^{-1}(z_i)f(z_i), \qquad i = 1, 2, 3, \ldots. \tag{7.72}$$

It may be rather cumbersome to evaluate the inverse of the Jacobian $J^{-1}(z_i)$ for each i. It has therefore been suggested that $J^{-1}(z)$ be kept fixed. Naturally, this will decrease the speed of convergence, but it can be shown that, if the first guess is sufficiently close to the solution, such a procedure still converges for a large class of functions $f_i(z)$. In actual numerical work, considerable care in preserving enough significant digits when evaluating the right-hand side of (7.72) may be required, since, particularly if the number of equations is large, the computation of $f(z_i)$ and $J^{-1}(z_i)$ can become rather difficult, owing to losses in significant digits.

Other methods, analogous to those given for the single equation, can be devised.

Minimizing Methods. In these methods, the problems (7.67) are replaced by the problem of finding the minimum of one function, $F(z)$, which is so defined that for the solutions of (7.67) it attains a minimum. Such a function may be defined, for instance, as

$$F(z) = \sum_{j=1}^{m} f_j(z)\bar{f}_j(z) \tag{7.73}$$

or

$$F(z) = \sum_{j=1}^{m} |f_j(z)|. \tag{7.74}$$

In numerical work, the form (7.73) is frequently preferable, since (7.74) leads often to a very narrow minimum, so that it may be very difficult to find an initial guess which—when applied with some iterative method—will lead to a solution. Therefore, only the case (7.73) is considered here.

Numerical methods for finding the minimum of $F(z)$ can be easily devised by using the geometrical picture. In the neighborhood of a solution x, $F(z)$ represents, according to the assumptions, a concave surface. If one starts, therefore, from an initial guess z_0 sufficiently close to x and proceeds in the proper direction d_0 along any straight line, except the one which is tangent to $F(z) = $ constant, one can always get to a point z_1 which is closer to x:

$$z_1 = z_0 + ad_0. \tag{7.75}$$

The closest point to x in the particular direction d_0 can be found by determining the minimum of $F(z_0 + ad_0)$ as a function of a; that is, a is given by the equation

$$\frac{dF(z_0 + ad_0)}{da} = 0, \tag{7.76}$$

which is, in general, nonlinear in a.

This process may be repeated with another direction d_1, and so on. For the directions, the following two choices are most frequently used:

1. The directions d_i are the gradients of F:

$$d_i = \operatorname{grad} F(z_i) \tag{7.77}$$

[where $\operatorname{grad} F(z_i)$ means $\operatorname{grad} F(z)$ for $z = z_i$]. This is combined with (7.76),

$$\frac{dF[z_i + a \operatorname{grad} F(z_i)]}{da} = 0, \tag{7.78}$$

leading to a_i, so that

$$z_{i+1} = z_i + a_i \operatorname{grad} F(z_i), \qquad i = 0, 1, 2, \dots . \qquad (7.79)$$

This method is called the method of steepest descent. It can be shown that the z_i converge to x for an appropriately chosen z_0, if $F(z)$ is analytic in a neighborhood of x.

In some cases, it may be rather difficult to evaluate grad $F(z_i)$. In these situations, it may be more convenient to use directions d_i parallel to the coordinate axis.

2. d_i is a set of unit vectors in the direction of a rectangular coordinate system. With this choice, the method used amounts to solving the set of generally nonlinear equations in a:

$$\frac{dF(z + ae_j)}{d\zeta_j} = 0, \qquad j = 1, 2, 3, \dots, m \qquad [z = (\zeta_1, \dots, \zeta_m)] \qquad (7.80)$$

—where e_j is a unit vector in the direction of the coordinate ζ_j—cyclically starting with an initial guess $z = z_0$. In each step, one of the equations (7.80) is solved, giving an a_i and z_{i+1} $(i = 0, 1, 2, \dots)$:

$$z_{i+1} = z_i + a_i e_{i_m}, \qquad \text{with } i_m = i - \left[\frac{i}{m}\right] m, \qquad (7.81)$$

where $[i/m]$ is the largest integer smaller or equal to the quotient i/m. One should perhaps note that the nonlinear equations (7.80) are not identical with the original equations (7.67).

This method is analogous to the Gauss-Seidel method for linear equations. The relative simplicity of computations for each of its iterations has to be paid for, in general, by a loss in the speed of convergence.

Some other methods, like the conjugate-gradient method, have been devised for finding the minimum of (7.73) (see [2]).

It should be pointed out here that in the case of systems of nonlinear equations, the choice of the initial guess z_0 is frequently a difficult problem, since all the methods described converge only if the initial guess z_0 is sufficiently close to the solution. For this reason, it will frequently be necessary to make a comprehensive tabulation of $F(z)$, which will indicate the behavior of this function.

Finally, one has to admit that the known numerical methods for the solution of large systems of nonlinear equations are sometimes far from satisfactory. If they converge at all to some values in a reasonable amount of time, there remains still the difficult question of the accuracy of the answer thus obtained. In most cases, there do not exist any practical estimates for the error, so that the only means of checking the solutions, at least to a certain extent, is the substitution of the computed values into the original equations.

Therefore, there remain still a number of problems in this field, which has become more and more important in the past few years, owing to the tremendous advances in science and technology.

REFERENCES

1. F. B. Hildebrand, "Introduction to Numerical Analysis," McGraw-Hill Book Company, Inc., New York, 1956.

2. A. S. Householder, "Principles of Numerical Analysis," McGraw-Hill Book Company, Inc., New York, 1953.

3. Fr. A. Willers, "Methoden der praktischen Analysis," 3d ed., Walter De Gruyter & Co., Berlin, 1958.

4. J. Peltier, "Résolution numérique des équations algébriques," Gauthier-Villars, Paris, 1957.

5. R. Adachi, On Newton's Method for the Approximate Solution of Simultaneous Equations, *Kumamoto J. Sci. Ser. A*, vol. 2, pp. 259–272, 1955.

6. A. C. Aitken, On the Iterative Methods of Lin and Friedman for Factorizing Polynomials, *Proc. Roy. Soc. Edinburgh*, sec. A, vol. 64, pp. 190–199, 1955.

7. F. L. Bauer, Quadratisch konvergente Durchführung der Bernoulli-Jacobischen Methode zur Nullstellenbestimmung von Polynomen, *S.–B. Math.-Nat. Kl., Bayer. Akad. Wiss.*, pp. 275–303, 1955.

8. F. L. Bauer, Direkte Faktorisierung eines Polynomes. *S.–B. Math.-Nat. Kl., Bayer. Akad. Wiss.*, pp. 163–203, 1957.

9. F. L. Bauer and K. Samelson, Polynomkerne und Iterationsverfahren, *Math. Z.*, vol. 67, pp. 93–98, 1957.

10. R. A. Brooker, The Solution of Algebraic Equations on the EDSAC, *Proc. Cambridge Philos. Soc.*, vol. 48, pp. 255–270, 1952.

11. G. Caldwell, A Note on the Downhill Method, *J. Assoc. Comput. Mach.*, vol. 6, pp. 223–225, 1959.

12. L. D. Eskin, Euler's Algorism for Extraction of Roots, *Uč. Zap. Kazan Univ.*, vol. 115, no. 14, pp. 139–143, 1955.

13. W. Everling, Eine Verallgemeinerung des Horner'schen Schemas, *Z. Angew. Math. ,Mech.,* vol. 37, p. 74, 1957.

14. M. Fiedler, Ueber das Graeffe'sche Verfahren, *Czechoslovak Math. J.*, vol. 5, no. 80, pp. 506–516, 1955.

15. E. Frank, On the Calculation of the Roots of Equations, *J. Math. Phys.*, pp. 187–197, 1955.

16. W. L. Frank, Finding Zeros of Arbitrary Functions, *J. Assoc. Comput. Mach.*, vol. 5, pp. 154–165, 1958.

17. S. Gorn, Maximal Convergence Intervals and a Gibb's Type Phenomenon for Newton's Approximation Procedure, *Ann. of Math.*, vol. 59, pp. 463–476, 1954.

18. D. Grohne, Bemerkungen zur Erweiterung des Verfahrens von Newton-Raphson auf die Berechnung einer mehrfachen Nullstelle, *Z. Angew. Math. Mech.*, vol. 37, p. 233, 1957.

19. W. Hart and T. S. Motzkin, A Composite Newton-Raphson Gradient Method for the Solution of Systems of Equations, *Pacific J. Math.*, vol. 6, pp. 691–707, 1956.

20. F. Heigl, Ueber die Abschätzung der Wurzeln algebraischer Gleichungen, *Monatsh. Math.*, vol. 62, pp. 16–55, 1958.

21. H. Heinrich, Zur Vorbehandlung algebraischer Gleichungen, *Z. Angew. Math. Mech.*, vol. 36, pp. 145–148, 1956.

22. A. Hirschleber, Ausnahmefälle des Graeffe'schen Verfahrens, *Z. Angew. Math. Mech.*, vol. 36, pp. 254–255, 1956.

23. A. Hirschleber, Praktische Auswertung von Ausnahmefällen beim Graeffe'schen Verfahren, *Z. Angew. Math. Mech.*, vol. 37, pp. 257–259, 1957.

24. G. N. Lance, Solutions of Algebraic and Transcendental Equations on an Automatic Digital Computer, *J. Assoc. Comput. Mach.*, vol. 6, pp. 97–101, 1959.

25. D. Markovitch, Les méthodes pratiques de factorisation approximative des polynomes, *Bull. Soc. Math. Phys. Macédoine*, vol. 7, pp. 5–16, 1956.

26. Č. Masaitis, Numerical Location of Zeros, *Aberdeen Proving Ground Ordn. Comput. Res. Rep.* 4, pp. 26–28, 1957.

27. D. Muller, A Method for Solving Algebraic Equations Using an Automatic Computer, *Math. Tables Aids Comput.*, vol. 10, pp. 208–215, 1956.

28. E. Pflanz, Zur Berechnung der Werte eines Polynomes mit dem Horner'schen Verfahren, *Z. Angew. Math. Mech.*, vol. 36, p. 152, 1956.

29. J. Schröder, Anwendung funktionalanalytischer Methoden zur numerischen Behandlung von Gleichungen, *Z. Angew. Math. Mech.*, vol. 36, pp. 260–261, 1956.

30. P. Wynn, Cubically Convergent Process for Zeros, *Math. Tables Aids Comput.*, vol. 10, pp. 97–100, 1956.

31. A. Zajta, Untersuchungen über die Verallgemeinerungen der Newton-Raphsonschen Wurzel-Approximationen I, II, *Acta Tech. Acad. Sci. Hungar.*, vol. 15, pp. 233–260, 1956; vol. 19, pp. 25–60, 1957.

32. A. M. Ostrowski, "Theory of the Solution of Equations and Systems of Equations," Academic Press, Inc., New York, 1960.

33. J. H. Wilkinson, The Evaluation of the Zeros of Ill-conditioned Polynomials, I, II, *Numer. Math.*, vol. 1, pp. 150–166, 167–180, 1959.

34. E. H. Bareiss, Resultant Procedure and the Mechanization of the Graeffe Process, *J. Assoc. Comput. Mach.*, vol. 7, pp. 346–386, 1960.

35. D. H. Lehmer, A Machine Method for Solving Polynomial Equations, *J. Assoc. Comput. Mach.*, vol. 8, pp. 151–162, 1961.

36. A. C. Aitken, On the Factorization of Polynomials by Iterative Methods, *Proc. Roy. Soc. Edinburgh*, sec. A, vol. 63, pp. 174–191, 1951.

37. A. C. Aitken, On the Theory of Factorizing Polynomials by Iterated Division, *Proc. Roy. Soc. Edinburgh*, sec. A, vol. 63, pp. 326–335, 1952.

38. F. W. J. Olver, The Evaluation of Zeros of High-degree Polynomials, *Philos. Trans. Roy. Soc. London*, ser. A., vol. 244, pp. 385–415, 1952.

39. J. J. Derr, A Unified Process for the Evaluation of the Zeros of Polynomials Over the Complex Number Field, *Math. Tables Aids Comput.*, vol. 13, pp. 29–36, 1959.

40. C. Flanagan and J. E. Maxfield, Estimates of the Roots of Certain Polynomials, *J. Soc. Indust. Appl. Math.*, vol. 7, pp. 367–373, 1959.

41. O. Gross and S. M. Johnson, Sequential Minimax Search for a Zero of a Convex Function, *Math. Tables Aids Comput.*, vol. 13, pp. 44–51, 1959.

42. S. Kulik, A Method of Approximating the Complex Roots of Equations, *Pacific J. Math.*, vol. 8, pp. 277–281, 1958; On the Solution of Algebraic Equations, *Proc. Amer. Math. Soc.*, vol. 10, pp. 185–192, 1959.

43. C. Mack, Routh Test Function Methods for the Numerical Solution of Polynomial Equations, *Quart. J. Mech. Appl. Math.*, vol. 12, pp. 365–378, 1959.

44. W. D. Munro, Some Iterative Methods for Determining Zeros of Functions of a Complex Variable, *Pacific J. Math.*, vol. 9, 555–566, 1959.

45. G. P. Weeg, Truncation Error in the Graeffe Root Squaring Method, *J. Assoc. Comp. Mach.*, vol. 7, pp. 69–71, 1960.

46. D. Greenspan, On Popular Methods and Extant Problems in the Solution of Polynomial Equations, *Math. Mag.*, vol. 31, pp. 239–253, 1957/58.

8

Eigenvalues of Finite Matrices

OLGA TAUSSKY

RESEARCH ASSOCIATE

CALIFORNIA INSTITUTE OF TECHNOLOGY

MARVIN MARCUS

ASSOCIATE PROFESSOR OF MATHEMATICS

UNIVERSITY OF BRITISH COLUMBIA

SOME TOPICS CONCERNING BOUNDS FOR EIGENVALUES OF FINITE MATRICES *by Olga Taussky*

8.1 Introduction

Most methods for finding the eigenvalues of a finite matrix lead to difficulties when applied to an arbitrary matrix. It is therefore of importance to obtain at least estimates for the eigenvalues. Some methods for finding the eigenvalues actually depend on the knowledge of such estimates. Furthermore, for many practical problems the exact eigenvalues are not even required, and bounds will quite often suffice.

Here only three types of bounds are discussed. Several others have been developed, some in quite recent years. The bounds to be discussed arise from (1) the field of values, (2) the Geršgorin circles, and (3) the majorization by nonnegative matrices. No completeness in material or bibliography is aimed at.

We note that the material presented here is becoming of increasing interest for numerical analysts. For instance, the theory of nonnegative matrices is being applied intensively (see Varga [56]) in the study of iterative solutions of the difference equations approximating partial differential equations arising from important technological problems. Also, the theory of stable matrices, that is, matrices whose eigenvalues are all in the left half plane, continues to develop (see Bellman [55], Gantmakher [9], Taussky [51, 52], Ostrowski and Schneider [53]).

THE FIELD OF VALUES

8.2 Definition and Basic Properties

Let $A = (a_{ik})$ be an $n \times n$ matrix whose elements are complex numbers. The field of values $F(A)$ of such a matrix is the set of all numbers

$$\sum_{i,k=1}^{n} a_{ik} x_i \bar{x}_k = (Ax,x) = \bar{x}'Ax$$

where x is a vector $(x_1, \ldots, x_n)$ with $\sum_{i=1}^{n} x_i \bar{x}_i = 1$. This concept was introduced by Hausdorff [13] and Toeplitz [37], who proved that $F(A)$ is a bounded, closed, and convex set. That $F(A)$ is bounded and closed follows, of course, immediately from the fact that it is a continuous function of the points of the unit sphere $\sum_{i=1}^{n} x_i \bar{x}_i = 1$. It can further be seen at once that $F(A)$ contains the eigenvalues λ_i of A. For $Ax = \lambda_i x$ with $\bar{x}'x = 1$ implies

$$\bar{x}'Ax = \lambda_i \bar{x}'x = \lambda_i.$$

8.3 The Field of Values of Hermitian Matrices

Let A be a real symmetric matrix $A = A'$ or a complex, but hermitian, matrix; that is, $A = \bar{A}' = A^*$. In this case we have

$$\overline{\bar{x}'Ax} = x'\bar{A}\bar{x} = \bar{x}'A^*x = \bar{x}'Ax.$$

(The second equality comes from the fact that we can transpose a scalar.) Hence $F(A)$ is real for an hermitian A. In particular, the eigenvalues are real. From the fact that $F(A)$ is closed, bounded, and convex, it follows then that for an hermitian A it is a closed interval on the real line. The end points are known to be the largest and smallest eigenvalues, $\lambda_{\max}$ and $\lambda_{\min}$, of A. Since the diagonal elements of A belong to $F(A)$, we have, in particular,

$$\lambda_{\max} \geq \max a_{ii}, \qquad \lambda_{\min} \leq \min a_{ii}.$$

8.4 The Convex Hull of the Eigenvalues

The fact that for an hermitian matrix the end points of $F(A)$ are $\lambda_{\max}$ and $\lambda_{\min}$ is a special case of a much more general fact: since $F(A)$ is convex and contains the eigenvalues $\lambda_1, \ldots, \lambda_n$, it contains the convex closure $C(\lambda)$ of the λ_i, that is, the smallest convex and closed set which includes them. The question arises; Is $C(\lambda) = F(A)$? If it is, then we know that the vertices of $C(\lambda)$ will be eigenvalues.

However, in general, $F(A) \neq C(\lambda)$. If, on the other hand, A is normal, then equality occurs, as is shown below.

8.5   Normal Matrices

A matrix A is called *normal* when

$$AA^* = A^*A$$

where $A^* = \bar{A}'$; for example, hermitian matrices are normal since they satisfy $A^* = A$.   Also, *unitary* matrices, that is, matrices with $A^{-1} = A^*$, are normal; in the case that A is real, they are called *orthogonal*.

One of the most important applications of unitary matrices is provided by the fact that every matrix A can be transformed to upper triangular form by a unitary similarity; that is, a unitary matrix U exists such that

$$U^{-1}AU = (b_{ik}),$$

with $b_{ik} = 0$ when $i > k$.   (For a proof of this result see Schwerdtfeger [54, p. 203]; note that the matrix B is not unique.)   Since U is unitary, this implies that $U^{-1}A^*U = (b_{ik})^* = (b_{ki})$.

If, further, A is normal, then $U^{-1}AU$ is normal too, which implies that

$$(b_{ik})(b_{ik})^* = (b_{ik})^*(b_{ik}).$$

Equating the diagonal elements of the two products above, we obtain

$$b_{ik} = 0, \qquad i \neq k.$$

This implies that every normal matrix can be transformed by a unitary similarity into a diagonal matrix.   Since similar matrices have the same eigenvalues, this diagonal matrix consists of the eigenvalues of the normal matrix.

8.6   Invariance of the Field of Values

Another property of $F(A)$ which is used to prove that $F(A)$ coincides with $C(\lambda)$ for a normal A is the fact that, for a unitary A,

$$F(A) = F(U^{-1}AU).$$

This follows immediately from the definition of $F(A)$ as the set of numbers $\bar{x}'Ax$ for $\bar{x}'x = 1$; replacing A by $U^{-1}AU$, we obtain $\bar{x}'U^{-1}AUx$, which belongs to $F(A)$, since $\bar{x}'U^{-1} = (\overline{Ux})'$ and $\bar{x}'U^{-1}Ux = 1$ for $\bar{x}'x = 1$.   On the other hand, every number $\bar{x}'Ax$ can be written in the form $(\bar{x}'U)(U^{-1}AU)(U^{-1}x) = (\overline{U^{-1}x})'(U^{-1}AU)(U^{-1}x)$, and again $\bar{x}'UU^{-1}x = 1$ for $x'x = 1$.

8.7   The Field of Values for Normal Matrices

Hence we need to prove the property $F(A) = C(\lambda)$ for A normal only for the diagonal matrix diag $(\lambda_1, \ldots, \lambda_n)$ formed by the eigenvalues of

A. For such a diagonal matrix the field of values is

$$\sum_{i=1}^{n} \lambda_i x_i \bar{x}_i.$$

Since $x_i \bar{x}_i \geq 0$ and $\sum_{i=1}^{n} x_i \bar{x}_i = 1$, it is clear that $F(A)$ is the convex closure of the λ_i's.

Normal matrices are not the only ones for which $F(A) = C(\lambda)$ unless $n \leq 4$. For all $n > 4$, there are nonnormal matrices with this property (see Moyls and Marcus [21]).

8.8   Generalizations of the Field of Values

The following generalization of the definition of $F(A)$ was suggested by Givens [12]:

$$F_H(A) = x^*HAx \quad \text{for } x^*Hx = 1$$

where H is a positive definite matrix.   It can then be shown that $C(\lambda)$ is the intersection of all $F_H(A)$ for all possible choices of H.

Another generalization was suggested by K. Fan (unpublished): let $F_r(A)$ be the set of all numbers $\sum_{i=1}^{r} (Ax^i, x^i)$ when the set x^i varies over all systems of r orthonormal vectors.

8.9   The Field of Values of Sums and Products

It is easy to see that the field of values of $A + B$ is contained in the set of numbers $F(A) + F(B)$ where $S_1 + S_2$ means here the set of all numbers $\sigma_1 + \sigma_2$ when $\sigma_1 \in S_1$ and $\sigma_2 \in S_2$.   Similarly the field of values of AB is contained in $F(A)F(B)$ for an analogous definition.

8.10   Singular Values of Matrices

If λ_i are the eigenvalues of A, then A^* has as eigenvalues $\bar{\lambda}_i$.   The eigenvalues of AA^* are in general not $\lambda_i \bar{\lambda}_i$.   For normal matrices they are $\lambda_i \bar{\lambda}_i$ and conversely (see Parker [27], Hoffman and Taussky [17]).   This can be shown by the methods used in Sec. 8.3.   The positive square roots of the eigenvalues of AA^* are called the singular values of A.   The following inequalities hold between the eigenvalues and the singular values (see Browne [6], Brauer [4], and Weyl [38]):

$$\lambda_{\min}(AA^*) \leq |\lambda_i(A)|^2 \leq \lambda_{\max}(AA^*).$$

These inequalities matter very much, for it is easier to find bounds for the eigenvalues of the hermitian matrix AA^* than for the general matrix *A*.   The inequalities can be proved easily, again by transforming A to triangular form by a unitary similarity.

8.11 Application of the Field of Values to Bounds of Eigenvalues

The exact form of the set $F(A)$ is complicated and not of immediate computational use (see Murnaghan [22]).

However, useful bounds can be obtained from $F(A)$ with little trouble:

$$|\sum a_{ik} x_i \bar{x}_k| \leq \sum |a_{ik}| \qquad \text{for } \sum x_i \bar{x}_i = 1;$$

hence

$$|\lambda_{\max}| \leq \sum |a_{ik}|.$$

This is a very crude estimate. A better bound,

$$|\lambda_{\max}| \leq (\sum |a_{ik}|^2)^{1/2},$$

can be obtained by applying the Schwarz inequality as follows:

$$|\sum a_{ij} x_i \bar{x}_k|^2 \leq \sum |a_{ij}|^2 \sum |x_i \bar{x}_k|^2 = \sum |a_{ik}|^2 \sum |x_i|^2 \sum |x_k|^2 = \sum |a_{ik}|^2.$$

Using $F(A)$, we also obtain

$$\left| \sum_{i,k=1}^{n} a_{ik} x_i \bar{x}_k \right| \leq \sum_{i,k=1}^{n} |a_{ik}|\, |x_i \bar{x}_k| \leq \max |a_{ik}| \sum_{i,k=1}^{n} |x_i|\, |\bar{x}_k|$$

$$= \max |a_{ik}| \sum_{i=1}^{n} |x_i| \sum_{i=1}^{n} |\bar{x}_i| \leq \max |a_{ik}|\, n.$$

The last inequality can be obtained by applying the Schwarz inequality $(\Sigma\, a_i b_i)^2 \leq \Sigma\, a_i^2 \Sigma\, b_i^2$ to the sets $a_i = |x_i|$, $b_i = 1$. This implies $\sum_{i=1}^{n} |x_i| \leq \sqrt{n}$. Hence

$$|\lambda_{\max}| \leq \max |a_{ik}|\, n.$$

Bounds can also be obtained for the real and imaginary parts of the eigenvalues. Observe that

$$\operatorname{Re}\left(\sum_{i,k=1}^{n} a_{ik} x_i \bar{x}_k \right) = \tfrac{1}{2} \sum_{i,k=1}^{n} (a_{ik} + \overline{a_{ki}}) x_i \bar{x}_k$$

and apply the above estimates to the matrix $\tfrac{1}{2}(A + A^*)$.
It follows that

$$|\operatorname{Re}(\lambda_i)| \leq \max \tfrac{1}{2} |a_{ik} + \overline{a_{ki}}|\, n.$$

By a similar argument

$$|\operatorname{Im}(\lambda_i)| \leq \max \tfrac{1}{2} |a_{ik} - \overline{a_{ki}}|\, n$$

is obtained. If $a_{ik} = \overline{a_{ki}}$, then $\operatorname{Im}(\lambda_i) = 0$ follows, which is a well-known fact for hermitian matrices. If $a_{ik} = -\overline{a_{ki}}$, then $\operatorname{Re}(\lambda_i) = 0$ follows, which is also well known for skew hermitian matrices.

The bounds for $|\lambda_i|$ and $|\mathrm{Re}\ (\lambda_i)|$ are best possible, as is seen by taking as A a matrix all of whose elements are 1. However, for real matrices the bound for $|\mathrm{Im}\ (\lambda_i)|$ can be improved to

$$|\mathrm{Im}\ (\lambda_i)| \leq \max \tfrac{1}{2} |a_{ik} - a_{ki}| \cot \frac{\pi}{2n} .$$

This bound is best possible, as can be seen by taking as A the matrix

$$\begin{pmatrix} 0 & 1 & 1 & \cdots \\ -1 & 0 & 1 & \cdots \\ -1 & -1 & 0 & \cdots \\ & \cdots & & \cdots \end{pmatrix}$$

whose characteristic equation is $(x + 1)^n + (x - 1)^n = 0$ and whose eigenvalues are $i \cot [(2k - 1)\pi/2n]$. These last bounds have been developed by Hirsch [16], Bendixson [2], and Pick [28].

8.12   The Norm of a Matrix

Although $F(A)$ is invariant under unitary similarity transformations, these last bounds are not invariant. An invariant bound mentioned earlier can also be found by using the following inequality due to Schur [32]:

$$\sum_{i=1}^{n} |\lambda_i|^2 \leq \sum_{i,k=1}^{n} |a_{ik}|^2.$$

This implies immediately the inequality

$$|\lambda_{\max}| \leq (\sum |a_{ik}|^2)^{1/2}.$$

The quantity $(\Sigma\ |a_{ik}|^2)^{1/2}$ is called norm A. To show that it is invariant under unitary transformations of A, use the fact that $(\text{norm } A)^2 = \mathrm{tr}\ (AA^*)$; since further $\mathrm{tr}\ [(U^{-1}AU)(U^{-1}AU)^*] = \mathrm{tr}\ (U^{-1}AA^*U)$ and the trace of a matrix is invariant under even arbitrary similarity transformations, the invariance of norm A is established.

Since norm A is invariant under unitary transformations, the inequality of Schur can be proved by assuming A in triangular form. This proof further exhibits that equality holds if and only if the triangular matrix is actually diagonal. This means for the original matrix that equality holds in the Schur inequality if and only if A is normal.

8.13   Row and Column Sums

It can be shown that

$$\max_{i} \sum_{k=1}^{n} |a_{ik}| \qquad \text{and} \qquad \max_{k} \sum_{i=1}^{n} |a_{ik}|$$

are bounds for the absolute values of the eigenvalues of A. Even these bounds can be replaced by a bound which is, in general, better. This is done in Sec. 8.15.

THE GERŠGORIN CIRCLES

8.14 A Determinant Theorem: Matrices with Dominant Diagonal

The bounds announced will be obtained easily from a simple theorem which has turned up again and again in totally different branches of mathematics (for a bibliography, see Taussky [34]). It deals with so-called "matrices with dominant diagonal," that is, matrices $A = (a_{ik})$ for which

$$|a_{ii}| > \sum_{\substack{k=1 \\ k \neq i}}^{n} |a_{ik}|, \qquad i = 1, \ldots, n.$$

Such matrices play a big role in computational problems, since they are not too remote from diagonal matrices. Many processes for finding the inverse of a matrix work particularly well for such matrices.

The determinant theorem in question states that a matrix with dominant diagonal has an inverse. This theorem can be generalized if we generalize the concept of dominant diagonal by including also the possibility of equality in the above relations. However, we must obviously exclude the case that equality holds for all n equations. It has further to be assumed that the matrix is *indecomposable**, that is, that it cannot be brought into the form $\begin{pmatrix} P & Q \\ O & R \end{pmatrix}$ by a simultaneous row and column permutation. Here P and R are square matrices, and O consists of zeros only. The theorem then finally becomes:

An indecomposable matrix with a dominant diagonal in the generalized sense, for which not all the relations

$$|a_{ii}| = \sum_{\substack{k=1 \\ k \neq i}}^{n} |a_{ik}|, \qquad i = 1, \ldots, n,$$

hold, has an inverse.

8.15 Application to Eigenvalues

If we apply the determinant theorem to an arbitrary matrix $A = (a_{ik})$, it follows that as long as the matrix $A - xI$ has a dominant diagonal, then it must also have an inverse; that is, if

$$|a_{ii} - x| > \sum_{\substack{k=1 \\ k \neq i}}^{n} |a_{ik}|,$$

---

* The term *irreducible* is also used.

then x is not an eigenvalue.   This implies that all the eigenvalues of A lie inside or on the boundary of the n circles:

$$|a_{ii} - x| \leq \sum_{\substack{k=1 \\ k \neq i}}^{n} |a_{ik}|.$$

Applying the generalized concept of dominant diagonal, we obtain the following theorem:

For an indecomposable matrix all eigenvalues lie inside the union of the above circles unless an eigenvalue is a common boundary point of all n circles.

The importance of these circles was first mentioned by Geršgorin [11]; later they were rediscovered by Brauer [3].

8.16   Generalization of the Determinant Theorem to the Study of the Rank of a Matrix

Another formulation of the determinant theorem is obviously the following:

Let A be an indecomposable matrix for which not all

$$|a_{ii}| = \sum_{\substack{k=1 \\ k \neq i}}^{n} |a_{ik}|, \qquad i = 1, \ldots, n,$$

and let rank $A \leq n - 1$;   then at least one inequality

$$|a_{ii}| < \sum_{\substack{k=1 \\ k \neq i}}^{n} |a_{ik}|$$

must hold.

A generalization of this was given by Taussky [35] and Stein [33]:
Let A be an indecomposable matrix for which not all

$$|a_{ii}| = \sum_{\substack{k=1 \\ k \neq i}}^{n} |a_{ik}|, \qquad i = 1, \ldots, n.$$

If rank $A \leq n - m$, then at least m inequalities

$$|a_{ii}| < \sum_{\substack{k=1 \\ k \neq i}}^{n} |a_{ik}|$$

hold.

8.17   Application to Multiple Eigenvalues of a Matrix

From the preceding theorem it follows immediately that for an indecomposable matrix an eigenvalue of multiplicity m with m linearly independent eigenvectors must be contained in at least m of the Geršgorin circles.

8.18   Disconnected Sets of Circles

Geršgorin showed that, if a set of n_1 ($\leq n$) circles has no point in common with the remaining $(n - n_1)$ circles, then this set contains exactly n_1 eigenvalues (multiple eigenvalues being counted with their proper multiplicities). He showed this by a continuity argument which is repeated here for the special case that $n_1 = 1$. The general case follows in exactly the same manner.

Assume that the circle in question corresponds to the ith row. Construct then a new matrix A' in which the ith row is replaced by $(0 \cdots 0\, a_{ii}\, 0 \cdots 0)$. This matrix has a_{ii} as an eigenvalue, and the remaining $n - 1$ eigenvalues come from the $(n - 1) \times (n - 1)$ matrix which is obtained if we omit the ith row and column. Clearly the Geršgorin circles of this matrix are contained in the $(n - 1)$ remaining circles of the original matrix and hence have no point in common with the ith circle. Use now the fact that the eigenvalues vary continuously with the elements of the matrix! We go back from A' to A in a continuous transition by increasing the absolute values of the elements in the ith row, but so that they do not exceed the original $|a_{ik}|$ at any time. It is then clear that the eigenvalue moving away from a_{ii} cannot leave the original ith circle and that the other $(n - 1)$ eigenvalues must stay inside the other $(n - 1)$ circles.

A special case arises when all circles are disconnected. If this happens to a real matrix, then all eigenvalues must be real. For the complex eigenvalues would have to lie symmetrically about the real axis; since the centers of the circles are on the real axis, the corresponding circle would have to contain two eigenvalues, which is a contradiction.

8.19   Real Matrices with Dominant Diagonal

It can be shown that a real matrix with dominant diagonal and positive diagonal elements not only is nonsingular but even has a positive determinant. Various lower bounds for the determinant of such a matrix have been given (see Ostrowski [23], Price [29], Brenner [5], Haynsworth [14], Schneider [30]).

The Geršgorin circles of such a matrix lie entirely on the right of the imaginary axis; hence real matrices with dominant and positive diagonal have all their eigenvalues with positive real parts.

8.20   Eigenvalues of Similar Matrices

Since similar matrices have the same eigenvalues but not the same circles, it is possible to obtain smaller regions inside which the eigenvalues lie. For if we consider all matrices $S^{-1}AS$ for all possible nonsingular matrices S, then the eigenvalues of A must lie in the intersection of all the circle regions obtained.   If A is in particular similar to a diagonal matrix, then the eigenvalues themselves, considered as point circles, are a special case of such a circle region.

For practical computations it is particularly helpful to use as S the matrices diag $(1, \ldots, 1, \alpha, 1, \ldots, 1)$. Such an S does not change the diagonal elements but can be used to decrease the radii of the circles.

8.21   Other Circle Sets

Since the transpose of a matrix has the same eigenvalues as the original matrix, the columns of the matrix can be used instead of the rows.   We denote the radii derived from the rows by r_i, that is,

$$r_i = \sum_{\substack{k=1 \\ k \neq i}}^{n} |a_{ik}|,$$

and the radii derived from the columns by c_i, that is,

$$c_i = \sum_{\substack{k=1 \\ k \neq i}}^{n} |a_{ki}|,$$

It was shown by Ostrowski [25] that the eigenvalues of A also lie in the circles with centers a_{ii} and radii $r_i^{\alpha} c_i^{1-\alpha}$, for all α with $0 \leq \alpha \leq 1$.

Other regions which contain the eigenvalues were studied by Schneider [31] by using the fact that a determinant vanishes simultaneously with the determinants obtained by permuting the rows. Applying this to a characteristic determinant and using the determinant theorems of Sec. 8.14, a region which contains the eigenvalues is obtained which consists partly of the interior of circles, and partly of the exterior.   This treatment provides a generalization of the fact, observed by Taussky [36] for $n = 2$, that in this case no eigenvalue can lie in the common part of the two Geršgorin circles.   For, by Schneider's remark, the eigenvalues for $n = 2$ have also to lie in the union of the exterior of the same two circles, hence cannot lie in the common part.

8.22   Cassini Ovals

The following generalization of the determinant theorem of Sec. 8.14 holds:

Let

$$|a_{ii}| \, |a_{kk}| > \sum_{\substack{r=1 \\ r \neq i}}^{n} |a_{ir}| \sum_{\substack{r=1 \\ r \neq k}}^{n} |a_{kr}|$$

hold for all $i, k = 1, \ldots, n$; $i \neq k$.   Then A is nonsingular.

This theorem was found by Ostrowski [24] and rediscovered by Brauer [4], who further utilized it in the same manner as Geršgorin applied the determinant theorem of Sec. 8.14 to obtain the circles.   In this way it is shown that the $\binom{n}{2}$ Cassini ovals

$$|a_{ii} - z|\,|a_{kk} - z| \le \sum_{\substack{r=1 \\ r\neq i}}^{n} |a_{ir}| \sum_{\substack{r=1 \\ r\neq k}}^{n} |a_{kr}|$$

form a region inside which all the eigenvalues must lie.

It was pointed out to the author by J. L. Brenner (unpublished) that this argument cannot, in general, be generalized to three or more factors.

NONNEGATIVE MATRICES

In the Geršgorin circles, as in most work on bounds for the eigenvalues, the absolute values of the elements of the matrix play a bigger role than the elements.   This idea is now exploited in more detail. See also Fan [46].

8.23   Majorization

If A is an arbitrary $m \times n$ matrix (a_{ik}) with complex elements and $B = (b_{ik})$ is another $m \times n$ matrix, such that $b_{ik} \ge |a_{ik}|$, then we say that B majorizes A, and we write $B \ge A$.   In particular, $B \ge 0$ means that all elements of B are nonnegative, in which case the matrix B is called nonnegative.   By $B > 0$ we mean that all elements of B are positive, in which case the matrix B is called positive.

If $B \ge A$ and $m = n$, then the absolute values of all the eigenvalues of A are at most as large as the absolute value of the maximum eigenvalue of B (which is actually itself a nonnegative number, as is shown below). This fact can be proved by using the well-known majorizing of power series; namely, if $|\alpha_i| \le \beta_i$, $i = 1, \ldots$, then the radius of convergence of the power series $\sum \alpha_i x^i$ is at least as large as the radius of convergence of the power series $\sum \beta_i x^i$.   Consider then the power series with matrix coefficients $(I - xA)^{-1}$ and $(I - xB)^{-1}$. It is known (see, e.g., Mac-Duffee [20], p. 98) that the radii of convergence of these series are $1/|\lambda_{\max}(A)|$, $1/\lambda_{\max}(B)$, respectively, which proves the assertion.

If some $b_{ik} > |a_{ik}|$, then it cannot be concluded, in general, that $\lambda_{\max}(B) > |\lambda_{\max}(A)|$, as is seen by the example

$$A = \begin{pmatrix} 0 & 0 \\ 0 & 0 \end{pmatrix}, \qquad B = \begin{pmatrix} 0 & 0 \\ 1 & 0 \end{pmatrix}.$$

However, for indecomposable matrices (see Sec. 8.14), the inequalities

$$b_{ik} \geq |a_{ik}|,$$

with strict inequality in at least one case, imply that

$$\lambda_{\max}(B) > \lambda_{\max}(A).$$

8.24   Primitive Matrices

An indecomposable matrix A which is nonnegative and has only one eigenvalue of maximal absolute value is called *primitive*. This definition can be shown to be equivalent to asking that $A^m > 0$ for some value $m = m_1$ (see, e.g., Herstein [15], Pták and Sedláček [57]). A positive matrix is by definition indecomposable.

8.25   The Fundamental Theorem Concerning Nonnegative Indecomposable Matrices

The main usefulness of positive and nonnegative matrices lies in the fact that important facts are known about their eigenvalues and vectors. A nonnegative indecomposable matrix has among its eigenvalues of maximal absolute value one which is real and positive. This eigenvalue is simple, and its corresponding eigenvector can be chosen to have positive components. No other eigenvalue has an eigenvector with positive (or even nonnegative) components.

The theorem concerning nonnegative indecomposable matrices goes back to Perron and Frobenius and can be proved in various ways. The existence of a positive eigenvalue with positive eigenvector for a positive matrix follows easily from the Brouwer fixed-point theorem (see Alexandroff and Hopf [1], p. 480). Here a proof will be given which follows rather closely Wielandt's treatment [39]. For other proofs see Brauer [44], Fan [45], and Householder [47].

(*a*) The main tool in this treatment is to assign to every vector $x = (x_1, \ldots, x_n)$ with all $x_i \geq 0$ (but at least one $x_i > 0$) the number r_x defined in the following way:

$$r_x = \min_i \frac{\sum a_{ik} x_k}{x_i}.$$

If $x_i = 0$, then the quotient is defined to have the value $+\infty$. This number is also definable as the largest number ρ for which

$$Ax - \rho x \geq 0.$$

It is clear that at least one component of $Ax - \rho x$ is zero; our aim is to find an x for which all are zero. It is easy to see that the set of numbers r_x, when x varies over all vectors described above, contains positive numbers and also that it is bounded. It can be shown that

$$r_x \leq \text{max column sum.}$$

For if we let s be the vector $(1,1,\ldots,1)$, then

$$Ax - r_x x \geq 0$$

implies

$$s'Ax - r_x s'x \geq 0$$

or

$$r_x \leq \frac{s'Ax}{s'x} \leq \text{max column sum.}$$

(No column sum is zero, since the matrix is indecomposable.)

Since the set r_x is bounded, it must have a least upper bound r. We now prove that there exists a vector x^* such that $r_{x^*} = r$.

Instead of considering the set of all vectors $x \geq 0$, we may restrict ourselves to considering only vectors x with $\Sigma\, x_i = 1$, since

$$\frac{\sum a_{ik}x_k}{x_i} = \frac{\sum a_{ik}x_k / \sum x_k}{x_i / \sum x_k}.$$

These vectors form a closed and bounded set. Hence, there exists among them a converging sequence of vectors $x^1, x^2, \ldots$ for which $\lim r_{x^i} = r$. Let $x^i \to \bar{x}$, where $\bar{x}$ is again a vector in the same space. We only have to show that $r_{\bar{x}} = r$. By assumption,

$$r \geq r_{\bar{x}}.$$

On the other hand,

$$Ax^i - r_{x^i}x^i \geq 0;$$

hence also

$$A\bar{x} - r\bar{x} \geq 0,$$

which, however, implies that

$$r \leq r_{\bar{x}},$$

so that we obtain

$$r_{\bar{x}} = r.$$

(b) We now prove that r is an eigenvalue of A and that every vector $\bar{x}$ for which $r_{\bar{x}} = r$ is an eigenvector. For this purpose the following lemma is used:

Let y be any (nonzero) nonnegative vector. Then

$$(I + A)^{n-1}y > 0.$$

This can be shown by proving that for all t the vector $(I + A)^t y$ contains nonzero elements wherever $(I + A)^{t-1}y$ has nonzero elements and at least one more nonzero element. This is a consequence of the fact that A is indecomposable.

Consider then a vector z such that

$$Az - rz = y \geq 0.$$

We know that $y > 0$ is impossible. However, we multiply the above inequality by $(I + A)^{n-1}$:

$$A(I + A)^{n-1}z - r(I + A)^{n-1}z = (I + A)^{n-1}y \geq 0.$$

The lemma implies that

$$A(I + A)^{n-1}z - r(I + A)^{n-1}z > 0,$$

which is impossible. This implies that $y = 0$.

This again implies that r is an eigenvalue of A and that z is an eigenvector.

(c) The extremal vectors are positive. Since with z, also, the positive vector $(I + A)^{n-1}z$ is an eigenvector and since $Az = rz$, the vector $(I + A)^{n-1}z$ coincides with $(1 + r)^{n-1}z$, a positive multiple of z. Hence z is positive.

(d) r is a maximal eigenvalue. Let α be any eigenvalue of A and let x be its corresponding eigenvector; then

$$\alpha x = Ax$$

holds. This implies

$$|\alpha|\, x^* \leq A^* x^* = Ax^*,$$

where x^*, A^* denote the vector and matrix obtained from x and A by replacing each element by its absolute value. The inequality

$$Ax^* - |\alpha|\, x^* \geq 0$$

implies, by definition,

$$|\alpha| \leq r.$$

(e) No eigenvalue which differs from r can have a positive eigenvector. This follows from the following lemma (see, e.g., Zurmühl [42], p. 161):

Let A be any matrix with eigenvalue α and corresponding vector x. Let $\beta \neq \alpha$ be also an eigenvalue of A, and let y be an eigenvector of β considered as an eigenvalue of the transpose of A. Then $y'x = 0$.

We apply this lemma to $\alpha = r$, considered as an eigenvalue of A', when $\beta \neq r$ is any eigenvalue of A. Since the corresponding eigenvector of r with respect to A' is also positive, it follows that the eigenvector of β cannot be nonnegative.

(f) r is a simple eigenvalue of A. First we show that r has only one linearly independent eigenvector. Let z be any vector for which $r_z = r$, and let x be another eigenvector of r, either extremal or not. Take a number c such that $x - cz = y \geq 0$, with at least one $y_i = 0$.

Since the vector y is also an extremal vector of r, a contradiction is found which implies $y = 0$ or $x = cz$.

Consider next $(-1)^n$ times the characteristic polynomial $\phi(x)$ of A, that is, $|xI - A|$. We know that $\phi(r) = 0$ and want to establish $\phi'(r) \neq 0$. Since $\phi'(r)$ can be written in the form ΣX_{ii}, where X_{ik} are the cofactors of $rI - A$, we see that $\phi'(r)$ is equal to the trace of (X_{ik}). The matrix (X_{ik}) has rank 1 for $x = r$, hence is not the zero matrix. We note that

$$(rI - A)(X_{ik}) = 0.$$

Hence, every column of (X_{ik}) is an eigenvector of r or consists of zeros. There is only one linearly independent eigenvector whose elements are all $\neq 0$ and have the same sign. Hence the elements in each column have the same sign; similarly, the elements in each row have the same sign, since they are the eigenvectors of r with respect to A'. Hence all elements of (X_{ik}) have the same sign, which implies that its trace is $\neq 0$.

8.26   An Inclusion Theorem for the Eigenvalues of an Indecomposable Nonnegative Matrix

Collatz [7] proved that the intervals spanned by the quotients $\Sigma a_{ik}x_k/x_i$ considered in Sec. 8.25, formed for an arbitrary positive vector, always include the dominant eigenvalue. This follows easily from Wielandt's treatment described in Sec. 8.25.

8.27   A Similar Inclusion Theorem for Real Symmetric Matrices and Other Inclusion Theorems

Collatz [7] later proved by a different method that for real symmetric matrices the quotients mentioned in Sec. 8.26, formed for an arbitrary real vector without zero components, span an interval which includes at least one eigenvalue of the matrix. A generalization of this valid for arbitrary normal matrices was obtained simultaneously by Walker and Weston [37a] and by Wielandt [40]. The formulation of Wielandt's theorem enables it to include various other previously found inclusion theorems. For other inclusion theorems concerning hermitian and normal matrices, see, in particular, Fan and Hoffman [8], Kato [18], Wielandt [41].

8.28   A Problem Concerning Positive Matrices and Symmetric Matrices

In Secs. 8.26 and 8.27 a theorem was mentioned which holds both for positive and for symmetric matrices but which necessitates, so far, different proofs. There are other theorems of this nature, and it seems desirable to find a unified treatment for both cases.   Examples of such theorems are:

1. The dominant root exceeds the diagonal elements; more generally, every principal minor of det $(\lambda I - A)$ is greater than zero if λ is larger than the dominant root (this is true for positive matrices and for symmetric matrices).

2. The inequality

$$\det_{i,k=1,\ldots,n} (a_{ik}) \leq \det_{i,k=1,\ldots,p} (a_{ik}) \det_{i,k=p+1,\ldots,n} (a_{ik})$$

is valid for matrices with nonnegative minors of all orders and for positive definite symmetric matrices.

3. A matrix with all its minors of all orders nonnegative has all eigenvalues real and nonnegative; a positive semidefinite symmetric matrix has all eigenvalues real and nonnegative.

4. The eigenvalues of the matrix are separated by the eigenvalues of a principal minor of order $n - 1$ (this is true for matrices all of whose minors are positive and for symmetric matrices).

Problem 2 was suggested to K. Fan, who subsequently found a unified treatment (unpublished).

8.29 Stochastic Matrices

From the last remark in Sec. 8.23 it follows that a positive (hence indecomposable) matrix cannot have its maximum eigenvalue equal to its maximum row sum unless all row sums are equal.   This can also be deduced from the fact that for an indecomposable matrix an eigenvalue cannot lie on the boundary of the Gershgorin circles unless it lies on the boundary of all the circles.   Finally, it can quite easily be proved independently by the following argument.   Let r be the maximum eigenvalue, let $x = (x_1, \ldots, x_n)$ be the corresponding eigenvector, and assume

$$r = \max_i \sum_{k=1}^{n} a_{ik}$$

$$rx_i = \sum a_{ik}x_k, \qquad i = 1, \ldots, n.$$

Let $x_M = \max x_i$; then

$$rx_M = \sum a_{Mk}x_k \leq x_M \sum a_{Mk} \leq x_M \max_i \sum_{k=1}^{n} a_{ik}.$$

Since

$$r = \max_i \sum_{k=1}^{n} a_{ik}$$

we have $x_i = x_M$; hence all row sums are equal too.

A nonnegative matrix for which all row sums are equal is called *stochastic*.   Matrices of this type play a great role in many branches of mathematics, as well as in applications—for example, in the study of the transition probability of Markoff chains. For references concerning stochastic matrices, see for example, Gantmakher [9].

8.30 Bounds for λ_{max} in a Positive Matrix

Since in a nonstochastic positive matrix, λ_{max} differs from the maximum row sum, we may put

$$\lambda_{max} = \text{max row sum} - p, \qquad p > 0.$$

A bound for p was given by Ledermann [19] and later improved by Ostrowski [26] and Brauer [43].

8.31 Completely Nonnegative (Positive) Matrices*

Completely nonnegative matrices are those in which all the minors of all dimensions are nonnegative (positive). Such matrices have been studied primarily by Gantmakher and Krein [10]. The eigenvalues of a completely nonnegative matrix are nonnegative. Of particular importance are the oscillatory matrices. They are completely nonnegative, but a power of the matrix is completely positive. All the eigenvalues of such a matrix are positive and simple. Let $\lambda_1 > \lambda_2 > \lambda_3 > \cdots$ be these eigenvalues. The number of changes of sign in the eigenvector which corresponds to λ_i is exactly $i - 1$. A special case of a completely positive matrix is the Hilbert matrix $\left(\dfrac{1}{i + k}\right)$ or, more generally, the matrices $\left(\dfrac{1}{x_i + y_k}\right)$ with $0 < x_1 < x_2 < \cdots < x_n$ and $0 < y_1 < y_2 < \cdots < y_n$.

REFERENCES

1. P. Alexandroff and H. Hopf, "Topologie, I," Springer-Verlag, Berlin, 1935.

2. J. Bendixson, Sur les racines d'une équation fondamentale, *Acta Math.*, vol. 25, pp. 359–365, 1902.

3. A. Brauer, Limits for the Characteristic Roots of a Matrix, I, *Duke Math. J.*, vol. 13, pp. 387–395, 1946.

4. A. Brauer, Limits for the Characteristic Roots of a Matrix, II, *Duke Math. J.*, vol. 14, pp. 21–26, 1947.

5. J. L. Brenner, A Bound for a Determinant with Dominant Main Diagonal, *Proc. Amer. Math. Soc.*, vol. 5, pp. 631–634, 1954.

6. E. T. Browne, The Characteristic Equation of a Matrix, *Bull. Amer. Math. Soc.*, vol. 34, pp. 363–368, 1928.

7. L. Collatz, Einschliessungssatz für die charakteristischen Zahlen von Matrizen, *Math. Z.*, vol. 48, pp. 221–226, 1942.

8. K. Fan and A. J. Hoffman, Lower Bounds for the Rank and Location of the Eigenvalues of a Matrix in O. Taussky, ed., "Contributions to the Solution of

* See also Sec. 8.28.

Systems of Linear Equations and the Determination of Eigenvalues," National Bureau of Standards Applied Mathematics Series, vol. 39, pp. 117–130, 1954.

9. F. R. Gantmakher, "Theory of Matrices," Moscow, 1954.

10. F. R. Gantmakher and M. Krein, Sur les matrices complètement non négatives et oscillatoires, *Compositio Math.*, vol. 4, pp. 445–476, 1937.

11. S. Geršgorin, Über die Abgrenzung der Eigenwerte einer Matrix, *Izv. Akad. Nauk. SSSR, Ser. Mat.*, vol. 7, pp. 749–754, 1937.

12. W. Givens, Fields of Values of a Matrix, *Proc. Amer. Math. Soc.*, vol. 3, pp. 206–209, 1952.

13. F. Hausdorff, Der Wertevorrat einer Bilinearform, *Math. Z.* vol. 3, pp. 314–316, 1919.

14. E. V. Haynsworth, Bounds for Determinants with Dominant Main Diagonal, *Duke Math. J.*, vol. 20, pp. 199–209, 1953.

15. I. N. Herstein, A Note on Primitive Matrices, *Amer. Math. Monthly*, vol. 61, pp. 18–20, 1959.

16. A. Hirsch, Sur les racines d'une équation fondamentale, *Acta Math.*, vol. 25, pp. 367–370, 1902.

17. A. J. Hoffman and O. Taussky, A Characterization of Normal Matrices, *J. Res. Nat. Bur. Standards*, vol. 52, pp. 17–19, 1944.

18. T. Kato, On Some Approximate Methods Concerning the Operators TT^*, *Math. Ann.*, vol. 126, pp. 253–262, 1953.

19. W. Ledermann, Bounds for the Greatest Latent Roots of a Positive Matrix, *J. London Math. Soc.*, vol. 25, pp. 265–268, 1950.

20. C. C. MacDuffee, "The Theory of Matrices," Springer-Verlag, Berlin, 1933.

21. B. N. Moyls and M. D. Marcus, Field Convexity of a Square Matrix, *Proc. Amer. Math. Soc.*, vol. 6, pp. 981–983, 1955.

22. F. D. Murnaghan, On the Field of Values of a Square Matrix, *Proc. Nat. Acad. Sci. U.S.A.*, vol. 18, pp. 246–248, 1932.

23. A. Ostrowski, Sur la détermination des bornes inférieures pour une classe de déterminants, *Bull. Sci. Math.*, vol. 61, pp. 1–32, 1937.

24. A. Ostrowski, Über die Determinanten mit überwiegender Hauptdiagonale, *Comment. Math. Helv.*, vol. 10, pp. 69–96, 1937.

25. A. Ostrowski, Über das Nichtverschwinden einer Klasse von Determinanten und die Lokalisierung der charakteristischen Wurzeln von Matrizen, *Compositio Math.*, vol. 9, pp. 209–226, 1951.

26. A. Ostrowski, Bounds for the Greatest Latent Root of a Positive Matrix, *J. London Math. Soc.*, vol. 27, pp. 254–256, 1952.

26a. A. Ostrowski, Note on Bounds for Determinants with Dominant Principal Diagonal, *Proc. Amer. Math. Soc.*, vol. 3, pp. 26–30, 1952.

27. W. V. Parker, The Characteristic Roots of Matrices, *Duke Math. J.*, vol. 12, pp. 519–526, 1945.

28. G. Pick, Über die Wurzeln der charakteristischen Gleichungen von Schwingungsproblemen, *Zeit. Angew. Math. Mech.*, vol. 2, pp. 353–357, 1922.

29. G. B. Price, Bounds for Determinants with Dominant Principal Diagonal, *Proc. Amer. Math. Soc.*, vol. 2, pp. 497–502, 1951.

30. H. Schneider, An Inequality for Latent Roots Applied to Determinants with a Dominant Diagonal, *J. London Math. Soc.*, vol. 28, pp. 8–20, 1953.

31. H. Schneider, Regions of Exclusion for the Latent Roots of a Matrix, *Proc. Amer. Math. Soc.*, vol. 5, pp. 320–322, 1954.

32. I. Schur, Über die charakteristischen Wurzeln einer linearen Substitution mit einer Anwendung auf die Theorie der Integralgleichungen, *Math. Ann.*, vol. 66, pp. 488–510, 1909.

33. P. Stein, A Note on Bounds for Multiple Characteristic Roots of Matrices, *J. Res. Nat. Bur. Standards*, vol. 48, pp. 59–60, 1952.

34. O. Taussky, A Recurring Theorem on Determinants, *Amer. Math. Monthly*, vol. 56, pp. 672–676, 1949.

35. O. Taussky, Bounds for Characteristic Roots of Matrices, II, *J. Res. Nat. Bur. Standards*, vol. 46, 124–125, 1951.

36. O. Taussky, Bounds for Characteristic Roots of Matrices, *Duke Math. J.*, vol. 15, pp. 1043–1044, 1948.

37. O. Toeplitz, Das algebraische Analogon zu einem Satze von Fejér, *Math. Z.*, vol. 2, pp. 187–197, 1918.

37a. A. G. Walker and J. D. Weston, Inclusion Theorems for the Eigenvalues of a Normal Matrix, *J. London Math. Soc.*, vol. 24, pp. 28–31, 1949.

38. H. Weyl, Inequalities between the Two Kinds of Eigenvalues of a Linear Transformation, *Proc. Nat. Acad. Sci. U.S.A.*, vol. 35, pp. 408–411, 1949.

39. H. Wielandt, Unzerlegbare, nicht negative Matrizen, *Math. Z.*, vol. 52, pp. 642–648, 1950.

40. H. Wielandt, Ein Einschliessungssatz für charakteristische Wurzeln normaler Matrizen, *Arch. Math.*, vol. 1, pp. 348–352, 1949.

41. H. Wielandt, Die Einschliessung von Eigenwerten normaler Matrizen, *Math. Ann.*, vol. 121, pp. 234–241, 1949.

42. R. Zurmühl, "Matrizen," Springer-Verlag, Berlin, 1950.

43. A. Brauer, The Theorems of Ledermann and Ostrowski on Positive Matrices, *Duke Math. J.*, vol. 2, pp. 265–274, 1957.

44. A. Brauer, A New Proof of Theorems of Perron and Frobenius on Nonnegative Matrices, I: Positive Matrices, *Duke Math. J.*, vol. 3, pp. 367–378, 1937.

45. K. Fan, Topological Proofs for Certain Theorems on Matrices with Nonnegative Elements, *Monatsh. Math.*, vol. 62, pp. 219–237, 1958.

46. K. Fan, Note on Circular Disks Containing the Eigenvalues of a Matrix, *Duke Math. J.*, vol. 25, pp. 441–446, 1958.

47. A. Householder, On Matrices with Nonnegative Elements, *Monatsh. Math.*, vol. 62, pp. 238–242, 1958.

48. P. Lax, Differential Equations, Difference Equations and Matrix Theory, *Comm. Pure Appl. Math.*, vol. 11, pp. 175–194, 1958.

49. M. Parodi, "La localisation des valeurs caractéristiques des matrices et ses applications," Gauthier-Villars, Paris, 1959.

50. H. Weinberger, Remarks on the Preceding Paper of Lax, *Comm. Pure Appl. Math.*, vol. 11, pp. 195–196, 1958.

51. O. Taussky, A Remark on a Theorem of Lyapunov, *J. Math. Analysis Appl.*, vol. 2, pp. 105–107, 1961.

52. O. Taussky, A Generalization of a Theorem of Lyapunov, *J. Soc. Indust. Appl. Math.*, vol. 9, 1961 (to appear).

53. A. M. Ostrowski and H. Schneider, Some Theorems on the Inertia of General Matrices, *J. Math. Analysis Appl.* (to appear).

54. H. W. E. Schwerdtfeger, "Introduction to Linear Algebra and the Theory of Matrices," P. Noordhoff, N. V., Groningen, Netherlands, 1950.

55. R. Bellman, "Matrix Analysis," McGraw-Hill Book Company, Inc., New York, 1960.

56. R. S. Varga, "Iterative Numerical Analysis," Prentice-Hall, Inc., Englewood Cliffs, N.J. (to appear).

57. V. Pták and J. Sedláček, On the Index of Imprimitivity of Nonnegative Matrices, *Czechoslovak Math. J.*, vol. 8(83), pp. 496–501, 1958 (in Russian, English summary).

HERMITIAN FORMS AND EIGENVALUES
by Marvin Marcus

8.32   Introduction

We attempt to survey here some of the more recent techniques used in investigating quadratic forms, eigenvalues, and singular values of linear transformations on the n-dimensional unitary space V_n to itself. The discussion is separated into three sections. The first of these is devoted to an exposition of those properties of the Grassmann product and compound transformations which we need here and which are useful in other problems (e.g., the totally positive matrices of Gantmakher and Krein). We then discuss some of the elementary properties of convex sets and functions and obtain the essential structure theorem for doubly stochastic (d.s.) matrices. From these we can easily derive inequalities connecting singular values, eigenvalues, and quadratic forms. The final section is devoted to a presentation of the more advanced results that have recently been completed.

Although some attempt has been made to make the material herein self-contained, we by no means prove every lemma. Rather we hope that the proofs that are presented will convey some idea of the techniques and devices that seem to work effectively in dealing with a rather wide class of problems. The knowledgeable reader will also recognize that the definitions and results are not always presented in their most general form. However, we have attempted to minimize complexity in the statements of the results, sometimes at the expense of generality. Notes and bibliography are deferred to the end.

8.33   Grassmann Products and Compounds

A useful and natural tool for dealing with products of eigenvalues of a linear transformation T is the compound of T. We list here the pertinent definitions and theorems for the exterior product and the induced compound in the order in which they are most readily proved.

We introduce some notation to diminish the number of subscripts usually attendant with these objects.

1. ϵ_i is the unit vector with ith coordinate 1. The binomial coefficient $\binom{n}{p}$ is $n!/p!(n-p)!$. By $\prod_1^p V_n$ we mean the cartesian product of V_n with itself p times.

2. If $1 \leq p \leq n$, let $Q_{pn} = \{(i_1, \ldots, i_p) \mid 1 \leq i_1 < \cdots < i_p \leq n\}$. That is, Q_{pn} is the totality of strictly increasing functions on the integers

$1, \ldots, p$ into the integers $1, \ldots, n$. If $\alpha = (i_1, \ldots, i_p)$ and $\omega = (j_1, \ldots, j_p)$ are two elements of Q_{pn}, then α comes before ω in *lexicographic order* if there is an integer m, $1 \leq m \leq p$, for which $i_t = j_t$, $t = 1, \ldots, m-1$, and $i_m < j_m$.

Definition 8.1. Let f be a function on $\prod_1^p V_n$ into a vector space W such that f is linear in each variable and

$$f(x_1, \ldots, x_p) = \text{sign } \pi f(x_{\pi(1)}, \ldots, x_{\pi(p)}) \tag{8.1}$$

for any permutation π of $1, \ldots, p$. Then f is called a *multilinear function* on $\prod_1^p V_n$ to W.

Theorem 8.1. *For each $p = 1, 2, \ldots, n$ there exists a multilinear function on $\prod_1^p V_n$ to $V_{\binom{n}{p}}$ such that the smallest vector space containing the range of f is $V_{\binom{n}{p}}$.*

Proof. Let $x_i = (x_{i1}, \ldots, x_{in})$, $i = 1, \ldots, p$, be any p vectors in V_n. For $\omega \in Q_{pn}$, choose p columns from $X = (x_{ij})$ with indices ω and form the p-square subdeterminant so obtained. Arrange these numbers in lexicographic order according to the choice of ω. The multilinearity is immediate, and the last assertion is made clear by choosing $x_j = \epsilon_j$, $j = 1, \ldots, p$.

We denote the function f in the proof of Theorem 8.1 by

$$f(x_1, \ldots, x_p) = x_1 \wedge \cdots \wedge x_p,$$

the usual notation for the exterior, or Grassmann, product. Note here that the mapping is in general not *onto* $V_{\binom{n}{p}}$. For example, if $n = 4$ and $p = 2$ and $v = x_1 \wedge x_2 = (v_1, \ldots, v_6)$, then $v_1 v_6 = v_2 v_5 - v_3 v_4$.

Theorem 8.2. *Let $y_1, \ldots, y_p$ belong to V_n and suppose*

$$y_i = \sum_{j=1}^n y_{ij} x_j, \qquad i = 1, \ldots, p. \tag{8.2}$$

Then

$$y_1 \wedge \cdots \wedge y_p = \sum_{\omega \in Q_{pn}} c_\omega x_\omega,$$

where, if $\omega = (i_1, \ldots, i_p)$, then

$$x_\omega = x_{i_1} \wedge \cdots \wedge x_{i_p}$$

and

$$c_\omega = \det \begin{pmatrix} y_{1i_1} & \cdots & y_{1i_p} \\ \cdot & & \cdot \\ \cdot & & \cdot \\ \cdot & & \cdot \\ y_{pi_1} & \cdots & y_{pi_p} \end{pmatrix}.$$

Proof

$$y_1 \wedge \cdots \wedge y_p = \left(\sum y_{1j} x_j \right) \wedge \cdots \wedge \left(\sum y_{pj} x_j \right)$$

$$= \sum_{j_1} y_{1j_1} \left(x_{j_1} \wedge \sum y_{2j} x_j \wedge \cdots \wedge \sum y_{pj} x_j \right)$$

$$= \sum_{j_1, \ldots, j_p} y_{1j_1} y_{2j_2} \cdots y_{pj_p} x_{j_1} \wedge \cdots \wedge x_{j_p}.$$

Now it is clear that, if any two indices in $x_{j_1} \wedge \cdots \wedge x_{j_p}$ are the same, the value is 0. Moreover, we may restrict our summation to those sequences which are in Q_{pn}, as follows:

$$y_1 \wedge \cdots \wedge y_p = \sum_\omega \left[\sum_\pi y_{1\pi(j_1)} \cdots y_{p\pi(j_p)} \right] x_\omega$$

$$= \sum c_\omega x_\omega.$$

From this result the following two theorems are immediate.

Theorem 8.3. *If x_j, $j = 1, \ldots, n$, constitute a basis for V_n, then the x_ω, $\omega \in Q_{pn}$, constitute a basis for $V_{\binom{n}{p}}$.*

Theorem 8.4. $x_1 \wedge \ldots \wedge x_p = 0$ *if and only if $x_1, \ldots, x_p$ are linearly dependent.*

The next result describes the form of the inner product of two vectors which are exterior products themselves.

Theorem 8.5.

$$(x_1 \wedge \cdots \wedge x_p, y_1 \wedge \cdots \wedge y_p) = \det \{(x_i, y_j)\}_{i,j=1,\ldots,p}. \tag{8.3}$$

Proof. Let

$$x_i = (x_{i1}, \ldots, x_{in}),$$

$$y_j = (y_{j1}, \ldots, y_{jn}),$$

$i, j = 1, \ldots, p$. Then

$$\det \{(x_i, y_j)\} = \det \left(\sum_{r=1}^n x_{ir} \bar{y}_{jr} \right)$$

$$= \sum_{r_1, \ldots, r_p} \bar{y}_{1r_1} \cdots \bar{y}_{pr_p} \det \begin{pmatrix} x_{1r_1} & \cdots & x_{1r_p} \\ \cdot & & \cdot \\ \cdot & & \cdot \\ \cdot & & \cdot \\ x_{pr_1} & \cdots & x_{pr_p} \end{pmatrix}$$

$$= \sum_\omega \left[\sum_\pi \bar{y}_{1\pi(r_1)} \cdots \bar{y}_{p\pi(r_p)} \operatorname{sign} \pi \right] \det \{x_{ir_j}\}.$$

$$= \sum \det \{x_{ir_j}\} \det \{\bar{y}_{ir_j}\}.$$

This calculation completes the proof.

As an immediate consequence we have the following result.

Theorem 8.6. *If $1 \le p \le n$ and $x_1, \ldots, x_n$ is an orthonormal (o.n.) set in V_n, then x_ω, $\omega \in Q_{pn}$, is an o.n. set in $V_{\binom{n}{p}}$.*

Definition 8.2. Let A be a linear transformation on V_n to V_n. Let $C_p(A)$, the pth *compound* of A, on $V_{\binom{n}{p}}$ to $V_{\binom{n}{p}}$ be defined by

$$C_p(A)\, \epsilon_{i_1} \wedge \cdots \wedge \epsilon_{i_p} = A\epsilon_{i_1} \wedge \cdots \wedge A\epsilon_{i_p} \tag{8.4}$$

for each basis vector ϵ_ω, $\omega \in Q_{np}$.

The following result is an immediate consequence of the properties of the exterior product and the relation (8.4).

Theorem 8.7. *If* $y_1 \wedge \cdots \wedge y_p \in V_{\binom{n}{p}}$, *then*

$$C_p(A) y_1 \wedge \cdots \wedge y_p = A y_1 \wedge \cdots \wedge A y_p.$$

The matrix representation of $C_p(A)$ is described as follows: If $x_1, \ldots, x_n$ is a basis for V_n, then the representation of $C_p(A)$ relative to the basis x_ω, $\omega \in Q_{pn}$, is an $\binom{n}{p}$-square matrix whose entries are the p-square subdeterminants of the representation of A relative to $x_1, \ldots, x_n$ arranged in doubly lexicographic order according to row and column selections from A. For example, if

$$A = \begin{pmatrix} a_{11} & a_{12} & a_{13} \\ a_{21} & a_{22} & a_{23} \\ a_{31} & a_{32} & a_{33} \end{pmatrix},$$

then

$$C_2(A) = \begin{pmatrix} \begin{vmatrix} a_{11} & a_{12} \\ a_{21} & a_{22} \end{vmatrix} & \begin{vmatrix} a_{11} & a_{13} \\ a_{21} & a_{23} \end{vmatrix} & \begin{vmatrix} a_{12} & a_{13} \\ a_{21} & a_{23} \end{vmatrix} \\[2ex] \begin{vmatrix} a_{11} & a_{12} \\ a_{21} & a_{22} \end{vmatrix} & \begin{vmatrix} a_{11} & a_{13} \\ a_{21} & a_{23} \end{vmatrix} & \begin{vmatrix} a_{12} & a_{13} \\ a_{32} & a_{33} \end{vmatrix} \\[2ex] \begin{vmatrix} a_{21} & a_{22} \\ a_{31} & a_{32} \end{vmatrix} & \begin{vmatrix} a_{21} & a_{23} \\ a_{31} & a_{33} \end{vmatrix} & \begin{vmatrix} a_{22} & a_{23} \\ a_{32} & a_{33} \end{vmatrix} \end{pmatrix}.$$

The following properties of $C_p(A)$ are immediate consequences of the definition.

Theorem 8.8. *If* $1 \leq p \leq n$, *then*

(i) $$C_p(AB) = C_p(A) C_p(B);$$

(ii) $$C_p^*(A) = C_p(A^*), \qquad A^* \text{ the conjugate transpose of } A;$$

(iii) $$C_p(A^{-1}) = C_p^{-1}(A).$$

(iv) *If* A *is normal, hermitian, positive definite (or nonnegative), unitary, so is* $C_p(A)$.

(v) *The eigenvalues of $C_p(A)$ are the $\binom{n}{p}$ numbers $\lambda_{i_1} \lambda_{i_2} \cdots \lambda_{i_p}$ for*

$(i_1, \ldots i_p) \in Q_{pn}$, *where $\lambda_1, \ldots, \lambda_n$ are the eigenvalues of A.*

Proof.

(i) If x_ω is a basis for $V_{\binom{n}{p}}$, then

$$C_p(AB)x_\omega = (AB)x_{i_1} \wedge \cdots \wedge (AB)x_{i_p}$$
$$= C_p(A)Bx_{i_1} \wedge \cdots \wedge Bx_{i_p}$$
$$= C_p(A)C_p(B)x_\omega.$$

(ii)
$$[C_p(A)x_1 \wedge \cdots \wedge x_p, y_1 \wedge \cdots \wedge y_p]$$
$$= \det\{(Ax_i, y_j)\} = \det\{(x_i, A^*y_j)\}$$
$$= [x_1 \wedge \cdots \wedge x_p, C_p(A^*)y_1 \wedge \cdots \wedge y_p].$$

(iii)
$$C_p(AA^{-1}) = C_p(I_n) = I_{\binom{n}{p}}.$$

(iv) For example, if A is normal,

$$C_p(A)C_p^*(A) = C_p(A)C_p(A^*) = C_p(AA^*)$$
$$= C_p(A^*A) = C_p(A^*)C_p(A)$$
$$= C_p^*(A)C_p(A).$$

(v) Assume that A is triangular. Then it is a direct calculation to see that $C_p(A)$ is triangular with diagonal elements [eigenvalues of $C_p(A)$] precisely the numbers $\lambda_{i_1} \cdots \lambda_{i_p}$. But any matrix can be unitarily triangulated, and $C_p(A)$ is similar to $C_p(U^{-1}AU) = C_p^{-1}(U)C_p(A)C_p(U)$.

This completes the proof.

Definition 8.3. If A is a linear transformation on V_n to V_n, then the *singular values* of A are the nonnegative square roots of the eigenvalues of A^*A.

Let

$$|\lambda_1| \geq \cdots \geq |\lambda_n|, \qquad \alpha_1 \geq \cdots \geq \alpha_n, \qquad (8.5)$$

where λ_j and α_j, $j = 1, \ldots, n$, are, respectively, the eigenvalues and singular values of A. It is clear that

$$|\lambda_1| = |(Ax, x)| \leq \|Ax\| = (Ax, Ax)^{1/2} = (A^*Ax, x)^{1/2}$$
$$\leq \alpha_1 \qquad (8.6)$$

for any A and x, the normalized eigenvector of A corresponding to λ_1. Now the singular values of $C_p(A)$ are nonnegative square roots of the eigenvalues of $C_p(A^*A)$, which are in turn the numbers $\alpha_{i_1} \cdots \alpha_{i_p}$. Hence, by (8.5) and (8.6) applied to $C_p(A)$, we have the following result.

Theorem 8.9.   *Let A be an arbitrary linear transformation on V_n to V_n with eigenvalues and singular values* (8.5).   *Then, for $1 \leq p \leq n$,*

$$\prod_{j=1}^{p} |\lambda_j| \leq \prod_{j=1}^{p} \alpha_j, \tag{8.7}$$

with equality for $p = n$.

In the next section we introduce some elementary properties of convex sets and functions and use them to obtain some of the easier consequences of (8.7).   It turns out that our methods also give us information on the extreme values of functions of quadratic forms associated with an hermitian matrix.

8.34   Convex Functions and D.S. Matrices

Definition 8.4.   A set M in real euclidean n space E_n is *convex* if the line segment joining any two points of M consists entirely of points in M: $x \in M$ and $y \in M$ and $0 \leq \theta \leq 1$ imply

$$\theta x + (1 - \theta) y \in M.$$

Definition 8.5.   A real-valued function f on the convex set M is *convex* if

$$f(\theta x + (1 - \theta) y) \leq \theta f(x) + (1 - \theta) f(y)$$

for $x \in M$, $y \in M$, $0 \leq \theta \leq 1$.

Definition 8.6.   An n-square real matrix S is *doubly stochastic* (d.s.) if all elements are nonnegative and any row and column sum is 1.   The totality of d.s. matrices of size $n \times n$ is denoted by M_n.

Definition 8.7.   If a_j, $j = 1, \ldots, m$, is a set of points in E_n, then $H(a_1, \ldots, a_m)$, the *convex hull* of the a_j, is the set of points defined by

$$x = \sum_{j=1}^{m} t_j a_j, \qquad t_j \geq 0, j = 1, \ldots, m,$$

$$\sum_{j=1}^{m} t_j = 1.$$

We remark that, if f is a convex function on $H(a_1, \ldots, a_m)$, then $x \in H(a_1, \ldots, a_m)$ implies that

$$f(x) = f\left(\sum_{j=1}^{m} t_j a_j\right) \leq \sum_{j=1}^{m} t_j f(a_j)$$

$$\leq \max_j f(a_j).$$

Hence the maximum value of f is achieved at a vertex.

Our first result concerning M_n is the following.   The proof is somewhat long but is constructive and entirely elementary.

Theorem 8.10.   *Let* $P_1, \ldots, P_m$, $m = n!$ *be the permutation matrices of size* n.   *Then*

$$M_n = H(P_1, \ldots, P_m). \tag{8.8}$$

Proof.   It is immediate that

$$H(P_1, \ldots, P_m) \subset M_n.$$

Now let a "general diagonal" of any n-square matrix A be a set of n positions in A each of which occurs precisely once in each row and column of A.   The first information we need is contained in the following lemma.

Lemma.   *Let S be a set of elements of A.   Then every general diagonal of A intersects S if and only if S contains an $s \times t$ submatrix with $s + t = n + 1$.*

Necessity: It is clear that, by permuting rows and columns, a general diagonal goes into a general diagonal.   Hence we lose no generality by assuming that A has the form

$$A = \begin{pmatrix} T_1 & T_2 \\ S & T_3 \end{pmatrix},$$

with dimensions as follows:

S: $s \times t$, $s + t = n + 1$

T_1: $(n - s) \times t$

T_2: $(n - s) \times (n - t)$

T_3: $s \times (n - t)$.

We may assume $t \geq s$ without loss of generality.   If d is a general diagonal not intersecting S, it must go through precisely t columns of T_1 and thus through precisely t rows of T_1.   Thus, since $t \geq s$, d does not intersect T_2, and hence intersects T_3 in precisely $(n - t)$ rows.   But

$$n - t = s - 1,$$

and hence d lies in at most $(s - 1)$ rows of T_3.   But T_3 has s rows and consequently d does not lie in every row of A, a contradiction.   Thus every diagonal hits S.

Sufficiency: The proof is by induction.   For $n = 1$ or $S = A$ the result is clear.   Otherwise we assume there exists an element a_{ij} not in S and let B be the minor of a_{ij}.   If d is a diagonal through a_{ij}, then, since $d \cap S \neq 0$, it must intersect S in elements of B.   On the other hand, any diagonal of B can be extended to a diagonal of A by adjoining a_{ij} and hence any diagonal of B hits S (since $a_{ij} \notin S$).   By induction, B

contains a $p \times q$ submatrix S_1 of elements of S with $p + q = n$. By permutation of rows and columns of A, we may assume A has the form

$$A = \begin{pmatrix} T_1 & T_2 \\ S_1 & T_3 \end{pmatrix},$$

where the dimensions are as follows:

S_1: $p \times q, \quad p + q = n$

T_1: $(n - p) \times q = q \times q$

T_2: $(n - p) \times (n - q) = q \times p$

T_3: $p \times (n - q) = p \times p.$

Suppose there is a diagonal d_1 of T_1 such that $d_1 \cap S = 0$. Then we adjoin any diagonal d_2 of T_3 to d_1 to get a diagonal d of A. But $d \cap S \neq 0$, so $d_2 \cap S \neq 0$. Hence, if some diagonal of T_1 does not hit S, then every diagonal of T_3 does (and conversely). So we assume that every diagonal of T_1 hits S. Then T_1 has a $u \times v$ submatrix S_2 consisting of elements of S with $u + v = q + 1$. It is clear that we may combine S_1 and S_2 to obtain a submatrix S_3 of A with dimensions $(u + p) \times v$ consisting of elements of S. Now

$$u + p + v = u + v + p = q + 1 + p = q + p + 1 = n + 1.$$

The lemma is thus established.

Proceeding to the proof of the theorem, we let $A \in M_n$ and let S be the set of zero entries of S. If every diagonal of A hit S, then there would exist an $s \times t$ submatrix S_1 of A consisting of zeros with $s + t = n + 1$. The complementary matrix of S_1—call it T_1—has dimensions $(n - s) \times (n - t)$. We may assume that A has the form

$$A = \begin{pmatrix} S_1 & T_2 \\ T_3 & T_1 \end{pmatrix}.$$

Now the sum of the elements in T_2 is s and in T_3 is t. Hence the sum over T_1 is $n - (s + t) = -1$, an impossibility. Now let d_1 be a diagonal of A with no zeros in it, and let t_1 be the least element in d_1. Then, if $t_1 = 1$, it is clear that A is a permutation matrix; otherwise we choose P_1, a permutation matrix with 1s in positions corresponding to d_1. Then $A_1 = \dfrac{A - t_1 P_1}{1 - t_1}$ is d.s. and has at least one less positive element than A. We then proceed as above, using A_1, and after at most $(n^2 - n)$

steps, we get a matrix with exactly n positive elements in it (fewer than n would contradict the d.s. property) which must all be 1s. Thus

$$A = \sum_{j=1}^{m} t_j P_j, \qquad t_j \geq 0.$$

Now $\sum_{j=1}^{m} t_j = 1$ is clear from the fact that A is d.s. This completes the proof of Theorem 8.10.

We note here that the proof shows that any particular $S \in M_n$ is in the convex hull of no more than $(n^2 - n + 1)$ permutation matrices.

Definition 8.8. If $x_1 \geq x_2 \geq \cdots \geq x_n$ is an ordered set of real numbers, we define $K_n(x)$ to be the intersection of half spaces and a hyperplane:

$$t_{i_1} + \cdots + t_{i_k} \leq x_1 + \cdots + x_k \tag{8.9}$$

$$t_1 + \cdots + t_n = x_1 + \cdots + x_n, \tag{8.10}$$

$$1 \leq k \leq n, \qquad 1 \leq i_1 < i_2 < \cdots < i_k \leq n.$$

If $t \in K_n(x)$, we indicate this with the notation $[t] < [x]$.

Theorem 8.11:
$$K_n(x) = \{y \mid y = Sx, S \in M_n\}. \tag{8.11}$$

In other words, $K_n(x)$ is the convex hull of the $n!$ points Px where P runs over all n-square permutation matrices.

Proof. The argument can be done directly in terms of the *support function F* of the convex hull $L = \{Px\}$ where P ranges over all n-square permutation matrices. This is defined as follows:

$$F(u) = \max_{z \in L} (u,z),$$

and it is clear that

$$(t,u) = F(u)$$

is by definition a support plane of L for any u. It is also true that L is the intersection of the half spaces $(t,u) \leq F(u)$ as u ranges over all n vectors. In our case we easily check that

$$F(u) = \max_{P} (u,Px).$$

Now suppose $t \in L$; then

$$t = \sum \omega_p Px, \qquad \omega_p \geq 0, \qquad \sum \omega_p = 1,$$

so
$$\sum_{j=1}^{n} t_j = \sum \omega_p \sum_{j=1}^{n} (Px)_j = \sum_{j=1}^{n} x_j.$$

Moreover, let u be a vector with coordinates $i_1, \ldots, i_k$ equal to 1 and the rest 0. Then we check that

$$\sum_{j=1}^{k} t_{i_j} = (u,t) \leq \max_{P} (u,Px) = \sum_{j=1}^{k} x_j.$$

Thus $L \subset K_n(x)$. On the other hand, let

$$f(t) = (u,t)$$

for a fixed u and $t \in K_n(x)$. Since f is linear in t, it must assume its maximum value on one of the support planes (8.9). Thus assume $\max f = f(\bar{t})$ and

$$\sum_{j=1}^{k} \bar{t}_{i_j} = \sum_{j=1}^{k} x_j, \qquad 1 \leq i_1 < \ldots < i_k \leq n - 1.$$

Let
$$\bar{t}^1 = (\bar{t}_{i_1}, \ldots, \bar{t}_{i_k}), \qquad \bar{t}^2 = (\bar{t}_{i_{k+1}}, \ldots, \bar{t}_{i_n}).$$
$$x^1 = (x_1, \ldots, x_k), \qquad x^2 = (x_{k+1}, \ldots, x_n).$$

Then we check easily that

$$[\bar{t}^1] < [x^1], \qquad [\bar{t}^2] < [x^2].$$

Since the theorem is true for $n = 1$, we obtain by induction that

$$\bar{t}^1 = S_1 x^1, \qquad S_1 \in M_k$$
and
$$\bar{t}^2 = S_2 x^2, \qquad S_2 \in M_{n-k}.$$

But then $\bar{t} = Q(\bar{t}_1 + \bar{t}_2) = Q(S_1 + S_2)x$, where $+$ indicates direct sum and Q is an appropriate permutation matrix. Thus

$$K_n(x) \subset L,$$

and the proof is complete.

Theorem 8.12. *If* $f(t_1, \ldots, t_k)$ *is a function such that* $f(e^{t_1}, \ldots, e^{t_k})$ *is convex, nondecreasing in each* t_j, *and symmetric and if* A *is an n-square complex matrix with eigenvalues and singular values given by (8.5), then*

$$f(|\lambda_1|, \ldots, |\lambda_k|) \leq f(\alpha_1, \ldots, \alpha_k) \tag{8.12}$$

where $1 \leq k \leq n$.

Proof. From (8.7) we have

$$\sum_{j=1}^{p} \log |\lambda_j| \leq \sum_{j=1}^{p} \log \alpha_j, \qquad 1 \leq p \leq k. \tag{8.13}$$

Let
$$x_j = \log \alpha_j \qquad j = 1, \ldots, k - 1,$$
$$x_k = \log \alpha_k - \left(\sum_{j=1}^{k} \log \alpha_j - \sum_{j=1}^{k} \log |\lambda_j| \right).$$

The first $(k - 1)$ inequalities (8.13) are unchanged when x_j replaces

$\log \alpha_j$ and the kth inequality is changed to equality. If we set $r = (\log |\lambda_1|, \ldots, \log |\lambda_k|)$ and observe that $x_1 \geq \cdots > x_k$, we conclude from (8.11) that

$$r = Sx,$$

where $S \in M_k$. Let $g(t) = f(e^{t_1}, \ldots, e^{t_k})$, and we observe that

$$\begin{aligned} f(|\lambda_1|, \ldots, |\lambda_k|) = g(r) = g(Sx) &\leq g(Px) = g(x) \\ &\leq g(\log \alpha_1, \ldots, \log \alpha_k) \\ &= f(\alpha_1, \ldots, \alpha_k). \end{aligned} \tag{8.14}$$

The first inequality in (8.14) follows from the fact that $g(Sx)$ is a convex function of S and hence assumes its largest value on a permutation matrix. The remaining steps are immediate consequences of the non-decreasing and symmetry properties. We remark that, if $f(t_1, \ldots, t_k) = t_1^\sigma + \cdots + t_k^\sigma$, $\sigma \geq 0$, then, from (8.12), we have

$$|\lambda_1|^\sigma + \cdots + |\lambda_k|^\sigma \leq \alpha_1^\sigma + \cdots + \alpha_k^\sigma \tag{8.15}$$

for $k = 1, \ldots, n$.

It is also clear that analogous results for f concave can be obtained in a similar way.

Fortunately the methods used to get results like (8.12) give us information on functions of quadratic forms with practically no labor. Consider, for example, the following theorem.

Theorem 8.13. *Let A be an n-square complex hermitian matrix with eigenvalues $\lambda_1 \geq \cdots \geq \lambda_n$. Let $x_1, \ldots, x_k$ be an o.n. set of vectors in V_n, $1 \leq k \leq n$. Then*

$$\sum_{j=1}^{k} \lambda_{n-j+1} \leq \sum_{j=1}^{k} (Ax_j, x_j) \leq \sum_{j=1}^{k} \lambda_j. \tag{8.16}$$

Proof. Let $u_1, \ldots, u_n$ be an o.n. set of eigenvectors of A with $(Au_i, u_i) = \lambda_i$, $i = 1, \ldots, n$. Then

$$(Ax_i, x_i) = \sum_{j=1}^{n} \lambda_j |(x_i, u_j)|^2.$$

Now, complete $x_1, \ldots, x_k$ to an o.n. basis for V_n by adjoining $x_{k+1}, \ldots, x_n$. It follows immediately from the o.n. properties that

$$S = (|(x_i, u_j)|^2) \in M_n.$$

Also,

$$(Ax_i, x_i) = (S_i, \lambda),$$

where S_i is the ith-row vector of S and $\lambda = (\lambda_1, \ldots, \lambda_n)$. So define

$$f(S) = \sum_{j=1}^{k} (S_j, \lambda),$$

and since f is linear in S, the proof is completed by noting Theorem 8.10.

In case A is positive definite, we can use the concavity of $\left(\prod_{j=1}^{k} t_j\right)^{1/k}$ in exactly the same way to get

$$\prod_{j=1}^{k} (Ax_j, x_j) \geq \prod_{j=1}^{k} \lambda_{n-j+1}. \tag{8.17}$$

A nice application of (8.17) is the following proof of the Minkowski inequality:

$$\begin{aligned} |A + B|^{1/n} &= \prod_{j=1}^{n} [(A + B)x_j, x_j]^{1/n} \\ &\geq \prod_{j=1}^{n} (Ax_j, x_j)^{1/n} + \prod_{j=1}^{n} (Bx_j, x_j)^{1/n} \\ &\geq |A|^{1/n} + |B|^{1/n}. \end{aligned} \tag{8.18}$$

Here A and B are positive definite hermitian matrices, and $x_1, \ldots, x_n$ are an o.n. set of eigenvectors of $A + B$. By choosing $x_j = \epsilon_j$ and $k = n$, the relation (8.17) becomes the statement of the Hadamard determinant theorem.

It is known that $E_r^{1/r}$ and E_r/E_{r-1} are concave, nondecreasing functions where E_r is the rth elementary symmetric function. It is clear that both (8.17) and (8.18) can be extended with little effort to similar results for these functions.

Actually, (8.17) can be considerably sharpened by using the fact that $C_k(A)$ is positive definite hermitian when A is; for

$$\prod_{j=1}^{k} \lambda_j \geq (C_k(A)x_1 \wedge \cdots \wedge x_k, x_1 \wedge \cdots \wedge x_k) \geq \prod_{j=1}^{k} \lambda_{n-j+1}, \tag{8.19}$$

and an application of the Hadamard determinant theorem to $\{(Ax_j, x_j)\}$ gives (8.17).

We just mention here that a function satisfying $f(Sx) \leq f(x)$ for $S \in M_n$ with equality if and only if S is a permutation matrix is called *Schur-convex*. It is clear that this property is made to order for proofs like those of Theorems (8.12) and (8.13).

Recently (8.19) was extended in a way that generalizes (8.16) for positive definite hermitian matrices. We do not include the proof.

Theorem 8.14. *Let A be positive definite and let $x_1, \ldots, x_k$ be an o.n. set of vectors in V_n. Then, for $1 \leq r \leq k \leq n$,*

$$E_r(\lambda_n, \ldots, \lambda_{n-k+1}) \leq \sum_{\omega \in Q_{rk}} [C_r(A)x_\omega, x_\omega] \leq E_r(\lambda_1, \ldots, \lambda_k). \tag{8.20}$$

We note that (8.20) is not an immediate consequence of (8.16). For although the sum in (8.20) is over a set of o.n. vectors in $V_{\binom{n}{r}}$, the bounds are not necessarily sums of the largest or smallest $\binom{k}{r}$ eigenvalues of $C_r(A)$. The reason for this is that we are not taking extreme values over *all* o.n. sets. A result related to (8.20) is the following:

If A and B are n-square complex matrices with singular values $\alpha_1 \geq \cdots \geq \alpha_n$ and $\beta_1 \geq \cdots \geq \beta_n$, respectively, then

$$|\text{tr }(UAVB)| \leq \sum_{j=1}^{n} \alpha_j \beta_j, \tag{8.21}$$

where U and V are any two unitary matrices.

Moreover, the upper bound in (8.21) is assumed for appropriate choices of U and V. This result has recently been generalized in several ways and references will be found in Sec. 8.36 and in the bibliography at the end of the chapter.

8.35   Intermediate Eigenvalues

A problem somewhat different from those considered in Sec. 8.34 is the following. Given a set of some of the eigenvalues of A—say λ_{i_1}, $\lambda_{i_2}, \ldots, \lambda_{i_k}$—and a function $f(t_1, \ldots, t_k)$, find an extremal characterization of $f(\lambda_{i_1}, \ldots, \lambda_{i_k})$ in terms of $f[(Ax_1,x_1), \ldots, (Ax_k,x_k)]$ for $x_1, \ldots, x_k$, an o.n. set in V_n. The well-known Courant-Fischer result is of this type, and the following theorem is a generalization of this as well as of Theorem 8.13.

Theorem 8.15.   *Let A be an hermitian matrix with eigenvalues $\lambda_1 \geq \cdots \geq \lambda_n$ and let $1 \leq i_1 < \cdots < i_k \leq n$. Let $c_1 \geq \cdots \geq c_k$ be k nonnegative real numbers. Then*

$$\sum_{j=1}^{k} c_j \lambda_{i_j} = \max_R \min_x \sum_{j=1}^{k} c_j(Ax_{i_j},x_{i_j}). \tag{8.22}$$

The notation here is the following. For fixed subspaces $R_{i_1} \subset \cdots \subset R_{i_k}$ with dim $R_{i_j} = i_j$, $\min\limits_x$ indicates the minimum over all possible o.n. sets $x_{i_1}, \ldots, x_{i_k}$ with $x_{i_j} \in R_{i_j}$. Then $\max\limits_R \min\limits_x$ is the largest of these minima as the spaces $R_{i_1} \subset \cdots \subset R_{i_k}$ vary.

A result which follows from (8.22) is the following (see also Wielandt [23]):

If $\lambda_1 \geq \cdots \geq \lambda_n$, $\mu_1 \geq \cdots \geq \mu_n$, and $\gamma_1 \geq \cdots \geq \gamma_n$ are, respectively, the eigenvalues of A, B, and $A + B$ (A and B hermitian), then

$$\gamma = \lambda + S\mu \tag{8.23}$$

for $S \in M_n$.

A further generalization of the type of Theorem 8.15 for symmetric functions is as follows.

Theorem 8.16. *Let* $\varphi(t_1, \ldots, t_k)$ *be symmetric and nondecreasing for* $t_j \in [\lambda_n, \lambda_1]$. *Then, if* $1 \le i_1 < \cdots < i_k \le n$,

$$\varphi(\lambda_{i_1}, \ldots, \lambda_{i_k}) = \sup_R \inf_x \tilde{\varphi}(x_1, \ldots, x_k). \qquad (8.24)$$

Here the notation is the same as above and $\tilde{\varphi}(x_1, \ldots, x_k)$ is by definition $\varphi(\tilde{\lambda}_1, \ldots, \tilde{\lambda}_k)$ for $\tilde{\lambda}_j$, the eigenvalues of A restricted to the space spanned by $x_1, \ldots, x_k$. (By this we mean $\tilde{\lambda}_j$ are the eigenvalues of PAP where P is the orthogonal projection into the space spanned by $x_1, \ldots, x_k$.)

From (8.24) various inequalities connecting singular values are obtained.

In the case in which A is simply hermitian, the extreme values of

$$\prod_{j=1}^{k} (Ax_j, x_j) \qquad (8.25)$$

have been investigated. Moreover, a theorem analogous to (8.20) for A indefinite is known for arbitrary r. Of interest would be a generalization of these kinds of results to a more general class of transformations. Results describing the structure of boundary points of M_n would also be useful in attacking these problems for a more general class of functions than the convex functions.

8.36   Notes

Sec. 8.33. The material on compounds can be found in [4], [15], and [21]. Theorem 8.9 was proved first in [22] in the way we have used here. Later a different method yielded the same result (see [6]).

Sec. 8.34. The proof of Theorem 8.10 used here is found in [5]. Another shorter (but not constructive) proof is found in [10]. The result was originally published in [3]. Theorem 8.11 is proved in [18] and [2], as well as in the book "Inequalities," by G. H. Hardy, J. E. Littlewood, and G. Pólya. Theorem 8.12 in the case in which f is Schur-convex may be found in [18] (the proof is the same). The argument, however, was originally used in [19] and also in [7]. Remark (8.15) is found in [22], [7], and [6]. Theorem 8.13 was proved first in [6], with a somewhat different argument. The proof given here has been used in various forms in [2] and [13]. Further extensions are to be found in [17]. The remark (8.17) is found in [9]. The extensions to symmetric functions are to be found in [12]. Theorem 8.14 is in [15] and in somewhat extended form in [16]. Actually it is easy to show that (8.24) implies (8.20). The result (8.21) appeared first in [20]. Later a new technique and a generalization of (8.21) appeared in [8]. In [16] some extensions of the results of [8] are obtained via (8.20) and the results in [11].

Sec. 8.35.   Theorem 8.15 was first proved for $c_j = 1$ in [23].   The form given here is found in [14].   The remark (8.23) is found in [23] also, and there certain inequalities for Schur-convex functions of the eigenvalues are obtained.   The result (8.24) is found in [1].   K. Fan obtained the same result for a more restrictive class of functions before the appearance of [1].   In a thesis at the University of British Columbia, R. Thompson independently obtained (8.24) for φ, an elementary symmetric function.   This work, however, was not submitted for publication after the appearance of [1].   The remark (8.25) is found in [17].

REFERENCES

1. A. R. Amir-Moez, Extreme Properties of Eigenvalues of a Hermitian Transformation, *Duke Math. J.*, vol. 28, pp. 463–476, 1956.

2. R. Bellman and A. J. Hoffman, On a Theorem of Ostrowski and Taussky, *Arch. Math.*, vol. 5, pp. 123–127, 1954.

3. G. Birkhoff, Three Observations on Linear Algebra, *Univ. Nac. Tucumán. Rev. Ser. A*, vol. 5, pp. 147–151, 1946.

4. N. Bourbaki, "Algebra Multilinéaire," Hermann, Paris, 1948.

5. L. Dulmage and I. Halperin, On a Theorem of Frobenius-König and J. von Neumann's Game of Hide and Seek, *Trans. Roy. Soc. Canada. Sect. III*, ser. 3, vol. 49, pp. 23–29, 1955.

6. K. Fan, On a Theorem of Weyl Concerning Eigenvalues of Linear Transformations, I, *Proc. Nat. Acad. Sci. U.S.A.*, vol. 36, pp. 652–655, 1949.

7. K. Fan, On a Theorem of Weyl Concerning Eigenvalues of Linear Transformations, II, *Proc. Nat. Acad. Sci. U.S.A.*, vol. 36, pp. 31–35, 1950.

8. K. Fan, Maximum Properties and Inequalities for the Eigenvalues of Completely Continuous Operators, *Proc. Nat. Acad. Sci. U.S.A.*, vol. 37, pp. 760–766, 1951.

9. K. Fan, A Minimum Property of the Eigenvalues of a Hermitian Transformation, *Amer. Math. Monthly*, vol. 60, pp. 48–50, 1953.

10. A. J. Hoffman and H. W. Wielandt, The Variation of the Spectrum of a Normal Matrix, *Duke Math. J.*, vol. 20, no. 1, pp. 37–39, 1953.

11. A. Horn, On the Singular Values of a Product of Completely Continuous Operators, *Proc. Nat. Acad. Sci. U.S.A.*, vol. 36, p. 374, 1950.

12. L. Lopes and M. Marcus, Inequalities for Symmetric Functions and Hermitian Matrices, *Canadian J. Math.*, vol. 9, pp. 305–312, 1957.

13. M. Marcus, Convex Functions of Quadratic Forms, *Duke J. Math.*, vol. 24, pp. 321–326, 1957.

14. M. Marcus and R. Thompson, A Note on Symmetric Functions of Eigenvalues, *Duke Math. J.*, vol. 24, pp. 43–46, 1957.

15. M. Marcus and J. L. McGregor, Extremal Properties of Hermitian Matrices, *Canadian J. Math.*, vol. 8, pp. 524–531, 1956.

16. M. Marcus and B. N. Moyls, On the Maximum Principle of Ky Fan, *Canadian J. Math.*, vol. 9, pp. 313–320, 1957.

17. M. Marcus, B. N. Moyls, and R. Westwick, Some Extreme Value Results for Indefinite Hermitian Matrices, *Illinois J. Math.*, vol. 1, pp. 449–457, 1957.

18. A. Ostrowski, Sur quelques applications des fonctions convexes et concaves au sens de I. Schur, *J. Math. Pures Appl.*, vol. 31, pp. 253–292, 1952.

19. G. Pólya, Remark on Weyl's Note: Inequalities between the Two Kinds of

Eigenvalues of a Linear Transformation, *Proc. Nat. Acad. Sci. U.S.A.*, vol. 36, pp. 49–51, 1950.

20. J. von Neumann, Some Matrix Inequalities and Metrization of Matrix Space, *Tomsk. Gos. Univ. Uč. Zap.*, vol. 1, pp. 286–300, 1937.

21. J. H. M. Wedderburn, "Lectures on Matrices," American Mathematical Society Colloquium Publications, vol. 17, 1934.

22. H. Weyl, Inequalities between the Two Kinds of Eigenvalues of a Linear Transformation, *Proc. Nat. Acad. Sci. U.S.A.*, vol. 35, pp. 408–411, 1949.

23. H. Wielandt, An Extremum Property of Sums of Eigenvalues, *Proc. Amer. Math. Soc.*, vol. 6, pp. 106–110, 1955.

9

Numerical Methods in Ordinary Differential Equations

HENRY A. ANTOSIEWICZ

PROFESSOR OF MATHEMATICS
UNIVERSITY OF SOUTHERN CALIFORNIA
LOS ANGELES

WALTER GAUTSCHI

OAK RIDGE NATIONAL LABORATORY

9.1 Introduction

We consider, throughout, methods for the numerical solution of the initial-value problem for systems of real ordinary differential equations of first order,

$$\frac{dy^{\mu}}{dx} = f^{\mu}(x, y^1, \ldots, y^m), \qquad y^{\mu}(x_0) = y_0{}^{\mu} \qquad (\mu = 1, 2, \ldots, m).$$

Our aim is to give the fundamental principles on which most of these methods are based, rather than to attempt a complete presentation of all such methods. For a more detailed treatment and a discussion of methods for the numerical solution of boundary-value and eigenvalue problems, we refer to the books listed in the bibliography—for example, to those of Collatz, where further references to the ample literature on the subject can be found.

In the following we always write the basic system in vector form,*

$$\frac{dy}{dx} = f(x, y), \qquad y(x_0) = y_0, \tag{9.1}$$

* To attain more symmetry, some authors write (9.1) as

$$\frac{dw}{dx} = F(w), \qquad w(x_0) = w_0,$$

by setting $w = \begin{pmatrix} x \\ y \end{pmatrix}$, $F = \begin{pmatrix} 1 \\ f \end{pmatrix}$, $w_0 = \begin{pmatrix} x_0 \\ y_0 \end{pmatrix}$. This artifice appears to go back to Nyström ([46], p. 9).

314

and denote by $\| y \|$ the usual euclidean length of y. Without further mention, we tacitly assume that there is a set $I \times R$ containing (x_0, y_0) in its interior on which $f(x,y)$ is continuous and satisfies

$$\| f(x,u) - f(x,v) \| \leq K \| u - v \| \tag{9.2}$$

for some constant $K > 0$, so that there exists on some interval $[x_0, X] \subset I$ a unique solution $y(x)$ with $y(x_0) = y_0$. Recall that, if $f(x,y)$ is of class C^s, $s \geq 1$, on $I \times R$, then $y(x)$ is of class C^{s+1} on $[x_0, X]$ and, if R is convex and $\| \partial f(x,y) / \partial y^\mu \|$ is bounded on $I \times R$ for each $\mu = 1, 2, \ldots, m$, then (9.2) holds.

All methods for the numerical solution of (9.1) considered in the following yield, for a sequence $\{x_n\}$ of abscissas $x_n > x_0$, a sequence $\{y_n\}$ of vectors y_n which approximate to the (exact) vectors $y(x_n)$ of the desired solution. In the first part, Secs. 9.2 to 9.5, we consider the so-called one-step methods, which define y_{n+1} as a function of x_{n+1}, x_n, y_n. A famous representative of this group of methods is Kutta's generalization of Simpson's rule. The second part, Secs. 9.6 to 9.10, is devoted to multi-step methods, in which y_{n+1} is defined as a function of x_{n+1}, $x_{n-\rho}$, $y_{n-\rho}$, $\rho = 0, 1, \ldots, k$ for some $k > 0$. Here, the classical example is Adams' method.

The kind of difficulty one is likely to face is illustrated by the simple equation,

$$\frac{dy}{dx} = \begin{pmatrix} 0 & 1 \\ 10a^2 & 9a \end{pmatrix} y, \qquad y(0) = \begin{pmatrix} 1 \\ -a \end{pmatrix}, \tag{9.3}$$

in which $a > 0$ is some constant. Its general solution is

$$y(x) = c_1 e^{-ax} \begin{pmatrix} 1 \\ -a \end{pmatrix} + c_2 e^{10ax} \begin{pmatrix} 1 \\ 10a \end{pmatrix},$$

and the particular solution desired is obtained for $c_1 = 1$, $c_2 = 0$. No matter what approximate method is used, it will introduce a c_2-component due to round-off errors, and if at $x = \xi$ this component is η, it will be ηe^{20a} at $x = \xi + 2$. Thus, it will ultimately totally overshadow the desired solution and lead to entirely spurious results, regardless of how many decimals are carried in the computation.

Though in a particular problem the situation may not be so bad, this example should serve nevertheless as a warning: numerical integration should not be undertaken when no definite information about the desired solution is available. Careful analysis of the problem at hand must always precede the start of computations.

RUNGE-KUTTA METHODS

9.2 Method of Taylor's Series and General Runge-Kutta Method

Every one-step method can be written in the form

$$y_{n+1} = y_n + h_n \varphi(x_n, y_n; h_n) \qquad (n = 0, 1, 2, \ldots), \qquad (9.4)$$

where $\varphi(x, y; h)$ is a vector-valued function and $h_n = x_{n+1} - x_n$. The choice of φ should be "reasonable" in the sense that for fixed $(x, y) \in I \times R$

$$\varphi(x, y; h) \to f(x, y) \qquad \text{as } h \to 0. \qquad (9.5)$$

If $y(x)$ is the exact solution of the differential equation and

$$r(x, h) = y(x) + h\varphi(x, y(x); h) - y(x + h), \qquad (9.6)$$

then for any fixed $x \in [x_0, X]$

$$r(x, h) = o(h) \qquad \text{as } h \to 0.$$

The vector $r(x, h)$ is called the *truncation error* at the point x. If p is the largest integer p' with the property that

$$r(x, h) = O(h^{p'+1}) \qquad \text{as } h \to 0, \qquad (9.7)$$

then p is called the *order* of the method (9.4).

The simplest choice of φ satisfying (9.5) is

$$\varphi(x, y; h) = f(x, y).$$

The corresponding method,*

$$y_{n+1} = y_n + hf(x_n, y_n), \qquad (9.8)$$

was proposed by Euler in 1768. If $f \in C^1$, it has the order $p = 1$, since

$$r(x, h) = y(x) + hf[x, y(x)] - y(x + h) = y(x) + hy'(x) - y(x + h) = O(h^2).$$

This also shows that the method, in essence, makes use of the first two terms of Taylor's series.

A natural extension of (9.8), then, is the so-called *method of Taylor's series* (also proposed by Euler), which takes into account the first $(p + 1)$ terms of Taylor's series. To describe it, let $f \in C^p$, $p > 1$, and set

$$f^{[0]}(x, y) = f(x, y), f^{[k+1]}(x, y) = \frac{\partial f^{[k]}(x, y)}{\partial x} + \frac{\partial f^{[k]}(x, y)}{\partial y} f(x, y)$$

$$(k = 0, 1, \ldots, p - 2) \qquad (9.9)$$

---

* In this and in similar formulas in the sequel, we write simply h instead of h_n, with the understanding that h may or may not depend on n.

where $\partial f^{[k]}/\partial y$ denotes the $m \times m$ matrix having as columns $\partial f^{[k]}/\partial y^\mu$ $(\mu = 1, 2, \ldots, m)$.   Clearly,

$$f^{[k]}(x,y(x)) = y^{(k+1)}(x). \tag{9.10}$$

Taking, then,

$$\varphi(x,y;h) = \sum_{k=0}^{p-1} \frac{h^k}{(k+1)!} f^{[k]}(x,y),$$

we are led to a method of order p, since, by (9.6), (9.10),

$$r(x,h) = y(x) + h \sum_{k=0}^{p-1} \frac{h^k}{(k+1)!} y^{(k+1)}(x) - y(x+h) = O(h^{p+1}).$$

Although for special systems of differential equations, notably linear systems, the method of Taylor's series may be used quite efficiently (for an example, see Chap. 2), its applicability in more general cases is rather limited, because of the rapidly increasing complexity of the expressions in (9.9).   It was Runge [52] who, in 1895, first pointed out a possibility of evading successive differentiations and of preserving at the same time the increased accuracy afforded by Taylor's series.   Runge's method was subsequently improved by Heun [26] and Kutta [32].

Kutta's proposal (somewhat more general than a similar one made by Heun) consists in setting up φ with undetermined parameters as follows:

$$\varphi(x,y;h) = \sum_{s=1}^{r} \alpha_s k_s,$$
$$k_1(x,y) = f(x,y), \tag{9.11}$$
$$k_s(x,y;h) = f\left(x + \mu_s h, y + h \sum_{j=1}^{s-1} \lambda_{sj} k_j\right) \qquad (s = 2, \ldots, r).$$

Given r, the number of "substitutions" into f, the parameters α_s, μ_s, λ_{sj} are to be determined so as to make the order p of (9.11) as large as possible.

We note that in (9.11) $f \in C^q$ implies $\varphi \in C^q$ for h sufficiently small.

Expanding the local truncation error formally into Taylor's series,

$$r(x,h) = \sum_{k=0}^{\infty} \frac{1}{k!} \left[\frac{\partial^k r(x,h)}{\partial h^k}\right]_{h=0} h^k,$$

and noting from (9.6) that $r(x,0) = 0$ and that

$$\left[\frac{\partial^k r(x,h)}{\partial h^k}\right]_{h=0} = k\left[\frac{\partial^{k-1} \varphi(x,y(x);h)}{\partial h^{k-1}}\right]_{h=0} - y^{(k)}(x) \qquad (k > 0),$$

we find that Kutta's method is of order p, if $f \in C^p$ and

$$\left[\frac{\partial^{k-1} \varphi(x,y(x);h)}{\partial h^{k-1}}\right]_{h=0} - \frac{1}{k} y^{(k)}(x) \quad \begin{cases} \equiv 0 & \text{for } 1 \le k \le p, \\ \not\equiv 0 & \text{for } k = p + 1. \end{cases} \tag{9.12}$$

More detailed calculations show that the p identities in (9.12) are equivalent to a set of, in general, nonlinear equations for the parameters α_s, μ_s, λ_{sj}. For each r, there will be a largest value of p, $p = p^*(r)$, for which these equations are solvable, and it turns out that

$$p^*(r) = r \qquad \text{if } 1 \leq r \leq 4.$$

The corresponding solutions have a certain degree of freedom, which is 1 for $r = 2$ and 2 for $r = 3$ and $r = 4$. Their actual derivation, however, is of considerable length, and the calculations become rapidly more complex as r is further increased. For example, if $r = 5$, Kutta [32] obtains 16 equations in 15 unknowns, and it appears as yet uncertain whether these equations are dependent. Thus, $p^*(5) \geq 4$; similarly one knows only that $p^*(6) \geq 5$. Corresponding formulas of order 4 and 5 are listed in [46]. Formulas of order 6 utilizing eight substitutions are derived in [28,29].

9.3 Examples of Runge-Kutta Formulas

To derive a particular set of Runge-Kutta formulas for a fixed $r(\geq 1)$, one proceeds as follows. First one obtains, in terms of the partial derivatives of $f(x,y)$, the partial derivatives of $\varphi(x,y;h)$ with respect to h, by using (9.11), and the (total) derivatives of $y(x)$, by using (9.1); this requires $(p-1)$ differentiations if a method of order p is desired. Then one substitutes these expressions into (9.12) and satisfies the p identities in (9.12) by equating to zero the coefficients of the various partial derivatives of $f(x,y)$. Under the natural assumption that

$$\mu_s = \sum_{j=1}^{s-1} \lambda_{sj} \qquad (s = 2, \ldots, r), \tag{9.13}$$

one finds, for example, for $p = 1$, 2, or 3, that the first, the first two, or all three of the following equations must be satisfied:

$$\sum_{s=1}^{r} \alpha_s = 1, \tag{9.14}$$

$$\sum_{s=2}^{r} \alpha_s \mu_s = \tfrac{1}{2}, \tag{9.15}$$

$$\sum_{s=2}^{r} \alpha_s \mu_s^{2} = 2 \sum_{s=3}^{r} \alpha_s \sum_{i=2}^{s-1} \lambda_{si} \mu_i = \tfrac{1}{3}. \tag{9.16}$$

Suppose we require only a method of order $p \geq 1$, so that solely (9.14) must hold. If $r = 1$, then (9.13) drops out, and $\alpha_1 = 1$, which yields Euler's point-slope formula (9.8). If $r > 1$, we have to satisfy r equations with $2r - 1 + \tfrac{1}{2}r(r-1)$ variables, which leaves us $r - 1 + \tfrac{1}{2}r(r-1)$ free parameters.

Similarly, for a Runge-Kutta method of order $p \geq 2$, both (9.14) and (9.15) must hold, which requires $r \geq 2$. There are $r - 2 + \tfrac{1}{2}r(r - 1)$ degrees of freedom in the choice of the parameters. For example, if $r = 2$, we have

$$\alpha_1 = 1 - \alpha_2, \qquad \mu_2 = \lambda_{21} = \frac{1}{2\alpha_2}.$$

Note that $r = 2$ violates the second relation in (9.16) so that $p^*(2) = 2$.

In the *modified Euler-Cauchy method* (or the improved point-slope formula) the choice $\alpha_2 = 1$ is made, for which (9.4) reads

$$y_{n+1} = y_n + hf[x_n + \tfrac{1}{2}h, \; y_n + \tfrac{1}{2}hf(x_n, y_n)]. \tag{9.17}$$

In *Heun's method* (or the improved Euler-Cauchy method) $\alpha_2 = \tfrac{1}{2}$ is chosen, for which (9.4) reduces to

$$y_{n+1} = y_n + \tfrac{1}{2}h\{f(x_n, y_n) + f[x_n + h, \; y_n + hf(x_n, y_n)]\}. \tag{9.18}$$

Runge-Kutta formulas of order $p \geq 3$ can be obtained if $r \geq 3$; they can be chosen from a set of formulas with degree of freedom $[r - 4 + \tfrac{1}{2}r(r - 1)]$. If $r = 3$, they are given by

$$\alpha_1 = \frac{2 - 3(\mu_2 + \mu_3) + 6\mu_2\mu_3}{6\mu_2\mu_3},$$

$$\alpha_2 = \frac{2 - 3\mu_3}{6\mu_2(\mu_2 - \mu_3)}, \qquad \alpha_3 = \frac{2 - 3\mu_2}{6\mu_3(\mu_3 - \mu_2)},$$

$$\lambda_{21} = \mu_2, \qquad \lambda_{31} = \frac{\mu_3(3\mu_2 - \mu_3 - 3\mu_2^2)}{\mu_2(2 - 3\mu_2)}, \qquad \lambda_{32} = \frac{\mu_3(\mu_3 - \mu_2)}{\mu_2(2 - 3\mu_2)},$$

as follows from (9.13) to (9.16). If $\mu_2 = \tfrac{1}{3}$, $\mu_3 = \tfrac{2}{3}$ is chosen, then (9.4) becomes

$$\begin{aligned}
y_{n+1} &= y_n + \tfrac{1}{4}h(k_1 + 3k_3), \\
k_1 &= f(x_n, y_n), \\
k_3 &= f\{x_n + \tfrac{2}{3}h, \; y_n + \tfrac{2}{3}hf[x_n + \tfrac{1}{3}h, \; y_n + \tfrac{1}{3}hf(x_n, y_n)]\},
\end{aligned} \tag{9.19}$$

which is also referred to as *Heun's formula*. The choice $\mu_2 = \tfrac{1}{2}$, $\mu_3 = 1$ yields *Kutta's third-order rule*:

$$\begin{aligned}
y_{n+1} &= y_n + \tfrac{1}{6}h(k_1 + 4k_2 + k_3), \\
k_1 &= f(x_n, y_n), \\
k_2 &= f[x_n + \tfrac{1}{2}h, \; y_n + \tfrac{1}{2}hf(x_n, y_n)], \\
k_3 &= f\{x_n + h, \; y_n - hf(x_n, y_n) + 2hf[x_n + \tfrac{1}{2}h, \; y_n + \tfrac{1}{2}hf(x_n, y_n)]\}.
\end{aligned} \tag{9.20}$$

To find Runge-Kutta formulas of order $p = 4$, we must have $r \geq 4$. If $r = 4$, there are obtained 11 equations containing 13 parameters. A particular solution suggested by Kutta is the set of constants

$$\alpha_1 = \alpha_4 = \tfrac{1}{6}, \qquad \alpha_2 = \alpha_3 = \tfrac{1}{3},$$
$$\mu_2 = \mu_3 = \tfrac{1}{2}, \qquad \mu_4 = 1,$$
$$\lambda_{21} = \lambda_{32} = \tfrac{1}{2}, \qquad \lambda_{43} = 1, \qquad \lambda_{31} = \lambda_{41} = \lambda_{42} = 0.$$

This is the choice made in Runge-Kutta's method, for which (9.4) reads

$$\begin{aligned}
y_{n+1} &= y_n + \tfrac{1}{6}h(k_1 + 2k_2 + 2k_3 + k_4), \\
k_1 &= f(x_n, y_n), \\
k_2 &= f(x_n + \tfrac{1}{2}h, y_n + \tfrac{1}{2}hk_1), \\
k_3 &= f(x_n + \tfrac{1}{2}h, y_n + \tfrac{1}{2}hk_2), \\
k_4 &= f(x_n + h, y_n + hk_3).
\end{aligned} \tag{9.21}$$

Note, that, if f is independent of y, both formulas (9.20) and (9.21) reduce to Simpson's rule.

Gill [19] proposes a solution for the same 11 equations under the additional requirement that the vectors $y_n + h(\lambda_{i1}k_1 + \lambda_{i2}k_2)$, $i = 3, 4$, and $y_n + h(\alpha_1 k_1 + \alpha_2 k_2)$ be linearly dependent. He adopts, from among others, the set of constants

$$\alpha_1 = \alpha_4 = \tfrac{1}{6}, \qquad \alpha_2 = \tfrac{1}{3}(1 - \sqrt{\tfrac{1}{2}}), \qquad \alpha_3 = \tfrac{1}{3}(1 + \sqrt{\tfrac{1}{2}}),$$
$$\mu_2 = \mu_3 = \tfrac{1}{2}, \qquad \mu_4 = 1,$$
$$\lambda_{21} = \tfrac{1}{2}, \qquad \lambda_{31} = -\tfrac{1}{2} + \sqrt{\tfrac{1}{2}}, \qquad \lambda_{32} = 1 - \sqrt{\tfrac{1}{2}},$$
$$\lambda_{41} = 0, \qquad \lambda_{42} = -\sqrt{\tfrac{1}{2}}, \qquad \lambda_{43} = 1 + \sqrt{\tfrac{1}{2}},$$

with which (9.4) becomes

$$\begin{aligned}
y_{n+1} &= y_n + \tfrac{1}{6}h[k_1 + 2(1 - \sqrt{\tfrac{1}{2}})k_2 + 2(1 + \sqrt{\tfrac{1}{2}})k_3 + k_4], \\
k_1 &= f(x_n, y_n), \\
k_2 &= f(x_n + \tfrac{1}{2}h, y_n + \tfrac{1}{2}hk_1), \\
k_3 &= f(x_n + \tfrac{1}{2}h, y_n - (\tfrac{1}{2} - \sqrt{\tfrac{1}{2}})hk_1 + (1 - \sqrt{\tfrac{1}{2}})hk_2), \\
k_4 &= f(x_n + h, y_n - \sqrt{\tfrac{1}{2}}hk_2 + (1 + \sqrt{\tfrac{1}{2}})hk_3).
\end{aligned} \tag{9.22}$$

Still other formulas are described in [31] and in [13, 38], where also their adoption for use on high-speed computing machines is discussed.

More accurate variants of Runge-Kutta's method, involving also substitutions into partial derivatives of f, are given in [17, 36, 47]. Further one-step methods with

$$\varphi(x,y;h) = \sum_{s=1}^{r} \alpha_s f(x + \mu_s h, y + \mu_s h \bar{\varphi}_s(x, y; \mu_1 h, \ldots, \mu_r h)),$$

where the $\bar{\varphi}_s$ represent auxiliary one-step methods, are considered in [23, 25].

9.4 Differential Equations of Higher Order

Because of their importance we consider in more detail systems of second-order differential equations

$$v'' = g(x, v, v'), \qquad v(x_0) = v_0, \qquad v'(x_0) = v_0', \qquad (9.23)$$

where v and g are vector-valued functions and g is sufficiently smooth on a suitable set $I \times R \times S$.

The system (9.23) can be written as a first-order system [of twice the size of (9.23)] if we introduce the column vector $w = v'$ and write

$$y = \begin{pmatrix} v \\ w \end{pmatrix}, \qquad f(x,y) = \begin{pmatrix} w \\ g(x,v,w) \end{pmatrix}, \qquad y_0 = \begin{pmatrix} v_0 \\ w_0 \end{pmatrix}. \qquad (9.24)$$

Then (9.23) is equivalent to

$$y' = f(x,y), \qquad y(x_0) = y_0. \qquad (9.25)$$

Any method of Sec. 9.3 can now be applied to the system (9.25). The resulting formulas may then again be separated into their v and w parts to obtain formulas for the computation of v and $w = v'$.

For the Runge-Kutta formula (9.21) we find, after a short calculation,

$$\begin{aligned} v_{n+1} &= v_n + h v_n' + \tfrac{1}{6} h^2 (l_1 + l_2 + l_3), \\ v_{n+1}' &= v_n' + \tfrac{1}{6} h (l_1 + 2l_2 + 2l_3 + l_4), \end{aligned} \qquad (9.26)$$

where
$$\begin{aligned} l_1 &= g(x_n, v_n, v_n'), \\ l_2 &= g(x_n + \tfrac{1}{2}h, \, v_n + \tfrac{1}{2}h v_n', \, v_n' + \tfrac{1}{2}h l_1), \\ l_3 &= g(x_n + \tfrac{1}{2}h, \, v_n + \tfrac{1}{2}h v_n' + \tfrac{1}{4}h^2 l_1, \, v_n' + \tfrac{1}{2}h l_2), \\ l_4 &= g(x_n + h, \, v_n + h v_n' + \tfrac{1}{2}h^2 l_2, \, v_n' + h l_3). \end{aligned} \qquad (9.27)$$

By construction, this method is of order 4, in the sense that

$$v_1 - v(x_0 + h) = O(h^5), \qquad v_1' - v'(x_0 + h) = O(h^5). \qquad (9.28)$$

In analogy with Kutta's procedure [see (9.11)], one could start from the outset with a system of formulas of type (9.26), (9.27) and use undetermined coefficients to search for more accurate or more convenient formulas.   This was done in 1925 by Nyström [46], who sets

$$v_{n+1} = v_n + hv'_n + h^2 \sum_{s=1}^{r} \alpha_s l_s,$$

$$v'_{n+1} = v'_n + h \sum_{s=1}^{r} \beta_s l_s,$$

(9.29)

with $l_1 = g(x_n, v_n, v'_n),$

$$l_s = g(x_n + \mu_s h,\, v_n + \mu_s h v'_n + h^2 \sum_{j=1}^{s-1} \lambda_{sj} l_j,\, v'_n + h \sum_{j=1}^{s-1} \kappa_{sj} l_j)$$

$$(s = 2, \dots, r). \quad (9.30)$$

He finds, among others, the following particular simple set of formulas:

$$l_1 = g(x_n, v_n, v'_n),$$
$$l_2 = g(x_n + \tfrac{1}{2}h,\, v_n + \tfrac{1}{2}hv'_n + \tfrac{1}{8}h^2 l_1,\, v'_n + \tfrac{1}{2}hl_1),$$
$$l_3 = g(x_n + \tfrac{1}{2}h,\, v_n + \tfrac{1}{2}hv'_n + \tfrac{1}{8}h^2 l_1,\, v'_n + \tfrac{1}{2}hl_2), \quad (9.31)$$
$$l_4 = g(x_n + h,\, v_n + hv'_n + \tfrac{1}{2}h^2 l_3,\, v'_n + hl_3),$$

from which v_{n+1}, v'_{n+1} is obtained as in (9.26).   The resulting method is also of order 4 but in general involves fewer calculations than (9.27), since the first two arguments in l_2 and l_3 are the same.

A method which extends Nyström's method (9.26), (9.31) to systems of mth-order equations

$$v^{(m)} = g(x, v, v', \dots, v^{(m-1)}), \qquad v^{(\mu)}(x_0) = v_0{}^{(\mu)} \qquad (\mu = 0, 1, \dots, m-1)$$

(9.32)

was developed by Zurmühl [72, 73].   To describe it, let

$$T_\mu(\alpha) = v_n{}^{(\mu)} + \alpha h v_n{}^{(\mu+1)} + \cdots + \frac{(\alpha h)^{m-\mu-1}}{(m-\mu-1)!}\, v_n{}^{(m-1)}$$

$$(0 \le \mu \le m-1)$$

denote truncated Taylor series for the μth derivative at $x = x_n + \alpha h$, based on the available derivatives at $x = x_n$.   Using the short-hand notation $g(x, u_\mu)$ for $g(x, u_0, u_1, \dots, u_{m-1})$, set

$$l_1 = g[x_n, T_\mu(0)],$$

$$l_2 = g\left[x_n + \tfrac{1}{2}h,\, T_\mu(\tfrac{1}{2}) + \frac{(h/2)^{m-\mu}}{(m-\mu)!}\, l_1\right],$$

(9.33)

$$l_3 = g\left[x_n + \tfrac{1}{2}h,\, T_\mu(\tfrac{1}{2}) + \frac{(h/2)^{m-\mu}}{(m-\mu)!}\, l^{(\mu)}\right], \qquad l^{(\mu)} = \begin{cases} l_1 \ (0 \le \mu \le m-2) \\ l_2 \ (\mu = m-1), \end{cases}$$

$$l_4 = g\left[x_n + h,\, T_\mu(1) + \frac{h^{m-\mu}}{(m-\mu)!}\, l_3\right].$$

Then

$$v_{n+1}^{(\mu)} = T_\mu(1) + \frac{h^{m-\mu}}{(m-\mu)!} \frac{1}{(m-\mu+1)(m-\mu+2)} [(m-\mu)^2 l_1$$
$$+ 2(m-\mu)(l_2+l_3) + (2-m+\mu)l_4] \qquad (\mu = 0,1,\ldots,m-1).$$
$$(9.34)$$

It was shown by Zurmühl that in case v is a scalar function one has

$$v_1^{(\mu)} - v^{(\mu)}(x_0 + h) = O(h^{p_\mu}), \qquad p_\mu = \begin{cases} m+3-\mu & (0 \le \mu \le m-2) \\ 5 & (\mu = m-1). \end{cases}$$
$$(9.35)$$

Thus, if $m > 2$, the function $v(x)$ is obtained with a local error of order h^{m+3}, and the order of accuracy in the sequence of derivatives decreases successively by 1 until it reaches $O(h^5)$ for the $(m-2)$nd derivative. It must be noted, however, that the accumulated error of v over a large number of steps is nevertheless of order h^4 for all m. Compare in this connection the remarks in [55].

Further Runge-Kutta methods for (9.32), involving also partial derivatives of g, are listed in [7, 17].

9.5   Error Analysis

For any one-step method we have, from (9.4) and (9.6),

$$y_{n+1} = y_n + h\varphi(x_n, y_n; h),$$
$$y(x_{n+1}) = y(x_n) + h\varphi(x_n, y(x_n); h) - r(x_n, h),$$

where $r(x,h)$ is the local truncation error. Thus, if $\epsilon_n = y_n - y(x_n)$ denotes the error vector at the nth step, we find by subtraction

$$\epsilon_{n+1} = \epsilon_n + h[\varphi(x_n, y_n; h) - \varphi(x_n, y(x_n), h)] + r(x_n, h). \qquad (9.36)$$

This shows that the increase of the accumulated error is composed of two parts: the truncation error $r(x_n, h)$ and the contribution arising from the second term on the right. It is, in fact, the nature of this additional term which is decisive for the behavior of ϵ_n as n becomes large.

To see this, write

$$\varphi(x_n, y_n; h) - \varphi(x_n, y(x_n); h) = \frac{\partial \varphi}{\partial y} [y_n - y(x_n)] = \frac{\partial \varphi}{\partial y} \epsilon_n,$$

where the derivatives making up the matrix $(\partial\varphi/\partial y)$ are taken at suitable points on the line segment between y_n and $y(x_n)$. We obtain then, from (9.36),

$$\epsilon_{n+1} = \left(I + h\frac{\partial\varphi}{\partial y}\right)\epsilon_n + r(x_n, h). \qquad (9.37)$$

The behavior of ϵ_n for large n, therefore, depends mainly on the matrices $I + h(\partial\varphi/\partial y)$, which are all close to the unit matrix I. If they have eigenvalues which are consistently (i.e., for all n) larger than 1, then one expects the sequence of error norms $\|\epsilon_n\|$ to increase ultimately like a geometric progression. If all eigenvalues are consistently less than 1, then the error norms will remain bounded. In view of this, the first term on the right in (9.37) is often called the "propagation error." Obviously, in case of simple quadratures, where $\partial\varphi/\partial y = 0$, there is no geometric propagation of errors.

An estimation of the propagation error for Runge-Kutta methods was already given by Runge [53]. Suppose that,* in $I \times R$,

$$\left\| \frac{\partial f(x,y)}{\partial y} \right\| \leq K,$$

and consider, for example, the Runge-Kutta method (9.21), with

$$
\begin{aligned}
\varphi(x,y;h) &= \sum_{s=1}^{4} \alpha_s k_s(x,y), \\
k_1(x,y) &= f(x,y), \\
k_s(x,y) &= f(x + \mu_s h, y + \lambda_s h k_{s-1}) \qquad (s > 1),
\end{aligned}
\tag{9.38}
$$

$$
\begin{aligned}
\alpha_1 &= \tfrac{1}{2}\alpha_2 = \tfrac{1}{2}\alpha_3 = \alpha_4 = \tfrac{1}{6}, \\
\mu_2 &= \mu_3 = \tfrac{1}{2}\mu_4 = \tfrac{1}{2}, \\
\lambda_2 &= \lambda_3 = \tfrac{1}{2}\lambda_4 = \tfrac{1}{2}.
\end{aligned}
\tag{9.39}
$$

Then, for any two points (x,y), $(x,\bar{y})$ in $I \times R$, we have

$$\|k_1(x,y) - k_1(x,\bar{y})\| = \left\| \frac{\partial f}{\partial y}(y - \bar{y}) \right\| \leq K\|y - \bar{y}\|,$$

$$\|k_s(x,y) - k_s(x,\bar{y})\| = \left\| \frac{\partial f}{\partial y}\{y - \bar{y} + \lambda_s h[k_{s-1}(x,y) - k_{s-1}(x,\bar{y})]\} \right\|$$

$$\leq K[\|y - \bar{y}\| + \lambda_s h \|k_{s-1}(x,y) - k_{s-1}(x,\bar{y})\|].$$

From this we obtain successively

$$\|k_2(x,y) - k_2(x,\bar{y})\| \leq K(1 + \lambda_2 hK)\|y - \bar{y}\|,$$
$$\|k_3(x,y) - k_3(x,\bar{y})\| \leq K(1 + \lambda_3 hK + \lambda_3\lambda_2 h^2 K^2)\|y - \bar{y}\|,$$
$$\|k_4(x,y) - k_4(x,\bar{y})\| \leq K(1 + \lambda_4 hK + \lambda_4\lambda_3 h^2 K^2 + \lambda_4\lambda_3\lambda_2 h^3 K^3)\|y - \bar{y}\|.$$

* For a different assumption in this connection (relative to scalar differential equations) see [11].

Therefore, by (9.38) and (9.39),

$$\|\varphi(x,y;h) - \varphi(x,\bar{y};h)\| \le K[\alpha_1 + \alpha_2(1 + \lambda_2 hK)$$
$$+ \alpha_3(1 + \lambda_3 hK + \lambda_3\lambda_2 h^2 K^2) + \alpha_4(1 + \lambda_4 hK + \lambda_4\lambda_3 h^2 K^2$$
$$+ \lambda_4\lambda_3\lambda_2 h^3 K^3)] \|y - \bar{y}\| = K(1 + \tfrac{1}{2}hK + \tfrac{1}{6}h^2K^2 + \tfrac{1}{24}h^3K^3) \|y - \bar{y}\|.$$

Letting now $x = x_n, y = y_n, \bar{y} = y(x_n)$, we find for the propagation term in (9.36) the following estimation

$$\| \epsilon_n + h\{\varphi(x_n,y_n;h) - \varphi(x_n,y(x_n);h)\}\|$$

$$\le \left(1 + hK + \frac{(hK)^2}{2!} + \frac{(hK)^3}{3!} + \frac{(hK)^4}{4!}\right) \| \epsilon_n\|. \quad (9.40)$$

The estimation of the truncation error is considerably more laborious. A first rigorous estimate for the Runge-Kutta method (9.38), (9.39) is stated in [4] and proved in [5] by Bieberbach.   We give it here for the case of a scalar first-order differential equation.   In $I \times R$, let

$$f \in C^4, \qquad |f| \le N, \qquad \left|\frac{\partial^l f}{\partial x^i \, \partial y^k}\right| \le \frac{M}{N^{k-1}} \qquad (0 < l \le 4, 0 \le k \le 4).$$
$$(9.41)$$

Then, for $x_n < X$,

$$|r(x_n,h)| \le MN(3.7 + 5.4M + 1.3M^2 + .017M^3)h^5. \quad (9.42)$$

Similar bounds are derived in [5] and [66] also for arbitrary systems of differential equations.   Analogous bounds for the truncation error of Zurmühl's method can be found in [18] (see also [8]).

Under the slightly different assumptions

$$\left|\frac{\partial^l f}{\partial x^i \, \partial y^k}\right| \le \frac{M^l}{N^{k-1}} \qquad (0 \le l \le 4) \quad (9.43)$$

(which contain, for $l = 0$, the assumption $|f| \le N$) Lotkin [35] derives the "asymptotic" estimate

$$r(x_n,h) = \rho h^5 + O(h^6), \qquad |\rho| \le \tfrac{73}{720}NM^4. \quad (9.44)$$

The constant M in (9.43) may be obtained by forming

$$\max_{I \times R} \left|\frac{\partial^l f}{\partial x^{l-k} \, \partial y^k}\right| = K_{lk}, \qquad \max_{0 \le k \le l} N^{k-1}K_{lk} = L_l, \qquad \max_{1 \le l \le 4} L_l^{l} = M$$

in this order.

Estimates which are based on a priori bounds for $y^{(5)}(x)$, $(d/dx)f_y[x, y(x)], f_{yy}[x,y(x)]$ are given in [1], and further estimates in [7, 10].

The estimation (9.40) of the propagation error can now be combined with any estimation

$$\| r(x_n, h) \| \leq T h^5$$

of the truncation error to give a bound for the total accumulated error in Runge-Kutta's method.   In fact, setting

$$1 + hK + \frac{(hK)^2}{2!} + \frac{(hK)^3}{3!} + \frac{(hK)^4}{4!} = 1 + hP,$$

we obtain, from (9.36) and (9.40),

$$\| \epsilon_{n+1} \| \leq (1 + hP) \| \epsilon_n \| + T h^5 \qquad (n = 0, 1, 2, \ldots),$$

and therefore, if $\epsilon_0 = 0$ and $P > 0$,

$$\| \epsilon_n \| \leq \frac{T h^4}{P} [(1 + hP)^n - 1].$$

In the light of example (9.3) it is not surprising that estimations of this kind, being necessarily satisfied in every instance, may lead to rather conservative bounds.   For example, if we apply (9.41), (9.42) to the equation

$$y' = f(x), \tag{9.45}$$

that is, to a simple problem of quadrature, we obtain

$$|r(x_n, h)| \leq 3.7 H h^5 (1 + \cdots), \qquad H = \max_{1 \leq l \leq 4} |f^{(l)}|, \tag{9.46}$$

where dots indicate additional positive terms.   On the other hand, the well-known remainder term for Simpson's rule, to which Runge-Kutta's method reduces in this case, leads to the estimate

$$|r(x_n, h)| \leq \frac{H^* h^5}{2880}, \qquad H^* = \max |f^{(4)}|. \tag{9.47}$$

Comparison between (9.46) and (9.47) shows that, for quadratures, Bieberbach's bound is too large by a factor of at least 10^4.   Somewhat better is the bound which derives from (9.44) [about 300 times too large in the case of (9.45)], but it has the drawback of being justified only for h sufficiently small.

In view of these difficulties, present-day efforts tend to appraise the error more realistically by stochastic methods [25, 50].   In practice, one makes use of various asymptotic devices to estimate the accuracy, notably Richardson's "deferred approach" to the limit [51] (see also [16, 21]).

DIFFERENCE METHODS

9.6 Linear Multistep Methods

The methods so far discussed replace the first-order system of differential equations (9.1) by a first-order system of difference equations (9.4). The local error committed thereby could be made as small as $O(h^5)$, but not smaller without considerable additional effort. We now replace (9.1) by difference equations of higher order, which will permit us to decrease the local error to any desired order of magnitude.

More specifically, we consider *linear multistep methods*, that is, methods which define y_{n+1} by a linear combination of vectors y_{n-s+1}, hf_{n+1}, hf_{n-s+1}, $s = 1, 2, \ldots, k$, where

$$f_n = f(x_n, y_n) \qquad (n = 0, 1, 2, \ldots). \qquad (9.48)$$

We write these methods in the form

$$y_{n+1} + \alpha_1 y_n + \cdots + \alpha_k y_{n-k+1} = h(\beta_0 f_{n+1} + \beta_1 f_n + \cdots + \beta_k f_{n-k+1}), \qquad (9.49)$$

where it is assumed that α_s, β_s are real constants, $k > 1$, $|\alpha_k| + |\beta_k| > 0$, and $h = x_{n+1} - x_n$ is independent of n. Once k initial vectors $y_0, y_1, \ldots,$ y_{k-1} are known, the relation (9.49) can be used to obtain successively all desired approximations y_n for $n \geq k$. The k initial vectors must be found independently by some other method (e.g., by a Runge-Kutta method).

It is customary to call the formula (9.49) *open* if $\beta_0 = 0$ and *closed* if $\beta_0 \neq 0$. Open formulas define the "new" approximation y_{n+1} explicitly in terms of "old" approximations, whereas closed formulas contain y_{n+1} implicitly as argument in f_{n+1}. In the latter case the relation (9.49) represents a system of m, in general, nonlinear equations for the m components of y_{n+1}. The existence and uniqueness of a solution of such a system, and a practical method of solving it, are discussed in Sec. 9.8.

We associate with the "k-step" method (9.49) the linear functional L defined by

$$Lw(t) = \sum_{s=0}^{k} [\alpha_s w(k - s) - \beta_s w'(k - s)], \qquad \alpha_0 = 1. \qquad (9.50)$$

Here $w(t)$ is considered to be a scalar function differentiable in $[0,k]$. We call k the *index* of L and say that the functional L is of order p if $L(t^r) = 0$ for $r = 0, 1, \ldots, p$ but $L(t^{p+1}) \neq 0$.*

---

* In place of the powers $\{t^r\}$ one may consider other systems of functions $\{\omega_r(t)\}$ and define analogously the order of L with respect to $\{\omega_r\}$. For the case $\omega_r(t) = \exp(\lambda_r t)$ with suitable constants λ_r, see [6].

If $w \in C^{p+1}$ in $[0,k]$, then, by Taylor's theorem,

$$w(t) = \sum_{r=0}^{p} \frac{w^{(r)}(0)}{r!} t^r + \frac{1}{p!} \int_0^k (t - u)^p_+ w^{(p+1)}(u) \, du$$

where $$(t - u)_+ = \max (0, t - u).$$

Every linear functional L of order p can therefore be represented in the form

$$Lw = \frac{1}{p!} \int_0^k \lambda_p(u) w^{(p+1)}(u) \, du, \qquad \lambda_p(u) = L[(t - u)^p_+], \qquad (9.51)$$

in which all characteristics of L are collected in the first factor of the integrand and all those of w in the second factor.   If $\lambda_p(u)$ does not change sign in $[0,k]$, then (9.51) can be simplified to

$$Lw = l_{p+1} w^{(p+1)}(\tau), \qquad l_{p+1} = \frac{L(t^{p+1})}{(p + 1)!}, \qquad 0 < \tau < k. \qquad (9.51')$$

In fact, by the mean-value theorem,

$$Lw = \frac{w^{(p+1)}(\tau)}{p!} \int_0^k \lambda_p(u) \, du,$$

and by (9.51), with $w(t) = t^{p+1}/(p + 1)!$,

$$\int_0^k \lambda_p(u) \, du = \frac{L(t^{p+1})}{p + 1}. \qquad (9.52)$$

The expressions in (9.51) and (9.51') are referred to as *remainder terms* of the functional L.

In analogy with (9.6) we define for the method (9.49) the local truncation error at the point x to be the vector

$$r(x,h) = y*(x,h) - y(x + h),$$

where $y*$ is the solution of

$$y* + \sum_{s=1}^{k} \alpha_s y(x - sh + h) - h \left[\beta_0 f(x + h, y*) + \sum_{s=1}^{k} \beta_s y'(x - sh + h) \right] = 0.$$

If the functional L in (9.50) has order p, then our method (9.49) is of order p in the sense of (9.7).   More precisely, it can be shown that if $f \in C^p$, then

$$\|r(x,h)\| = |l_{p+1}| \, \|y^{(p+1)}(x)\| \, h^{p+1} + o(h^{p+1}).$$

Multistep methods of a more general form than (9.49) have also been considered.   Some of them make use of certain "advanced" points (x_{n+l}, y_{n+l}), $l > 1$, others of partial derivatives of f.   For a study of these we refer to [9, 15, 33, 44].

9.7 Multistep Methods of Maximal Order

We turn now to the question of determining suitable functionals (9.50). In order to obtain a functional L of order p, we must have

$$L(t^r) = \sum_{s=0}^{k} \alpha_s (k-s)^r - r \sum_{s=0}^{k} \beta_s (k-s)^{r-1} = 0 \quad (r = 0, 1, \ldots, p). \quad (9.53)$$

Since $\alpha_0 = 1$, these relations represent an inhomogeneous system of $(p+1)$ linear equations in $(2k+1)$ unknowns α_s, β_s. If $p < 2k$, such a system has always infinitely many solutions, so that there is an infinite number of functionals L with index k and order $p < 2k$. On the other hand, it can be shown that (9.53) has a unique solution if $p = 2k$ and no solution if $p > 2k$. The corresponding functional L of maximum order can be constructed in closed form by using Hermite's interpolation formula (details are given in [14], numerical values in [56]).

The resulting k-step methods of order $2k$ are mainly of theoretic interest, in spite of their high local accuracy. It turns out that the corresponding recurrence (9.49) is very sensitive to small disturbances, which are quickly amplified during repeated application of (9.49). This phenomenon, known as numerical instability, is examined in more detail in Sec. 9.10. Here, we mention only that the stability properties of (9.49) depend on the location of the zeros of the polynomial

$$a(z) = z^k + \alpha_1 z^{k-1} + \cdots + \alpha_k, \quad (9.54)$$

which is called the *generating polynomial* of the functional L. In fact, a necessary condition for stability is that all zeros of $a(z)$ be located within or on the unit circle and that all zeros on the unit circle be simple [14, 59]:

$$\text{If} \qquad a(\zeta) = 0, \qquad \text{then} \qquad \begin{cases} \text{either } |\zeta| < 1 \\ \text{or } |\zeta| = 1 \quad \text{and} \quad a'(\zeta) \neq 0. \end{cases} \quad (9.55)$$

Following Dahlquist [14], we call a functional L (and also the corresponding multistep method) *stable* if the generating polynomial $a(z)$ of L satisfies condition (9.55).

From the practical point of view, therefore, the interesting question is to maximize the order of a functional L among all stable functionals with given index. We can assume, henceforth, that L has order $p \geq 0$, so that certainly

$$a(1) = 1 + \alpha_1 + \alpha_2 + \cdots + \alpha_k = 0. \quad (9.56)$$

We note then, first of all, the following theorem.

Theorem 9.1. *If for a given generating polynomial (9.54) there exists a corresponding functional L with index k and order $p \geq k + 1$, then it is unique.*

The proof follows readily from (9.53), in which the α_s are to be considered as prescribed and the β_s as unknowns.

A functional L of the type indicated in Theorem 9.1 always exists. Indeed, let us write (9.50) equivalently in the form

$$
\begin{aligned}
Lw(t) &= \sum_{s=0}^{k} [\alpha_s w(k - s) - \gamma_{ks} \nabla^s w'(k)] \\
&= a(E)E^{-k}w(k) - \sum_{s=0}^{k} \gamma_{ks} \nabla^s w'(k), \quad (9.57)
\end{aligned}
$$

where E, ∇ denote the displacement and the backward difference operator, respectively. By means of the formal calculus of operators, we transform (9.57) into

$$
Lw(t) = \left\{ -\frac{a[1/(1 - \nabla)](1 - \nabla)^k}{\ln(1 - \nabla)} - \sum_{s=0}^{k} \gamma_{ks} \nabla^s \right\} w'(k),
$$

which certainly holds whenever $w(t)$ is a polynomial. Let

$$
-\frac{a[1/(1 - z)](1 - z)^k}{\ln(1 - z)} = \sum_{s=0}^{\infty} c_{ks} z^s, \quad (9.58)
$$

and define

$$
\gamma_{ks} = c_{ks} \quad (s = 0, 1, \ldots, k). \quad (9.59)
$$

Then

$$
Lw(t) = \left(\sum_{s=k+1}^{\infty} c_{ks} \nabla^s \right) w'(k). \quad (9.60)
$$

Hence, $Lw = 0$ if w is a polynomial of degree $\le k + 1$; that is, L is of order $p \ge k + 1$.

If L is stable, it can be shown, moreover, that $c_{k,k+1} \ne 0$ unless k is even and

$$
\alpha_{k-s} = -\alpha_s \quad (s = 0, 1, \ldots, k; k \text{ even}), \quad (9.61)
$$

in which case $c_{k,k+1} = 0$, $c_{k,k+2} \ne 0$. In view of (9.60) and Theorem 9.1, this implies the following result.

Theorem 9.2 (*Dahlquist* [14]). *The maximal order among all stable functionals L with index k is equal to $k + 1$ if k is odd and is equal to $k + 2$ if k is even.*

It is characteristic of a stable functional of even index and maximal order that its generating polynomial $a(z)$ has the zeros $z = 1$ and $z = -1$ and that all other zeros, if any, are on the unit circle arranged in conjugate pairs. In fact, (9.61) is equivalent to $z^k a(1/z) + a(z) \equiv 0$; hence $a(1) = a(-1) = 0$, and $a(\zeta) = 0$ implies $a(1/\zeta) = 0$. Since no zero is allowed to fall outside the unit circle, we have $|\zeta| = 1$ for each zero ζ, and then $1/\zeta = \bar{\zeta}$ is a zero whenever ζ is.

Conversely, if $a(z)$ has the zeros

$$\zeta_1 = 1, \qquad \zeta_2 = -1, \qquad \zeta_{2r-1} = \bar{\zeta}_{2r} = e^{i\theta_r}$$
$$(r = 2, \ldots, k/2; \, 0 < \theta_r < \pi),$$

then
$$a(z) = (z^2 - 1) \prod_{r=2}^{k/2} [z^2 - (2\cos\theta_r)z + 1],$$

so that

$$z^k a(1/z) + a(z) = (1 - z^2) \prod_{r=2}^{k/2} [1 - (2\cos\theta_r)z + z^2]$$
$$+ (z^2 - 1) \prod_{r=2}^{k/2} [z^2 - (2\cos\theta_r)z + 1] \equiv 0.$$

The gain in order, if k is even, can be explained by the existence of an expansion of L in central differences,

$$Lw = \sum_{s=0}^{k} \alpha_s w(k-s) - \sum_{s=0}^{k/2} \tau_{ks} \, \delta^{2s} w'(\tfrac{1}{2}k) \qquad (k \text{ even}; \, \alpha_{k-s} = -\alpha_s), \quad (9.62)$$

where the coefficients τ_{ks} are found from*

$$\frac{a(u)}{u^{(k/2)} \ln u} = \sum_{s=0}^{\infty} \tau_{ks} z^{2s}, \qquad u = 1 + \tfrac{1}{2}z^2 + z\sqrt{1 + \tfrac{1}{4}z^2}. \quad (9.63)$$

Formula (9.62), for example, contains for $k = 2$, $a(z) = z^2 - 1$, Simpson's formula

$$w(2) - w(0) - \tfrac{1}{3}[w'(2) + 4w'(1) + w'(0)] = -\tfrac{1}{90}w^{(5)}(\tau), \quad (9.64)$$

and for $k = 4$, $a(z) = z^4 + z^3 - z - 1$ a formula due to Dahlquist [14]:

$$w(4) + w(3) - w(1) - w(0) - 3[w'(3) + w'(1)$$
$$+ \tfrac{1}{10}\delta^4 w'(2)] = -\tfrac{1}{140}w^{(7)}(\tau). \quad (9.65)$$

The remainder terms are obtained from (9.51'), which is applicable in these cases, as can be verified.

Stable functionals L of maximal order are always closed [14]. Open functionals of index k and order k can be constructed by a formula analogous to (9.57):

$$Lw = \sum_{s=0}^{k} \alpha_s w(k-s) - \sum_{s=0}^{k-1} \sigma_{ks} \nabla^s w'(k-1), \quad (9.66)$$

where
$$\frac{(1-z)^{k-1} a[1/(1-z)]}{-\ln(1-z)} = \sum_{s=0}^{\infty} \sigma_{ks} z^s. \quad (9.67)$$

---

* Note that the left-hand side in (9.63) is an even function of z, since $u(-z) = 1/u(z)$ and

$$\frac{a(1/u)}{u^{-(k/2)} \ln(1/u)} = \frac{-u^k a(1/u)}{u^{(k/2)} \ln u} = \frac{a(u)}{u^{(k/2)} \ln u}$$

by virtue of (9.61).

For example, if $k = 4$ and $a(z) = z^4 - 1$, we obtain from (9.66) and (9.51'),

$$w(4) - w(0) - \tfrac{4}{3}[2w'(3) - w'(2) + 2w'(1)] = \tfrac{14}{45}w^{(5)}(\tau). \quad (9.68)$$

In view of the representations (9.57) and (9.66), multistep methods are often called *finite-difference methods*. Extensive lists or various examples of difference methods can be found in [22, 48, 65, 69]. The classical difference methods are based on the functional L with $a(z) = z^k - z^{k-1}$ and are discussed in more detail in Sec. 9.9.

9.8 Predictor-Corrector Schemes

We return now to the question of solving the equation

$$y_{n+1} + \alpha_1 y_n + \cdots + \alpha_k y_{n-k+1} = h[\beta_0 f(x_{n+1}, y_{n+1})$$
$$+ \beta_1 f_n + \cdots + \beta_k f_{n-k+1}] \quad (\beta_0 \neq 0) \quad (9.69)$$

for the vector y_{n+1}, assuming that the vectors $y_n, y_{n-1}, \ldots; f_n, f_{n-1}, \ldots$ are known. We shall show that, for h sufficiently small, (9.69) has a unique solution, which can be obtained by a method of successive approximations.

Theorem 9.3. *If*

$$|\beta_0| Kh < 1, \quad (9.70)$$

$K > 0$ *being a constant satisfying* (9.2), *then Eq.* (9.69) *has a unique solution* y_{n+1}. *If we define the iteration*

$$y_{n+1}^{[\nu+1]} + \alpha_1 y_n + \cdots + \alpha_k y_{n-k+1} = h[\beta_0 f(x_{n+1}, y_{n+1}^{[\nu]})$$
$$+ \beta_1 f_n + \cdots + \beta_k f_{n-k+1}] \quad (\nu = 0, 1, 2, \ldots),$$
$$(9.71)$$

then $y_{n+1}^{[\nu]} \to y_{n+1}$ *as* $\nu \to \infty$ *for any initial vector* $y_{n+1}^{[0]}$. *Moreover,*

$$\|y_{n+1}^{[\nu]} - y_{n+1}\| \leq \frac{(|\beta_0| Kh)^\nu}{1 - |\beta_0| Kh} \|y_{n+1}^{[1]} - y_{n+1}^{[0]}\|. \quad (9.72)$$

(It is tacitly assumed that $y_{n+1}^{[0]} \in R$ and that, with any $y_{n+1}^{[\nu]} \in R$, also $y_{n+1}^{[\nu+1]} \in R$, where R is a closed set in euclidean space E_m.)

Proof. Define the operator

$$Tu = h\beta_0 f(x_{n+1}, u) - \sum_{s=1}^{k} (\alpha_s y_{n-s+1} - h\beta_s f_{n-s+1}),$$

which maps R into itself, and let $\mu = |\beta_0| Kh$; by assumption, $\mu < 1$. Then, for any two vectors u and v of R, we have, by (9.2),

$$\|Tu - Tv\| = \|h\beta_0[f(x_{n+1}, u) - f(x_{n+1}, v)]\| \leq \mu \|u - v\|,$$

so that T is a contraction operator.   For such operators it is well known that the iteration $y_{n+1}^{[\nu+1]} = T y_{n+1}^{[\nu]}$, that is, (9.71), converges to a unique solution y_{n+1} of (9.69) for which (9.72) holds.

Practical use of Theorem 9.3 is made in the *predictor-corrector methods.* These consist in "predicting" an initial approximation $y_{n+1}^{[0]}$ to y_{n+1} by means of an open multistep formula and "correcting" it then successively by means of the iteration (9.71), based on a closed multistep formula. If L_1 and L_2 denote the functionals corresponding to the predictor and corrector formulas, respectively, then they are usually chosen in such a way that L_1 and L_2 have the same order p but that L_2 has a smaller remainder term than L_1; that is,

$$\text{order } L_1 = \text{order } L_2 = p, \qquad |L_1(t^{p+1})| > |L_2(t^{p+1})|. \quad (9.73)$$

As an example of such a predictor-corrector scheme, we mention *Milne's method* [40], which uses the functional in (9.68) for L_1 and the functional in (9.64) for L_2:

$$y_{n+1}^{[0]} = y_{n-3} + \tfrac{4}{3}h(2f_n - f_{n-1} + 2f_{n-2}), \qquad (9.74)$$
$$y_{n+1}^{[\nu+1]} = y_{n-1} + \tfrac{1}{3}h[f(x_{n+1}, y_{n+1}^{[\nu]}) + 4f_n + f_{n-1}] \quad (\nu = 0, 1, 2, \ldots).$$

Here, $p = 4$ and $L_1[t^5] = {}^{112}\!/_{3}$, $L_2[t^5] = -\tfrac{4}{3}$.   Other pairs of predictor and corrector formulas are given in the next section.   See also [24, 57], for alternative formulas, and [30], for a procedure of changing the step length in Milne's method.

The number of iterations required to obtain y_{n+1} with a given accuracy is seen from (9.72) to depend, in part, on the size of Kh.   Since this quantity should be kept considerably less than unity, not more than two or three iterations should turn out to be necessary.   If more are needed, there is evidence that the step length h is too large.

We note also that the relations

$$y_{n+1}^{[\nu+1]} = y_{n+1}^{[\nu]} + h\beta_0[f(x_{n+1}, y_{n+1}^{[\nu]}) - f(x_{n+1}, y_{n+1}^{[\nu-1]})] \quad (\nu \geq 1) \quad (9.75)$$

can be substituted for (9.71) to compute the second iterate and all higher iterates.

The predictor-corrector scheme described above for systems of first-order differential equations applies also to a single differential equation of order $m > 1$,

$$v^{(m)} = g(x, v, v', \ldots, v^{(m-1)}), \qquad (9.76)$$

if (9.76) is transformed in the usual manner into a system of m first-order equations.   One would predict then the unknown function v and all its first $(m - 1)$ derivatives, before any corrections are applied.   In practice, however, one predicts only once, namely, the value $v_{n+1}^{(m-1)}$, by a predictor formula P, say, and from then on uses a corrector formula C to obtain $v_{n+1}^{(m-2)}$, $v_{n+1}^{(m-3)}$, $\ldots$, v_{n+1} in this order.   The values obtained are then inserted into the differential equation (9.76), giving $v_{n+1}^{(m)}$, after which $v_{n+1}^{(m-1)}$ can be recalculated by the corrector formula C.   If this new value differs from that obtained previously by P, the cycle is repeated.

9.9   Adams' Method

Difference methods which correspond to the generating polynomial

$$a(z) = z^k - z^{k-1} \qquad (k > 0)$$

are always stable in the sense of Sec. 9.7 since $a(z)$ has the simple zero $z = 1$ and all remaining zeros are zero if $k > 1$.   The corresponding open and closed methods of index k and maximal order are called *Adams' extrapolation method* and *Adams' interpolation method*, respectively.   The latter is of order $k + 1$, by virtue of Theorem 9.2, whereas the former is of order k, as follows from (9.66) and Theorem 9.1.

The functional L_1 for the extrapolation method is obtained from (9.66) and (9.67),

$$L_1 w = w(k) - w(k - 1) - \sum_{s=0}^{k-1} \sigma_s \nabla^s w'(k - 1), \qquad (9.77)$$

where the constants σ_s are determined by the expansion

$$\frac{z}{-(1 - z) \ln (1 - z)} = \sum_{s=0}^{\infty} \sigma_s z^s. \qquad (9.78)$$

Here, the coefficients no longer depend on k, which has the practical advantage that the index and order of L_1 can be simultaneously increased by simply adding more terms to the sum in (9.77).

Adams' extrapolation method of order k can thus be written in the form

$$y_{n+1} = y_n + h \sum_{s=0}^{k-1} \sigma_s \nabla^s f_n. \qquad (9.79)$$

The coefficients σ_s allow the following representation as a definite integral:

$$\sigma_s = \int_0^1 \binom{t + s - 1}{s} dt \qquad (s = 0, 1, 2, \ldots). \qquad (9.80)$$

In fact, since L_1 is of order k, we have, for $k \geq 1$,

$$0 = L_1 \left[\int_0^t \binom{u}{k - 1} du \right] = \int_0^k \binom{t}{k - 1} dt - \int_0^{k-1} \binom{t}{k - 1} dt$$

$$- \sum_{s=0}^{k-1} \sigma_s \binom{k - 1 - s}{k - 1 - s} = \int_{k-1}^k \binom{t}{k - 1} dt - \sum_{s=0}^{k-1} \sigma_s,$$

where the well-known relation

$$\nabla^s \binom{t}{r} = \binom{t-s}{r-s}$$

was used.   Hence

$$\sum_{s=0}^{k-1} \sigma_s = \int_{k-1}^{k} \binom{t}{k-1} dt,$$

and since k is arbitrary,

$$\sigma_k = \sum_{s=0}^{k} \sigma_s - \sum_{s=0}^{k-1} \sigma_s = \int_{k}^{k+1} \binom{t}{k} dt - \int_{k-1}^{k} \binom{t}{k-1} dt$$

$$= \int_{k-1}^{k} \left[\binom{t+1}{k} - \binom{t}{k-1} \right] dt = \int_{k-1}^{k} \binom{t}{k} dt = \int_{0}^{1} \binom{t+k-1}{k} dt,$$

which proves (9.80) for $s \geq 1$.   If $s = 0$, then $\sigma_0 = 1$ follows directly from (9.78).

As to the remainder term of L_1, it can be shown that

$$L_1 w = \sigma_k w^{(k+1)}(\tau), \qquad 0 < \tau < k. \tag{9.81}$$

For the interpolation method we obtain the corresponding functional L_2 from (9.57) to (9.59),

$$L_2 w = w(k) - w(k-1) - \sum_{s=0}^{k} \gamma_s \nabla^s w'(k), \tag{9.82}$$

where

$$\frac{z}{-\ln(1-z)} = \sum_{s=0}^{\infty} \gamma_s z^s. \tag{9.83}$$

By an argument similar to that following (9.80) one finds

$$\gamma_s = \int_{0}^{1} \binom{t+s-2}{s} dt \qquad (s = 0, 1, 2, \ldots). \tag{9.84}$$

Also, the remainder term of L_2 can be written in the form

$$L_2 w = \gamma_{k+1} w^{(k+2)}(\tau), \qquad 0 < \tau < k. \tag{9.85}$$

If we increase by 1 the index (and order) of the functional L_1 in (9.77), we can combine it with L_2 to form a pair of predictor and corrector formulas (both having order $k+1$).   This leads to the following method:

$$y_{n+1}^{[0]} = y_n + h \sum_{s=0}^{k} \sigma_s \nabla^s f_n,$$
$$y_{n+1}^{[\nu+1]} = y_n + h \sum_{s=0}^{k} \gamma_s \nabla^s f_{n+1}^{[\nu]} \qquad (\nu = 0, 1, 2, \ldots), \tag{9.86}$$

where $f_{n+1}^{[\nu]} = f(x_{n+1}, y_{n+1}^{[\nu]})$.   It is easily verified from (9.80) and (9.84) that

$$|\gamma_{s+1}| < \sigma_{s+1} \qquad (s \geq 1),$$

so that the criterion (9.73) for a proper choice of predictor and corrector formulas is fulfilled.

Adams [3] derives both formulas (9.86) by integration of appropriate interpolation polynomials.   He does not use the first formula but predicts $y_{n+1}^{[0]}$ by extrapolation of the last difference retained and successive "advancing" of the difference table.

As indicated in (9.75), the calculation for the iteration in (9.86) can be shortened by using

$$y_{n+1}^{[\nu+1]} = y_{n+1}^{[\nu]} + h\gamma_0(f_{n+1}^{[\nu]} - f_{n+1}^{[\nu-1]}) \qquad \text{for } \nu \geq 1.$$

In the case where $y_{n+1}^{[0]}$ is predicted according to (9.86), also the first iterate can be obtained directly by means of the formula [58]:

$$y_{n+1}^{[1]} = y_{n+1}^{[0]} + h\gamma_k \nabla^{k+1} f_{n+1}^{[0]}. \tag{9.87}$$

In order to use (9.87), however, one has to carry along an extra column of the $(k + 1)$st differences.

A detailed error analysis for Adams' method was first given by von Mises [41] and since then has been the subject of numerous investigations (e.g., [2, 37, 39, 43, 61 to 64, 67, 68]).   We refer the reader to these original papers or to the treatments in the texts by Hildebrand and Collatz.

9.10   Stability of Difference Methods

In numerical work it is usually impossible to carry out all required calculations with unlimited precision.   One is forced to round numbers to finitely many figures and, if infinite processes are involved, to reduce these to finite ones.   Thus, in the case of multistep method (9.49), the actual results z_n one obtains do not satisfy (9.49), that is,

$$\sum_{s=0}^{k} \alpha_s y_{n+1-s} = h \sum_{s=0}^{k} \beta_s f(x_{n+1-s}, y_{n+1-s}), \tag{9.88}$$

but rather

$$\sum_{s=0}^{k} \alpha_s z_{n+1-s} = h \sum_{s=0}^{k} \beta_s f(x_{n+1-s}, z_{n+1-s}) + r_n, \tag{9.89}$$

where the vectors r_n are "small" in norm.   If the initial vectors z_κ ($\kappa = 0$, $1, \ldots, k - 1$) differ from y_κ only slightly and if all r_n are sufficiently small, one expects that the vectors z_n will also differ only slightly from y_n for all n.   Regarding (9.89) as a perturbation of (9.88), one may then say, loosely speaking, that (9.88) is stable if it is indeed insensitive to small perturbances r_n.

In the following we consider a somewhat stronger notion of stability, which is uniform with respect to h in the sense that, if $z_\kappa - y_\kappa$ and r_n are suitably restricted, stability takes place no matter how small h.   Since

(9.88) will generally be used for $n = k - 1, k, \ldots, N - 1$, with N such that $x_0 + Nh < X$, this implies that we shall have stability for arbitrarily large N.

We say that the perturbations in (9.89) are of class $C(\delta)$ if, for some $h_0 > 0$,

$$\sum_{\kappa=0}^{k-1} \|z_\kappa - y_\kappa\| + \sum_{n=k-1}^{N-1} \|r_n\| \leq \delta \qquad (9.90)$$

uniformly for all $h \leq h_0$ and all N with $x_0 + Nh < X$. For example, perturbations such that $\|z_\kappa - y_\kappa\| \leq \delta/2k$, $\|r_n\| \leq \delta h/[2(X - x_0)]$ are of class $C(\delta)$.

The multistep method (9.88) is then called stable with respect to a class Γ of functions $f(x, y)$ if for each $f \in \Gamma$ and for any $\epsilon > 0$ there exists a $\delta(\epsilon) > 0$ such that the errors produced by perturbations of class $C(\delta)$ satisfy $\|z_n - y_n\| \leq \epsilon$ $(n = k, k + 1, \ldots, N)$ uniformly for all $h \leq h_0$ and all N with $x_0 + Nh < X$.†

In the following we consider the class Γ^* of functions f continuous on $I \times R$ and satisfying (9.2).

Theorem 9.4.‡ *A multistep method (9.88) is stable relative to the class Γ^* if and only if condition (9.55) is fulfilled.*

Before proving Theorem 9.4, we establish the following useful lemma on linear nonhomogeneous difference equations with constant coefficients.

Lemma 9.1. *Let e_n satisfy the difference equation*

$$\sum_{s=0}^{k} \alpha_s e_{n+1-s} = g_n \qquad (n \geq k - 1, \alpha_0 = 1) \qquad (9.91)$$

and denote by $H_{n\kappa}(\kappa = 0, 1, \ldots, k - 1)$ the solutions of the corresponding homogeneous equation (with $g_n = 0$) satisfying the initial conditions

$$H_{n\kappa} = \delta_{n\kappa} \qquad (n = 0, 1, \ldots, k - 1). \qquad (9.92)$$

($\delta_{n\kappa}$ is the Kronecker symbol.) *Then*

$$e_n = \sum_{\kappa=0}^{k-1} H_{n\kappa} e_\kappa + \sum_{\nu=k-1}^{n-1} H_{n+k-\nu-2, k-1} g_\nu \qquad (n \geq k). \qquad (9.93)$$

Proof of Lemma 9.1. It is clear from (9.91) that e_n must be of the form

$$e_n = \sum_{\kappa=0}^{k-1} K_{n\kappa} e_\kappa + \sum_{\nu=k-1}^{n-1} L_{n\nu} g_\nu \qquad (n \geq k). \qquad (9.94)$$

---

† For other definitions of stability, see, for example, [34, 49].

‡ Theorem 9.4 is essentially due to Dahlquist [14]. We follow here, with minor deviations, the exposition given in [27].

By considering the special case where all $g_\nu = 0$ and $e_\kappa = \delta_{\kappa\lambda}$ for some fixed λ, $0 \le \lambda < k$, we infer from (9.94) that $e_n = K_{n\lambda}$ and from the uniqueness of the corresponding solution that

$$K_{n\lambda} = H_{n\lambda} \qquad (n \ge k; \lambda = 0, 1, \ldots, k-1).$$

Considering next the case where $g_\nu = \delta_{\nu\mu}$ for some fixed $\mu \ge k-1$ and $e_\kappa = 0$ for $\kappa = 0, 1, \ldots, k-1$, we conclude from (9.94) that $L_{n\nu}$ is a solution of

$$\sum_{s=0}^{k} \alpha_s L_{n+1-s} = \delta_{n\nu} \qquad (n \ge k-1) \tag{9.95}$$

satisfying the initial conditions

$$L_\kappa = 0 \qquad (\kappa = 0, 1, \ldots, k-1). \tag{9.96}$$

For all $n < \nu$, (9.95) is homogeneous, so that $L_{n\nu} = 0$ $(n \le \nu)$, because of (9.96). Setting $n = \nu$ in (9.95), we find $L_{\nu+1,\nu} = 1$. For $n > \nu$, (9.95) is again homogeneous. Hence, $L_{n\nu}$ is a solution, for $n > \nu$, of the homogeneous difference equation associated with (9.91), satisfying

$$L_{\nu-k+2,\nu} = L_{\nu-k+3,\nu} = \cdots = L_{\nu\nu} = 0, \qquad L_{\nu+1,\nu} = 1.$$

Since $H_{n+k-\nu-2,k-1}$ is another such solution, it follows that

$$L_{n\nu} = H_{n+k-\nu-2,k-1}.$$

Lemma 9.1 is proved.

Proof of Theorem 9.4.   Let

$$e_n = z_n - y_n \qquad (n = 0, 1, 2, \ldots).$$

Subtracting (9.88) from (9.89), we find

$$\sum_{s=0}^{k} \alpha_s e_{n+1-s} = g_n,$$

$$g_n = h \sum_{s=0}^{k} \beta_s [f(x_{n+1-s}, z_{n+1-s}) - f(x_{n+1-s}, y_{n+1-s})] + r_n. \tag{9.97}$$

Thus, each component e_n^μ of e_n satisfies a difference equation (9.91) with g_n^μ as inhomogeneous term.

To prove the necessity of (9.55), we need only consider the particular case where $f(x, y) \equiv 0$ and $r_n = 0$ $(n \ge k-1)$. Then $g_n = 0$, and e_n^μ is a solution of the homogeneous difference equation associated with (9.91). The general solution of this equation is a linear combination (with, in general, complex coefficients) of the k solutions

$$\zeta_i^n n^j \qquad (j = 0, 1, \ldots, q_i - 1; i = 1, 2, \ldots, q), \tag{9.98}$$

where the ζ_i denote the distinct zeros of the generating polynomial $a(z)$ and the q_i denote the respective multiplicities. Suppose (9.55) is not fulfilled. Then either $|\zeta_i| > 1$ for some i, or $|\zeta_i| = 1$ and $j > 0$ for some i and j. In both cases the corresponding solution (9.98) is not bounded in absolute value as $n \to \infty$. It can always be made a component of e_n^μ by a suitable choice of the initial values e_κ^μ. Since, furthermore, e_n^μ does not depend on h, we can choose h so small and n correspondingly so large as to make $|e_n^\mu|$, and thus $\|e_n\|$, as large as we please, no matter how small the initial errors are. This contradicts stability as defined above.

To prove the sufficiency part of the theorem, we assume that (9.55) holds. Then all solutions (9.98) are bounded as $n \to \infty$. Since the solutions $H_{n\kappa}$ of Lemma 9.1 are linear combinations of the solutions (9.98), it follows that

$$|H_{n\kappa}| \leq H \qquad (n \geq 0, \kappa = 0, 1, \ldots, k-1)$$

for some $H \geq 1$. From (9.93), isolating the term with $\nu = n - 1$ in the second sum, we then have

$$|e_n^\mu| \leq H\left(\sum_{\kappa=0}^{k-1} |e_\kappa^\mu| + |g_{n-1}^\mu| + \sum_{\nu=k-1}^{n-2} |g_\nu^\mu|\right).$$

Summing over μ,

$$\sum_{\mu=1}^m |e_n^\mu| \leq H\left(\sum_{\kappa=0}^{k-1}\sum_{\mu=1}^m |e_\kappa^\mu| + \sum_{\mu=1}^m |g_{n-1}^\mu| + \sum_{\nu=k-1}^{n-2}\sum_{\mu=1}^m |g_\nu^\mu|\right).$$

Since $\|u\| \leq \sum_{\mu=1}^m |u^\mu| \leq \sqrt{m}\,\|u\|$ for any vector $u \in E_m$, we find

$$\|e_n\| \leq H\sqrt{m}\left(\sum_{\kappa=0}^{k-1} \|e_\kappa\| + \|g_{n-1}\| + \sum_{\nu=k-1}^{n-2} \|g_\nu\|\right).$$

From (9.97) and (9.2) we obtain the estimates

$$\|g_{n-1}\| \leq h\beta K \|e_n\| + h\beta K \sum_{s=1}^k \|e_{n-s}\| + \|r_{n-1}\|,$$

$$\|g_\nu\| \leq h\beta K \sum_{s=0}^k \|e_{\nu+1-s}\| + \|r_\nu\|,$$

where $\beta = \max_s |\beta_s|$, so that, after some grouping together, and further enlargement,

$$(1 - h\beta KH\sqrt{m})\,\|e_n\| \leq h\beta KH(k+1)\sqrt{m} \sum_{\nu=0}^{n-1} \|e_\nu\|$$

$$+ H\sqrt{m}\left(\sum_{\kappa=0}^{k-1} \|e_\kappa\| + \sum_{\nu=k-1}^{n-1} \|r_\nu\|\right).$$

Assume now that $h \leq h_0$, $1 - h_0 \beta K H \sqrt{m} > 0$ and that the perturbations in (9.89) are of class $C(\delta)$. Then

$$\|e_n\| \leq hA \sum_{\nu=0}^{n-1} \|e_\nu\| + B\delta \qquad (n = 1, 2, \ldots), \qquad (9.99)$$

where $A = \dfrac{\beta K H(k + 1)\sqrt{m}}{1 - h_0 \beta K H \sqrt{m}} > 0$, $B = \dfrac{H \sqrt{m}}{1 - h_0 \beta K H \sqrt{m}} > 1$.

Observe that the difference equation

$$E_n = hA \sum_{\nu=0}^{n-1} E_\nu + B\delta \qquad (n = 1, 2, \ldots), \qquad E_0 = B\delta \quad (9.100)$$

has the solution

$$E_n = B\delta(1 + hA)^n.$$

Obviously, $\|e_0\| \leq E_0$, and subtracting (9.100) from (9.99), we get

$$\|e_n\| - E_n \leq hA \sum_{\nu=0}^{n-1} (\|e_\nu\| - E_\nu) \qquad (n = 1, 2, \ldots).$$

Therefore, by induction, $\|e_n\| - E_n \leq 0$. Thus, for $n \leq N$,

$$\|e_n\| \leq E_n \leq E_N \leq B\delta(1 + hA)^{(X - x_0)/h} \leq B\delta e^{A(X - x_0)}.$$

Choosing then $\delta = B^{-1} e^{-A(X - x_0)} \epsilon$, we obtain $\|e_n\| \leq \epsilon$, which proves stability. This completes the proof of Theorem 9.4.

As interesting as stability is the question of convergence, that is, the question of whether $\max\limits_{0 \leq n \leq N} \|z_n - y(x_n)\| \to 0$ as $h \to 0$ whenever

$$\sum_{\kappa=0}^{k-1} \|z_\kappa - y(x_\kappa)\| + \sum_{n=k-1}^{N-1} \|r_n\| = O(h).$$

Convergence in this sense implies stability. Conversely, it can be shown [14, 27] that *every stable method of order ≥ 1 is also convergent*. For further results along these lines, see [20].

A stable method, though producing satisfactory results for h sufficiently small, may very well fail to do so if h is not small enough. This is likely to occur if the solution of the differential equation decreases exponentially, whereas the approximating difference equation has solutions which increase exponentially. Instabilities of this weaker type are studied in [12, 45, 49, 54, 70, 71].

REFERENCES

Among the books specifically devoted to the numerical solution of differential equations are those numbered 6, 13, 14, 22, 41, and 46 in the bibliography in Sec. 2.43, together with

Š. E. Mikeladze, "New Methods of Integration of Differential Equations and their Applications to Problems in the Theory of Elasticity," Gosudarstv. Izdat. Tehn.-Teor. Lit., Moscow, 1951 (in Russian).

H. von Sanden, "Praxis der Differentialgleichungen," 4th ed., Walter de Gruyter & Co., Berlin, 1955.

Various texts on numerical analysis pay substantial attention to the present subject, notably those numbered 9, 27, 29, 35, 36, 38, 48, 51, 59, 70, 71, and 73 in the bibliography in Sec. 2.43.

Among the other relevant works are the following:

1. J. Albrecht, Beiträge zum Runge-Kutta-Verfahren, *Z. Angew. Math. Mech.*, vol. 35, pp. 100–110, 1955.

2. N. S. Bahvalov, On the Estimation of the Error in the Numerical Integration of Differential Equations by Adams' Extrapolation Method, *Dokl. Akad. Nauk SSSR*, vol. 104, pp. 683–686, 1955 (in Russian).

3. F. Bashforth and J. C. Adams, "An Attempt to Test the Theories of Capillary Action . . . with an Explanation of the Method of Integration Employed," Cambridge University Press, London, 1883.

4. L. Bieberbach, "Theorie der Differentialgleichungen," Springer-Verlag, Berlin, 1923.

5. L. Bieberbach, On the Remainder of the Runge-Kutta Formula in the Theory of Ordinary Differential Equations, *Z. Angew. Math. Phys.*, vol. 2, pp. 233–248, 1951.

6. P. Brock and F. J. Murray, The Use of Exponential Sums in Step by Step Integration, *Math. Tables Aids Comput.*, vol. 6, pp. 63–78, 138–150, 1952.

7. E. Bukovics, Eine Verbesserung und Verallgemeinerung des Verfahrens von Blaess zur numerischen Integration gewöhnlicher Differentialgleichungen, *Österreich. Ing.-Arch.*, vol. 4, pp. 338–349, 1950.

8. E. Bukovics, Beiträge zur numerischen Integration, II, III, *Monatsh. Math.*, vol. 57, pp. 333–350, 1954; vol. 58, pp. 258–265, 1954.

9. V. Capra, Nuove formule per l'integrazione numerica delle equazioni differenziali ordinarie del 1° e del 2° ordine, *Univ. e Politec. Torino. Rend. Sem. Mat.*, vol. 16, pp. 301–359, 1956–1957.

10. V. Capra, Valutazione degli errori nella integrazione numerica dei sistemi di equazioni differenziali ordinarie, *Atti Accad. Sci. Torino. Cl. Sci. Fis. Mat. Nat.*, vol. 91, pp. 188–203, 1956–1957.

11. J. W. Carr, III, Error Bounds for the Runge-Kutta Single-step Integration Process, *J. Assoc. Comput. Mach.*, vol. 5, pp. 39–44, 1958.

12. L. Collatz, Über die Instabilität beim Verfahren der zentralen Differenzen für Differentialgleichungen zweiter Ordnung, *Z. Angew. Math. Phys.*, vol. 4, pp. 153–154, 1953.

13. S. D. Conte and R. F. Reeves, A Kutta Third-order Procedure for Solving Differential Equations Requiring Minimum Storage, *J. Assoc. Comput. Mach.*, vol. 3, pp. 22–25, 1956.

14. G. Dahlquist, Convergence and Stability in the Numerical Integration of Ordinary Differential Equations, *Math. Scand.*, vol. 4, pp. 33–53, 1956.

15. G. Dahlquist, Stability and Error Bounds in the Numerical Integration of Ordinary Differential Equations, *Kungl. Tekn. Högsk. Handl. Stockholm*, no. 130, pp. 1–87, 1959.

16. W. J. Duncan, Technique of the Step-by-step Integration of Ordinary Differential Equations, *Phil. Mag.*, ser. 7, vol. 34, pp. 493–509, 1948.

17. E. Fehlberg, Eine Methode zur Fehlerverkleinerung beim Runge-Kutta-Verfahren, *Z. Angew. Math. Mech.*, vol. 38, pp. 421–426, 1958.

18. W. Gautschi, Über den Fehler des Runge-Kutta-Verfahrens für die numerische Integration gewöhnlicher Differentialgleichungen n-ter Ordnung, *Z. Angew. Math. Phys.*, vol. 6, pp. 456–461, 1955.

19. S. Gill, A Process for the Step-by-step Integration of Differential Equations in an Automatic Digital Computing Machine, *Proc. Cambridge Philos. Soc.*, vol. 47, pp. 96–108, 1951.

20. A. D. Gorbunov and B. M. Budak, On the Convergence of Certain Finite Difference Processes for the Equations $y' = f(x, y)$ and $y'(x) = f(x, y(x), y(x - \tau(x)))$, *Dokl. Akad. Nauk SSSR*, vol. 119, pp. 644–647, 1958 (in Russian).

21. S. Gorn and R. Moore, "Automatic Error Control; The Initial Value Problem in Ordinary Differential Equations," Ballistic Research Laboratory Report 893, 1954.

22. "Interpolation and Allied Tables," H.M. Stationery Office, London, 1956.

23. P. C. Hammer and J. W. Hollingsworth, Trapezoidal Methods of Approximating Solutions of Differential Equations, *Math. Tables Aids Comput.*, vol. 9, pp. 92–96, 1955.

24. R. W. Hamming, Stable Predictor-Corrector Methods for Ordinary Differential Equations, *J. Assoc. Comput. Mach.*, vol. 6, pp. 37–47, 1959.

25. P. Henrici, Theoretical and Experimental Studies on the Accumulation of Error in the Numerical Solution of Initial Value Problems for Systems of Ordinary Differential Equations, pp. 36–44 in *Proc. Intern. Conf. on Information Processing, Paris, 1959*, UNESCO, Paris, 1960.

26. K. Heun, Neue Methode zur approximativen Integration der Differentialgleichungen einer unabhängigen Variable, *Z. Math. Phys.*, vol. 45, pp. 23–38, 1900.

27. T. E. Hull and W. A. J. Luxemburg, Numerical Methods and Existence Theorems for Ordinary Differential Equations, *Numer. Math.*, vol. 2, pp. 30–41, 1960.

28. A. Huťa, Une amélioration de la méthode de Runge-Kutta-Nyström pour la résolution numérique des équations différentielles du premier ordre, *Acta Fac. Nat. Univ. Comenian. Math.*, vol. 1, pp. 201–224, 1956.

29. A. Huťa, Contribution à la formule de sixième ordre dans la méthode de Runge-Kutta-Nyström, *Acta Fac. Nat. Univ. Comenian. Math.*, vol. 2, pp. 21–24, 1957.

30. G. H. Keitel, An Extension of Milne's Three-point Method, *J. Assoc. Comput. Mach.*, vol. 3, pp. 212–222, 1956.

31. J. Kuntzmann, Deux formules optimales du type de Runge-Kutta, *Chiffres*, vol. 2, pp. 21–26, 1959.

32. W. Kutta, Beitrag zur näherungsweisen Integration totaler Differentialgleichungen, *Z. Math. Phys.*, vol. 46, 435–453, 1901.

33. E. Lindelöf, Remarques sur l'intégration numérique des équations différentielles ordinaires, *Acta Soc. Sci. Fenni. Nova Ser. A*, vol. 2, pp. 1–21, 1938.

34. W. Liniger, Zur Stabilität der numerischen Integrationsmethoden für Differentialgleichungen, Dissertation, Lausanne, 1956; Zürich, 1957.

35. M. Lotkin, On the Accuracy of Runge-Kutta's Method, *Math. Tables Aids Comput.*, vol. 5, pp. 128–133, 1951.

36. M. Lotkin, A New Integrating Procedure of High Accuracy, *J. Math. Phys.*, vol. 31, pp. 29–34, 1952.

37. S. M. Lozinskiĭ, Error Estimation in the Numerical Integration of Ordinary Differential Equations, I, *Izv. Vysš. Učebn. Zavedeniĭ Mat.*, no. 5, pp. 52–90, 1958 (in Russian).

38. D. W. Martin, Runge-Kutta Methods for Integrating Differential Equations on High-speed Digital Computers, *Comput. J.*, vol. 3, pp. 118–123, 1958.

39. P. Matthieu, Über die Fehlerabschätzung beim Extrapolationsverfahren von Adams, I, II, *Z. Angew. Math. Mech.*, vol. 31, pp. 356–370, 1951; vol. 33, pp. 26–41, 1953.

40. W. E. Milne, Numerical Integration of Ordinary Differential Equations, *Amer. Math. Monthly*, vol. 33, pp. 455–460, 1926.

41. R. von Mises, Zur numerischen Integration von Differentialgleichungen, *Z. Angew. Math. Mech.*, vol. 10, pp. 81–92, 1930.

42. A. R. Mitchell and J. W. Craggs, Stability of Difference Relations in the Solution of Ordinary Differential Equations, *Math. Tables Aids Comput.*, vol. 7, pp. 127–129, 1953.

43. E. Mohr, Über das Verfahren von Adams zur Integration gewöhnlicher Differentialgleichungen, *Math. Nachr.*, vol. 5, pp. 209–218, 1951.

44. I. S. Muhin, Application of the Markov-Hermite Interpolation Polynomials for the Numerical Integration of Ordinary Differential Equations, *Prikl. Mat. Meh.*, vol. 16, pp. 231–238, 1952 (in Russian).

45. I. S. Muhin, On the Accumulation of Errors in Numerical Integration of Differential Equations, *Prikl. Mat. Meh.*, vol. 16, pp. 753–755, 1952 (in Russian).

46. E. J. Nyström, Über die numerische Integration von Differentialgleichungen, *Acta Soc. Sci. Fenn.*, vol. 50, no. 13, pp. 1–55, 1925.

47. E. Pflanz, Bemerkungen über die Methode von G. Duffing zur Integration von Differentialgleichungen, *Z. Angew. Math. Mech.*, vol. 28, pp. 167–172, 1948.

48. W. Quade, Numerische Integration von gewöhnlichen Differentialgleichungen durch Interpolation nach Hermite, *Z. Angew. Math. Mech.*, vol. 37, pp. 161–169, 1957.

49. W. Quade, Über die Stabilität numerischer Methoden zur Integration gewöhnlicher Differentialgleichungen erster Ordnung, *Z. Angew. Math. Mech.*, vol. 39, pp. 117–134, 1959.

50. H. Rademacher, On the Accumulation of Errors in Processes of Integration on High-speed Calculating Machines, *Ann. Comput. Lab. Harvard Univ.*, vol. 16, pp. 176–187, 1948.

51. L. F. Richardson, The Deferred Approach to the Limit, *Philos. Trans. Roy. Soc. London Ser. A*, vol. 226, pp. 299–349, 1927.

52. C. Runge, Über die numerische Auflösung von Differentialgleichungen, *Math. Ann.*, vol. 46, pp. 167–178, 1895.

53. C. Runge, Ueber die numerische Auflösung totaler Differentialgleichungen, *Nachr. K. Ges. Wiss. Göttingen*, pp. 252–257, 1905.

54. H. Rutishauser, Über die Instabilität von Methoden zur Integration gewöhnlicher Differentialgleichungen, *Z. Angew. Math. Phys.*, vol. 3, pp. 65–74, 1952.

55. H. Rutishauser, Bemerkungen zur numerischen Integration gewöhnlicher Differentialgleichungen *n*-ter Ordnung, *Z. Angew. Math. Phys.*, vol. 6, pp. 497–498, 1955.

56. H. E. Salzer, Osculatory Extrapolation and a New Method for the Numerical Integration of Differential Equations, *J. Franklin Inst.*, vol. 262, pp. 111–119, 1956.

57. T. H. Southard and E. C. Yowell, An Alternative "Predictor-Corrector" Process, *Math. Tables Aids Comput.*, vol. 6, pp. 253–254, 1952.

58. K. Stohler, Eine Vereinfachung bei der numerischen Integration gewöhnlicher Differentialgleichungen, *Z. Angew. Math. Mech.*, vol. 23, pp. 120–122, 1943.

59. M. R. Šura-Bura, Error Estimates in Numerical Integration of Ordinary Differential Equations, *Prikl. Mat. Meh.*, vol. 16, pp. 575–588, 1952 (in Russian).

60. J. Todd, Notes on Modern Numerical Analysis, I: Solution of Differential Equations by Recurrence Relations, *Math. Tables Aids Comput.*, vol. 4, pp. 39–44, 1950.

61. W. Tollmien, Über die Fehlerabschätzung beim Adamsschen Verfahren zur Integration gewöhnlicher Differentialgleichungen, *Z. Angew. Math. Mech.*, vol. 18, pp. 83–90, 1938.

62. W. Tollmien, Bemerkung zur Fehlerabschätzung beim Adamsschen Interpolationsverfahren, *Z. Angew. Math. Mech.*, vol. 33, pp. 151–155, 1953.

63. W. Uhlmann, Fehlerabschätzungen bei Anfangswertaufgaben gewöhnlicher Differentialgleichungssysteme 1. Ordnung, *Z. Angew. Math. Mech.*, vol. 37, pp. 88–99, 1957.

64. W. Uhlmann, Fehlerabschätzungen bei Anfangswertaufgaben einer gewöhnlichen Differentialgleichung höherer Ordnung, *Z. Angew. Math. Mech.*, vol. 37, pp. 99–111, 1957.

65. M. Urabe and T. Tsushima, On Numerical Integration of Ordinary Differential Equations, *J. Sci. Hiroshima Univ. Ser. A*, vol. 17, pp. 193–219, 1953.

66. O. Vejvoda, Error Estimate for the Runge-Kutta Formula, *Aplikace Mat.*, vol. 2, pp. 1–23, 1957 (in Czech).

67. J. Weissinger, Eine verschärfte Fehlerabschätzung zum Extrapolationsverfahren von Adams, *Z. Angew. Math. Mech.*, vol. 30, pp. 356–363, 1950.

68. J. Weissinger, Eine Fehlerabschätzung für die Verfahren von Adams und Störmer, *Z. Angew. Math. Mech.*, vol. 32, pp. 62–67, 1952.

69. H. S. Wilf, An Open Formula for the Numerical Integration of First Order Differential Equations, *Math. Tables Aids Comput.*, vol. 11, pp. 201–203, 1957; vol. 12, pp. 55–58, 1958.

70. H. S. Wilf, A Stability Criterion for Numerical Integration, *J. Assoc. Comput. Mach.*, vol. 6, pp. 363–365, 1959.

71. B. Zondek and J. W. Sheldon, On the Error Propagation in Adams' Extrapolation Method, *Math. Tables Aids Comput.*, vol. 13, pp. 52–55, 1959.

72. R. Zurmühl, Zur numerischen Integration gewöhnlicher Differentialgleichungen zweiter und höherer Ordnung, *Z. Angew. Math. Mech.*, vol. 20, pp. 104–116, 1940.

73. R. Zurmühl, Runge-Kutta-Verfahren zur numerischen Integration von Differentialgleichungen *n*-ter Ordnung, *Z. Angew. Math. Mech.*, vol. 28, pp. 173–182, 1948.

Added in proof. Since the preparation of this manuscript many results have appeared or come to our attention which have direct bearing on the subject matter treated here. While it has been impossible for us to include all of them in detail, we append a selected list of them for further reference:

1′. R. Alonso, A Starting Method for the Three-point Adams Predictor-Corrector Method, *J. Assoc. Comput. Mach.*, vol. 7, pp. 176–180, 1960.

2′. R. Ansorge and W. Töring, Zur Stabilität des Nyströmschen Verfahrens, *Z. Angew. Math. Mech.*, vol. 40, pp. 568–570, 1960.

3′. I. S. Berezin and N. P. Židkov, "Numerical Methods," vols. 1 and 2, Moscow, 1959 (in Russian).

4′. Ch. Blanc, Sur les formules d'intégration approchée d'équations différentielles, *Arch. Math.*, vol. 5, pp. 301–308, 1954.

5′. B. M. Budak and A. D. Gorbunov, Stability of Calculation Processes Involved in the Solution of the Cauchy Problem for the Equation $dy/dx = f(x,y)$ by Multi-point Difference Methods, *Dokl. Akad. Nauk SSSR*, vol. 124, pp. 1191–1194, 1959 (in Russian).

6′. F. Ceschino and J. Kuntzmann, Impossibilité d'un certain type de formule d'intégration approchée à pas liés, *Chiffres*, vol. 1, pp. 95–101, 1958.

7′. F. Ceschino and J. Kuntzmann, Faut il passer à la forme canonique dans les problèmes différentielles de conditions initiales?, pp. 33–36, in *Proc. Intern. Conf. on Information Processing, Paris, 1959*, UNESCO, Paris, 1960.

8′. S. C. R. Dennis, The Numerical Integration of Ordinary Differential Equations Possessing Exponential Type Solutions, *Proc. Cambridge Philos. Soc.*, vol. 56, pp. 240–246, 1960.

9′. E. Fehlberg, Neue genauere Runge-Kutta-Formeln für Differentialgleichungen zweiter Ordnung, *Z. Angew. Math. Mech.*, vol. 40, pp. 252–259, 1960.

10′. E. Fehlberg, Neue genauere Runge-Kutta-Formeln für Differentialgleichungen *n*-ter Ordnung, *Z. Angew. Math. Mech.*, vol. 40, pp. 449–455, 1960.

11′. E. Fehlberg, Numerisch stabile Interpolationsformeln mit günstiger Fehlerfortpflanzung für Differentialgleichungen erster und zweiter Ordnung, *Z. Angew. Math. Mech.*, vol. 41, pp. 101–110, 1961.

12′. C. V. D. Forrington, Extensions of the Predictor-Corrector Method for the Solution of Systems of Ordinary Differential Equations, *Comput. J.*, vol. 4, pp. 80–84, 1961.

13′. P. Henrici, "Discrete Variable Methods for Ordinary Differential Equations," John Wiley & Sons, Inc., New York (to appear).

14′. T. E. Hull and A. C. R. Newbery, Error Bounds for a Family of Three-point Integration Procedures, *J. Soc. Indust. Appl. Math.*, vol. 7, pp. 402–412, 1959.

15′. T. E. Hull and A. C. R. Newbery, Integration Procedures which Minimize Propagated Errors, *J. Soc. Indust. Appl. Math.*, vol. 9, pp. 31–47, 1961.

16′. V. I. Krylov, Convergence and Stability of the Numerical Solution of a Differential Equation of Second Order, *Dokl. Akad. Nauk BSSR*, vol. 4, pp. 187–189, 1960 (in Russian).

17′. W. E. Milne and R. R. Reynolds, Stability of a Numerical Solution of Differential Equations, *J. Assoc. Comput. Mach.*, vol. 6, pp. 196–203, 1959; vol. 7, pp. 46–56, 1960.

18′. National Physical Laboratory, "Modern Computing Methods," Notes on Applied Science, No. 16, 2d ed., H. M. Stationery Office, London, 1961.

19′. A. Ralston, Numerical Integration Methods for the Solution of Ordinary Differential Equations, pp. 95–109, in "Mathematical Methods for Digital Computers," A. Ralston and H. S. Wilf (eds.), John Wiley & Sons, Inc., New York, 1960.

20′. A. Ralston, Some Theoretical and Computational Matters Relating to Predictor-Corrector Methods of Numerical Integration, *Comput. J.*, vol. 4, pp. 64–67, 1961.

21′. J. R. Rice, Split Runge-Kutta Method for Simultaneous Equations, *J. Res. Nat. Bur. Standards*, vol. 64B, pp. 151–170, 1960.

22′. W. Richter, Sur l'erreur commise dans la méthode d'intégration de Milne, *C. R. Acad. Sci. Paris*, vol. 233, pp. 1342–1344, 1951.

23′. W. Richter, Estimation de l'erreur commise dans la méthode de M. W. E. Milne pour l'intégration d'un système de *n* équations différentielles du premier ordre, Thèse, Université de Neuchâtel, 1952.

24′. M. J. Romanelli, Runge-Kutta Methods for the Solution of Ordinary Differential Equations, pp. 110–120, in "Mathematical Methods for Digital Computers," A. Ralston and H. S. Wilf (eds.), John Wiley & Sons, Inc., New York, 1960.

25′. H. Rutishauser, Bemerkungen zur numerischen Integration gewöhnlicher Differentialgleichungen *n*-ter Ordnung, *Numer. Math.*, vol. 2, pp. 263–279, 1960.

26′. E. Schechter, On the Error of Runge-Kutta's Method of Numerical Integration, *Acad. Repub. Pop. Romîne. Fil. Cluj. Stud. Cerc. Mat.*, vol. 8, pp. 115–124, 1957 (in Romanian).

27′. E. Schechter, Error Estimation in Some Methods of Numerical Integration of Differential Equations, *Acad. Repub. Pop. Romîne. Fil. Cluj. Stud. Cerc. Mat.*, vol. 9, pp. 343–350, 1958 (in Romanian).

28′. J. Schröder, Fehlerabschätzung mit Rechenanlagen bei gewöhnlichen Differentialgleichungen erster Ordnung, *Numer. Math.*, vol. 3, pp. 39–61, 1961.

29′. J. Schröder, Verbesserung einer Fehlerabschätzung für gewöhnliche Differentialgleichungen erster Ordnung, *Numer. Math.*, vol. 3, pp. 125–130, 1961.

30′. L. Stoller and D. Morrison, A Method for the Numerical Integration of Ordinary Differential Equations, *Math. Tables Aids Comput.*, vol. 12, pp. 269–272, 1958.

31′. S. S. Toktalaeva, Ordinate Formulas for Numerical Integration of Ordinary Differential Equations of First Order, *Vyčisl. Mat.*, vol. 5, pp. 3–57, 1959 (in Russian).

32′. M. Urabe and S. Mise, A Method of Numerical Integration of Analytic Differential Equations, *J. Sci. Hiroshima Univ. Ser. A*, vol. 19, pp. 307–320, 1955.

33′. M. Urabe, Theory of Errors in Numerical Integration of Ordinary Differential Equations, *J. Sci. Hiroshima Univ. Ser. A-I*, vol. 25, pp. 3–62, 1961.

34′. R. Zanovello, Sul metodo di Runge-Kutta per l'equazione differenziale $y' = f(x,y)$, *Rend. Sem. Mat. Univ. Padova*, vol. 30, pp. 349–360, 1960.

10

Orthonormalizing Codes in Numerical Analysis

PHILIP J. DAVIS

NATIONAL BUREAU OF STANDARDS

10.1 Introduction

Orthonormal sets of vectors or functions have for years played an important role in many theoretical discussions of algebra and analysis. They are of great use in matrix theory, approximation theory, differential and integral equations, boundary-value problems of mathematical physics, etc. In short, there is hardly a region of linear analysis in which the employment of orthonormal systems does not lend great simplicity and elegance to the theory. Despite this fact, the use of such sets for the purposes of numerical analysis has been thus far quite limited. The reason for this is that the algebraic features of the orthonormalizing process are somewhat involved when only hand computation techniques are available. However, the current availability of high-speed computation machines with a reasonably large memory capacity has altered this situation substantially, and orthonormal systems should, in the near future, become part of the stock in trade of every numerical analyst.

Orthonormalization codes can be written with sufficient generality and flexibility so as to be immediately utilizable in a wide variety of problems. With small changes in input and appropriate interpretation of the output, such a code can, in the hands of a competent numerical analyst, be made to tackle problems of seemingly diverse natures. It will have the precise advantages and disadvantages of any multiple-purpose tool. The purpose of this chapter is to discuss the manner in which such an orthonormalization code can be set up, to outline the variety of problems that it can handle, and to describe a number of concrete problems that have been solved in this way.

347

10.2   Orthonormal Vectors and Expansions

We deal with vectors f of dimension N possessing components $y_1, \ldots, y_N$. We employ this notation inasmuch as we are frequently concerned with the situation in which the components y_k are the values of a function f at a set of points $x_k : y_k = f(x_k)$. If a vector f_1 has components $y_{11}, \ldots, y_{1N}$ and a vector f_2 has components $y_{21}, \ldots, y_{2N}$, we introduce the expression

$$(f_1, f_2) = \sum_{k=1}^{N} w_k y_{1k} y_{2k} \qquad (10.1)$$

as an *inner product*. The w_k are a set of nonnegative weights which are considered fixed throughout this discussion. As the definition of the norm of a vector f, we take

$$\| f \| = (f, f)^{1/2}. \qquad (10.2)$$

In the case of complex-valued components, we take as the definition of the inner product

$$(f_1, f_2) = \sum_{k=1}^{N} w_k y_{1k} \overline{y_{2k}}, \qquad \overline{(x + iy)} = x - iy. \qquad (10.1')$$

The most general inner product for vectors of dimension N can be written in the form

$$(f_1, f_2) = (f_1)(W)(f_2)', \qquad (10.1'')$$

where (f_i) indicates the $(1 \times N)$-row vector $(y_{i1}, \ldots, y_{iN})$ and the prime denotes the transpose. Here $W = W'$ is a fixed positive definite matrix of order N. There have been a number of problems in statistics and eigenvalue theory in which it has been essential to use the inner product $(10.1'')$.

A set of vectors $\phi_1, \phi_2, \ldots$ is said to be *orthonormal* with respect to an inner product if and only if

$$(\phi_j, \phi_k) = \delta_{jk} = \begin{cases} 0 & \text{if } j \neq k \\ 1 & \text{if } j = k. \end{cases} \qquad (10.3)$$

The components of an orthonormal set $\phi_1, \phi_2, \ldots$ are designated here by $z_{k1}, z_{k2}, \ldots, z_{kN}$ for $k = 1, 2, \ldots$. In terms of a set of orthonormal functions $\phi_1, \ldots, \phi_n$, $n \leq N$, a given vector f possesses an orthonormal (or Fourier) expansion

$$f \sim \sum_{k=1}^{n} (f, \phi_k) \phi_k \equiv f^*, \qquad (10.4)$$

with a discrepancy given by

$$\delta = f - \sum_{k=1}^{n} (f, \phi_k) \phi_k. \qquad (10.5)$$

The vector δ has components $\delta_1, \delta_2, \ldots, \delta_N$. For each $n \leq N$, the Fourier expansion (10.4) possesses the familiar least-square property

$$\|\delta\| = \left\| f - \sum_{k=1}^{n} (f, \phi_k) \phi_k \right\| = \min \tag{10.6}$$

from among all the possible approximations of f of the form

$$\sum_{k=1}^{n} a_k \phi_k.$$

Let $f_1, \ldots, f_n$ be a set of n vectors $(n \leq N)$ which are assumed to be linearly independent. The object of the Gram-Schmidt orthonormalization process is to produce a set of linear combinations of the vectors $f_1, \ldots, f_n$:

$$\phi_1 = a_{11} f_1$$
$$\phi_2 = a_{21} f_1 + a_{22} f_2$$
$$\phi_2 = a_{31} f_1 + a_{32} f_2 + a_{33} f_3 \tag{10.7}$$
$$\cdot$$
$$\cdot$$
$$\cdot$$

such that the set $\phi_1, \phi_2, \ldots$ are orthonormal. If this is accomplished, the Fourier expansion (10.4) may be expressed directly in terms of the vectors f_k:

$$f \sim \sum_{n=1}^{k} (f, \phi_k) \phi_k = \sum_{k=1}^{n} (f, \phi_k) \sum_{j=1}^{k} a_{kj} f_j$$
$$= \sum_{j=1}^{n} \left[\sum_{k=j}^{n} (f, \phi_k) a_{kj} \right] f_j = \sum_{j=1}^{n} d_j f_j, \tag{10.8}$$

where

$$d_j = \sum_{k=j}^{n} (f, \phi_k) a_{kj}, \qquad j = 1, 2, \ldots, n. \tag{10.9}$$

It is easy to see that the coefficients d_j solve the problem of minimizing $\|\delta\|$ from among all the possible approximations of the form

$$\sum_{k=1}^{n} a_k f_k.$$

10.3 The Gram-Schmidt Orthonormalization in Recursive Form

The Gram-Schmidt process may be put into the following recursive form, which is convenient for machine work. Let $f_1, \ldots, f_n$ be the

n given vectors to be orthogonalized.   Set

$$D_1 = (f_1, f_1)^{1/2}$$

$$c_{11} = \frac{1}{D_1} \tag{10.10a}$$

$$\phi_1 = c_{11} f_1$$

$$D_2 = [(f_2, f_2) - |(f_2, \phi_1)|^2]^{1/2}$$

$$c_{12} = -\frac{(f_2, \phi_1)}{D_2}$$

$$c_{22} = \frac{1}{D_2} \tag{10.10b}$$

$$\phi_2 = c_{12}\phi_1 + c_{22}f_2,$$

and, in general,

$$D_k = [(f_k, f_k) - |(f_k, \phi_1)|^2 - |(f_k, \phi_2)|^2 - \cdots - |(f_k, \phi_{k-1})|^2]^{1/2}$$

$$c_{1k} = -\frac{(f_k, \phi_1)}{D_k}$$

$$c_{2k} = -\frac{(f_k, \phi_2)}{D_k}$$

$$\cdot$$
$$\cdot \tag{10.10c}$$
$$\cdot$$

$$c_{k-1,\,k} = -\frac{(f_k, \phi_{k-1})}{D_k}$$

$$c_{kk} = \frac{1}{D_k}$$

$$\phi_k = c_{1k}\phi_1 + c_{2k}\phi_2 + \cdots + c_{k-1,k}\phi_{k-1} + c_{kk}f_k.$$

It may be verified immediately that

$$(\phi_i, \phi_j) = \delta_{ij}$$

We shall also give a second form of (10.10).

$$\psi_1 = f_1$$
$$D_1 = (\psi_1, \psi_1)^{1/2} \tag{10.11a}$$
$$\phi_1 = \psi_1/D_1$$

$$\psi_2 = f_2 - (f_2, \phi_1)\phi_1$$
$$D_2 = (\psi_2, \psi_2)^{1/2} \tag{10.11b}$$
$$\phi_2 = \psi_2/D_2$$

and, in general,

$$\psi_k = f_k - (f_k,\phi_1)\phi_1 - (f_k,\phi_2)\phi_2 - \cdots - (f_k,\phi_{k-1})\phi_{k-1}$$
$$D_k = (\psi_k,\psi_k)^{1/2} \qquad (10.11c)$$
$$\phi_k = \psi_k/D_k$$

The vectors ψ_k are orthogonal but not necessarily normal, whereas the ϕ_k are orthonormal.

The auxiliary quantities D_k are interesting in themselves in view of the identity

$$(D_1 D_2 \cdots D_n)^2 = G(f_1,f_2, \ldots,f_n)$$

$$= \begin{vmatrix} (f_1,f_1) & \cdots & (f_1,f_n) \\ \cdot & & \cdot \\ \cdot & & \cdot \\ \cdot & & \cdot \\ (f_n,f_1) & \cdots & (f_n,f_n) \end{vmatrix} \qquad (10.12)$$

The determinant G is known as the *Gram determinant* of the system of vectors, and $G^* = G(f_1,f_2, \ldots,f_n)/\|f_1\|^2 \|f_2\|^2 \cdots \|f_n\|^2$ is a "measure" of the linear independence of the vectors $f_1, \ldots, f_n$. We always have

$$0 \le G^* \le 1. \qquad (10.13)$$

The lower value is attained if and only if the vectors f_i are linearly dependent, and the upper value is attained if and only if the vectors are orthogonal. A second expression for G is

$$G(f_1,f_2, \ldots,f_n) = (a_{11}a_{22} \cdots a_{nn})^{-2} \qquad (10.14)$$

In the special case where $n = N$, we have

$$G(f_1, f_2, \ldots, f_n) = [\det (f_1, f_2, \ldots, f_n)]^2 \qquad (10.15)$$

and so

$$\det(f_1,f_2, \ldots,f_n) = D_1 D_2 \cdots D_n = (a_{11}a_{22} \cdots a_{nn})^{-1}. \qquad (10.16)$$

10.4 Coding with a Matrix Multiplication Subroutine

It is possible to avoid excess coding by using a matrix multiplication subroutine. The scheme described in this section is due to E. Haynsworth. It is assumed that we have available a subroutine which will multiply an $m \times n$ matrix stored in location A by an $n \times n$ matrix stored in location B and store the result in location C. The locations and dimensions must be specified at each multiplication. The central and recurrent feature of the orthonormalization scheme is the construction of a vector of the form

$$g^* = g - (g,\phi_1)\phi_1 - (g,\phi_2)\phi_2 - \cdots - (g,\phi_k)\phi_k, \qquad (10.17)$$

where $k = 1, 2, \ldots, n$ and g may be any one of the vectors $f_1, \ldots, f_n, f$.

This form also appears in the correction formula (10.26).   We have

$$\overset{1 \times N}{(g)} \; \overset{N \times N}{(W)} \; \overset{N \times k}{(\phi_1, \phi_2, \ldots, \phi_k)} = \overset{1 \times k}{[(g,\phi_1), (g,\phi_2), \ldots, (g,\phi_k)]}. \quad (10.18)$$

Furthermore,

$$\overset{1 \times k}{[(g,\phi_1), (g,\phi_2), \ldots, (g,\phi_k)]} \; \overset{k \times N}{\begin{pmatrix} \phi_1 \to \\ \phi_2 \to \\ \cdots \\ \phi_k \to \end{pmatrix}} = (g,\phi_1)\phi_1 + \cdots + (g,\phi_k)\phi_k.$$

Hence, if we designate the $N \times k$ matrix $(\phi_1, \phi_2, \ldots, \phi_k)$ by Φ_k, we have

$$g^* = g(I - W\Phi_k\Phi_k').$$

We also need (g^*,g^*), and this can be expressed as

$$\overset{1 \times N}{(g^* \to)} \; \overset{N \times N}{(W)} \; \overset{N \times 1}{(g^* \downarrow)} = (g^*,g^*). \quad (10.19)$$

The coding may now be based upon these identities.

The coding of a complex orthonormalization process follows the same pattern as that of the real case, with the obvious modification of working with complex numbers in the form of their real and imaginary parts.   We must insist, however, that the weights in (10.1) be nonnegative, or that the matrix W in (10.1″) be positive definite; otherwise (ψ_i, ψ_i) need not be ≥ 0, and the extraction of its square root becomes meaningless.

10.5   The Orthonormalization of Functions

In theoretical discussions of orthonormal functions, the inner product is usually found to be of the form

$$(f,g) = \int w(x) f(x) g(x) \, dx \quad (10.20a)$$

in the real case and

$$(f,g) = \int w(x) f(x) \, \overline{g(x)} \, dx \quad (10.20b)$$

in the complex case.   Here $w(x)$ is a fixed nonnegative weighting function, and x is a real variable which ranges over a certain interval. Double and multiple integrals also occur.   For numerical work, it is most convenient to replace the above integrals by an appropriate rule for numerical integration.   That is, we introduce a fixed set of abscissas $x_1, \ldots, x_N$ and assume that

$$(f,g) = \int w(x) f(x) g(x) \, dx \doteq \sum_{i=1}^{N} w_i f(x_i) g(x_i) \quad (10.21)$$

is sufficiently accurate for the problem in question. A function, therefore, is represented by a vector of dimension N whose components are the values of the function at $x_1, \ldots, x_N$. In order to avoid linear dependency, the number N of points x_k must be selected at least as large as the number n of functions dealt with. The constants w_i must account for the weighting function $w(x)$ as well as for the integration process itself.

10.6 Scaling

Overflow in the computation of the inner products (f_j, ϕ_i) can be avoided by individually scaling down the f_i sufficiently, since the scale factor of any f_j does not affect the orthonormalization process. A second source of overflow occurs in the computation ψ_k/D_k, inasmuch as the orthonormal functions may take on large values at certain points of their range even though their value in the mean is one. This must be expected in general; for instance, in the case of the normalized Legendre polynomials $P_n(x)$ we have $P_n(1) = (n + \frac{1}{2})^{\frac{1}{2}}$. This situation occurs regardless of how the f_k are scaled and can be corrected only by scaling up the weights w_k. When doing this, we must be careful to scale down the f_j to avoid overflow in the computation of the inner products. This scaling should be carried out, not in the code itself, but when the specific data are prepared for insertion. The effect of scaling up the weights by a factor k is that the orthonormal functions are scaled down by a factor $1/\sqrt{k}$. This device has the limitation that there is an upper limit to the quantity k max w_i in fixed-point machines. If the weights are initially chosen so that there is a wide spread in their values and some are close to the largest number the machine can handle, then k cannot be very large; hence the scaling down of the orthonormal functions is negligible, and overflow occurs. In addition, any scaling down decreases the number of significant figures available for the computation. These scaling problems can be avoided by using floating-point routines, at the cost of much more time spent in computation and less storage capacity left for data.

10.7 Round-off

Round-off occurs principally in the computation of ψ_k/D_k, because, when k is large, the vectors ψ_k and D_k both become small. In adverse circumstances it may be so severe as to produce a meaningless computation. Round-off may show its effects in several ways. the theoretically orthonormal vectors ϕ_k become less and less orthonormal as k becomes large; quantities in the brackets in (10.10c) may become negative, for large h, contrary to the Bessel inequality. A very good way of spotting round-off is the following. Suppose we are approximating f by 4, 5,

6, ... functions f_i. For each n, there will be computed the norm $\|\delta_n\|$ of the least-square approximation of f by n functions f_i. Theoretically, $\|\delta_n\|$ is monotonically decreasing, but it may be found that, after decreasing for a while, it actually increases! This indicates the presence of serious round-off, and the computations should be stopped at this point.

A method for alleviating some of the effects of round-off consists in a progressive "straightening out" of the orthonormal vectors. Let us suppose that we have a system of n vectors $\phi_1, \phi_2, \ldots, \phi_{n-1}, \bar{\phi}_n$ of which the first $(n-1)$ are substantially orthonormal,

$$(\phi_i, \phi_j) = \delta_{ij} \qquad (i, j = 1, 2, \ldots, n-1), \qquad (10.22)$$

whereas the nth vector $\bar{\phi}_n$ is normal but is slightly nonorthogonal to the first $(n-1)$ vectors (these last two conditions actually occur in practice):

$$(\bar{\phi}_n, \phi_j) = \epsilon_j \qquad (j = 1, 2, \ldots, n-1), \qquad (10.23)$$

$$(\bar{\phi}_n, \bar{\phi}_n) = 1. \qquad (10.24)$$

Write

$$\phi_n = \bar{\phi}_n + h,$$

where ϕ_n is the true (improved) nth orthonormal vector and h is a correction vector whose norm is assumed to be small. Expanding h in its Fourier series, we have

$$h = \phi_n - \bar{\phi}_n = \sum_{j=1}^{n-1} (h, \phi_j)\phi_j + (h, \phi_n)\phi_n. \qquad (10.25)$$

From (10.23) we have

$$(\phi_n - h, \phi_j) = \epsilon_j$$

or

$$(\phi_n, \phi_j) - (h, \phi_j) = \epsilon_j$$

or

$$(h, \phi_j) = -\epsilon_j = -(\phi_j, \bar{\phi}_n), \qquad j = 1, 2, \ldots, n-1.$$

From (10.24) we have

$$(\phi_n - h, \phi_n - h) = 1$$

or, neglecting (h, h),

$$(h, \phi_n) = 0.$$

Thus,
$$\phi_n = \bar{\phi}_n - \sum_{j=1}^{n-1} (\phi_j, \bar{\phi}_n)\phi_j \qquad (10.26)$$

gives us a formula for proceeding from a first approximation $\bar{\phi}_n$ to a better approximation ϕ_n.

10.8 Input and Output

The Computation Laboratory of the National Bureau of Standards has developed five orthonormalizing codes. Codes I and II, written for the SEAC by P. Rabinowitz, are fixed-point codes, real and complex, respectively.   Code III, written for the SEAC by J. Bram, is real and in floating point.   Code IV, written by E. Haynsworth, incorporates the general inner product (10.1″) into Code III.   Code V, written for the IBM 704 by E. Haynsworth, is in floating point.   Codes I to IV are in single precision, yielding 11S for the fixed-point routines and 8S for the floating-point routines.   Code V is in 704 single precision, yielding 8S.

The codes, as developed, read in N weights, N values for each of the n functions $f_j (n \leq N)$ and N values of a function f.   Then they compute and print out the N values of each of the orthonormal functions ϕ_i and the residues δ.   In addition, they can print out the $n(n-1)/2$ inner products $(f_j, \phi_i)(i < j)$, the n values D_j, and the n values (f, ϕ_i), which are the Fourier coefficients in (10.4).   This material is sufficient in many cases.   However, at other times, it is desirable to have the coefficient d_i in the expansion (10.8) and the coefficients a_{ij} in the expansions (10.7).   These can be obtained without additional coding by using the same code and augmenting the input data as follows (see Fig. 10.1).   Read in $(N + n)$ weights where the last n weights are zero and $(N + n)$ values for each of the vectors f_j where the last n values of the augmented vector f_j are equal to $\delta_{ij}(i = 1, 2, \ldots, n)$ and $(N + n)$ values for f where the last n values are zero.   The orthonormalization procedure will then give the values a_{ji} and $-d_i$ in addition to everything else mentioned above.   Since we know that $f_i = D_i \phi_i - \sum_{j<i} (\phi_j, f_i)\phi_j$, we have a complete description of the relationship between the f_j and the ϕ_j and hence of the relationship among f, f_j, and ϕ_j.   It is convenient to have key-word insertions which control the information printed out, since this may vary from problem to problem.

Orthonormalizing codes must frequently be employed in conjunction with auxiliary data-preparation codes, which prepare the input data. As we see further on, the inputs may consist of successive powers of one fixed vector, of the values at a set of fixed points of a sequence of harmonic functions, or of solutions of certain linear differential equations. The most frequent input, at least from the point of view of production computation, is the sequence of powers $f_j: (x_1^j, x_2^j, \ldots, x_N^j), j = 0,$ $1, \ldots, n$, and it was found convenient in developing Code III to have this input inserted automatically by means of a key word.

10.9   General Augmented Inputs

We have pointed out that, by augmenting the vectors f_i with an $n \times n$ unit matrix, we obtain pertinent information without additional coding.   What do we obtain when we augment (f_i) with an arbitrary

Vector Input

	Weights	f_1	f_2	$\cdots$	f_n	f
	w_1	y_{11}	y_{21}	$\cdots$	y_{n1}	y_1
N	.	.	.	.	.	.
	w_N	y_{1N}	y_{2N}	$\cdots$	y_{nN}	y_N
	0	1	0	$\cdots$	0	0
	0	0	1	$\cdots$	0	0
n	0	0	0	$\cdots$	0	0
	.	.	.	.	.	.
	0	0	0	$\cdots$	1	0

Vector Output

	ϕ_1	ϕ_2	$\cdots$	ϕ_n	δ
	z_{11}	z_{21}	$\cdots$	z_{n1}	δ_1
N	.	.	.	.	.
	z_{1N}	z_{2N}	$\cdots$	z_{nN}	δ_N
	a_{11}	a_{21}	$\cdots$	a_{n1}	$-d_1$
	0	a_{22}	$\cdots$	a_{n2}	$-d_2$
n	0	0	$\cdots$	a_{n3}	$-d_3$
	.	.	.	.	.
	0	0	$\cdots$	a_{nn}	$-d_n$

Fig. 10.1   Illustrating use of augmented
vector inputs.

$p \times n$ matrix T and the vector f with an arbitrary vector g?   Designate the $N \times n$ matrix $(f_1, f_2, \ldots, f_n)$ by F, the $N \times n$ matrix $(\phi_1, \phi_2, \ldots, \phi_n)$ by ϕ, the $n \times n$ matrix* (a_{ij}) by A, the augmented portion of the orthonormal output matrix by E, and the augmented portion of the δ vector by h (see Fig. 10.2).   Then we have

$$TA = E. \tag{10.27}$$

If T is itself given by

$$T = LF \tag{10.28}$$

* Here, and elsewhere, it is convenient to define $a_{ij} = 0$, $i < j$.

Vector Input

Weights	f_1	f_2	$\cdots$	f_n	f
w_1	y_{11}	y_{21}	$\cdots$	y_{n1}	y_1
.	.	.	.	.	.
.	.	.	.	.	.
w_N	y_{1N}	y_{2N}	$\cdots$	y_{nN}	y_N
0	t_{11}	t_{21}	$\cdots$	t_{n1}	g_1
0	t_{12}	t_{22}	$\cdots$	t_{n2}	g_2
.	.	.	.	.	.
.	.	.	.	.	.
0	t_{1p}	t_{2p}	$\cdots$	t_{np}	g_p

(N spans the first block of rows, p spans the t rows.)

Vector Output

ϕ_1	ϕ_2	$\cdots$	ϕ_n	δ
z_{11}	z_{21}	$\cdots$	z_{n1}	δ_1
.	.	.	.	.
.	.	.	.	.
z_{1N}	z_{2N}	$\cdots$	z_{nN}	δ_N
e_{11}	e_{21}	$\cdots$	e_{n1}	h_1
e_{12}	e_{22}	$\cdots$	e_{n2}	h_2
.	.	.	.	.
.	.	.	.	.
e_{1p}	e_{2p}	$\cdots$	e_{np}	h_p

(N spans the first block of rows, p spans the e rows.)

Fig. 10.2   Notation for general augmentation.

for some $p \times N$ matrix L, then, in view of (10.7), $FA = \phi$, and we have

$$E = L\phi. \tag{10.29}$$

The vector h is given by

$$h = g - \sum_{k=1}^{n} (f,\phi_k)e_k \tag{10.30}$$

where $e_k - (e_{k1}, e_{k2}, \ldots, e_{kp})$ are the rows of E.

In Sec. 10.12, we give an interpretation of (10.29) which is of use in numerical work.

In the case where $p = N = n$, we may eliminate A in (10.27) and obtain

$$E = TF^{-1}\phi \tag{10.31}$$

Since ϕ is orthonormal with respect to the inner product (10.1″), we have $\phi'W\phi = I$, and hence,

$$F^{-1} = T^{-1}E\phi'W. \tag{10.32}$$

If we make the particular selection $T = I$, $W = I$ (the first augmented situation described), then $E = A$ and

$$F^{-1} = A\phi'. \tag{10.33}$$

10.10 Uses for Orthonormalizing Codes

We shall now indicate some areas where orthonormalizing codes have been found useful.   The following list should be regarded as suggestive rather than exhaustive, and the reader will surely be able to augment it. A number of the following topics are discussed in detail in later sections.

1. Expansion of a given function in a series of orthogonal functions—for example, in a series of Legendre polynomials, Chebyshev polynomials, or trigonometric functions.   This is equivalent to a harmonic analysis or a "Chebyshev analysis," depending on the set selected.

2. Approximation in a least-square sense of a given function by linear combinations of powers, rational functions, trigonometric exponentials, other special sets of functions, or of sets of functions which are defined numerically by a set of values.

3. Curve fitting of empirical data in two dimensions and in a higher number of dimensions.   Smoothing.   Extrapolation.   The dual problem of finding the best (least-square) solution to a system of N linear equations in n unknowns, $n \leq N$.   In any computation laboratory, these are likely to be "bread-and-butter" problems for an orthonormalizing code.

4. Matrix inversion and solution of linear systems of equations.

5. Approximation theory as applied to boundary-value problems of potential theory or of more general linear partial differential equations of elliptic type.

6. Least-square methods as applied to boundary-value problems of ordinary differential equations.

7. Least-square methods as applied to integral equations and other linear functional equations.

8. Use of complex orthogonal functions for conformal mapping and for certain auxiliary conformal quantities.

It should be pointed out that, although somewhat more efficient codes could be devised for the problems of the above list, the adaptability of a single code to a variety of purposes is a very attractive feature. The inputs for these problems have been found especially easy to handle.

10.11 Least-square Approximations and Orthonormal Expansions

Least-square approximations and orthonormal expansions are essentially identical.   We deal with a finite interval which, for simplicity, has been taken as $-1 \leq x \leq 1$. If the functions f_k are selected as $f_k = x^k \, (k = 0, 1, \ldots)$ and $w(x) = 1$, then the orthonormalizing process generates the Legendre polynomials. If $f_k = x^k$ and $w(x) = (1 - x^2)^{-\frac{1}{2}}$ or $w(x) = (1 - x^2)^{\frac{1}{2}}$, the process generates the Chebyshev polynomials of the first and second kinds, respectively. More generally, if $w(x) = (1 - x)^{\alpha}(1 + x)^{\beta}$, $\alpha > -1$, $\beta > -1$, the process will generate the so-called Jacobi polynomials $P_n^{(\alpha,\beta)}(x)$. Because of the approximate nature of the integration rule (10.21), there will be some deviation between the polynomials obtained numerically and those obtained by an exact integration, but in any case the orthonormal expansions resulting are exact with respect to the inner product (10.21) which has been set up, and the least-square property $\| f - f^* \|^2 = \min$ is valid.

If we take for the functions f_k the set $1, \sin x, \cos x, \ldots, \sin mx, \cos mx$, computed at $2m$ equally spaced points on an interval of length 2π, and if $w_i = 1$, the orthonormalization process will leave these functions unaltered, and a Fourier expansion (really a trigonometric interpolation series) results.

If the function f which is to be approximated is given in closed form or can be otherwise computed on a set of nonequally spaced abscissas $x_1, \ldots, x_N$, then there is the possibility of using integration rules of great accuracy (such as the Gaussian).

There is also the possibility of computing the orthonormal functions exactly in certain cases and obtaining an interpolation series in these orthonormal functions. Thus, for example, for Chebyshev polynomials of the first kind $[T_k = P_k^{(-\frac{1}{2}, -\frac{1}{2})}]$, we have the orthogonality relationship

$$\sum_{i=0}^{N} T_j(x_i) \, T_k(x_i) = \begin{cases} 0 & j, k < N + 1, \quad j \neq k, \\ 1/2(N + 1) & j = k, \end{cases} \quad (10.34)$$

where $\qquad x_i = \cos \dfrac{\pi}{2N + 2} (2i + 1) \qquad (i = 0, 1, \ldots, N).$ $\qquad (10.35)$

Hence, if we select for f_k the functions x^k tabulated at the $(N + 1)$ abscissas (10.35) and take $w_i = 1$ in (10.21), the orthonormalization procedure will yield the T_k exactly.

The general phenomenon of which (10.34) is but a special instance may be described as follows. Let $p_0(x), p_1(x), \ldots$ be the set of orthonormal polynomials which result from the inner product (10.20a). Let an integer N be fixed, and let the zeros of the polynomial $p_{N+1}(x)$ be designated by $x_1, \ldots, x_{N+1}$. Then, by a classical result (see, e.g., Szegö [30], p. 46), we have

$$\int_{-1}^{+1} p(x)w(x) \, dx = \sum_{i=1}^{N+1} \lambda_i p(x_i) \qquad (10.36)$$

whenever $p(x)$ is a polynomial of degree $2N + 1$ at most. Here λ_k are the Christoffel numbers corresponding to x_k and defined by

$$\lambda_k = \int_{-1}^{+1} \left[\frac{p_n(x)}{p_n'(x_k)(x - x_k)} \right]^2 w(x) \, dx. \tag{10.37}$$

Thus, we must have

$$\int_{-1}^{+1} p_j(x)p_k(x)w(x) \, dx = \delta_{jk} = \sum_{i=1}^{N+1} \lambda_i p_j(x_i)p_k(x_i) \qquad j, k < N. \tag{10.38}$$

We may conclude from (10.38) that, if in the numerical orthonormalizing process we take for f_k the functions x^k ($k = 0, 1, \ldots, < N$) computed at the Jacobi abscissas $x_1, \ldots, x_{N+1}$ of order $N + 1$ and use the Christoffel numbers λ_k as weights in the inner product (10.21), then the exact orthonormal polynomials will result.

The appropriate zeros and weights are available in a number of instances. In the Legendre case ($\alpha = \beta = 0$) they have been listed (Davis and Rabinowitz [12]) to order 48. For Chebyshev polynomials of the first kind ($\alpha = \beta = -\frac{1}{2}$), the zeros are given by (10.35) and the weights λ_k by $\lambda_k = \text{const}$ ($k = 1, \ldots, N + 1$). Thus (10.38) yields (10.34). For the Chebyshev polynomials of the second kind, $U_n(z)$ (see, e.g., Szegö [30], pp. 343–344; see also pp. 59, 369), the zeros of U_{N+1} are given by $x_k = \cos[k\pi/(N + 2)]$ ($k = 1, 2, \ldots, N + 1$), whereas the Christoffel numbers are $\lambda_k = \text{const} \, \sin^2[k\pi/(N + 2)]$ ($k = 1, 2, \ldots, N + 1$). Asymptotic values of x_k and λ_k are available in more general situations.

10.12   Curve Fitting

We assume that N pieces of data take the values $y_1, \ldots, y_N$ at the points $x_1, x_2, \ldots, x_N$, yielding the points (x_k, y_k). These points need not be distinct and may be listed in any convenient order, but we assume here that there are at least $(n + 1)$ distinct abscissas among them. Repetitions may therefore occur among the points (x_k, y_k). It is desired to pass that polynomial of degree $n < N$ through these points which fits them best in the least-square sense. To this end, we need only select $f: (y_1, \ldots, y_N)$ and $f_k: (x_1^k, x_2^k, \ldots, x_N^k)$ ($k = 0, 1, \ldots, n$). The selection $w_k = 1$ places equal emphasis on each piece of data, but an unequal selection of weights may be called for from time to time. A similar scheme may be employed in the case of two or more independent variables. The quantities d_j [see (10.9) and Fig. 10.1] will be the coefficients of the minimal polynomial and the δ_i the individual discrepancies. If all that is required is a plot of the minimal curve, this can be obtained directly from the discrepancies. In such a case the unaugmented scheme can be used. However, if this polynomial is required explicitly, the augmented matrix scheme is convenient.

Assuming that the least-square fit of experimental data $f: (y_1, \ldots, y_N)$ by means of linear combinations of functions $f_i: (y_{i1}, y_{i2}, \ldots, y_{iN})$ $(i = 1, 2, \ldots, n)$ is given by $f^* = \sum_{i=1}^{n} d_i f_i$, the *variance* of d_i, var d_i, and the *covariance* of d_i and d_j, cov (d_i, d_j) [var d_i = cov (d_i, d_i)] are frequently desired in statistical analysis. These statistical quantities are easily expressed in terms of the quantities a_{ij}. Utilizing (10.9) and (10.21) and assuming that

$$\text{cov } (y_i, y_j) = \delta_{ij}/N w_i, \tag{10.39}$$

it may be shown that

$$\text{cov } (d_i, d_j) = \frac{1}{N} \sum_{p=1}^{n} a_{pi} a_{pj}. \tag{10.40}$$

In (10.40) we have written $a_{pi} = 0$ for $p < i$.

The dual of the above in the multidimensional linear case consists in a least-square fitting of a point to a system of hyperplanes. This may be described algebraically as follows (see, e.g., Whittaker and Robinson [32], p. 209). Let there be given a set of N linear equations in n unknowns, $n \le N$:

$$a_{i1}x_1 + a_{i2}x_2 + \cdots + a_{in}x_n = \beta_i \qquad (i = 1, \ldots, N). \tag{10.41}$$

It is desired to determine that vector $(x_1^*, \ldots, x_n^*)$ such that

$$\sum_{i=1}^{n} (\beta_i - a_{i1}x_1^* - a_{i2}x_2^* - \cdots - a_{in}x_n^*)^2 = \text{min.} \tag{10.42}$$

We assume that the system (10.41) is such that this problem has a unique solution. To employ the orthonormalization code, we take $f: (\beta_1, \ldots, \beta_N)$ and $f_i: (a_{1i}, a_{2i}, \ldots, a_{Ni})$. Weights $w_k = 1$ should be taken. The quantities d_j will be the required solution, and the δ_j will be the individual discrepancies.

In many working examples, one is asked to approximate data by, say, a polynomial. But what one may really want is, not the least-square polynomial itself, but some further quantity obtained from the polynomial, by a linear process—perhaps an integral or a derivative at specified points. If L designates a linear operator and f a function (or a vector), this reflects the working rule

$$\text{Approximation to } L(f) = L(\text{approximation to } f). \tag{10.43}$$

Now $L(\text{approximation to } f)$ may be conveniently computed by utilizing the scheme of general augmented input as follows. Augment each vector $f_i (i = 1, \ldots, n)$ by the vector $L(f_i)$ and augment f by $(0, \ldots, 0)$.

Then, according to (10.29) and (10.30), the augmented δ vector h will yield

$$-h = \sum_{k=1}^{n} (f,\phi_k)e_k = \sum_{k=1}^{n} (f,\phi_k)L\phi_k = L\sum_{k=1}^{n} (f,\phi_k)\phi_k \quad (10.44)$$

$$= L(\text{approximation to } f).$$

10.13   Solution of Linear Systems of Equations and Matrix Inversion

A special case of (10.41) arises when $n = N$, that is, a system of N linear equations in N unknowns. If the matrix (a_{ij}) is nonsingular, there is a unique solution which must coincide with the minimal solution $x_1^*, \ldots, x_N^*$ in (10.42), the discrepancies in this case being theoretically all zero. The technique of solution is therefore the same as in the last paragraph, but the following observations should be made. The δ column prints out the discrepancies from the theoretical zero which arise from round-off. If it is necessary to save storage space, we do not have to augment the input vectors in the full way explained previously. Instead, we augment f_i by the single value β_i and use a corresponding weight equal to zero. The vector f we take as $(\beta_1, \ldots, \beta_n, 0)$. If we denote by γ_i the number which then appears in the output vectors in the places corresponding to the augmented β_i, then the solution $x_1^*, \ldots, x_N^*$ is given by

$$x_i^* = \sum_{k=1}^{N} z_{ki}\gamma_k, \quad i = 1, 2, \ldots, N. \quad (10.45)$$

10.14   Partial Differential Equations of Elliptic Type

We have already discussed the principal elementary uses for ortho-normalizing codes. However, there are many problems of a more advanced character in which orthonormalization or least-square approximation can occur as an important intermediate step. In the subsequent sections we review a number of such problems.

The technique may be applied to the solution of boundary-value problems of linear partial differential equations of elliptic type. As a simple case, let us suppose that we are dealing with the differential equation

$$\frac{\partial^2 u}{\partial x^2} + \frac{\partial^2 u}{\partial y^2} - A(x,y)u = 0, \quad A(x,y) \geq 0, \quad (10.46)$$

and are required to find a function u which satisfies (10.46) and which, along the boundary b of a simply connected region B, takes on pre-scribed values f: $u(s) = f(s)$ (the Dirichlet problem). Here s is a length parameter along b. Suppose, first, that we have succeeded in constructing a number of *particular solutions* u_n of the differential

equation (10.46).   By a particular solution, we mean any function
which is a solution of (10.46) but which need satisfy no boundary conditions.   In the case of the potential equation $(A = 0)$, for example,
we may take for u_n the harmonic polynomials.   We denote by $u_n(s)$ the
values which $u_n(x,y)$ takes on b.   We then solve the problem

$$\int_b [f(s) - \sum_{k=1}^{n} a_k u_k(s)]^2 \, ds = \min. \tag{10.47}$$

To arrive at this solution using our procedure, we introduce N points
(x_i, y_i) on the contour b.   For the vector f we take $[f(x_1, y_1), \ldots,$
$f(x_N, y_N)]$, and for the vectors f_i we take $[u_i(x_1, y_1), \ldots, u_i(x_N, y_N)]$.
Weights w_i appropriate to the distribution of the points (x_i, y_i) should be
selected.   The constants d_k of the output will then be the required a_k, and
the approximate solution $u^*(x,y) = \sum_{i=1}^{n} a_k u_k(x,y)$ may be computed.
Appropriate modifications can be introduced whenever the boundary
conditions involve normal derivatives.

10.15   Some Theoretical Remarks on the Solution of Elliptic Partial Differential Equations

The numerical procedure just described must be reviewed against the
following theoretical background.   The first problem is that of obtaining a family of particular solutions of the differential equation.   If the
differential equation is sufficiently simple, then particular solutions are
immediately available.   For instance, for the harmonic equation
$\Delta u = 0$, we may take the harmonic polynomials.

$$\text{Re}(z^m) \quad (m = 0, 1, \ldots) \quad \text{and} \quad \text{Im}(z^m) \quad (m = 1, 2, \ldots),$$
$$\tag{10.48}$$

where $z = x + iy$.   For the harmonic equation in three dimensions,
we may take the spherical harmonics

$$r^n P_n^{(m)}(\cos \theta) e^{im\phi}. \tag{10.49}$$

For the biharmonic equation $\Delta \Delta u = 0$ in two dimensions, we may take

$$\text{Re}(\bar{z}z^m + z^n) \quad (z = x + iy; m, n = 0, 1, \ldots). \tag{10.50}$$

We cannot record here all the differential equations for which families
of particular solutions are available in elementary form or in the form of
special functions.   For further information on this subject, the interested reader is referred to Bergman [5, 7], Vekua [31], and Henrici
[21, 21a].   Nor can we enter into the details of obtaining particular

solutions of general differential equations. This is a complicated problem to which much study has been devoted.

The second theoretical problem which arises is that of the "completeness" of the family of particular solutions which has been selected. By this is meant the possibility of arbitrarily close approximation of the boundary data by means of the boundary values of linear combinations of the particular solutions. When the selected set of particular solutions is complete, then, as $n \to \infty$, the approximate solutions $\sum_{k=1}^{n} a_k u_k(x,y)$ will converge uniformly to the theoretical solution, and hence the numerical computation has, at least, a theoretical chance of being nearly correct. If the set is incomplete, then it may not have this chance. The completeness of a given set may be related to the geometrical nature of the boundary, the connectivity of the region, and the type of boundary data which is allowed. On theoretical problems relating to completeness, see Bergman [5] and Fichera [20]. Here we record only that, for simply connected regions with smooth boundaries and boundary data which belong to L^2, the harmonic polynomials (10.48) form a complete set of solutions for the harmonic equation.

In numerical practice one works with only a finite number of particular solutions, that is, with a system which is not complete. This directs attention to the third theoretical problem: that of developing error estimates for the discrepancy between the theoretical solution u and the approximate solution u^*. This has recently been done by Nehari in the case of the two-dimensional harmonic equation with a variety of normalizations [26]. Nehari also points out that his methods are applicable to the more general equation (10.46).

Nehari's error estimates are such that, having dealt with n particular solutions and having gone through the necessary orthonormalizations, one can then estimate the error incurred. It is not possible to use the estimate to tell at the beginning of the computation how many particular solutions must be employed in order to achieve a prescribed accuracy. We quote here one of Nehari's theorems which is related to the type of experimental computations we have carried out:

Let $u(x,y)$ be harmonic in a convex domain A and let $U(s)$ denote the values of u on the boundary C of A. Let $u_1(x,y), \ldots, u_n(x,y)$ be functions which are harmonic in A and which are orthonormalized by the conditions

$$\int_C u_m(s)u_n(s) \, ds = \delta_{mn}. \tag{10.51}$$

If $a_1, \ldots, a_n$ are the Fourier coefficients

$$a_n = \int_C U(s)u_n(s) \, ds, \tag{10.52}$$

then

$$[u(x,y) - \sum_{k=1}^{n} a_k u_k(x,y)]^2$$

$$\leq \left[\int_C U^2(s)\, ds - \sum_{k=1}^{n} a_k^2\right]\left[\frac{1}{2\pi^2} \int_C \frac{ds}{(x-x')^2 + (y-y')^2}\right.$$

$$\left. - \sum_{k=1}^{n} u_k^2(x,y)\right], \qquad (x',y') \text{ on } C.$$

The right-hand side of this estimate tends to zero if $n \to \infty$ and $\{u_n(x,y)\}$ is an infinite set which is complete in the space of harmonic functions $u(x,y)$ for which
$$\int_C u^2(x,y)\, ds < \infty.$$

The order in which the particular solutions are orthonormalized may also be of importance in numerical work. It is obviously better to insert first those functions which will approximate the boundary data in the best way. There may be cases in which one can tell beforehand which functions are better, but in general one merely adopts some arbitrary order.

10.16 Conformal Mapping and Related Quantities

It has been known for some time that the interior mapping function of a simply connected domain B, as well as its exterior mapping function, can be obtained from the complex polynomials which have been orthogonalized over the boundary of B.

Let B designate a simply connected region lying in the complex z plane whose boundary C is rectifiable. Let $w(z)$ designate a positive and continuous weight function defined on C (or on $B + C$). In the space of analytic functions which are regular in $B + C$, we may introduce the inner product

$$(f,g) = \int_C f(z)\overline{g(z)}w(z)\, ds \qquad (10.53)$$

and orthonormalize the powers $1, z, z^2, z^3, \ldots$ with respect to this inner product. We designate the polynomials which arise in this fashion by

$$p_n(z) = k_n z^n + \ldots, \qquad k_n > 0. \qquad (10.54)$$

We designate by $\phi(z)$ the function which maps the exterior of C conformally onto the exterior of $|w| = 1$, $\phi(\infty) = \infty$, $\phi'(\infty) = 1$. If z is exterior to C, we have

$$\lim_{n \to \infty} \frac{p_{n+1}(z)}{p_n(z)} = \phi(z), \qquad (10.55)$$

$$\lim_{n \to \infty} \frac{k_{n+1}}{k_n} = \frac{1}{c}, \qquad (10.56)$$

where c is the transfinite diameter of C. These results are independent of the weight function $w(z)$.

Let $\psi(z)$ map the interior of C conformally onto the interior of $|w| = 1$. Let the weight $w(z) = 1$; then

$$\sum_{n=0}^{\infty} p_n(z)\overline{p_n(t)} = \frac{L}{2\pi} [\psi'(z)\overline{\psi'(t)}]^{\frac{1}{2}}, \qquad (10.57)$$

where L is the length of C. For details on these matters and for some information on the rapidity of convergence, see Szegö [30], pp. 355–366).

Orthogonal polynomials will also arise from the inner product $(f,g) = \displaystyle\int\int_B f(z)\overline{g(z)}\, dx\, dy$. For identities parallel to those above, see Bergman [5].

The quantity c in (10.56), known as the *transfinite diameter* of B, was originally introduced into analysis in a different form by Fekete [18]. According to Fekete's original work, the transfinite diameter of an arbitrary closed bounded point set E, $\tau(E)$, is defined as

$$\tau(E) = \lim_{n\to\infty} \sqrt[\binom{n}{2}]{V_n}, \qquad \binom{n}{2} = \frac{n(n-1)}{2} \qquad (10.58)$$

where
$$V_n = \max_{z_i \in E} |V(z_1, z_2, \ldots, z_n)| \qquad (10.59)$$

and where V is the Vandermonde determinant for the indicated arguments. The identification between $\tau(E)$ and certain conformal and potential theoretic quantities has been carried out by both Fekete and Szegö [29]. A generalization of the relationship (10.56) has recently been obtained by Fekete and Walsh ([19], p. 61):

Let E consist of a finite number of rectifiable Jordan arcs. Let

$$p_n(z) = a_n z^n + \cdots, a_n > 0 \ (n = 0, 1, \ldots)$$

be complex polynomials that are orthonormal over E in the sense that

$$\int_E p_m(z)\, \overline{p_n(z)}\, ds = \delta_{mn}.$$

Then we have
$$\tau(E) = \lim_{n\to\infty} (1/a_n)^{1/n}. \qquad (10.60)$$

10.17   Some Linear Functional Equations

In the above scheme for a partial differential equation, we have satisfied the equation and approximated the boundary conditions. There are situations in which we want to do the reverse. One such occurs in the solution of linear functional equations by the least-square method (see, e.g., Collatz [9], pp. 130, 321, 384).   Let $L(y) = f(x)$ be a nonhomogeneous linear functional equation with solution $y(x)$ subject to certain homogeneous or nonhomogeneous auxiliary conditions.   To solve this problem, we let

$$y^*(x) = y_0(x) + \sum_{k=1}^{N} a_k y_k(x), \tag{10.61}$$

where $y_0(x)$ satisfies the nonhomogeneous auxiliary conditions and y_n the homogeneous ones.   We then choose the a_k so that

$$\|L(y^*) - f(x)\| = \min,$$

where some appropriate norm has been introduced.   The way these a_k are computed using the orthonormalizing code is as follows: for f_i $(i = 1, \ldots, N)$ the values of $L[y_i(x)]$ are set at a fixed set of N points, $n \leq N$, and for f the values of $f(x) - L[y_0(x)]$ are set at these same points.   The d_j are then the a_j required.   For example, let there be given a second-order linear differential equation $y'' + g(y)y' + h(x)y = f(x)$ with the boundary conditions $y(a) = c$ and $y(b) = d$.   We choose $y_0(x)$ so that $y_0(a) = c$ and $y_0(b) = d$ and choose $y_j(x)$, $j > 0$, so that $y_j(a) = y_j(b) = 0$.   Then f_j is the vector whose components are

$$y_j''(x_i) + g(x_i)y_j'(x_i) + h(x_i)y_j(x_i) \qquad (i = 1, 2, \ldots, N).$$

As a second example, let us take the linear integral equation of the second kind

$$y(x) - \lambda \int_a^b k(x,t)y(t)\, dt = f(x).$$

We set

$$y^*(x) = \sum_{k=1}^{n} a_k y_k(x),$$

where $y_k(x)$ are conveniently chosen functions.   Then the components of f_j should be

$$y_j(x_i) - \lambda \int_a^b k(x_i,t)y_j(t)\, dt \qquad (i = 1, 2, \ldots, N).$$

Finally, we mention the method of upper and lower bounds for estimating quadratic functionals (such as capacity and torsional rigidity) where an orthonormalization process occurs at an intermediate level.   For a description of these matters, the reader is referred to Diaz [15].

10.18   Experimental Computations Using Orthonormalizing Codes

We now give the details of a number of problems, principally in potential theory and conformal mapping, that have been handled by the methods just outlined.   The computations can be described briefly as follows:

1. Solution of a Dirichlet problem for a "bean-shaped" region.

2. Computation of the system of orthonormal polynomials for the bean-shaped region.

3. Computation of the system of orthonormal polynomials for a square.

4. Solution of a Dirichlet problem for an irregular pentagon and utilization of Nehari's error estimate.

5. Computation of the transfinite diameter of two collinear line segments.

10.19   Dirichlet Problem for a Bean-shaped Region (Code I)

For complete details, see Davis and Rabinowitz [13].   A bean-shaped region (see Fig. 10.3) was obtained from a freehand drawing on

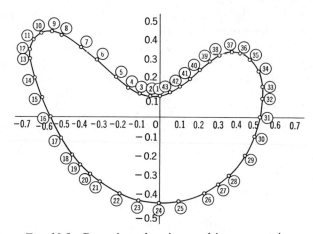

FIG. 10.3   Bean-shaped region used in computation.

coordinate paper.   The region itself is "defined" by means of 43 points on the contour (see Table 10.1).   These points are not distributed equally on the boundary; somewhat more points appear where the curvature is greatest.

Although certain theoretical difficulties occur when nonconvex regions are employed, we were interested in testing the process for a fairly intricate region.   Since the region was not specified analytically, no attempt was made to incorporate into the weights w_k [see (10.21)] a very exact line element ds or a very exact rule of numerical integration. For this region, weights w_k were taken proportional to the distance between the successive points given on the contour.   These are listed in column 4 of Table 10.1.

TABLE 10.1   LEAST-SQUARES SOLUTION FOR DIRICHLET PROBLEM FOR BEAN-SHAPED REGION

Pt. no.	Abscissa	Ordinate	Weight	Boundary value	Discrepancy	
1	.000	.110	.01414	.76089	—.0030	Boundary value $=$
2	—.050	.108	.01427	.72025	—.0031	$e^x \cos y +$ log
3	—.100	.115	.01963	.66721	—.0032	$[(1 - y)^2 + x^2]$
4	—.160	.150	.02300	.55236	—.0034	
5	—.220	.205	.03897	.40068	—.0032	Least-square harmonic
						polynomial
6	—.320	.300	.02792	.17014	—.00006	1.0017261087
7	—.400	.358	.03324	.06949	.0044	$+.997339446$ Re (z)
8	—.500	.420	.01483	.02006	.0069	-1.991187716 Im (z)
9	—.550	.436	.01423	.04590	.0023	$+1.48065453$ Re (z^2)
10	—.600	.430	.01505	.12037	—.0042	$-.00949996$ Im (z^2)
						$+.1889575$ Re (z^3)
11	—.644	.400	.01483	.22850	—.0069	$+.6236775$ Im (z^3)
12	—.660	.350	.01420	.33248	—.0026	$-.355600$ Re (z^4)
13	—.655	.300	.02881	.41180	.0014	$+.024526$ Im (z^4)
14	—.635	.200	.03043	.56168	.0038	$-.11960$ Re (z^5)
15	—.595	.100	.03076	.70060	.0009	$-.28034$ Im (z^5)
16	—.552	.000	.03311	.84177	—.0019	
17	—.500	—.105	.03175	.98915	—.0023	
18	—.440	—.200	.01809	1.12198	.0001	
19	—.400	—.250	.01998	1.19326	.0018	Discrepancies at points
20	—.350	—.300	.01882	1.26792	.0029	interior to bean
						x $Discrepancy$
21	—.300	—.344	.03140	1.33734	.0027	
22	—.204	—.400	.03450	1.44504	.0000	.4 $+.0009$
23	—.100	—.436	.02846	1.54875	—.0025	.3 $-.0001$
24	.000	—.448	.02831	1.64168	—.0017	.2 $-.0007$
25	.100	—.442	.03860	1.73582	.0015	.1 $-.0013$
						.0 $-.0017$
26	.230	—.400	.02431	1.85882	.0037	—.1 $-.0017$
27	.300	—.350	.02059	1.91643	.0014	—.2 $-.0015$
28	.353	—.300	.03566	1.95563	.0012	—.3 $-.0011$
29	.430	—.200	.03122	1.99206	—.0030	—.4 $-.0010$
30	.477	—.100	.02975	1.96611	.0004	—.5 $-.0014$
31	.510	.000	.02846	1.89648	.0041	
32	.522	.100	.01696	1.75623	.0030	
33	.520	.160	.02330	1.63625	—.0006	
34	.500	.240	.02102	1.41224	—.0057	
35	.456	.300	.01795	1.14765	—.0038	
36	.400	.330	.01147	.91523	.0028	
37	.360	.337	.01762	.78912	.0058	
38	.300	.320	.01648	.68785	.0054	
39	.250	.290	.01901	.66231	.0027	
40	.200	.245	.01901	.69067	—.0001	
41	.150	.200	.01809	.72694	—.0017	
42	.100	.160	.01677	.75642	—.0025	
43	.050	.128	.01501	.77202	—.0028	

As boundary-value data, we used the values of the harmonic function

$$u(x,y) = \text{Re}[e^z + \log(z - i)] \tag{10.62}$$

at the 43 points on the boundary. These are listed in column 5 of Table 10.1. These boundary data were approximated by linear combinations of the 11 harmonic functions 1, $\text{Re}(z), \ldots, \text{Re}(z^5)$, $\text{Im}(z^5)$.

The input data for this problem were, accordingly, w_i = weights of column 4, Table 10.1,

$$y_{jk} = \begin{cases} \text{Re} \\ \text{Im} \end{cases} (x_k + iy_k)^j,$$

$$f_k = \text{Re}\,[e^{x_k + iy_k} + \log\,(x_k + iy_k - i)] \tag{10.63}$$

Column 6, Table 10.1, lists the discrepancy between the specified values and the computed (least-square) values along the contour. It will be seen that the highest deviation is .0069. If one knew that this was the greatest deviation over the whole contour, then the maximum principle for harmonic functions would indicate that this is also the greatest deviation in the interior. Unfortunately, it is impossible theoretically to make such a conclusion (for a theoretical discussion of this point, see Payne and Weinberger [27] and Nehari [24, 26]), but one feels that in the interior these deviations are also of the same order of magnitude. We have computed the deviations at 10 points along the real axis in the interior of the region and have listed them in Table 10.1. These results bear out this feeling.

10.20   Orthogonal Polynomials for a Bean-shaped Region (Code II)

The input data here were as follows: w_j = weights of column 4, Table 10.1, $y_{jk} = (x_k + iy_k)^j$, y = arbitrary. As part of the output data, we obtained the coefficients of the orthonormal polynomials and the values of each orthonormal polynomial at each of the 43 points on the contour. We obtained the orthonormal polynomials up to and including those of degree 21. For reasons which are explained presently, it is not felt that the polynomials of degree greater than 11 are of great significance numerically.

Table 10.2 presents the ratios k_n/k_{n+1} for $n = 0, \ldots, 10$. According to (10.56) these ratios approach the transfinite diameter of the region. The convergence of this sequence is not too rapid, but the table suggests that we have determined this constant to 2 decimal places. We have computed these ratios also for $n = 11, \ldots, 20$, but have not tabulated them here. Their behavior is steady for a while and then, as $n \gg 11$, they begin to increase rapidly toward 1. This is the result of two things.

TABLE 10.2 DETERMINATION OF TRANSFINITE DIAMETER
OF BEAN-SHAPED REGION

n	k_n/k_{n+1}
0	.485511
1	.513294
2	.503448
3	.503615
4	.506216
5	.506834
6	.508043
7	.507085
8	.507510
9	.505941
10	.508073

In the first place, there is a considerable loss of significance in the co-efficients of high order, since these values have to be scaled down sufficiently to fit on the machine. Secondly, because only crude integration rules were employed in computing $\int_C z^n \bar{z}^m \, ds$, the ortho-normal polynomials themselves tend more to those corresponding to finite-sum inner product as n approaches the number of points on the contour.

According to (10.55), the ratio $p_{n+1}(z)/p_n(z)$ tends to the exterior mapping function. We have tested this out for $n = 10$. The worst agreement can be expected on the boundary of the region, where a theoretical value of $|\phi(z)| = 1$, $z \in C$, should be obtained. Table 10.3 lists the values of $|p_{11}(z)/p_{10}(z)|$ on the contour C. A maximum error of 10 per cent from the theoretical value of 1 was obtained. The average error appears to be about 5 per cent. From the values of $p_{10}(z)$ on the contour it was a fairly simple matter to trace the variation in arg $p_{10}(z)$, $z \in C$, and to verify that all the zeros of $p_{10}(z)$ lie in B. Thus, p_{11}/p_{10} is regular outside of B.

As might have been foreseen from the behavior of the ratios k_{n+1}/k_n for $n > 11$, no improvement in the quantities

$$|p_{n+1}(z)/p_n(z)|$$

was observed for $n > 11$.

10.21 Orthogonal Polynomials for a Square (Code II)

For machine purposes, it was convenient to have all distances from the boundary to the origin ≤ 1, and so the side of the square was taken to be $a = 1.4$. Since the boundary of the square consists of elementary curves, it is not too difficult to employ high accuracy integration formulas in (10.21). In computing with the square, we selected along

TABLE 10.3   THE QUANTITY $\left|\dfrac{p_{11}(z)}{p_{10}(z)}\right|$ EVALUATED ON THE BOUNDARY OF THE BEAN

Pt. no.	$\lvert p_{11}/p_{10}\rvert$	Pt. no.	$\lvert p_{11}/p_{10}\rvert$
1	.882	23	.937
2	.906	24	1.018
3	.944	25	1.016
4	.987	26	.968
5	.999	27	1.069
6	.983	28	.985
7	.992	29	.996
8	1.017	30	1.056
9	.993	31	.940
10	.980	32	1.050
11	1.019	33	1.026
12	.989	34	.976
13	.974	35	1.034
14	1.004	36	.984
15	1.032	37	.981
16	.994	38	1.029
17	.943	39	1.057
18	1.089	40	1.033
19	1.040	41	.981
20	.930	42	.928
21	.962	43	.890
22	1.067		

each of the sides a 16-point Gaussian integration formula. Inasmuch as the function $z^k = (x + iy)^k$ is, along either $x = $ const or $y = $ const, a polynomial in y or in x of degree k, this Gaussian integration formula will produce inner products which are completely accurate, neglecting machine round-off, up to the terms $\int_C z^{15}\bar{z}^{15}\, ds$. No particular use of the symmetries of the square was made, and the cyclic occurrence of many zero coefficients in the orthonormal polynomials served as a running check on the accuracy of the process at the machine end of the job. The orthonormal polynomials are listed in Table 10.4. Table 10.5 lists the ratios k_n/k_{n+1} which approach the transfinite diameter of the square. The theoretical value for this quantity (see Pólya and Szegö [28], p. 252) is

$$c = 1.4\,\frac{[\Gamma(1/4)]^2}{4\pi^{3/2}} = .826238.$$

Thus, using orthonormal polynomials of degree 15, we have secured this quantity to 3 significant figures.

TABLE 10.4   ORTHONORMAL POLYNOMIALS FOR A SQUARE;
SIDE $= 1.4$; SUM OF GAUSSIAN WEIGHTS $= 1.0$

1.0000000000			
1.2371791483 Z			
1.4937246015 Z^2			
1.7603713248 Z^3			
2.2025044571 Z^4	$+0.4230570561$		
2.6608221383 Z^5	$+0.7301295947$ Z		
3.220657584 Z^6	$+1.1572896252$ Z^2		
3.905515952 Z^7	$+1.7238789614$ Z^3		
4.737815070 Z^8	$+2.4298575834$ Z^4	$-.0188295964$	
5.737742726 Z^9	$+3.3915415979$ Z^5	$+.0646244543$ Z	
6.949286858 Z^{10}	$+4.645751758$ Z^6	$+.2286090195$ Z^2	
8.416037589 Z^{11}	$+6.274558086$ Z^7	$+.5137415655$ Z^3	
10.19384526 Z^{12}	$+8.381528538$ Z^8	$+.9916706683$ Z^4	$+.0261223727$
12.34288234 Z^{13}	$+11.102777658$ Z^9	$+1.7111406242$ Z^5	$+.0433444223$ Z
14.94442510 Z^{14}	$+14.597987726$ Z^{10}	$+2.782242918$ Z^6	$+.0869122976$ Z^2
18.09361812 Z^{15}	$+19.073026420$ Z^{11}	$+4.339843064$ Z^7	$+.1803740299$ Z^3

TABLE 10.5   DETERMINATION OF TRANSFINITE DIAMETER
OF SQUARE; SIDE $= 1.4$

n	k_n/k_{n+1}
0	.808290377
1	.828251169
2	.848528137
3	.799258916
4	.827753357
5	.826173559
6	.824643305
7	.824328492
8	.825728043
9	.825659214
10	.825719560
11	.825599896
12	.825888555
13	.825918846
14	.825950067

10.22 Boundary-value Problems for an Irregular Pentagon (Code III)

For complete details, see Hochstrasser [22].   An irregular pentagon, inscribable in a circle, was selected (see Fig. 10.4), and the following boundary value problems were set up:

1. Boundary values given by $u(x,y) = \mathrm{Re}\,(\cos z)$, $z = x + iy$.
2. Boundary values given by $u(x,y) = \mathrm{Re}\,[1/(z + 4)]$, $z = x + iy$.
3. Boundary values equal 1 on one fixed side and 0 on all other sides (harmonic measures).

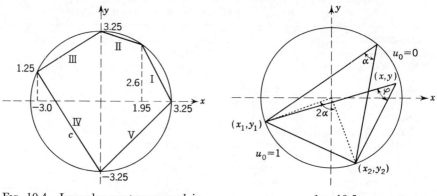

FIG. 10.4   Irregular pentagon used in computation.

ᖴIG. 10.5

We report here only on problem 3.   The harmonic measures of the sides of a polygon are intimately related to the constants of the Schwarz-Christoffel formula (see Ahlfors [3], p. 45).

In view of the discontinuity of the prescribed boundary values at two successive vertices of the pentagon, (x_1, y_1) and (x_2, y_2), it seems best to proceed by subtracting out the discontinuity.   This can be accomplished by finding a harmonic function which possesses the same jumps at (x_1, y_1) and (x_2, y_2) and using it as the first approximation.   Such a function is given by

$$u_0(x,y) = \frac{\varphi(x,y) - \alpha}{\pi - 2\alpha} \qquad (10.64)$$

where φ is the angle subtended at the point (x,y) by the fixed points (x_1, y_1) and (x_2, y_2) (see Fig. 10.5).   This function u_0 is the harmonic measure of the arc of the circle joining (x_1, y_1) and (x_2, y_2), which means that it takes on the value 1 on this arc and the value 0 on the complementary arc.   The approximation to the given values on the pentagon was accomplished by using the functions u_0, 1, Re (z), Im (z), Re (z^2), Im (z^2), . . . , $z = x + iy$.   A total of 12 harmonic functions was employed.   For the evaluation of the inner products, the integrals along the sides of the pentagon were evaluated by a Radau rule.   This is an 8-point modified Gaussian quadrature formula which involves the end points of the intervals and is exact for polynomials of degree 13 or less.

Table 10.6 presents for the harmonic measures of sides I to V the Nehari estimates (Sec. 10.15) at the point $x = y = 0$, as well as the maximum discrepancy between the prescribed boundary values and those given by the least-square solution.   For the boundary-value

TABLE 10.6   ERRORS FOR HARMONIC MEASURES OF SIDES OF PENTAGON

Side	I	II	III	IV	V
Nehari estimate at $x = y = 0$ ...	.0146	.00556	.0239	.00945	.0201
Maximum error on boundary ...	−.0520	−.0279	−.0945	.0335	.0788

problems 1 and 2, the exact difference between the theoretical value and the computed value can be computed, and it was found that the predicted error was in excess of the observed error by factors which ran from 4 to 100.   In the case of the harmonic measures, the exact values of the solutions are not known, and the predicted error must, therefore, be viewed in the light of this remark.

The values show, however, that the predicted error bound is better at $x = y = 0$ than the one suggested by the maximum error on the boundary.

10.23   Numerical Computation of the Transfinite Diameter of Two Collinear Line Segments (Code III)

For complete details, see Davis [14].   The transfinite diameter is known explicitly for a number of elementary geometrical configurations, but, in general, its numerical evaluation is attended by considerable difficulty.   For two collinear line segments of equal length placed symmetrically with respect to 0, say E: $-1 \leq x \leq -a$, $a \leq x \leq 1$, $0 < a < 1$, the value of $\tau(E)$ is known theoretically and is simply

$$\tau(E) = \tfrac{1}{2}\sqrt{1 - a^2}. \tag{10.65}$$

For two collinear line segments of unequal length, the value of $\tau(E)$ has been obtained by Achieser [1] and can be expressed as the ratio of certain elliptic functions.   For more than two line segments, a closed-form value of $\tau(E)$ is not known to the author.

The relationship (10.60) was tested to see what could be achieved by way of accuracy.   In these computations, the value $a = 1/2$ was selected, leading, in (10.65), to

$$\tau = \tfrac{1}{4}\sqrt{3} \doteq .4330127. \tag{10.66}$$

The inner products were computed by means of a 10-point Gaussian quadrature rule on each of the two segments $(-1, -\tfrac{1}{2})$ and $(\tfrac{1}{2}, 1)$. The machine was programmed to print out the coefficients of the orthonormal polynomials, as well as the values of these polynomials at the

Gaussian abscissas employed. In this way, it was possible to monitor the obvious global properties of the orthonormal polynomials, as well as to see where the accumulated round-off began to vitiate the computations. One way in which this was done was as follows. The polynomials $p_n(x)$, orthonormal over the set E: $(-1, -\tfrac{1}{2})$, $(\tfrac{1}{2}, 1)$, are alternately even and odd. As n increases, the theoretical zero values for the alternate coefficients of p_n become contaminated by round-off, and these "zeros" begin to assume the proportions of the nonzero coefficients and of the values of the orthonormal polynomials themselves (see Table 10.7). It was found that all significance was

TABLE 10.7   ORTHONORMAL POLYNOMIALS ON $(-1, -\tfrac{1}{2})$, $(\tfrac{1}{2}, 1)$ EXHIBITING EFFECT OF ROUND-OFF

Coefficient of:	1	x	x^2	x^3	x^4
p_0	1.0000000				
p_1	.00000000001	1.3093073			
p_2	-2.6843775	-.00000000003	4.6017900		
p_3	-.0000000002	-4.1140778	.0000000002	6.1932355	
p_4	7.6721535	-.0000000004	-28.177018	.0000000004	23.822212
p_5	.000000007	11.694401	-.00000003	-40.918493	.00000003
p_6	-22.558405	-.0000005	131.20021	.0000017	-230.99467
p_7	-.0000083	-34.093102	.000048	189.08749	-.000085
p_8	66.959357	.000078	-524.56943	-.00043	1435.1255
p_9	.00065	100.83287	-.005	-763.6782	.013
p_{10}	-199.48833	-.0021	1963.8362	.015	-7312.7657

Coefficient of:	x^5	x^6	x^7	x^8	x^9	x^{10}
p_0						
p_1						
p_2						
p_3						
p_4						
p_5	31.868611					
p_6	-.0000014	125.35317				
p_7	-319.27433	.000046	167.38838			
p_8	.00071	-1637.5651	-.00037	663.46546		
p_9	2022.6110	-.015	-2241.6237	.0059	885.36970	
p_{10}	-.039	12922.714	.041	-10891.666	-.0157	3521.15 97

lost when an attempt was made to go beyond $n = 10$. The last value of $(1/a_n)^{1/n}$ gave the value of $\tau(E)$ correct to within .009. Additional accuracy is obtainable only by employing double-precision coding and going beyond $n = 10$.

Although closed-form expressions for the orthonormal polynomials over E: $(-1, -\tfrac{1}{2})$, $(\tfrac{1}{2}, 1)$ are not available, such expressions are available for the Chebyshev polynomials for E (see [2], p. 287). Here the even and odd polynomials have a totally different structure. Using the latter polynomials as a guide (in the theory of domain polynomials these two sets frequently behave alike), we can confirm the slightly higher values for $(1/a_n)^{1/n}$ registered in Table 10.8 for odd n.

TABLE 10.8   COMPUTATION OF TRANSFINITE DIAMETER FROM
LEADING COEFFICIENTS OF ORTHONORMAL POLYNOMIALS

n	a_n	$1/\sqrt[n]{a_n}$	$\sqrt{a_n/a_{n+2}}$
1	1.3093073	.76376	.45979
2	4.6017900	.46616	.43951
3	6.1932355	.54454	.44084
4	23.822212	.45264	.43594
5	31.868611	.50041	.43633
6	125.35317	.44700	.43467
7	167.38858	.48120	.43481
8	663.46546	.44389	.43408
9	885.36970	.47048	
10	3521.1597	.44191	

Theoretical value:
.4330127

We can also conclude from the form of the Chebyshev polynomials that the ratio $(a_n/a_{n+2})^{1/2}$ would be a good estimator for $\tau(E)$. Table 10.8 also presents these values, and it will be seen that the last entry, $(a_8/a_{10})^{1/2}$, yields $\tau(E)$ correctly to within .001.

REFERENCES

1. N. Achieser, Über einige Funktionen welche in zwei gegebenen Intervallen am wenigsten von Null abweichen, *Bull. Acad. Sci. Leningrad*, pp. 1163–1202, 309–344, 449–536, 1932–1933.

2. N. Achieser, "Vorlesungen über Approximationstheorie," Akademie-Verlag G.m.b.H., Berlin, 1953.

3. L. Ahlfors, Two Numerical Methods in Conformal Mapping, in J. Todd, ed., "Experiments in the Computation of Conformal Maps," National Bureau of Standards Applied Mathematics Series, vol. 42, pp. 45–52, 1955.

4. E. Aparo, Risoluzione numerica di un problema di minimi quadrati, *Ricerca Sci.*, vol. 25, pp. 3039–3044, 1955.

5. S. Bergman, "The Kernel Function and Conformal Mapping," Mathematical Surveys, no. 5, American Mathematical Society, Providence, R.I., 1950.

6. S. Bergman, Operatorenmethoden in der Gasdynamik, *Z. Angew. Math. Mech.*, vol. 32, 1952.

7. S. Bergman and M. Schiffer, "Kernel Functions and Elliptic Differential Equations in Mathematical Physics," Academic Press, Inc., New York, 1953.

8. L. Bers and A. Gelbart, On a Class of Differential Equations in the Mechanics of Continua, *Quart. Appl. Math.*, vol. 1, pp. 168–188, 1943.

9. L. Collatz, "Numerische Behandlung von Differentialgleichungen," 2d ed., Springer-Verlag, Berlin, 1955.

10. P. Davis and P. Rabinowitz, Some SEAC Computations of Subsonic Fluid Flows by Bergman's Method of Integral Operators, Appendix, pp. 148–172, in

378 SURVEY OF NUMERICAL ANALYSIS

M. Z. v. Krzywoblocki, "Bergman's Linear Integral Operator Method in the Theory of Compressible Fluid Flow," Springer-Verlag, Vienna, 1960.

11. P. Davis and P. Rabinowitz, A Multiple Purpose Orthonormalizing Code and Its Uses, *J. Assoc. Comput. Mach.*, vol. 1, pp. 183–191, 1954.

12. P. Davis and P. Rabinowitz, Abscissas and Weights for Gaussian Quadratures of High Order, *J. Res. Nat. Bur. Standards*, vol. 56, pp. 35–37, 1956.

13. P. Davis and P. Rabinowitz, Numerical Experiments in Potential Theory Using Orthonormal Functions, *J. Wash. Acad. Sci.*, vol. 46, pp. 12–17, 1956.

14. P. Davis, Numerical Computation of the Transfinite Diameter of Two Collinear Line Segments, *J. Res. Nat. Bur. Standards*, vol. 58, pp. 155–156, 1957.

15. J. B. Diaz, "Inequalities and Minimal Principles in Mathematical Physics," Institute for Fluid Dynamics and Applied Mathematics Lecture Series, no. 18, College Park, Md., 1951.

16. S. Faedo, Sul metodo di Ritz e su quelli fondati sul principio dei minimi quadrati per la risoluzione approssimata dei problemi della fisica matematica, *Univ. Roma, Ist. Naz. Alta Mat. Rend. Mat. Appl.*, ser. 5, vol. 6, pp. 73–94, 1947.

17. E. Fehlberg, Bemerkungen zur Entwicklung gegebener Funktionen nach Legendreschen Polynome mit Anwendung auf die numerische Integration gewöhnlicher linearer Differentialgleichungen, *Z. Angew. Math. Mech.*, vol. 31, pp. 104–114, 1951.

18. M. Fekete, Über die Verteilung der Wurzeln bei gewissen algebraischen Gleichungen mit ganzzahligen Koeffizienten, *Math. Z.*, vol. 17, pp. 228–249, 1923.

19. M. Fekete and J. L. Walsh, On the Asymptotic Behavior of Polynomials with Extremal Properties, and of Their Zeros, *J. Analyse Math.*, vol. 4, pp. 49–87, 1955.

20. G. Fichera, Resultati concernenti la risoluzione delle equazioni funzionali lineari dovuti all' Istituto Nazionale per le applicazioni del calcolo, *Atti Accad. Naz. Lincei. Mem. Cl. Sci. Fis. Mat. Nat.*, ser. 8, vol. 3, pp. 1–81, 1950.

21. P. Henrici, Zur Funktionentheorie der Wellengleichung mit Anwendungen auf spezielle Reihen und Integrale mit Besselschen, Whittakerschen und Mathieuschen Funktionen, *Comment. Math. Helv.*, vol. 27, pp. 235–293, 1953.

21a. P. Henrici, A Survey of I. N. Vekua's Theory of Elliptic Partial Differential Equations with Analytic Coefficients, *Z. Angew. Math. Phys.*, vol. 8, pp. 169–203, 1957.

22. U. W. Hochstrasser, Numerical Experiments in Potential Theory Using the Nehari Estimates, *Math. Tables Aids Comput.*, vol. 12, pp. 26–33, 1958.

23. C. Lanczos, Trigonometric Interpolation of Empirical and Analytic Functions, *J. Math. Phys.*, vol. 17, pp. 123–199, 1938.

24. Z. Nehari, On the Numerical Computation of Mapping Functions by Orthogonalization, *Proc. Nat. Acad. Sci.*, vol. 37, pp. 369–372, 1951.

25. Z. Nehari, "Conformal Mapping," McGraw-Hill Book Company, Inc., New York, 1952.

26. Z. Nehari, On the Numerical Solution of the Dirichlet Problem, Proceedings of the Conference on Differential Equations (dedicated to A. Weinstein), pp. 157–178, University of Maryland Bookstore, College Park, Md., 1956.

27. L. E. Payne and H. F. Weinberger, New Bounds in Harmonic and Biharmonic Problems, *J. Math. Phys.*, vol. 33, pp. 291–307, 1955.

28. G. Pólya and G. Szegö, "Isoperimetric Inequalities in Mathematical Physics," Annals of Mathematics Studies, no. 27, Princeton University Press, Princeton, N.J., 1951.

29. G. Szegö, Bemerkung zu einer Arbeit von Herrn M. Fekete, *Math. Z.*, vol. 21, pp. 203–208, 1924.

30. G. Szegö, "Orthogonal Polynomials," Colloquium Publications, vol. 23, American Mathematical Society, Providence, R.I., 1959.

31. I. N. Vekua, "New Methods for Solving Elliptic Equations," Moscow, 1948 (in Russian).

32. E. T. Whittaker and G. Robinson, "The Calculus of Observations," 4th ed., Blackie & Son, Ltd., Glasgow, 1944.

33. P. J. Davis and P. Rabinowitz, Advances in Orthonormalizing Computation, in "Advances in Computers" vol. 2, F. L. Alt, ed., Academic Press, Inc., New York, 1961. This article includes a more comprehensive survey of the material in this chapter, together with an account of some recent computations.

11

The Numerical Solution
of Elliptic and Parabolic
Partial Differential Equations

DAVID YOUNG*

PROFESSOR OF MATHEMATICS AND
DIRECTOR, COMPUTATION CENTER
THE UNIVERSITY OF TEXAS

GENERAL INTRODUCTION

Finite-difference methods afford a powerful tool for the solution of many problems involving partial differential equations. The domain of the independent variables is replaced by a finite set of points, usually referred to as mesh points, and one seeks to determine approximate values for the desired solution at these points. The values at the mesh points are required to satisfy difference equations obtained either by replacing partial derivatives by partial difference quotients or by certain other more sophisticated techniques.

In practice, the decision regarding how many mesh points should be used to achieve a desired accuracy is usually based on intuition and experience, since practical error estimates are not available. Sometimes approximate solutions are obtained with two different sets of mesh points, one a refinement of the other, and the results compared, it being assumed that the accuracy of either of the two approximate solutions is about the same as the difference between them. The main problem from the computational standpoint, however, and the one primarily

* The chapter was written while the author was on the staff of the Ramo-Wooldridge Corporation, Los Angeles, Calif. It was submitted on June 9, 1958, and revised on May 21, 1959; some further changes have been made during the printing. The author wishes to acknowledge the helpful criticisms and suggestions of the following: Dr. S. D. Conte; Prof. G. E. Forsythe; Dr. L. D. Gates; Prof. P. Henrici; Dr. J. D. Riley; Dr. J. W. Sheldon; Prof. R. S. Varga; Dr. W. Kahan; and E. L. Wachspress.

considered here, is that of actually computing the solution of the difference equation.   For an elliptic equation the problem is that of solving a system of linear algebraic equations

$$Au + d = 0, \tag{11.1}$$

whereas for parabolic equations one has to solve a system of ordinary differential equations

$$\frac{du}{dt} = Au + d. \tag{11.2}$$

Here A is a given square matrix, d is a given column matrix, and u is an unknown column matrix.

It is not difficult to show that the matrix A in (11.1) is nonsingular and hence that a unique solution exists.   However, since there is one equation for each mesh point and since there may be several thousand mesh points, great care must be taken in the choice of the method for solving (11.1), lest the computing time, even for a very fast computing machine, becomes excessive.   Iterative methods are indicated because of the large number of zero elements of A and are nearly always used. With such methods one guesses an initial approximation to the solution of (11.1) and successively modifies this approximate solution, according to a given rule, until convergence has been achieved to within a prescribed tolerance.   The primary purpose of the first part of this chapter, Secs. 11.1 to 11.13, is to describe a number of iterative methods and to give results on the rates of convergence of these methods.   Methods for setting up finite-difference analogues for problems involving elliptic equations are also discussed in this part.

Depending on what numerical procedure is used to solve (11.2), it may or may not be necessary to solve systems of linear algebraic equations. With "explicit" methods no such systems are involved.   However, in such cases the increment in t is limited by stability considerations.   Such limitations can be partially or wholly removed by use of "implicit" methods, which may, however, involve solving systems of equations.   The second part, Secs. 11.14 to 11.18, describes explicit and implicit methods for solving parabolic equations with one or two space variables in addition to the time variable.   Also contained in this part is a discussion of the relation of some of these methods to certain iterative methods for solving problems involving elliptic equations.

ELLIPTIC EQUATIONS

11.1   Introduction

As already noted, the rate of convergence of the iterative method used is of critical importance in the solution of a boundary-value problem

involving a linear elliptic partial differential equation.   Following introductory discussions in Secs. 11.2 to 11.4 on the setting up of finite-
difference analogues of such problems and on the accuracy of the
numerical solutions, we present in Secs. 11.5 to 11.7 discussions of
several iterative methods.   Point iterative methods such as the Gauss-
Seidel method and the successive-overrelaxation method are considered
as well as line relaxation methods and an alternating-direction implicit
method.   The various methods are described, and rules and suggestions
are given for their use and for estimating the convergence rates.   Theoretical discussions are postponed until Secs. 11.8 to 11.12.   Here, discussions of the theory on which some of the methods are based are given,
together with some proofs.   Certain generalizations and extensions are
given, particularly for the successive-overrelaxation method.   The
reader who is interested in the use of the methods but not in the underlying theory can omit these later sections.   Applications and numerical
experiences are described in Sec. 11.13.

11.2   Boundary-value Problems

We restrict our attention here to the following class of problems.   Let
R be a bounded plane region with boundary S and let f be a function
defined and continuous on S.   Find a function $U(x,y)$ which is continuous on $R + S$, is twice differentiable in R, satisfies in R the linear
second-order partial differential equation

$$AU_{xx} + CU_{yy} + DU_x + EU_y + FU = G, \qquad (11.3)$$

and satisfies on S the condition

$$U = f. \qquad (11.4)$$

Here A, C, D, E, F, and G are analytic functions of the independent
variables x and y in R and satisfy in $R + S$ the conditions $A > 0, C > 0$,
$F \leq 0$.   Because of the conditions on A and C, Eq. (11.3) is said to be
elliptic.   More generally, an equation of the form

$$AU_{xx} + 2BU_{xy} + CU_{yy} = D(x,y,U,U_x,U_y) \qquad (11.5)$$

is said to be elliptic in R if $B^2 - AC < 0$ in R.   We remark that, by
introducing new variables ξ and η satisfying the conditions

$$\frac{\xi_y}{\xi_x} = \sqrt{\frac{A}{C}}, \qquad \frac{\eta_y}{\eta_x} = -\sqrt{\frac{A}{C}}, \qquad (11.6)$$

we obtain an equation of the form

$$\alpha U_{\xi\xi} + \gamma U_{\eta\eta} = \delta(\xi,\eta,U,U_\xi,U_\eta), \qquad (11.7)$$

where $\alpha > 0, \gamma > 0$ in R', the region in the (ξ,η) plane corresponding
to R.   Equation (11.7) is similar to (11.3) as far as the terms involving

the second-order derivatives are concerned. Much of our subsequent discussion applies to (11.7) as well as to (11.3). Much of our later discussion also applies to cases where, instead of prescribing U on S, we prescribe the normal derivative $\partial U/\partial n$ or a linear combination of U and $\partial U/\partial n$.

11.3 Construction of the Difference-equation Analogue

Since the problems formulated in Sec. 11.2 cannot be solved analytically except in a very few special cases, it is usually necessary to resort to approximate numerical methods. Of these, the method of finite differences seems best adapted for the solution of most problems on high-speed computers.

Let $(\bar{x}, \bar{y})$ denote an arbitrary but fixed point in the (x, y) plane and let h be a fixed positive number, which we call the *mesh size*. Let Σ_h denote the set of points (x, y) such that both $h^{-1}(x - \bar{x})$ and $h^{-1}(y - \bar{y})$ are integers. Two points (x, y) and (x', y') of Σ_h are *adjacent* if $(x - x')^2 + (y - y')^2 = h^2$. We let R_h denote the set of all points belonging to both Σ_h and R. Points of R_h are called *interior net points*. We determine the set S_h of *boundary net points* as follows. For each point (x, y) of R_h, consider the 4 adjacent points of Σ_h, which we denote by $(x_i, y_i), i = 1, 2, 3, 4$. For each i, consider the open line segment l_i joining (x, y) to (x_i, y_i). Three cases can occur:

1. If l_i does not intersect S and if (x_i, y_i) is a point of R_h, then no point of S_h belongs to l_i.

2. If l_i does not intersect S and if (x_i, y_i) is a point of S, then (x_i, y_i) is a point of S_h.

3. If l_i intersects S, then we let the point of intersection nearest to (x_i, y_i) belong to S_h. The set S_h consists of all points found by considering each point of R_h and the corresponding four line segments l_i.

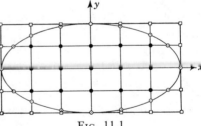

FIG. 11.1

As an example, consider the ellipse $(x/3)^2 + (y/2)^2 = 1$, with $\bar{x} = \bar{y} = 0$ and with $h = 1$ (Fig. 11.1). Points of R_h and S_h are indicated by solid black circles ● and open circles ○, respectively. Points of Σ_h not belonging to R_h or S_h are *exterior points* and are indicated by open squares □.

The simplest and most direct method of deriving a difference-equation representation of (11.3) is to replace the partial derivatives by suitable difference quotients involving the values of U at points of R_h and/or S_h. If this is done for each point of R_h, one then obtains a system of N linear algebraic equations involving the N unknown values of U at points of R_h. We recall that the values of U at the boundary points of S_h are given.

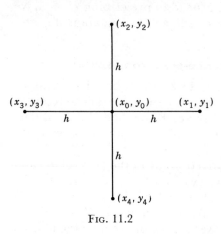

FIG. 11.2

To illustrate the derivation of the difference equations, let us first consider a point (x_0, y_0) of R_h such that the 4 adjacent points in Σ_h also belong either to R_h or to S_h. Such a point is known as a *regular point*. We seek to determine a difference expression corresponding to (11.3) which involves values of U corresponding to the 5 points shown in Fig. 11.2. Clearly more accurate difference expressions could be found if one were to consider additional points, but at the sacrifice of simplicity.

We first obtain difference quotients corresponding to U_{xx}. These difference quotients involve U_0, U_1, U_3, where we let $U_i = U(x_i, y_i)$, $i = 0, 1, 2, 3, 4$. Similarly, we let $(U_x)_i = U_x(x_i, y_i)$, etc. Assuming that $U(x, y)$ has continuous partial derivatives of fourth order in a sufficiently large neighborhood about (x_0, y_0), we have, by Taylor's theorem,

$$U_1 = U_0 + (U_x)_0 h + (U_{xx})_0 \frac{h^2}{2} + (U_{xxx})_0 \frac{h^3}{3!} + (\bar{U}_{xxxx})_{0,1} \frac{h^4}{4!}, \quad (11.8)$$

where $(\bar{U}_{xxxx})_{0,1} = U_{xxxx}(\xi, y_0)$,

where $x_0 < \xi < x_1$.

Similarly,

$$U_3 = U_0 - (U_x)_0 h + (U_{xx})_0 \frac{h^2}{2} - (U_{xxx})_0 \frac{h^3}{3!} + (\bar{U}_{xxxx})_{0,3} \frac{h^4}{4!}. \quad (11.9)$$

Combining (11.8) and (11.9), we have

$$(U_{xx})_0 = \frac{U_1 + U_3 - 2U_0}{h^2} - \frac{h^2}{4!} [(\bar{U}_{xxxx})_{0,1} + (\bar{U}_{xxxx})_{0,3}]. \quad (11.10)$$

Using the same method, we can also obtain the following:

$$(U_{yy})_0 = \frac{U_2 + U_4 - 2U_0}{h^2} - \frac{h^2}{4!} [(\bar{U}_{yyyy})_{0,2} + (\bar{U}_{yyyy})_{0,4}], \quad (11.11)$$

$$(U_x)_0 = \frac{U_1 - U_3}{2h} - \frac{h^2}{12} [(\bar{U}_{xxx})_{0,1} + (\bar{U}_{xxx})_{0,3}], \quad (11.12)$$

$$(U_y)_0 = \frac{U_2 - U_4}{2h} - \frac{h^2}{12} [(\bar{U}_{yyy})_{0,2} + (\bar{U}_{yyy})_{0,4}]. \quad (11.13)$$

Neglecting the remainder terms in (11.10) to (11.13) and substituting in (11.8), we obtain for each regular point (x, y) in R_h the difference equation

$$(A + \tfrac{1}{2}Dh)U(x + h, y) + (A - \tfrac{1}{2}Dh)U(x - h, y)$$
$$+ (C + \tfrac{1}{2}Eh)U(x, y + h) + (C - \tfrac{1}{2}Eh)U(x, y - h)$$
$$- 2(A + C - \tfrac{1}{2}Fh^2)U(x, y) = Gh^2, \quad (11.14)$$

where A, C, D, E, F, and G are to be evaluated at (x, y).   Writing (11.14) in the form

$$\alpha_1 U(x + h, y) + \alpha_3 U(x - h, y) + \alpha_2 U(x, y + h)$$
$$+ \alpha_4 U(x, y - h) - \alpha_0 U(x, y) = t(x, y), \quad (11.15)$$

where the α_i $(i = 0, 1, 2, 3, 4)$ are functions of (x, y), we observe that, because $A > 0, C > 0$, and $F \leq 0$,

$$\alpha_0 \geq \alpha_1 + \alpha_2 + \alpha_3 + \alpha_4. \quad (11.16)$$

Even for *irregular points* of R_h, that is, points of R_h which are not regular points, we can write the difference equation in the form (11.15).   Thus, if $x_1 - x_0 = s_1 h, x_0 - x_3 = s_3 h$, where $0 < s_1 \leq 1, 0 < s_3 \leq 1$, we can, with the aid of Taylor's theorem, easily derive the following formulas:

$$(U_x)_0 \doteq h^{-1}\left[\frac{s_3}{s_1(s_1 + s_3)} U_1 - \frac{s_1}{s_3(s_1 + s_3)} U_3 - \frac{s_3 - s_1}{s_1 s_3} U_0\right], \quad (11.17)$$

$$(U_{xx})_0 \doteq 2h^{-2}\left[\frac{1}{s_1(s_1 + s_3)} U_1 + \frac{1}{s_3(s_1 + s_3)} U_3 - \frac{1}{s_1 s_3} U_0\right]. \quad (11.18)$$

Similar expressions can be derived for $(U_y)_0$ and $(U_{yy})_0$.   If the resulting expressions are substituted into (11.3), one obtains

$$\alpha_1 U(x + s_1 h, y) + \alpha_3 U(x - s_3 h, y) + \alpha_2 U(x, y + s_2 h)$$
$$+ \alpha_4 U(x, y - s_4 h) - \alpha_0 U(x, y) = t(x, y), \quad (11.19)$$

where

$$\alpha_1 = \frac{2A}{s_1(s_1 + s_3)} + \frac{hs_3 D}{s_1(s_1 + s_3)}, \qquad \alpha_3 = \frac{2A}{s_3(s_1 + s_3)} - \frac{hs_1 D}{s_3(s_1 + s_3)},$$

$$\alpha_2 = \frac{2C}{s_2(s_2 + s_4)} + \frac{hs_4 E}{s_2(s_2 + s_4)}, \qquad \alpha_4 = \frac{2C}{s_4(s_2 + s_4)} - \frac{hs_2 E}{s_4(s_2 + s_4)},$$

$$\alpha_0 = \alpha_1 + \alpha_2 + \alpha_3 + \alpha_4 - Fh^2, \qquad t = Gh^2. \quad (11.20)$$

The proof of the existence of a unique solution of the difference equation and of the convergence of many of the numerical procedures for solving the difference equation is greatly simplified if the α_i appearing in

(11.15) are all positive.   Evidently all the α_i will be positive provided h is chosen so small that

$$h < \min \left\{ \frac{2A}{|D|}, \frac{2C}{|E|} \right\}, \tag{11.21}$$

the minimum being taken over all points of $R + S$.   Since $A > 0, C > 0$, and since A, C, D, E are continuous and hence bounded in $R + S$, it is clear that a positive minimum exists.

In the important special case in which (11.3) is *essentially self-adjoint*, that is, the case in which

$$\left(\frac{D - A_x}{A} \right)_y = \left(\frac{E - C_y}{C} \right)_x, \tag{11.22}$$

one can obtain a difference equation for which local accuracy is as good as that for (11.14), both for regular and for irregular points, and for which the coefficients α_i are positive for all $h > 0$.   Moreover, if there are no irregular points in R_h, the difference equation is *symmetric*, in the sense that the coefficient of $U(x',y')$ in the equation for (x,y) is the same as the coefficient of $U(x,y)$ in the equation for (x',y').   In such a case the matrix of the linear system corresponding to the difference equation would be symmetric.

We recall that an equation of the form (11.3) is *self-adjoint* if it can be written in the form

$$(AU_x)_x + (CU_y)_y + FU = G. \tag{11.23}$$

In order for this to be possible, it is clearly necessary and sufficient that we have

$$D = A_x, \qquad E = C_y. \tag{11.24}$$

Now the condition (11.22) guarantees the existence of a function $\mu(x,y)$ such that, if both sides of (11.3) are multiplied by $\mu(x,y)$, then the resulting equation is self-adjoint.   In our present discussion we assume that the process of finding $\mu(x,y)$ has been carried out and that the differential equation has been reduced to the form (11.23).

In deriving the difference equation for the neighborhood configuration shown in Fig. 11.2, we use difference representations of the following form:

$$(AU_x)_x = \frac{A(x + \frac{1}{2}s_1 h, y)\left(\dfrac{U_1 - U_0}{s_1 h} \right) - A(x - \frac{1}{2}s_3 h, y)\left(\dfrac{U_0 - U_3}{s_3 h} \right)}{\left(\dfrac{s_1 + s_3}{2} \right) h}$$

$$\tag{11.25}$$

and derive a difference equation

$$\alpha_1 U(x + s_1 h, y) + \alpha_3 U(x - s_3 h, y) + \alpha_2 U(x, y + s_2 h) + \alpha_4 U(x, y - s_4 h)$$
$$- \alpha_0 U(x, y) = t(x, y)$$

where $\quad \alpha_1 = \dfrac{A(x + \tfrac{1}{2} s_1 h, y)}{s_1 (s_1 + s_3)}, \qquad \alpha_2 = \dfrac{C(x, y + \tfrac{1}{2} s_2 h)}{s_2 (s_2 + s_4)},$

$$\alpha_3 = \dfrac{A(x - \tfrac{1}{2} s_3 h, y)}{s_3 (s_1 + s_3)}, \qquad \alpha_4 = \dfrac{C(x, y - \tfrac{1}{2} s_4 h)}{s_4 (s_2 + s_4)}, \qquad (11.26)$$

$$\alpha_0 = \alpha_1 + \alpha_2 + \alpha_3 + \alpha_4 - \tfrac{1}{2} h^2 F(x, y), \qquad t = \tfrac{1}{2} h^2 G(x, y).$$

We remark that, if there are irregular points in R_h, then the matrix of the linear system which one obtains will not in general be symmetric. This is probably not a serious disadvantage as far as the convergence rate of the iterative process is concerned. However, one could obtain a symmetric difference equation by using variational methods. We note that the problem of solving (11.23) in R with prescribed boundary values on S is equivalent to that of minimizing the integral

$$\iint\limits_{R} (A U_x{}^2 + C U_y{}^2 - F U^2 + 2 G U) \; dx \; dy$$

subject to the same boundary conditions. Now, if one represents the above integral by an expression involving appropriate sums of difference quotients, one obtains a quadratic form. The conditions for minimizing this quadratic form lead to Eqs. (11.15) and (11.26) for regular points and to somewhat more complicated equations for irregular points. The matrix of the system of equations is symmetric.

The methods just described are by no means the only methods for deriving the difference equations. One can, for instance, seek to represent the differential operator by a linear combination of functional values at neighboring points. By the use of Taylor series, one determines the coefficients occurring in the linear combination, in order to achieve the greatest local accuracy. Greater accuracy can sometimes be obtained by using the fact that the derivatives of the solution of the differential equation are related not only by the differential equation but by all differential equations obtained by differentiating that equation. Another method, based on the use of integration, was used by Varga [43].

Here and subsequently we assume that our difference equation can be written in the form

$$\alpha_1(x, y) u(x + s_1 h, y) + \alpha_2(x, y) u(x, y + s_2 h) + \alpha_3(x, y) u(x - s_3 h, y)$$
$$+ \alpha_4(x, y) u(x, y - s_4 h) - \alpha_0 u(x, y) = t(x, y), \quad (11.27)$$

where the $\alpha_i(x,y)$ are positive and where

$$\alpha_0 \geq \alpha_1 + \alpha_2 + \alpha_3 + \alpha_4. \tag{11.28}$$

We further assume that the region R_h is *connected*, that is, that any 2 points of R_h can be joined by a broken line consisting of line segments connecting adjacent points of R_h.

We now show that (11.27) has a unique solution. To do this, it is clearly necessary and sufficient to show that the determinant of the related linear system does not vanish. This will be the case provided that the homogeneous system, obtained by letting the boundary values and $t(x,y)$ vanish, has only the trivial solution which vanishes everywhere in R_h. Suppose the homogeneous system has a nontrivial solution. Then for some point of R_h we have $u \neq 0$. We can assume $u > 0$ at this point, since otherwise we could consider $(-u)$, which would also be a solution of the homogeneous system. Let M denote the largest positive value of u in R_h, and let $u(x_0, y_0) = M$. From (11.27) and (11.28) it follows that u must assume the value M at each of the 4 adjacent points. Continuing this process and using the connectedness of R_h, we conclude that $u(x,y) = M$ for all (x,y) in R_h and also in S_h. This contradicts the assumption that u vanishes on S_h and proves that u vanishes identically in $R_h + S_h$. It then follows that (11.27) has a unique solution.

11.4   Accuracy

It can be shown that, under rather general conditions [9], as h tends to zero, the solutions of the difference equation approach the solution of the differential equation. However, very little is known about the accuracy of the solution of the difference equation for a given value of h. Geršgorin [21] has obtained bounds for the maximum error in terms of the local error. In the case of Laplace's equation

$$U_{xx} + U_{yy} = 0 \tag{11.29}$$

for a region containing only regular interior points, we have, for all (x,y) in R_h,

$$|u_h(x,y) - U(x,y)| \leq \tfrac{1}{24} M_4 r^2 h^2,$$

where r is the radius of any circle containing the given region and where

$$M_4 = \max \left\{ \max_{(x,y) \in R+S} |U_{xxxx}|, \quad \max_{(x,y) \in R+S} |U_{yyyy}| \right\}.$$

Here u_h denotes the solution of the difference equation (11.14) corresponding to the mesh size h. Since the fourth partial derivatives of the solution are seldom known unless the solution itself is known, this estimate cannot usually be applied. In some cases these derivatives may not even be bounded. On the other hand, one can sometimes estimate U_{xxyy} by means of the difference quotient

$$U_{xxyy} \doteq h^{-2}\{u_h(x + h, y + h) - 2u_h(x, y + h) + u_h(x - h, y + h)$$
$$- 2[u_h(x + h, y) - 2u_h(x,y) + u_h(x - h, y)]$$
$$+ u_h(x + h, y - h) - 2u_h(x, y - h) + u_h(x - h, y - h)\}$$

and then estimate U_{xxxx} and U_{yyyy} by the relations

$$U_{xxyy} = -U_{xxxx} = -U_{yyyy},$$

which can be derived from (11.29).

Another method of estimating the accuracy of the finite-difference solution is to solve the difference equation with two different mesh sizes. If the difference between these solutions is small, then one may feel justified in assuming that the error is small. If one assumes more about the behavior of $u_h - U$, namely, that $u_h - U$ is proportional to h^2, then one can, by computing u_h and $u_{h/2}$, "extrapolate to zero grid size," using the formula

$$U(x, y) \doteq \tfrac{4}{3} u_{h/2}(x, y) - \tfrac{1}{3} u_h(x, y).$$

Although this process is somewhat dangerous, it sometimes gives a remarkable improvement in the accuracy.

Some empirical studies on the accuracy of finite-difference methods for solving Laplace's equation are reported in [57]. For problems where the boundary had no corners with interior angle greater than 180° and where the boundary values were continuous, the error was very small, and the extrapolation process yielded good results. However, if the boundary did have a corner with an interior angle of 270° or if the function defining the boundary values was not continuous, then the error was much larger, and the extrapolation process was not satisfactory.

None of the papers which have been written on error estimation (e.g., [51, 52, 47, 48, 49, 35, 65]) can be said to come close to satisfying the needs of the practical computer user. The field is very much open for further research.

11.5 Point Iterative Methods

As pointed out in the preceding section, little is known concerning the accuracy of numerical results obtained by solving difference equations corresponding to elliptic differential equations. Because of this, it would appear desirable to use an extremely fine mesh size in order to increase the likelihood of obtaining a desired accuracy. However, since the number of interior net points increases as h^{-2}, the number of linear equations to be solved also increases as h^{-2}. The problem of solving the difference equation presents a serious practical difficulty, despite the fact that the existence of a unique solution is known.

For linear systems of the size encountered in practice, the use of direct methods such as Cramer's rule, involving the use of determinants, and the Gauss elimination method are not practical, except possibly for certain very special cases involving rectangles. One is led, instead, to consider iterative methods, where one assumes an arbitrary initial approximation to the solution and then improves this approximation according to a prescribed procedure.*

In this section we describe some methods wherein the approximate solution is improved point by point. In the next two sections we consider methods involving simultaneous changes at groups of points. We present here, without proof, descriptions of the methods as well as rules and suggestions for their efficient use. Later, we present some of the underlying theory.

If we solve (11.27) for $u(x,y)$, we get

$$u(x, y) = \beta_1 u(x + h_1, y) + \beta_3 u(x - h_3, y) + \beta_2 u(x, y + h_2)$$
$$+ \beta_4 u(x, y - h_4) + \tau(x, y), \quad (11.30)$$

where
$$\tau = -\frac{t(x, y)}{\alpha_0}$$

and where, for $i = 1, 2, 3, 4,$

$$\beta_i = \frac{\alpha_i}{\alpha_0}, \quad (11.31)$$

$$h_i = h s_i. \quad (11.32)$$

For our present discussion it is sufficient to know that the β_i are all positive and that

$$\sum_{i=1}^{4} \beta_i \le 1. \quad (11.33)$$

The usual procedure is to compute all the β_i initially and to store them in the relatively slow-speed auxiliary memory of the computer, such as is provided by magnetic drums or tapes. This avoids the necessity of recomputing the β_i for each iteration, which would be a wasteful process, and at the same time saves the high-speed memory for other use. Large blocks of the β_i can be read into the high-speed memory conveniently when needed. Of course, if the differential equation is sufficiently simple, it may happen that many or all of the β_i are identical. In such

---

* With relaxation methods, which are more suited for hand computation than for machine use, one continually improves the approximate solution, varying the procedure from time to time in accordance with the judgment of the human computer.

cases a different scheme should be used, since it would be inefficient to store all the β_i.

Perhaps the simplest of the point iterative methods is the *Gauss-Seidel method*, also known as the *method of successive displacements*, where, starting with arbitrary initial values $u^{(0)}(x,y)$ for all points of R_h, one improves the values at points of R_h in an arbitrary but fixed order, using (11.30) and using improved values as soon as available. Thus, if we consider the ordering where (x,y) follows (x',y'), provided that either $y > y'$ or $y = y'$ and $x > x'$, then the improvement formula is

$$u^{(n+1)}(x,y) = \beta_1 u^{(n)}(x + h_1, y) + \beta_3 u^{(n+1)}(x - h_3, y) + \beta_2 u^{(n)}(x, y + h_2)$$
$$+ \beta_4 u^{(n+1)}(x, y - h_4) + \tau(x,y). \quad (11.34)$$

A complete iteration consists of improving the approximate values at all points of R_h. Having traversed the points of R_h, one starts over again at the "first" point and repeats the process until $d_n < \epsilon$, where ϵ is a prescribed tolerance and where

$$d_n = \max_{(x,y) \in R_h} |u^{(n)}(x,y) - u^{(n-1)}(x,y)|. \quad (11.35)$$

We remark that in a similar method, known as the *Jacobi method* or the *method of simultaneous displacements*, one does not use improved values until after a complete iteration. The improvement formula for this method is

$$u^{(n+1)}(x,y) = \beta_1 u^{(n)}(x + h_1, y) + \beta_3 u^{(n)}(x - h_3, y) + \beta_2 u^{(n)}(x, y + h_2)$$
$$+ \beta_4 u^{(n)}(x, y - h_4) + \tau(x,y). \quad (11.36)$$

In Sec. 11.8 we show that the Gauss-Seidel method converges exactly twice as fast as the Jacobi method, where the rate of convergence can be defined in a mathematically precise way.

As an example of the Gauss-Seidel method, let us consider a problem involving Laplace's equation

$$U_{xx} + U_{yy} = 0 \quad (11.37)$$

for the unit square $0 \leq x \leq 1, 0 \leq y \leq 1$ with $h = M^{-1}$, where M is an integer. For boundary values let us assume that $u = 1000$ on the side of a square where $y = 1$ and that $u = 0$ elsewhere. Evidently we have $\beta_1 \equiv \beta_2 \equiv \beta_3 \equiv \beta_4 \equiv \frac{1}{4}$, $h_1 \equiv h_2 \equiv h_3 \equiv h_4 \equiv 1$, and $\tau \equiv 0$. Table 11.1 illustrates the computational procedure for the case $M = 3$. The initial approximation to the solution was assumed to be zero for all 4 interior net points. The ordering of the points was $(\frac{1}{3}, \frac{1}{3})$, $(\frac{2}{3}, \frac{1}{3})$, $(\frac{1}{3}, \frac{2}{3})$, $(\frac{2}{3}, \frac{2}{3})$.

After seven complete iterations the values converged. For convenience, the $d^{(n)} = u^{(n)} - u^{(n-1)}$ are given as well as the $u^{(n)}$. The ratios

TABLE 11.1   An Example of the Use of the Gauss-Seidel Method

		$x = \frac{1}{3}$				$x = \frac{2}{3}$	
	n	$u^{(n)}$	$d^{(n)}$		n	$u^{(n)}$	$d^{(n)}$
$y = \frac{2}{3}$	0	0			0	0	
	1	250	250		1	312	312
	2	344	94		2	360	48
	3	368	24		3	372	12
	4	374	6		4	375	3
	5	375	1		5	375	0
	6	375	0		6	375	0
	7	375	0		7	375	0
$y = \frac{1}{3}$	0	0			0	0	
	1	0	0		1	0	0
	2	62	62		2	94	94
	3	110	48		3	118	24
	4	122	12		4	124	6
	5	124	2		5	125	1
	6	125	1		6	125	0
	7	125	0		7	125	0

$d^{(n)}/d^{(n-1)}$ give an indication of how rapidly the errors are decreasing. In this case it can be seen that the ratios are approximately $\frac{1}{4}$; hence the convergence is rapid. However, the general formula for λ, the limiting ratio, is

$$\lambda = \cos^2 \frac{\pi}{M} \sim 1 - \left(\frac{\pi}{M}\right)^2 \qquad (11.38)$$

(see, e.g., [55]). We refer to λ as the *spectral radius** of the Gauss-Seidel method. Thus, for instance, if $M = 20$, we have $\lambda = .975$, and the convergence is very slow.

By a simple modification of (11.34) we can make a substantial improvement in the rate of convergence. We use the following formula:

$$u^{(n+1)}(x,y) = \omega[\beta_1 u^{(n)}(x + h_1,y) + \beta_3 u^{(n+1)}(x - h_3,y)$$
$$+ \beta_2 u^{(n)}(x,y + h_2) + \beta_4 u^{(n+1)}(x,y - h_4) + \tau(x,y)] - (\omega - 1)u^{(n)}(x,y). \qquad (11.39)$$

Here ω is a parameter known as a *relaxation factor*, the choice of which determines the rate of convergence of the method. Evidently, when $\omega = 1$, the method reduces to the Gauss-Seidel method.

The method defined by (11.39) is known as the *successive-overrelaxation*

* Actually λ is the spectral radius of the matrix of the linear transformation associated with the Gauss-Seidel method. In general, as in [55], where the term "spectral norm" is used, we define the spectral radius of a matrix as the maximum of the moduli of its eigenvalues.

method (see [55]) and, when applied to Laplace's equation, as the *extrapolated Liebmann method* (see [16]). Its use will be illustrated by applying it to the example involving Laplace's equation which was considered previously in connection with the Gauss-Seidel method. Table 11.2 shows the results obtained using a relaxation factor of 1.1.

TABLE 11.2   An Example of the Use of the Successive-overrelaxation Method

		$x = \frac{1}{3}$				$x = \frac{2}{3}$	
	n	$u^{(n)}$	$d^{(n)}$		n	$u^{(n)}$	$d^{(n)}$
$y = \frac{2}{3}$	0	0			0	0	
	1	275	275		1	351	351
	2	365	90		2	373	22
	3	376	11		3	376	3
	4	376	0		4	376	0
$y = \frac{1}{3}$	0	0			0	0	
	1	0	0		1	0	0
	2	76	76		2	118	118
	3	126	50		3	126	8
	4	126	0		4	126	0

We note that convergence was achieved after four iterations.   The converged values are slightly in error because of the fact that only 3 significant figures were retained.   The erratic behavior of the ratios $d^{(n)}/d^{(n-1)}$ should be noted.

Actually, the best value of ω would have been 1.072.   The general formula for the best value is

$$\omega_b = 1 + \frac{\lambda}{(1 + \sqrt{1 - \lambda})^2}, \tag{11.40}$$

where λ is the limiting value of d_n/d_{n-1} for the Gauss-Seidel method. The value of 1.072 for our example is readily obtained by substituting $\lambda = \frac{1}{4}$ into (11.40).   It is possible to compute λ exactly for rectangles as well as for squares [see (11.38) for the square].   It can be shown that the convergence of the successive-overrelaxation method with the best value of ω is approximately as rapid as it would be if d_{n+1}/d_n tended to λ^* where

$$\lambda^* = \omega_b - 1 \sim 1 - \frac{2\pi}{M}.$$

Here λ^* is the spectral radius of the successive-overrelaxation method. In the case $M = 20$, we get $\omega = 1.73$ and hence $\lambda^* = .73$, compared with $\lambda = .975$ for the Gauss-Seidel method.   The rapidity of convergence for the successive-overrelaxation method is thus seen to be very much larger than for the Gauss-Seidel method.

Some rules and suggestions for choosing λ are given in [57], where numerical experiments involving the use of the method are also described. If, as in the case of Laplace's equation, one can determine λ exactly for a general rectangle, one should do so for a rectangle which wholly contains $R + S$. The ω determined in this way will be larger than the best value. This is fortunate, since the theory indicates that it is much better to overestimate than to underestimate ω. In spite of this, it may be better to use a somewhat smaller rectangle which has the same area as the given region. Another method of choosing λ is to perform a number of iterations using $\omega = 1$ and to attempt to estimate the limiting value of the ratio d_n/d_{n-1}.

Two other point iterative methods should be mentioned. The first is due to Richardson and is described in [33]. The convergence of the method has been discussed in [56, 37, 28]. Although Richardson's method as a method of solving linear systems is of wider applicability than the successive-overrelaxation method, it is considerably less effective for linear systems arising from elliptic difference equations (see the discussion in [55, 56, 61]). We discuss Richardson's method again in Sec. 11.18.

Another very interesting method, presented by Sheldon [36], is one which combines ideas used in Aitken's "to-and-fro" method [1], the successive-overrelaxation method, and Richardson's method. Pending the development of a rigorous analysis of the convergence rate of the method, at least in some special cases, it appears doubtful that the method will be used as much as either the successive-overrelaxation method or the alternating-direction implicit methods, which are discussed in Sec. 11.7.

11.6   Line Iterative Methods

With line iterative methods one improves the values of the approximate solution simultaneously on an entire line of points. The iterative formula for *successive row iteration* is

$$u^{(n+1)}(x, y) = \beta_1 u^{(n+1)}(x + h_1, y) + \beta_3 u^{(n+1)}(x - h_3, y)$$
$$+ \beta_2 u^{(n)}(x, y + h_2) + \beta_4 u^{(n+1)}(x, y - h_4) + \tau(x, y). \quad (11.41)$$

As indicated, the rows are improved in the order of increasing y. For *simultaneous row iteration* the improved values are not used until the end of a complete iteration. The improvement formula is

$$u^{(n+1)}(x, y) = \beta_1 u^{(n+1)}(x + h_1, y) + \beta_3 u^{(n+1)}(x - h_3, y)$$
$$+ \beta_2 u^{(n)}(x, y + h_2) + \beta_4 u^{(n)}(x, y - h_4) + \tau(x, y). \quad (11.42)$$

For each y the determination of the improved values involves the solution of a system of M linear equations with M unknowns, where M is the number of interior net points on the given row. Fortunately, because the matrix of the linear system is tridiagonal, that is, has no nonzero elements except on the main diagonal and on the diagonals adjacent to the main diagonal, there is a very simple algorithm for solving the equations. This algorithm, which is easily derived by using the Gaussian elimination method, involves a number of arithmetic operations which is proportional to M, as opposed to the approximately $\frac{1}{3}M^3$ operations required with a general matrix.   The algorithm appears to have been presented first by Thomas [41].   It was first used in connection with parabolic partial differential equations by Bruce, Peaceman, Rachford, and Rice [7].

We describe the procedure for the linear system

$$B_1 T_1 + C_1 T_2 = D_1,$$
$$A_i T_{i-1} + B_i T_i + C_i T_{i+1} = D_i \qquad (i = 2, 3, \ldots, M - 1), \quad (11.43)$$
$$A_M T_{M-1} + B_M T_M = D_M,$$

where the A_i, B_i, C_i, D_i are given and where the T_i are to be determined. The solution can be determined by the following formulas:

$$
\begin{aligned}
b_1 &= \frac{C_1}{B_1}, & b_i &= \frac{C_i}{B_i - A_i b_{i-1}} & (i &= 2, 3, \ldots, M - 1), \\
q_1 &= \frac{D_1}{B_1}, & q_i &= \frac{D_i - A_i q_{i-1}}{B_i - A_i b_{i-1}} & (i &= 2, 3, \ldots, M), \\
T_M &= q_M, & T_i &= q_i - b_i T_{i+1} & (i &= M - 1, M - 2, \ldots, 1).
\end{aligned}
\qquad (11.44)
$$

Successive line overrelaxation can be defined in an obvious way as follows:

$$u^{(n+1)}(x,y) = u^{(n)}(x,y) + \omega[\bar{u}^{(n+1)}(x,y) - u^{(n)}(x,y)], \qquad (11.45)$$

where

$$\bar{u}^{(n+1)}(x,y) = \beta_1 \bar{u}^{(n+1)}(x + h_1, y) + \beta_3 u^{(n+1)}(x - h_3, y)$$
$$+ \beta_2 u^{(n)}(x, y + h_2) + \beta_4 u^{(n+1)}(x, y - h_4) + \tau(x,y). \quad (11.34a)$$

We shall see in Sec. 11.10 that the rates of convergence of the three methods of row iteration which we have just defined bear the same relation to each other as do the corresponding point iteration methods. Thus, for instance, the rate of convergence of the method of successive row iteration is exactly twice that of simultaneous row iteration. Furthermore, the optimum value of ω is given by

$$\omega_b = 1 + \frac{\lambda}{(1 + \sqrt{1 - \lambda})^2},$$

where λ is the spectral norm of the method of successive row iteration.

Let us now compare the point iteration methods for the case of Laplace's equation in the unit square with $h = M^{-1}$.   It is not difficult to show (see, e.g., [3]) that

$$\lambda = \left(\frac{\cos \pi h}{2 - \cos \pi h}\right)^2 \sim 1 - 2\pi^2 h^2,$$

compared with $1 - \pi^2 h^2$ for successive point relaxation. Thus successive row iteration converges approximately twice as fast as successive point iteration. Later, in Sec. 11.10, we show that the method of successive row overrelaxation converges approximately $\sqrt{2}$ times as fast as successive point overrelaxation. At first sight, this relatively small improvement would not seem to be worth the extra effort involved in using (11.44) to perform the row iteration. However, Cuthill and Varga [64] showed that it is practical in some cases to compute and store once and for all certain coefficients, such as the coefficients of the inverse of the tridiagonal matrix, which can be used to carry out the line relaxation process much more readily than would be possible with the algorithm defined by (11.44). As a matter of fact, using the procedure of Cuthill and Varga, the computational effort per point is the same for block relaxation as for point relaxation.

11.7 Alternating-direction Implicit Methods

Two methods which are somewhat similar to line relaxation have been developed recently. One, which was presented by Peaceman and Rachford [32], is related to a method developed by Douglas [11] for solving the equation $u_t = u_{xx} + u_{yy}$. In Sec. 11.17 the relation between Douglas's method and the method of Peaceman and Rachford is discussed in more detail.

Douglas and Rachford [12] presented a method rather similar to that of Peaceman and Rachford. The former method can be generalized to three dimensions, whereas the latter apparently cannot. Nevertheless, since the Peaceman-Rachford method is superior to the Douglas-Rachford method in certain elementary cases and since the two methods and the analysis of their properties are quite similar, we discuss only the Peaceman-Rachford method here. For convenience, we consider Laplace's equation and a uniform mesh with $h_1 = h_2 = h_3 = h_4 = h$. The basic formulas are

$$u^{(n+\frac{1}{2})}(x,y) = u^{(n)}(x,y) + r[u^{(n+\frac{1}{2})}(x + h, y) + u^{(n+\frac{1}{2})}(x - h, y)$$
$$-2u^{(n+\frac{1}{2})}(x,y)] + r[u^{(n)}(x, y + h) + u^{(n)}(x, y - h)$$
$$- 2u^{(n)}(x,y)],$$

$$\tag{11.46}$$

$$u^{(n+1)}(x,y) = u^{(n+\frac{1}{2})}(x,y) + r[u^{(n+\frac{1}{2})}(x + h, y) + u^{(n+\frac{1}{2})}(x - h, y)$$
$$- 2u^{(n+\frac{1}{2})}(x,y)] + r[u^{(n+1)}(x, y + h) + u^{(n+1)}(x, y - h)$$
$$- 2u^{(n+1)}(x,y)].$$

We note that the first equation of (11.46), with $r = \frac{1}{4}$, defines a process which is very similar to but which is *not* the same as simultaneous row iteration.   The Peaceman-Rachford procedure is essentially a kind of a row iteration followed by a column iteration.   Although r need not be held fixed, it is important that the same value of r be used for both parts of an iteration.   The choice of the values of r is discussed in [32] and [45].

We describe the use of the method for the case of a unit square with mesh size h, following the results given in [45].   Starting with a positive integer t, whose selection is discussed later, determine z from the relation

$$z = \sigma^{1/(t-1)}$$

where

$$\sigma = \frac{a}{b},$$

$$b = 4\cos^2 \frac{\pi h}{2},$$

$$a = 4\sin^2 \frac{\pi h}{2}.$$

The r_k are then determined by*

$$r_k = \frac{1}{b z^{k-1}}, \qquad k = 1, 2, \ldots, t.$$

According to [45], the factor of reduction of the error achieved after t double sweeps is approximately, for small σ,

$$P_t = \left[\frac{1 - z^{\frac{1}{2}}}{1 + z^{\frac{1}{2}}} e^{-z^{\frac{3}{2}}/(1-z)} \right]^4.$$

Since the *average* factor of reduction per double sweep is $S_t = (P_t)^{1/t}$, one should choose t so as to minimize S_t.   Because of the complicated nature of S_t as a function of t, it is probably best to determine the best value of t by computing S_t for a number of different values of t.

As an example, let us consider the case $h = 20^{-1}$.   Here

$$a = 4\sin^2 \frac{\pi}{40} = .024623,$$

$$b = 4\cos^2 \frac{\pi}{40} = 3.97538,$$

$$\sigma = \frac{a}{b} = .0061940.$$

* Wachspress reports, in a private communication, that it is preferable to use the r_k in the order $r_k = z^{k-1}/a$, $k = 1, 2, \ldots, t$.

We compute S_t for various values of t, obtaining

$$S_6 = .3152 \qquad S_9 = .3056$$
$$S_8 = .3060 \qquad S_{10} = .3064$$

The optimum value for S_t is .3056, which is assumed for $t = 9$. The corresponding values of r_k are

$$r_1 = .25155 \qquad r_6 = 6.03450$$
$$r_2 = .47492 \qquad r_7 = 11.39320$$
$$r_3 = .89666 \qquad r_8 = 21.51045$$
$$r_4 = 1.69291 \qquad r_9 = 40.61191$$
$$r_5 = 3.19623$$

For the successive-overrelaxation method with the optimum value of ω, namely, 1.73, the average factor of reduction of the error is .73, as compared with .3056 per double sweep for the Peaceman-Rachford method. In general, it can be shown that the number of iterations needed to achieve a specified accuracy varies as $|\log h|^{-1}$ for the Peaceman-Rachford method, which is much more favorable than the h^{-1} required for the successive-overrelaxation method. Thus, decreasing h by a factor of 2 in the above example would double the number of iterations required for the successive-overrelaxation method, whereas there would be an increase by only a factor of $|\log \frac{1}{20}|/|\log \frac{1}{40}| = 1.23$ for the Peaceman-Rachford method.

In spite of the apparent advantages of the Peaceman-Rachford method, there are several reasons why one might hesitate to use it for some problems in preference to successive overrelaxation. The latter method is undoubtedly simpler. Not only are the basic formulas for the Peaceman-Rachford method considerably more complicated, but there is also a problem of obtaining the necessary data first by columns and then by rows, particularly if this information is stored on tape. The Peaceman-Rachford method may well be better for sufficiently small h, but it is not clear whether, for a given case, it will be better for the particular value of h being used. Moreover, although the theory underlying the successive-overrelaxation method has been extended to include a wide class of partial differential equations, including Laplace's, and to include nonrectangular regions, the theory for the Peaceman-Rachford method is limited to problems involving a very restricted class of partial differential equations and the rectangle. Generalizations of the Peaceman-Rachford method are discussed further in Sec. 11.12.

11.8 Theoretical Discussion of the Successive-overrelaxation Method

In this section we give a sketch of the underlying theory on which the analysis of the successive-overrelaxation method is based. The discussion here is not intended to be either as detailed or as rigorous as that given in [55]. Instead, a simplified and more intuitive discussion is presented. The simplified presentation is based, in part, on conversations with Prof. B. Friedman and on [17].

It is convenient to consider the following linear system:

$$\sum_{j=1}^{N} a_{i,j} u_j + d_i = 0, \qquad i = 1, 2, \ldots, N, \qquad (11.47)$$

where N is the number of points of R_h and where

$$a_{i,i} > 0, \qquad i = 1, 2, \ldots, N, \qquad (11.48a)$$

$$a_{i,i} \geq \sum_{\substack{j=1 \\ j \neq i}}^{N} |a_{i,j}| \qquad \text{and for at least one } i \text{ the strict inequality holds.} \qquad (11.48b)$$

The matrix A is *irreducible*: given any two nonempty disjoint subsets S and T of the set W of the first N positive integers such that $S + T = W$, there exists $a_{i,j} \neq 0$ such that $i \in S$ and $j \in T$. (11.48c)

The matrix A has property A: there exist two disjoint subsets S and T of W, the set of the first N positive integers, such that $S + T = W$ and such that, if $a_{i,j} \neq 0$, then either $i = j$ or $i \in S$ and $j \in T$ or $i \in T$ and $j \in S$. (11.48d)

Condition (11.48c) was formulated by Geiringer [20] and by Frobenius [18]. Condition (11.48d), which was formulated in [55], is equivalent to stating that the matrix A, by a suitable permutation of its rows and the corresponding columns, can be written in the form

$$A = \begin{pmatrix} D_1 & F \\ G & D_2 \end{pmatrix}, \qquad (11.49)$$

where D_1, D_2 are square diagonal matrices and where the rectangular matrices G and F are arbitrary. Actually, a matrix with this property belongs to the class of p-cyclic matrices studied by Frobenius [18] and Romanovsky [34] (see Sec. 11.11). It is easy to show that conditions (11.48) hold for any linear system arising from the difference equation (11.27) provided that the α_i are all positive and that (11.28) holds (see, e.g., [55]). We remark that the terms of (11.27) involving boundary values are absorbed into the d_i of (11.47). The nonzero coefficients $a_{i,j}$ with $i \neq j$ correspond to the $\alpha_i (i = 1, 2, 3, 4)$ of (11.27), and the diagonal elements $a_{i,i}$ correspond to α_0 in (11.27). That (11.48c) holds follows from the fact that the region R_h is assumed to be connected. Condition (11.48d) follows from consideration of a "coloring" of the points of R_h with two colors in such a way that every pair of adjacent points of R_h has different colors.   It is easy to see that such a coloring is possible.   In order to obtain the form (11.49) it is necessary only to label the points in an ordering so that all the points of one color occur before any point of the other color.   For it is clear from (11.27) that the difference equation for a point of one color only involves values of u at points of the opposite color.

We may write (11.47) in the form

$$Au + d = 0, \qquad (11.47')$$

where A is an $N \times N$ matrix and where u and d are column matrices. It is convenient to consider the matrix B defined by

$$B = -D^{-1}C, \qquad (11.50)$$

where

$$A = D + C. \qquad (11.51)$$

Here D is a diagonal matrix, and the diagonal elements of C vanish. Evidently the diagonal elements of B vanish, and we may write

$$B = L + U, \qquad (11.52)$$

where L and U have no nonzero elements above and below the main diagonal, respectively.   We may write

$$u = Bu + c, \qquad (11.47'')$$

where

$$c = -D^{-1}d.$$

We remark that B is the matrix corresponding to the Jacobi method of iteration, discussed in the previous section.

It is easy to show that, if A is symmetric, then B, though not necessarily symmetric, is similar to a symmetric matrix.   Consider the matrix $D^{\frac{1}{2}}BD^{-\frac{1}{2}}$, which is similar to B.   We have, by (11.50),

$$D^{\frac{1}{2}}BD^{-\frac{1}{2}} = -D^{-\frac{1}{2}}CD^{-\frac{1}{2}}, \qquad (11.53)$$

which is symmetric, since C is symmetric and $D^{-\frac{1}{2}}$ is diagonal.

We next show that, if μ is an eigenvalue of B, then so is $-\mu$.   Since the eigenvalues of B do not depend on the ordering of the rows and corresponding columns, we can assume that A is in the form (11.49) with D_1 and D_2 of order r and s, respectively.   Evidently B has the form

$$B = \begin{pmatrix} O_1 & H \\ K & O_2 \end{pmatrix}, \qquad (11.54)$$

where O_1 and O_2 are square null matrices of order r and s, respectively. If μ is an eigenvalue of B, we have

$$\det (B - \mu I) = \begin{vmatrix} -\mu I_1 & H \\ K & -\mu I_2 \end{vmatrix} = 0,$$

where I_1 and I_2 are square identity matrices of order r and s, respectively.

If we multiply the first r rows and the last s columns of the determinant by -1, the equality is preserved, and we obtain

$$0 = \begin{vmatrix} \mu I_1 & H \\ K & \mu I_2 \end{vmatrix} = \det (B + \mu I).$$

Hence $-\mu$ is an eigenvalue of B.

Condition (11.48d) shows us that, by starting with A and by rearranging, if necessary, the rows and the corresponding columns of A in a certain *ordering*, we may obtain the form (11.49). More generally, we say that any ordering of the rows and columns of A is *consistent* if, starting from the ordering, we can permute the rows and corresponding columns in such a way that if $a_{i,j} \neq 0$, the ordering relation between the ith and jth rows is unchanged and so that the matrix has the form

$$A = \begin{pmatrix} D_1 & F_1 & 0 & . & . & . & . & 0 \\ G_1 & D_2 & F_2 & . & . & . & . & 0 \\ 0 & G_2 & D_3 & . & . & . & . & 0 \\ 0 & 0 & G_3 & . & . & . & . & 0 \\ . & . & . & . & . & . & . & . \\ . & . & . & . & . & . & . & . \\ 0 & 0 & 0 & . & . & G_{p-2} & D_{p-1} & F_{p-1} \\ 0 & 0 & 0 & . & . & 0 & G_{p-1} & D_p \end{pmatrix}, \qquad (11.55)$$

where D_i is a square $r_i \times r_i$ matrix and where the F_i and G_i are $r_i \times r_{i+1}$ and $r_{i+1} \times r_i$ rectangular matrices, respectively. That such orderings exist follows from (11.49). The matrix B likewise has the form

$$B = \begin{pmatrix} O_1 & H_1 & 0 & . & . & 0 & 0 \\ K_1 & O_2 & H_2 & . & . & 0 & 0 \\ 0 & K_2 & O_3 & . & . & 0 & 0 \\ . & . & . & . & . & . & . \\ 0 & 0 & 0 & . & . & K_{p-1} & O_p \end{pmatrix}.$$

The method of successive overrelaxation is defined by the formula, given in [55],

$$u_i^{(n+1)} = \omega \left[\sum_{j=1}^{i-1} b_{i,j} u_j^{(n+1)} + \sum_{j=i+1}^{N} b_{i,j} u_j^{(n)} + c_i \right] - (\omega - 1) u_i^{(n)}$$

or, in matrix notation,

$$u^{(n+1)} = \omega [L u^{(n+1)} + U u^{(n)} + c] - (\omega - 1) I u^{(n)}.$$

If we let

$$L_\omega = (I - \omega L)^{-1} [\omega U - (\omega - 1) I],$$

we have

$$u^{(n+1)} = L_\omega u^{(n)} + (I - \omega L)^{-1}\omega c.$$

We remark that the nonsingularity of $(I - \omega L)$ follows from the fact that its determinant equals unity.

To study the rate of convergence, we consider

$$e^{(n)} = u^{(n)} - u,$$

where u is the true solution of (11.47'). Since $u = L_\omega u + (I - \omega L)^{-1}\omega c$ for any ω, we have

$$e^{(n+1)} = L_\omega e^{(n)}. \tag{11.56}$$

The rapidity of convergence depends on the largest eigenvalue of the matrix L_ω. We seek to relate the eigenvalues of L_ω to those of the simpler matrix B. Suppose $\omega > 0$ and λ is a nonzero eigenvalue of L_ω. Then

$$0 = \det (L_\omega - \lambda I) = \det \{(I - \omega L)^{-1}[\omega U - (\omega - 1)I] - \lambda I\}$$
$$0 = \det [\omega U - (\omega - 1)I - \lambda(I - \omega L)]$$
$$0 = \det \left[(U + \lambda L) - \left(\frac{\lambda + \omega - 1}{\omega}\right)I \right].$$

If the ordering is consistent, then we may assume A has the form (11.55) since the permutations of the rows and columns necessary to obtain this form clearly do not affect the $u^{(n)}$. Therefore the matrix $\left[U + \lambda L - \left(\dfrac{\lambda + \omega - 1}{\omega}\right)I\right]$ may be written in the form

$$\begin{pmatrix}
-aI_1 & H_1 & O & . & . & . & O & O \\
\lambda K_1 & -aI_2 & H_2 & . & . & . & O & O \\
O & \lambda K_2 & -aI_3 & . & . & . & O & O \\
. & . & . & . & . & . & . & . \\
O & O & O & . & . & . & \lambda K_{p-1} & -aI_p
\end{pmatrix},$$

where for convenience we have set $a = (\lambda + \omega - 1)/\omega$. Let*

$$\Gamma = \begin{pmatrix}
I_1 & O & O & . & . & . & . & . \\
O & \lambda^{1/2}I_2 & O & . & . & . & . & . \\
O & O & \lambda I_3 & . & . & . & . & . \\
 & & & . & & & & \\
 & & & & . & & & \\
. & . & . & & . & . & . & \lambda^{(p-1)/2}I_p
\end{pmatrix}.$$

* The matrix Γ was used by Friedman [17]. One could also obtain explicit expressions for the eigenvectors of L_ω as given in [53].

It follows that

$$\Gamma^{-1}\left[U + \lambda L - \left(\frac{\lambda + \omega - 1}{\omega}\right)I\right]\Gamma = \left[\lambda^{\frac{1}{2}}(U + L) - \left(\frac{\lambda + \omega - 1}{\omega}\right)I\right],$$

and we have

$$0 = \det\left[(U + L) - \left(\frac{\lambda + \omega - 1}{\omega\lambda^{\frac{1}{2}}}\right)I\right]$$

$$= \det\left[B - \left(\frac{\lambda + \omega - 1}{\omega\lambda^{\frac{1}{2}}}\right)I\right].$$

But since $\qquad\qquad \det(B - \mu I) = \prod_{i=1}^{N}(\mu_i - \mu),$

where the μ_i are the eigenvalues of B, we have

$$0 = \prod_{i=1}^{N}\left[\mu_i - \left(\frac{\lambda + \omega - 1}{\omega\lambda^{\frac{1}{2}}}\right)\right].$$

Thus, if λ is an eigenvalue of L_ω, then for some eigenvalue of B we have

$$\frac{\lambda + \omega - 1}{\omega\lambda^{\frac{1}{2}}} = \mu_i.$$

It can also be shown that, if μ is an eigenvalue of B and if λ satisfies

$$(\lambda + \omega - 1) = \mu\omega\lambda^{\frac{1}{2}}, \tag{11.57}$$

then λ is an eigenvalue of L_ω (see [55]). We remark that, since the eigenvalues of B are clearly independent of the ordering chosen, the eigenvalues of L_ω are the same for all consistent orderings. Of course, the eigenvectors will in general be different, and this may have some effect on the time required to obtain convergence in practice.

Let us now assume that A is symmetric. Hence the eigenvalues of B are real and occur in pairs $-\mu, \mu$. Let $\bar\mu$ denote the largest eigenvalue of B. By considering the mapping between the μ plane and the λ plane defined by (11.57), it can be shown (see [55]) that ω_b defined by

$$\omega_b{}^2\bar\mu^2 = 4(\omega_b - 1), \tag{11.58}$$
$$1 \le \omega_b < 2,$$

or, equivalently,

$$\omega_b = 1 + \left(\frac{\bar\mu}{1 + \sqrt{1 - \bar\mu^2}}\right)^2 = \frac{2}{1 + \sqrt{1 - \bar\mu^2}} \tag{11.58'}$$

is the optimum value of ω in the sense that the spectral radius of L_{ω_b} is less than that for L_ω with $\omega \ne \omega_b$. Surprisingly, for ω in the range

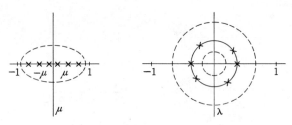

FIG. 11.3

$2 > \omega \geq \omega_b$ all the eigenvalues of L_ω have the same modulus, namely, $\omega - 1$; hence

$$\lambda(L_\omega) = \omega - 1, \qquad (2 \geq \omega \geq \omega_b). \tag{11.59}$$

Consequently, $\lambda(L_{\omega_b}) = \left(\dfrac{\bar{\mu}}{1 + \sqrt{1 - \bar{\mu}^2}}\right)^2 = \dfrac{1 - \sqrt{1 - \bar{\mu}^2}}{1 + \sqrt{1 - \bar{\mu}^2}}. \tag{11.60}$

In order to compare the effectiveness of the methods which we have considered, we introduce the concept of the *rate of convergence*, $R(A)$, of a method whose matrix is A.   This is defined by

$$R(A) = -\log \lambda(A), \tag{11.61}$$

where, here and elsewhere, we let $\lambda(A)$ denote the spectral radius of A. The motivation here is that the number of iterations necessary to reduce an initial error by a prescribed factor is, approximately, inversely proportional to the rate of convergence.

If $\omega = 1$, the method of successive overrelaxation reduces to the Gauss-Seidel method.   By (11.57) we have

$$\lambda(L_1) = [\lambda(B)]^2; \tag{11.62}$$

hence $$R(L_1) = 2R(B). \tag{11.63}$$

Thus the rate of convergence of the Gauss-Seidel method is just twice that of the Jacobi method.   By the use of (11.60) it can be shown (see [55]) that, asymptotically as $\lambda(B)$ tends to zero,

$$R(L_{\omega_b}) \sim 2\sqrt{R(L_1)}. \tag{11.64}$$

It can be seen that the gain in the rate of convergence is very large in cases where the Gauss-Seidel method is slow.

The statements made in Sec. 11.5 concerning the effect of overestimating and underestimating ω can be shown by the use of (11.57).

As an example, let us consider the linear system arising from the usual difference-equation analogue of the Dirichlet problem for a rectangle with sides $a = Mh$, $b = Nh$, where h is the mesh size and where M and N are integers.   The difference equation is

$$4u_{i,j} - u_{i+1,j} - u_{i-1,j} - u_{i,j+1} - u_{i,j-1} = 0, \quad i = 1, 2, \ldots, M - 1;$$
$$j = 1, 2, \ldots, N - 1.$$
$$(11.65)$$

Here $u_{i,j} = u(ih,jh)$.   We assume that the $u_{i,0}$ and $u_{i,N}$ $(i = 1, 2, \ldots, M - 1)$ are given and that the $u_{0,j} = u_{M,j}(j = 1, 2, \ldots, N - 1)$ are given.
   The (point) Jacobi method is defined by

$$u_{i,j}^{(n+1)} = \tfrac{1}{4}(u_{i+1,j}^{(n)} + u_{i-1,j}^{(n)} + u_{i,j+1}^{(n)} + u_{i,j-1}^{(n)}). \qquad (11.66)$$

Let $e_{i,j}^{(n)} = u_{i,j}^{(n)} - u_{i,j}$, where $u_{i,j}$ is the true solution of (11.65).   Evidently, $e^{(n+1)}$ and $e^{(n)}$ satisfy (11.66) but vanish on the boundary.   If we write (11.66) in the form

$$e^{(n+1)} = Be^{(n)}$$

where $e^{(n)}$ is a column matrix with elements $e_{i,j}^{(n)}$, we are led to seek the eigenvalues μ of B.   Evidently, for p,q integers and for

$$v_{i,j} = \sin \frac{p\pi ih}{a} \sin \frac{q\pi jh}{b}$$

we have

$$Bv = \mu v,$$

where

$$\mu = \tfrac{1}{2}\left(\cos \frac{p\pi h}{a} + \cos \frac{q\pi h}{b}\right).$$

Clearly $\bar{\mu} = \lambda(B)$ is given by

$$\bar{\mu} = \tfrac{1}{2}\left(\cos \frac{\pi h}{a} + \cos \frac{\pi h}{b}\right).$$

The (point) successive-overrelaxation method is given by

$$u_{i,j}^{(n+1)} = \omega[\tfrac{1}{4}(u_{i-1,j}^{(n+1)} + u_{i,j-1}^{(n+1)} + u_{i+1,j}^{(n)} + u_{i-1,j}^{(n)})] - (\omega - 1)u_{i,j}^{(n)}.$$

Here the ordering is $(1,1)$, $(2,1)$, $\ldots$, $(M - 1, 1)$, $(1,2)$, $\ldots$, $(M - 1, 2)$, etc.   The optimum value of ω is given by

$$\omega_b = 1 + \left(\frac{\bar{\mu}}{1 + \sqrt{1 - \bar{\mu}^2}}\right)^2.$$

If $a = b = 1$ and h is small, we have

$$\bar{\mu} = \cos \pi h \sim 1 - \frac{\pi^2 h^2}{2}$$

and, by (11.63),

$$R(L_1) \sim 2R(B) \sim \pi^2 h^2.$$

By (11.64) we have

$$R(L_{\omega_b}) \sim 2\sqrt{R(L_1)} \sim 2\pi h.$$

Thus the successive-overrelaxation method converges approximately $(2/\pi h)$ times as fast as the Gauss-Seidel method.

11.9 Extensions of the Generality of the Successive-overrelaxation Method

The question naturally arises whether the results obtained for the successive-overrelaxation method might hold under somewhat weaker assumptions than were made in Sec. 11.8.   That the results do not hold in general is illustrated in [61], where a problem involving a positive definite matrix is considered and it is shown that the successive-over-relaxation method is much less effective than would be the case if the overrelaxation theory did apply.   On the other hand, numerical experiments described in [57] indicate that the successive-overrelaxation method is about as effective when applied to the usual 9-point finite-difference equation corresponding to Laplace's equation as when applied to the 5-point equation.   Since the matrix corresponding to the 9-point equation,

$$4[u(x + h, y) + u(x - h, y) + u(x, y + h) + u(x, y - h)]$$
$$+ u(x + h, y + h) + u(x - h, y + h) + u(x + h, y - h)$$
$$+ u(x - h, y - h) - 20u(x,y) = 0, \qquad (11.67)$$

does not have property A, it appeared that at least some weakening of the assumptions would be possible.

Garabedian [19] has developed a method for obtaining estimates for the rate of convergence of the successive-overrelaxation method as applied to the 5-point and to the 9-point difference-equation analogues of the Dirichlet problem for the rectangle.   For the 5-point formula the result agrees with that obtained by the use of the overrelaxation theory. Indeed, for the unit square the formula for ω obtained from Garabedian's method is

$$\omega = \frac{2}{1 + \pi h},$$

whereas using (11.40), with $\lambda = \cos^2 \pi h$, gives

$$\omega = 1 + \left(\frac{\cos \pi h}{1 + \sin \pi h}\right)^2 \sim \frac{2}{1 + \pi h}.$$

On the other hand, for the 9-point formula we obtain, by Garabedian's method,

$$\omega = \frac{2}{1 + (\sqrt{26}/5)\pi h} \sim \frac{2}{1 + 1.02\pi h},$$

which is slightly less than for the 5-point formula. This result, which does not appear to have been obtained by any other means, agrees with the results of [57].

The method used by Garabedian involves relating the iterative formula for the successive-overrelaxation method to a certain hyperbolic partial differential equation and studying the latter equation. The technique is illustrated by a simple one-dimensional example in Sec. 11.18.

Kahan [27] has investigated the rate of convergence of the successive-overrelaxation method for cases where the matrix A does not have property A. He assumes instead that the diagonal elements of A are positive and that the other elements are nonpositive. He proves a number of interesting results without making further assumptions on A. However, probably the most interesting and useful results apply for the case where A is symmetric and positive definite. Kahan shows that there exists ω_b such that, asymptotically for small values of $R(L_1)$,

$$\sqrt{R(L_1)} \le R(L_{\omega_b}) \le 2\sqrt{R(L_1)}.$$

Here $R(L_1)$ and $R(L_{\omega_b})$ are the rates of convergence, as defined in Sec. 11.18, for the Gauss-Seidel method and for the successive-overrelaxation method, with $\omega = \omega_b$, respectively. Thus, as when property A holds [in which case $R(L_{\omega_b}) \sim 2\sqrt{R(L_1)}$], the successive-overrelaxation method converges much more rapidly than the Gauss-Seidel method. The best value of ω does not differ very much from

$$1 + \frac{\lambda(L_1)}{(1 + \sqrt{1 - \lambda(L_1)})^2},$$

where, as before, we let $\lambda(L_1)$ denote the spectral radius of L_1. Kahan gives suggestions for a more effective determination of the best value of ω.

11.10 Block Iteration Methods

In point iteration methods one essentially solves each equation for a certain unknown, using approximate values of the other unknowns and possibly also using overrelaxation. Natural extensions of these methods are the block iteration methods which are discussed in [3] and [17]. Here one divides the equations into a set of groups. The basic step in the block iterative process is to solve the subsystem of equations belonging to a given group for the corresponding unknowns, using approximate values for the other unknowns. For instance, suppose we consider the linear system

$$\sum_{j=1}^{m} a_{i,j} u_j + d_i = 0, \qquad i = 1, 2, \ldots, m, \tag{11.68}$$

or
$$Au + d = 0, \tag{11.68'}$$

and assume that the equations and unknowns are partitioned into N groups such that $u_1, u_2, \ldots, u_{m_1}$ belong to the first group, $u_{m_1+1}, u_{m_1+2}, \ldots,$ u_{m_2} belong to the second group, and, in general, $u_i, m_{k-1} < i \leq m_k$ belong to the kth group. (Here for convenience we let $m_0 = 0$.) Evidently, we may subdivide A into blocks.

$$A = \begin{vmatrix} A_{1,1} & A_{1,2} & \cdots & A_{1,N} \\ A_{2,1} & A_{2,2} & \cdots & A_{2,N} \\ \cdot \cdot \cdot \cdot \cdot \cdot \cdot \cdot \cdot \cdot \cdot \cdot \cdot \\ A_{N,1} & A_{N,2} & \cdots & A_{N,N} \end{vmatrix}, \tag{11.69}$$

where $A_{i,j}$ is an $(m_i - m_{i-1}) \times (m_j - m_{j-1})$ rectangular matrix.

Simultaneous block iteration may be defined by the following equations:

$$Du^{(n+1)} + Cu^{(n)} + d = 0 \tag{11.70}$$

or
$$u^{(n+1)} = Bu^{(n)} + c, \tag{11.70'}$$

where
$$B = -D^{-1}C \tag{11.71}$$

and
$$c = -D^{-1}d. \tag{11.72}$$

Here $A = D + C$ and

$$D = \begin{pmatrix} A_{1,1} & O & \cdots & O \\ O & A_{2,2} & \cdots & O \\ \cdot \cdot \cdot \cdot \cdot \cdot \cdot \cdot \cdot \cdot \cdot \cdot \cdot \\ O & O & \cdots & A_{N,N} \end{pmatrix}. \tag{11.73}$$

The method of successive block overrelaxation is defined by

$$u^{(n+1)} = \omega[Lu^{(n+1)} + Uu^{(n)} + c] - (\omega - 1)u^{(n)} \tag{11.74}$$

or
$$u^{(n+1)} = L_\omega u^{(n)} + f, \tag{11.74'}$$

where
$$L_\omega = (I - \omega L)^{-1}[\omega U - (\omega - 1)I] \tag{11.75}$$

and
$$f = (I - \omega L)^{-1}\omega c. \tag{11.76}$$

Here $B = L + U$, and L and U have no nonzero elements above and below the main diagonal, respectively.

In order to relate the eigenvalues of B to those of L_ω, we introduce, following [3], the concept of block property A.   A matrix A which has been partitioned in the form (11.69) has block property A if by a suitable rearrangement of the rows and corresponding columns it can be put into the form

$$A = \begin{pmatrix} D_1 & F \\ G & D_2 \end{pmatrix},$$ (11.77)

where D_1 and D_2 are matrices with matrix elements whose diagonal elements are nonsingular square matrices and whose other elements are null matrices. F and G are rectangular matrices whose elements are rectangular matrices.

An ordering of the rows and corresponding columns of blocks of A is *consistent* if A has the form

$$A = \begin{pmatrix} D_1 & F_1 & 0 & \cdots & 0 & 0 \\ G_1 & D_2 & F_2 & \cdots & 0 & 0 \\ 0 & G_2 & D_3 & \cdots & 0 & 0 \\ \multicolumn{6}{c}{\cdot\ \cdot\ \cdot\ \cdot\ \cdot\ \cdot\ \cdot\ \cdot\ \cdot\ \cdot\ \cdot\ \cdot\ \cdot\ \cdot} \\ 0 & 0 & 0 & \cdots & D_{p-1} & F_{p-1} \\ 0 & 0 & 0 & \cdots & G_{p-1} & D_p \end{pmatrix},$$ (11.78)

where D_i are matrices with matrix elements with square matrices on the main diagonal and null matrices elsewhere and the F_i and G_i are rectangular arrays of matrices.   Again, as in Sec. 11.8, we allow the permutation of rows and columns of A provided that if $A_{i,j} \neq 0$ the ordering relation between the ith row and the jth row is preserved.

It is easy to show that the matrix B defined by (11.71) has (point) property A.   Since L_ω bears exactly the same relation to D here as was the case with point relaxation, all the results given in Sec. 11.8 hold. Thus, for instance, if $\bar{\mu} = \lambda(B)$, the optimum value of ω is given by

$$\omega_b = 1 + \left(\frac{\bar{\mu}}{1 + \sqrt{1 - \mu^2}} \right)^2,$$ (11.79)

and as $\lambda(B)$ tends to zero, we have

$$R(L_{\omega_b}) \sim 2\sqrt{R(L_1)} = 2\sqrt{2}\sqrt{R(B)}.$$ (11.80)

To illustrate the foregoing, let us consider the application of line iteration to the example which was treated in Sec. 11.8.   We consider blocks each consisting of all the points on a row.   Methods based on the use of such blocks are called *line iteration methods* and have been discussed in Sec. 11.6.

For simultaneous line iteration, we have, by (11.65) and (11.42),

$$u_{i,j}^{(n+1)} = \tfrac{1}{4}(u_{i-1,j}^{(n+1)} + u_{i+1,j}^{(n+1)} + u_{i,j+1}^{(n)} + u_{i,j-1}^{(n)})$$
$$(i = 1, 2, \ldots, M-1; \; j = 1, 2, \ldots, N-1). \quad (11.81)$$

Even without solving the above equations we can find the eigenvalues of the matrix B associated with the method of simultaneous line iteration. Letting $e_{i,j}^{(n)} = u_{i,j}^{(n)} - u_{i,j}$, where $u_{i,j}$ is the true solution of the Laplace difference equation, we observe that $e^{(n+1)}$ and $e^{(n)}$ satisfy (11.81) and vanish on the boundary. We write (11.81) in the form

$$e^{(n+1)} = Be^{(n)} \quad (11.82)$$

where $e^{(n)}$ is a column matrix with elements $e_{i,j}^{(n)}$. Evidently, for p,q integers and for

$$v_{i,j} = \sin \frac{p\pi i h}{a} \sin \frac{q\pi j h}{b}, \quad (11.83)$$

we have

$$Bv = \mu v \quad (11.84)$$

where

$$\mu = \frac{\cos (q\pi h/b)}{2 - \cos (p\pi h/a)}. \quad (11.85)$$

If $a = b = 1$, we have, for the spectral radius of B,

$$\bar{\mu} = \frac{\cos \pi h}{2 - \cos \pi h} \sim 1 - \pi^2 h^2, \quad (11.86)$$

and the rate of convergence of successive line relaxation is

$$\lambda = \bar{\mu}^2 = \left(\frac{\cos \pi h}{2 - \cos \pi h}\right)^2 \sim 1 - 2\pi^2 h^2 \quad (11.87)$$

so that

$$R(L_1) = 2R(B) \sim 2\pi^2 h^2,$$

which is twice as large as for the method of successive point iteration, that is, the Gauss-Seidel method.

By (11.80) we have, for the method of successive line overrelaxation,

$$R(L_{\omega_b}) \sim 2\sqrt{R(L_1)} \sim 2\sqrt{2}\pi h.$$

Thus, as stated in Sec. 11.6, the rate of convergence of the method of successive line overrelaxation is approximately $\sqrt{2}$ times that of successive point overrelaxation.

11.11 p-cyclic Matrices

It was pointed out by Birkhoff and Varga [6, 44] that matrices with property A belong to a larger class of p-cyclic matrices essentially considered by Frobenius [18] and Romanovsky [34]. A matrix A is said to be *p-cyclic* ($p \geq 2$) if, by a permutation of the rows and of the corresponding columns of A, it can be placed in the form

$$A = \begin{pmatrix} D_1 & L_1 & 0 & \cdots & 0 \\ 0 & D_2 & L_2 & \cdots & 0 \\ & \cdots\cdots\cdots\cdots & & \\ & \cdots\cdots\cdots\cdots & & \\ 0 & 0 & 0 & \cdots & L_{p-1} \\ L_p & 0 & 0 & \cdots & D_p \end{pmatrix}, \tag{11.88}$$

where the submatrices L_i are rectangular matrices and where the diagonal submatrices D_i are square diagonal matrices.* Clearly, matrices with property A are 2-cyclic. As shown in [44], many results analogous to those discussed in Sec. 11.8 can be proved. For instance, if μ is an eigenvalue of B, then so is $\mu \exp(2\pi i k/p)$, $k = 1, 2, \ldots, p - 1$. The relation between the eigenvalues λ of L_ω and those of B is

$$(\lambda + \omega - 1)^p = \lambda^{p-1}\omega^p\mu^p,$$

from which it follows, for instance, that

$$R(L_1) = pR(B),$$

that is, the rate of convergence of the Gauss-Seidel method is p times that of the Jacobi method.

If all eigenvalues of B^p are real and nonnegative and if $0 < \lambda(B) < 1$, then the optimum relaxation factor ω_b is given by

$$\frac{(\omega_b - 1)}{\omega_b{}^p} \frac{p^p}{(p-1)^{p-1}} = [\lambda(B)]^p.$$

Evidently, when $p = 2$, we get $4(\omega_b - 1) = \omega_b{}^2[\lambda(B)]^2$, which is equivalent to (11.58). Moreover,

$$\lambda(L_{\omega_b}) = (\omega_b - 1)(p - 1),$$

and for $2 > \omega > \omega_b$ and $p \geq 2$,

$$\lambda(L_{\omega_b}) < \lambda(L_\omega) < (\omega - 1)(p - 1).$$

Asymptotically as $\lambda(B)$ tends to zero, we have

$$R(L_{\omega_b}) \sim \left(\frac{2p}{p-1}\right)^{1/2} [R(L_1)]^{1/2}.$$

* Actually, according to the original definition of a cyclic matrix, the D_i should be null matrices. However, if the diagonal elements of A are positive, the B matrix corresponding to A will be cyclic in the strict sense.

Thus the order-of-magnitude improvement which was seen to hold for $p = 2$ also holds for larger p.

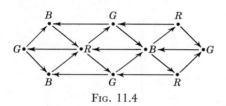

FIG. 11.4

An example of a problem with $p = 3$ is the use of a difference equation with a triangular net, shown in Fig. 11.4 where the difference equations for the points labeled R involve values of u at points labeled G, where the difference equations for points labeled G involve values of u at points labeled B, and where the difference equations for points labeled B involve only values of u at points labeled R.

11.12   Generalized Alternating-direction Implicit Method

The alternating-direction implicit method of Peaceman and Rachford can be generalized to include somewhat more general linear systems. The discussion here is based on [45, 5, 46].

Let us consider the linear system

$$(H + V)\,u + d = 0, \tag{11.89}$$

where H and V are symmetric positive definite square matrices and where u and d are unknown and known column matrices, respectively.   The basic assumption is made that H and V commute, that is, that

$$HV = VH. \tag{11.90}$$

The alternating-direction method of Peaceman and Rachford can be generalized as follows:

$$u^{(n+\frac{1}{2})} = u^{(n)} - r(Hu^{(n+\frac{1}{2})} + Vu^{(n)} + d), \tag{11.91}$$
$$u^{(n+1)} = u^{(n+\frac{1}{2})} - r(Hu^{(n+\frac{1}{2})} + Vu^{(n+1)} + d).$$

Here r is a parameter which may vary with n.   Usually H and V will be tridiagonal matrices, and the vectors $u^{(n+\frac{1}{2})}$ and $u^{(n)}$ can be found by solving successively the linear systems

$$(I + rH)u^{(n+\frac{1}{2})} = (I - rV)u^{(n)} - rd,$$
$$(I + rV)u^{(n+1)} = (I - rH)u^{(n+\frac{1}{2})} - rd,$$

using the algorithm described in Sec. 11.6.   Eliminating $u^{(n+\frac{1}{2})}$ from (11.91), we get

$$u^{(n+1)} = Q_r u^{(n)} + c, \tag{11.92}$$

where

$$Q_r = (I + rV)^{-1}(I - rH)(I + rH)^{-1}(I - rV),$$
$$c = -[(I + rV)^{-1}(I - rH)(I + rH)^{-1} + (I + rV)^{-1}]rd. \tag{11.93}$$

Since H and V are symmetric positive definite matrices, there exists a common basis of eigenvectors for both H and V (see, e.g., [46], Appendix A). Consequently, if λ and μ are eigenvalues of H and V, respectively, with common eigenvector v, then v is also an eigenvector of $(I + rV)^{-1}$, $(I - rH)$, $(I + rH)^{-1}$, $(I - rV)$, and hence of Q_r. The corresponding eigenvalue of Q_r is

$$F(\lambda,\mu,r) = \frac{(1 - r\lambda)(1 - r\mu)}{(1 + r\lambda)(1 + r\mu)}. \tag{11.94}$$

Moreover, every eigenvalue of Q_r is given by (11.94) for some eigenvalues of λ and μ of H and V, respectively.

The successive use of $r_1, r_2, \ldots, r_t$ leads to eigenvalues

$$\prod_{k=1}^{t} F(\lambda,\mu,r_k) = \prod_{k=1}^{t} \frac{(1 - r_k\lambda)(1 - r_k\mu)}{(1 + r_k\lambda)(1 + r_k\mu)}$$

of the matrix $\prod_{k=1}^{t} Q_{r_k}$. For a given t, it is desired to choose the r_k so that we can minimize the maximum absolute value of this expression, the maximum being taken over all eigenvalues λ and μ of H and V, respectively. The method suggested in [45] and [46] for choosing the r_k is according to the following formula:

$$r_k = \frac{1}{bx^{k-1}}, \qquad k = 1, 2, \ldots, t,$$

where

$$x = \left(\frac{a}{b}\right)^{1/(t-1)}.$$

Here all values of λ and μ are assumed to lie in the range $0 < a \leq \lambda$, $\mu \leq b$. An estimate for the factor of reduction after the t double sweeps is

$$P_t = \left[\frac{1 - \sqrt{x}}{1 + \sqrt{x}} e^{-x^{3/2}/(1-x)}\right]^4.$$

As remarked in Sec. 11.7, one should choose the integer t so that $S_t = (P_t)^{1/t}$ is minimized, though this choice is subject, of course, to the restriction that P_t should not be too small. Thus, if we desire to reduce the initial error to a fraction ρ of its initial value, then P_t should not be less than ρ. On the other hand, it may prove to be advantageous to choose t such that $P_t > \rho$. In this case, several sets of t double sweeps each would be required in order to achieve the desired convergence.

The analysis of the example considered in Sec. 11.7 is included in the foregoing discussion. The matrices H and V correspond to the difference operators

$$2u(x,y) - [u(x + h, y) + u(x - h, y)]$$

and

$$2u(x,y) - [u(x, y + h) + u(x, y - h)],$$

respectively.   They are easily seen to be symmetric and positive definite and, for the case of a rectangular region, they commute with each other. Clearly the sum of these two difference operators is the negative of the Laplace difference operator.   Finally, we remark that for the unit square with mesh size h, the eigenvalues of both H and V lie in the range

$$4 \sin^2 \frac{\pi h}{2} \le \lambda, \mu \le 4 \cos^2 \frac{\pi h}{2}.$$

The basic theory underlying the Peaceman-Rachford method cannot be extended to include all self-adjoint elliptic equations or to apply to nonrectangular regions, as is possible for the successive-overrelaxation method.*   In fact, Birkhoff and Varga [5] have shown that for Laplace's equation the condition (11.90) can hold only for a rectangle.   Although the alternating-direction method may well be very useful in more general cases than those involving Laplace's equation in the rectangle, it would appear that either more theoretical work or a great deal of successful computational experience is needed before the method can be recommended without reservation for general use.

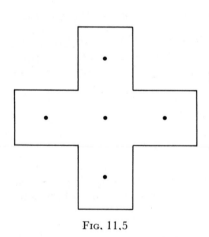

Even in the case of Laplace's difference equation for the region shown in Fig. 11.5, which contains only 5 net points, the matrix Q_r, with $r = 1$, has complex eigenvalues with relatively large imaginary parts.   If the theory which holds for the rectangle could be extended to more general regions, then, by (11.94), no complex eigenvalues could occur for real r.   The five eigenvalues of Q_1 are

FIG. 11.5

⅑,   ⅑,   0.2164, $-0.05039 + 0.08909i$, $-0.05039 - 0.08909i$.

* However, Wachspress, in a private communication, pointed out that, by using generalized conditions on H and V as formulated in [45], one can treat the case where the mesh spacings in both coordinate directions are not uniform.   To satisfy the generalized conditions, neither H nor V need be symmetric as long as there exists a positive definite matrix F such that HF and VF are positive definite.   It can be shown that, using the generalized conditions, one can apply the theory to problems involving the partial differential equations

$$\frac{\partial}{\partial x}\left[F(x)G(y)\frac{\partial u}{\partial x} \right] + \frac{\partial}{\partial y}\left[H(x)K(y)\frac{\partial u}{\partial y} \right] = S(x,y)$$

and the rectangle.

One important positive result concerning the Peaceman-Rachford method should be mentioned.   It has been proved in [46] that for any positive r the spectral radius of Q_r is less than one.   It is assumed that H and V are symmetric and positive definite, but they need not commute with each other.

11.13   Applications and Numerical Experiences

In this section some experiences derived from solving certain problems on high-speed computers are described.   Some problems were designed primarily to test the numerical methods, whereas others were actual practical problems.

As described in [57], a program was prepared for the ORDVAC computer at the Aberdeen Proving Ground, Maryland, for solving, for a class of regions, either the 5-point or the 9-point finite-difference analogue of the Dirichlet problem.   The main purpose in preparing this program, other than to study the accuracy of the finite-difference methods, as described in Sec. 11.4, was to evaluate the successive-overrelaxation method.   A number of Dirichlet problems were solved for different regions and using different values of ω.   As many as $19^2 = 361$ interior net points could be handled.   The behavior of the successive-over-relaxation method was very much as expected from the theory.   The effect of using the best relaxation factor reduced the number of iterations necessary for convergence by a factor which was as large as 10 in some cases.   For the square where the theoretical optimum ω is known exactly, the observed best ω was found to agree very closely.   It was also observed that, in accordance with the theory, the effect of using a value of ω slightly greater than optimum was much less serious than the effect of using one which was too small.   It was also observed that, if a certain value of ω was used, the number of iterations required was the same for all problems for which the optimum value was less than the value used.   This also agrees with the theory.   It was concluded that, if only a few problems are to be solved for a given region, then it is best to base the choice of ω on the computed value for an appropriate rectangle of the same area.   On the other hand, if a great many problems are to be solved, then it may pay to perform a number of iterations with $\omega = 1$ and to estimate $\lambda(L_1)$, from which ω can be computed by means of (11.40).   The variation of the number of iterations with ω for the 9-point formula was approximately the same as for the 5-point formula. As expected (see Sec. 11.9), the optimum ω for the 9-point formula was slightly smaller than for the 5-point formula.

A similar set of numerical experiments were performed in connection with the equation $U_{xx} + (k/y)U_y + U_{yy} = 0$ for various values of the constant k, as described in [59].   Boundary-value problems for the region $0 \leq A < y < A + B, C < x < D$ were treated. It was found that the methods developed by Warlick [50] for estimating the optimum value of ω were very satisfactory. On the other hand, values derived by assuming $k = 0$ gave results which were almost as good. It was observed that, although the use of the equation in the form given above rather than in the self-adjoint form $(y^k U_x)_x + (y^k U_y)_y = 0$ leads to equations which are not symmetric, the rates of convergence were almost the same as when the self-adjoint form of the equation was used.*

Among the important applications of elliptic partial differential equations are problems in weather prediction, nuclear-reactor physics, and in flow studies. Charney and Phillips describe in [8] the methods used at the Institute for Advanced Study with the IAS computer for weather prediction. Although the problem is, of course, three-dimensional and time-dependent, a basic step in the numerical process is the solution of a two-dimensional problem. The method of successive overrelaxation was used, with apparently satisfactory results.

As described in [58] and [4], an approximate solution was obtained to the problem of determining the axially symmetric flow past a pair of disks between which there is assumed to be a cavity, as shown in Fig. 11.6. The problem is unusually difficult because the boundary of the cavity is not known. It is necessary to assume a trial boundary, to solve an elliptic boundary-value problem, to test certain auxiliary boundary conditions, and, if these are not satisfied, to modify the boundary and repeat the process.

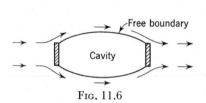

Free boundary

Cavity

Fig. 11.6

Since it is clearly necessary to solve many boundary-value problems before one can even hope to find the proper boundary, the rate of convergence of the iterative method used to solve the difference equation is of critical importance. This was particularly true in the computation described, since there were more than 1000 mesh points. Unfortunately, the use of the successive-overrelaxation method, although considerably better than the Gauss-Seidel method, was not so effective as was expected. Since the use of the estimated best value of ω led to a divergent process, it was necessary to use a much smaller value, with an accompanying loss in convergence speed. It is believed that this phenomenon was caused by the use of special difference formulas for points connecting regions of the fine and the coarse mesh. Different mesh sizes were used, since near the edges of the disks a mesh size was

* An explanation is given in [50].

needed which, if used throughout the entire region, would have involved too many mesh points.

Thus, suppose that the numbered points 1, 2, 4, 5 in Fig. 11.7 belong

$$.1 \quad .2 \qquad .a \quad .b \quad .c$$

$$.(z) \quad .d \quad .e \quad .f$$

$$.4 \quad .5 \qquad .g \quad .h \quad .i$$

Fig. 11.7

to the coarse mesh and that the points a to i belong to the fine mesh. The difference equations for points 2 and 5 involve certain adjacent points of the coarse mesh, as well as points b and h, respectively. The difference equations for b, c, e, f, h, and i involve points of the fine mesh. The only questions arise in connection with points like a, d, and g. Clearly, for a and g we can use adjacent points of the fine mesh and points 2 and 5, respectively. Now, in the work described in [58, 4] for point d a special formula was used which involved points 2, b, 5, and h. The use of this formula led to a system of linear equations with a matrix which was not symmetric and which did not have property A. Although these conditions are by no means *necessary* for convergence, the fact that they were not satisfied here had a very unfavorable effect.

Two methods are suggested for improving this situation. In the first of these, one introduces the point z and, instead of trying to represent the difference equation, one simply uses linear interpolation; that is, one lets $u_z = \frac{1}{2}(u_2 + u_5)$. Although the resulting linear system is not symmetric and does not have property A, the convergence is reported by Dr. R. J. Arms to be much improved, at least for some problems.

An alternative procedure would be to use a variational approach, already mentioned in Sec. 11.3. This would lead to a linear system with a symmetric and positive definite matrix. It would be necessary, however, to try to prevent the occurrence of negative coefficients. Kahan's results would indicate that the presence of negative coefficients would be a much more serious disadvantage than the fact that the matrix would not in general have property A. Further studies along these lines are indicated.*

A great deal of work is currently being done on two- and three-dimensional multigroup diffusion calculations arising in nuclear-reactor

*Note added in proof: Kahan (in a private communication) reports that in a number of numerical experiments the occurrence of small negative coefficients did not have a serious effect on the convergence. In every such case the matrix was symmetric.

studies (see, e.g., [39, 43, 46, 22]). Mathematically, a typical problem consists of a system of n simultaneous elliptic differential equations, each corresponding to one of n "groups" or neutron energy levels.* It is desired to determine a single parameter η, sometimes called the *criticality parameter*, which appears in one of the equations.

The usual procedure is to iterate with respect to the parameter η. Each such iteration is known as an "outer" iteration. Each outer iteration consists of solving successively each of the n equations for the corresponding function, assuming that the other $(n - 1)$ functions are known. The process of finding such a function is precisely that of solving an elliptic partial differential equation in a two- (or three-) dimensional region. Each iteration of the iterative process which is used to do this is known as an "inner" iteration. Thus, each outer iteration consists of n sets of inner iterations. Here more than ever, because of the large number of elliptic boundary-value problems which must be solved, the rate of convergence of the iterative procedure is crucial.

Varga describes in ⌊43⌋ a program for the IBM 704 computer for solving two group problems. This program, known as the QED code, has since been modified so as to handle four groups. The modified program is known as the PDQ code [62]. With a computer having 16000 words of core storage, up to 6500 mesh points can be handled in a rectangular region where, however, the coefficients of the differential equation are allowed to be discontinuous across straight lines known as *interfaces*. Across interfaces certain continuity conditions involving the functions u_i and their normal derivatives are imposed.

As described in [62], before beginning the iterative process, the best overrelaxation factor corresponding to each differential equation is estimated. The largest eigenvalue of the matrix B (see Sec. 11.8) is found by an iteration scheme due to Hestenes and Karush [63]. Considerable success with the method has been obtained, with the result that the PDQ code is now regarded as among the best nuclear-reactor programs presently available.

Wachspress describes in [46] the CURE program for the IBM 704 computer which can be used to solve neutron diffusion problems involving three groups and as many as 3000 mesh points. The Peaceman-Rachford method of iteration is used. The convergence of the method has been reported to be extremely satisfactory even for cases where the present theory does not apply.

---

* It may also be considered as a single equation relating an elliptic differential operator to a derivative with respect to a "timelike" variable (see, e.g., [39]). This equation is known as the *age diffusion equation*.

PARABOLIC EQUATIONS

11.14 Introduction

We shall consider the class of parabolic partial differential equations

$$U_t = U_{xx} + \phi(x,t,U) \qquad (11.95)$$

and

$$U_t = U_{xx} + U_{yy} + \psi(x,y,t,U), \qquad (11.96)$$

where U is the dependent variable and $\phi = \phi(x,t,U)$ and $\psi = \psi(x,y,t,U)$ are analytic functions of their arguments. It is easy to show that the types of boundary conditions which can be imposed for parabolic equations and which lead to problems with unique solutions are quite different from those for elliptic equations. For instance, with (11.95) we cannot in general prescribe values of U over a closed curve in the (x,t) plane. We can, however, impose the following boundary conditions:

$$U(0,t) = g_1(t), \qquad (11.97a)$$

$$U(1,t) = g_2(t), \qquad (11.97b)$$

$$U(x,0) = f(x). \qquad (11.97c)$$

The functions $g_1(t)$, $g_2(t)$, and $f(x)$ are given functions of their arguments which are continuous except for a finite number of finite jumps. Here we are considering the region K: $0 < x < 1, t > 0$. Since t frequently refers to the time variable, we sometimes refer to (11.97c) as an *initial condition*.

Whereas for elliptic equations the value of the solution at any one point depends on all the boundary values, in problems defined by (11.95) and (11.97) the value of $u(x_0,t_0)$ depends only on the values of $f(x)$ and on the values of $g_1(t)$ and $g_2(t)$ for values of t in the range $0 \le t \le t_0$. This has important implications for the determination of numerical solutions by the use of finite-difference methods. In problems involving parabolic equations one can construct numerical solutions step by step, using a so-called "marching" process. For elliptic problems, on the other hand, the solution cannot be found at any single point until it is found at all points.

Although the foregoing would tend to indicate that it is much simpler to compute the numerical solution of parabolic problems than of elliptic problems, the use of marching procedures introduces a difficulty not present in elliptic problems, namely, the problem of *stability*. Considerations of stability make it necessary to reject certain otherwise satisfactory methods. However, as shown in the next two sections, the stability problem can be overcome in an entirely satisfactory manner by the use of so-called "implicit" methods.

In Sec. 11.17 we discuss the solution of problems involving two space variables in addition to the time variable. The alternating-direction implicit method of Douglas [11] appears to be among the most promising for such problems. The close relation between the methods used to solve these problems and certain iterative methods for solving elliptic equations is brought out in Sec. 11.17. In Sec. 11.18 a procedure developed by Garabedian [19] is used to study the rate of convergence of the successive-overrelaxation method by considering a certain hyperbolic differential equation.

11.15   The Forward Difference Method

Although the discussion here and in the following section is limited to problems in two variables, x and t, involving Eqs. (11.95) and (11.97), much of what is said applies also to problems involving (11.96).

Perhaps the simplest finite-difference method for solving problems defined by (11.95) and (11.97) is the *forward difference method*. First one considers a network of points (x,t) such that $x = ih, i = 0, 1, 2, \ldots, M$, where M is an integer and $h = M^{-1}$, and such that $t = jk$. Here h and k represent the space and time increments, respectively. Let us consider a typical 4-point configuration, as shown in Fig. 11.8.

We represent the space derivative by

$$(U_{xx})_0 \doteq \frac{U_1 + U_3 - 2U_0}{h^2} \tag{11.98}$$

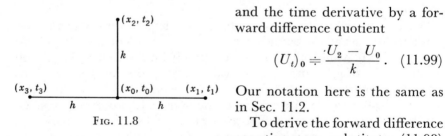

FIG. 11.8

and the time derivative by a forward difference quotient

$$(U_t)_0 \doteq \frac{U_2 - U_0}{k}. \tag{11.99}$$

Our notation here is the same as in Sec. 11.2.

To derive the forward difference equation, we substitute (11.98) and (11.99) in (11.95), obtaining, upon replacement of x_0 by x and t_0 by t, etc.,

$$u(x, t + k) = r[u(x + h, t) + u(x - h, t)] \\ + (1 - 2r)u(x,t) + rh^2\phi[x,t,u(x,t)], \tag{11.100}$$

where, for convenience, we let

$$r = \frac{k}{h^2}. \tag{11.101}$$

If we let $u_{i,j} = u(ih, jk)$, $\phi_{i,j} = \phi(ih, jk, u_{i,j})$, $f_i = f(ih)$, etc., then we have

$$u_{i,j+1} = r(u_{i+1,j} + u_{i-1,j}) + (1 - 2r)u_{i,j} + rh^2\phi_{i,j},$$
$$i = 1, 2, \ldots, M - 1; \quad j = 1, 2, \ldots . \quad (11.102)$$

Since $u_{i,0} = f_i$, $u_{0,j} = (g_1)_j$, $u_{M,j} = (g_2)_j$, one can readily compute successively $u_{i,1}$ for each i, then $u_{i,2}$, etc.

In [25] it is shown that, for the case $\phi \equiv 0$, $g_1 \equiv g_2 \equiv 0$, the solutions of the difference equation converge to the solution of (11.95) and (11.97), provided r is fixed and $r \leq \frac{1}{2}$. For the same case, Leutert [30] has shown the existence of a set of solutions of the difference equation with $r > \frac{1}{2}$ which converge to the solution of (11.95) and (11.97). This set of solutions was constructed, not to be used in practice, but simply to demonstrate the distinction between *convergence* and *stability*.

The problem of stability and its relation to the problem of convergence have been treated in a number of papers (e.g., [42, 29, 23, 31, 13]). It is very difficult to define precisely what is meant by the term "stability." Roughly speaking, if a process is unstable and if an error, such as a rounding error, is made at any stage af the computation, this error will increase exponentially as j increases. It frequently happens that an unstable process is not convergent, although Leutert's example shows that this is not always the case.

We shall try to illustrate some of the foregoing by an example. Let us assume $g_1 \equiv g_2 \equiv 0$ and $\phi \equiv 0$. Let $f(x) \equiv 1$, $0 < x < 1$, $f(0) = f(1) = 0$. Let $h = \frac{1}{4}$ and $r = \frac{1}{2}$. Our difference equation (11.102) becomes

$$u_{i,j+1} = \frac{1}{2}(u_{i+1,j} + u_{i-1,j}) \quad (i = 1, 2, 3; j = 0, 1, 2, \ldots),$$
$$u_{i,0} = 1 \quad (i = 1, 2, 3), \quad (11.103)$$
$$u_{0,j} = u_{4,j} = 0 \quad (j = 0, 1, 2, \ldots).$$

The numerical solution may be given by the following table. (The quantities in parentheses should be temporarily ignored.)

j \ i	0	1	2	3	4
0	0	1.000	1.000	1.000	0
1	0	.500	1.000	.500	0
2	0	.500	.500 $(+\epsilon)$	.500	0
3	0	.250 $(+\epsilon/2)$	.500	.250 $(+\epsilon/2)$	0
4	0	.250	.250 $(+\epsilon/2)$	.250	0
5	0	.125 $(+\epsilon/4)$	.250	.125 $(+\epsilon/4)$	0

It is not difficult to believe that, even though the values obtained for any given h are not "smooth," the numbers obtained by this process would approach the exact solution of the differential equation as h and

k were decreased.   To study the stability, let us introduce an error of ϵ in $u_{2,2}$.   Because the problem is linear, we can study the error separately, as indicated in the above table.   We note that in this case the error decreases with j and the process is stable.

Let us next consider the case where $r = 1$.   Equation (11.102) becomes

$$u_{i,j+1} = u_{i+1,j} + u_{i-1,j} - u_{i,j},$$

and we obtain the following results:

j \ i	0	1	2	3	4
0	0	1	1	1	0
1	0	0	$1(+\epsilon)$	0	0
2	0	$1(+\epsilon)$	$-1(-\epsilon)$	$1(+\epsilon)$	0
3	0	$-2(-2\epsilon)$	$3(+3\epsilon)$	$-2(-2\epsilon)$	0
4	0	$5(+5\epsilon)$	$-7(-7\epsilon)$	$5(+5\epsilon)$	0
5	0	$-12(-12\epsilon)$	$17(+17\epsilon)$	$-12(-12\epsilon)$	0

Since it is easy to show that in this problem all values of u lie between zero and unity, it is clear that the above numbers are considerably in error and that the error is increasing rapidly with j.   We are not surprised to learn that this process is not convergent.   Moreover, a stability analysis similar to the one performed previously for the case $r = \frac{1}{2}$ indicates that the process is not stable.

If the initial values were defined by $f(x) \equiv \sin x$, then the method would be convergent, though not stable.   Thus we would obtain the following results:

j \ i	0	1	2	3	4
0	0	.707	1.000	.707	0
1	0	.293	.414	.293	0
2	0	.121	.172	.121	0
3	0	.051	.070	.051	0
4	0	.019	.032	.019	0
5	0	.013	.006	.013	0
6	0	-.007	.020	-.007	0

Here the values are "respectable" until we reach $j = 5$, when, because of rounding errors, they begin to oscillate.   If we had carried more decimal places in our calculations, the occurrence of the oscillation would have been delayed.   Finally, if we had used exact values throughout, that is, if we had used $\sqrt{2}/2$ instead of .707, etc., the oscillations would never have occurred.   Naturally, these latter considerations are largely academic, and one must in practice use $r \leq \frac{1}{2}$ with the forward difference method.

11.16   The Crank-Nicolson Method

The requirement that the ratio r ($= k/h^2$) be fixed implies that, as h tends to zero, k tends to zero very rapidly.   This means that, if one is interested in the value of u for a particular point (x,t) and if one halves h, then the number of time steps must be increased by a factor of 4.   The amount of computation required would thus be increased by a factor of 8.

This difficulty may be overcome at a moderate cost by the use of the implicit difference equation used by Crank and Nicolson [10].   The difference equation is the same as the forward difference equation except that in the approximation to U_{xx} one uses, not the difference quotient involving values of u for the current value of t, but the average of the difference quotients for the current and for the new value of t.

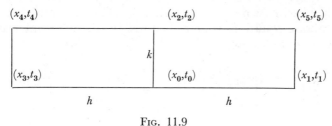

(x_4,t_4) (x_2,t_2) (x_5,t_5)

k

(x_3,t_3) (x_0,t_0) (x_1,t_1)

h h

FIG. 11.9

Accordingly, we use the following formula for $(U_{xx})_0$:

$$(U_{xx})_0 \doteq \frac{1}{2}\left(\frac{U_1 + U_3 - 2U_0}{h^2} + \frac{U_5 + U_4 - 2U_2}{h^2}\right)$$

and obtain, upon substitution into (11.95) and replacement of U by u,

$$u_{i,j+1} = \frac{r}{2}\left(u_{i+1,i} + u_{i-1,i} + u_{i+1,j+1} + u_{i-1,j+1} - 2u_{i,j+1}\right) + (1 - r)u_{i,j}$$
$$+ rh^2\phi_{i,j}, \qquad i = 1, 2, \ldots, M - 1; j = 0, 1, 2, \ldots. \tag{11.104}$$

Since Eq. (11.104) involves $u_{i+1,j+1}$ and $u_{i-1,j+1}$ as well as $u_{i,j+1}$, it is said to be an *implicit* difference equation.   Given $u_{i,j}$ for $i = 1, 2, \ldots, M - 1$ as well as $u_{0,j}$, $u_{M,j}$, $u_{0,j+1}$, and $u_{M,j+1}$, in order to find $u_{i,j+1}$ for $i = 1, 2, \ldots, M - 1$ we must solve a system of $(M - 1)$ linear algebraic equations with $(M - 1)$ unknowns.   One way of doing this would be to use the successive-overrelaxation method.   It is not difficult to show that $\bar{\mu} \le 1/(1 + r)$, from which the optimum value of ω can be found by the following formula:

$$\omega_b = 1 + \left(\frac{\bar{\mu}}{1 + \sqrt{1 - \bar{\mu}^2}}\right)^2.$$

Such a procedure was used in [60].   Evidently the rate of convergence decreases as r increases.   If k is chosen proportional to h as h decreases, then the total computational effort varies as $h^{-5/2}$ with the above procedure, as compared with h^{-3} for the forward difference method.

We remark that greater accuracy can be obtained by using

$$(rh^2/2)(\phi_{i,j} + \phi_{i,j+1})$$

instead of $rh^2\phi_{i,j}$ in (11.104).   Experience has indicated (see [60]) that the number of iterations necessary with the successive-overrelaxation method changes very little when this modification is introduced.

Since the matrix of the linear system to be solved at each time step is tridiagonal, one can use the method described in Sec. 11.6 [see (11.43) and (11.44)] to solve the linear system involved in passing from a given time step to the next.   As mentioned earlier, the first use of this algorithm to solve parabolic equations is described in [7].   The formulas as applied to (11.104) are as follows:

$$D_{i,j} = \frac{r}{2(1+r)}(u_{i-1,j} + u_{i+1,j}) + \frac{1-r}{1+r}u_{i,j} + \frac{rh^2}{1+r}\phi_{i,j},$$
$$i = 1, 2, \ldots, M-1;$$

$$b_{0,j} = 0, \qquad b_{i,j} = -\frac{r}{2(1+r)}\Big/\Big[1 + \frac{r}{2(1+r)}b_{i-1,j}\Big],$$
$$i = 1, 2, \ldots, M-2;$$

$$\hspace{8cm}(11.105)$$

$$q_{1,j} = D_{1,j}, \qquad q_{i,j} = \Big[D_{i,j} + \frac{r}{2(1+r)}q_{i-1,j}\Big]\Big/$$
$$\Big[1 + \frac{r}{2(1+r)}b_{i-1,j}\Big], i = 2, 3, \ldots, M-1;$$

$$u_{M-1,j+1} = q_{M-1,j}, \qquad u_{i,j+1} = q_{i,j} - b_{i,j}u_{i+1,j+1},$$
$$i = M-2, M-3, \ldots, 1.$$

Let us consider now the example given in Sec. 11.15 with $r = 1$. Proceeding from $j = 0$ to $j = 1$, we obtain the following:

i $\diagdown$ j	0	1	2	3	4
0 $u_{i,j}$	0	1.000	1.000	1.000	0
D_{ij}	...	.250	.500	.250	...
$b_{i,j}$	0	−.250	−.266	...	...
$q_{i,j}$	...	.250	.600	.428	...
1 $u_{i,j}$	0	.428	.714	.428	0

We see that the amount of work necessary per time step is approximately four times as great as for the forward difference method.   However, the size of time step k can be made much larger.   If we assume that k varies as h, as h tends to zero, then the work involved increases as h^{-2} with the Crank-Nicolson method, compared with h^{-3} with the forward difference method.   Of course the constants of proportionality are different.   We have already seen how a factor of approximately 4 is introduced by using the algorithm for solving the special linear system.   Also, if ϕ occurring in the differential equation is nonlinear, one may need to apply the formulas (11.105) two or more times.   After the first application of (11.105) we would normally replace $\phi_{i,j}$ by $\tfrac{1}{2}(\phi_{i,j} + \phi_{i,j+1})$ and reapply (11.105).   Generally speaking, one such iteration should be sufficient to obtain an accuracy consistent with that which is inherent in the basic difference equation.   Therefore, even for nonlinear equations there is still an important order-of-magnitude advantage of the Crank-Nicolson method over the forward difference method.

The Crank-Nicolson method is stable for all values of r and, in fact, is stable for any pair of positive values h and k.   Moreover, for cases where $\phi \equiv 0$ and where $g_1 \equiv g_2 \equiv 0$, Juncosa and Young [26] have proved that the method is convergent, provided $f(x)$ is piecewise continuous and provided $k = O(h/|\log h|)$ as h tends to zero.   This of course implies convergence for all r.   We remark that an error in logic which is frequently made when discussing such matters is to assume that, since there are no restrictions on r, then there are no restrictions on k.   We also remark that, although convergence has been proved only for $k = O(h/|\log h|)$, it appears likely that it holds also for $k = O(h)$.   This assumption has been made in the previous comparisons of the Crank-Nicolson and the forward difference methods.

11.17   Problems Involving Two Space Dimensions

Let us consider the following problem: given a bounded plane region R with boundary S and given functions $f(x,y)$ defined in R and $g(x,y,t)$ defined on S', find a function $U(x,y,t)$ which is continuous in $R' + S'$ and satisfies

$$U_{xx} + U_{yy} = U_t \quad \text{in } R',$$

$$U(x,y,0) = f(x,y), \qquad (x,y) \in R, \qquad (11.106)$$

$$U(x,y,t) = g(x,y,t), \qquad (x,y,t) \in S'.$$

Here R' and S' are the sets of all points (x,y,t) such that $t > 0$ and $(x,y) \in R$ and such that $t \geq 0$ and $(x,y) \in S$, respectively.   It is assumed that U is twice differentiable with respect to x and y and once differentiable with respect to t in R'.

For simplicity, we restrict our attention to the case where $R + S$ is a rectangle with sides $a = Mh$, $b = Nh$ (M, N integers) and $h = \Delta x = \Delta y$ is the common space increment. It should be noted, however, that much of what follows applies to considerably more general regions.

The simplest method again is the forward difference method. The formulas and the method are direct extensions of those discussed in Sec. 11.15. The formula is

$$
\begin{aligned}
u(x, y, t + \Delta t) = u(x, y, t) + r[u(x + \Delta x, y, t) + u(x - \Delta x, y, t) \\
+ u(x, y + \Delta y, t) + u(x, y - \Delta y, t) - 4u(x, y, t)].
\end{aligned}
$$
$$(11.107)$$

We remark that the condition on $k = \Delta t$ for stability and convergence is now

$$
r = \frac{k}{h^2} \leq \frac{1}{4}.
$$
$$(11.108)$$

As before, although the computational scheme is explicit and straightforward, the requirement of (11.108) imposes such a severe limitation on the size of k that the method is of doubtful practicality.

It is perhaps interesting to note that there is a very close connection between the method just described and Richardson's method of iteration [33] for solving Laplace's equation, of which the Jacobi method of simultaneous displacements is, in this instance, a special case. Thus, if we replace $u(x, y, t)$ by $u^{(n)}(x, y)$ and $u(x, y, t + k)$ by $u^{(n+1)}(x, y)$ in (11.107), we get

$$
\begin{aligned}
u^{(n+1)}(x, y) = u^{(n)}(x, y) + r[u^{(n)}(x + h, y) + u^{(n)}(x - h, y) \\
+ u^{(n)}(x, y + h) + u^{(n)}(x, y - h) - 4u^{(n)}(x, y)],
\end{aligned}
$$
$$(11.109)$$

which for $r = \frac{1}{4}$ reduces to the Jacobi method.

For the rectangle the eigenvalues associated with this method are

$$
\mu_{p,q} = 1 - 4r\left(\sin^2 \frac{p\pi h}{2a} + \sin^2 \frac{q\pi h}{2b}\right)
$$
$$(p = 1, 2, \ldots, M - 1; \qquad q = 1, 2, \ldots, N - 1). \quad (11.110)$$

These correspond to the eigenvectors

$$
(v_{p,q})_{i,j} = \sin \frac{p\pi i h}{a} \sin \frac{q\pi j h}{b},
$$
$$(11.111)$$

which vanish on the boundary of the rectangle.

Roughly speaking, the number of iterations needed for convergence for the elliptic equation is closely related to the number of time increments needed to achieve "steady state" in the associated transient heat-flow problem.   Since the larger the t variable, the closer one is to a steady-state condition (assuming that the boundary values for u are constant), one would like to take as large a value of k as possible.   However, by (11.110), we are limited by stability considerations for the transient problem.   If we wish to use a fixed value of r, we can take r only very slightly greater than $\frac{1}{4}$.   Actually the r for which the maximum of $\mu_{p,q}$ over all p,q is minimized is $r = \frac{1}{4}$.

On the other hand, by taking r considerably larger than $\frac{1}{4}$, we may reduce certain components of the error [corresponding to some of the pairs (p,q)], but at the same time we may increase others.   By choosing a sequence of values of r based on Chebyshev polynomials and by using these values repeatedly in a cyclic order—as described, for instance, in [56]—the components of the error can all be reduced by more or less uniform amounts.   There are two major practical difficulties associated with the method.   First, it was found in [56, 54, 61] that, even when care was exercised in the choice of the order in which the values of r were used, the control of rounding errors was a serious problem.   It appears that this difficulty can be at least partially overcome by the use of a formula which is analogous to (11.109) but which involves $u^{(n-1)}$ as well as $u^{(n)}$ and $u^{(n+1)}$ (see, e.g., [40] and [46], Appendix C).   This formula is based on the use of a three-term recurrence relation for Chebyshev polynomials.   The use of the new formula also appears preferable because after m iterations, for any m, the result which one obtains is equivalent to that which one would have obtained by applying (11.109) m times using the best set of m values of r.   If one uses (11.109) itself, however, with a fixed number, say s, of different values of r, the only intermediate results which would in general have significance would be those obtained after each set of s iterations.

The second difficulty, or limitation, associated with Richardson's method essentially rests on the fact that, in significantly reducing some error components, others may be substantially increased.   It would be very desirable to have a method by means of which one could reduce any error component without increasing others.   Both the methods of Peaceman and Rachford [32] and of Douglas and Rachford [12], the first of which is described later in this section, have this property, at least in certain special cases.

The Crank-Nicolson method for problems involving two or more space variables is likewise a direct generalization of the method described in Sec. 11.16 for one space variable.   In order to proceed from one time step to another, one must solve the difference analogue of a Dirichlet problem in two dimensions.   Unfortunately there does not appear to be any simple scheme for doing this, as there was in the case of one space dimension.   In a manner similar to that described in Sec. 11.16, a good estimate of the optimum relaxation function for the iterative process is very easy to make.   Indeed, a good value of $\bar{u}$ to be used in the formula for the optimum relaxation factor would be $\bar{u} = 2r/(1 + 2r)$.   There are no limitations on k and h as far as stability is concerned and, as in the one-dimensional case, it appears that convergence could be proved for $k = O(h)$; consequently the work required varies as $h^{-\frac{7}{2}}$, compared with h^{-4} with the forward difference method.

There does not appear to be any useful interpretation of the Crank-Nicolson method to iterative methods for solving elliptic difference equations.   The reason for this is that no techniques other than any of the already-known iterative methods have been used to carry out the process.

Two methods for solving time-dependent problems have led to new techniques for solving elliptic equations.   We restrict our attention here to the method of Douglas, Peaceman, and Rachford [11] and [32], even though the method of Douglas and Rachford is somewhat more general, in that it can be extended to apply to three dimensions.   The former method appears to be somewhat more efficient in certain special cases.

The basic process of passing from t to $t + k$ is performed in two parts. Each part involves an implicit formula for which, however, the associated matrix is tridiagonal.   In the first part one has to solve an implicit system for the rows, whereas in the second part one has an implicit system for the columns.   The actual formulas are the following:

$$u\left(x, y, t + \frac{k}{2}\right) = u(x,y,t) + r\left[u\left(x + h, y, t + \frac{k}{2}\right) + u\left(x - h, y, t + \frac{k}{2}\right)\right.$$

$$\left. - 2u\left(x, y, t + \frac{k}{2}\right) + u(x, y + h, t) + u(x, y - h, t) - 2u(x,y,t)\right],$$

$$u(x, y, t + k) = u\left(x, y, t + \frac{k}{2}\right) + r\left[u\left(x + h, y, t + \frac{k}{2}\right)\right. \tag{11.112}$$

$$+ u\left(x - h, y, t + \frac{k}{2}\right) - 2u\left(x, y, t + \frac{k}{2}\right) + u(x, y + h, t + k)$$

$$\left. + u(x, y - h, t + k) - 2u(x, y, t + k)\right].$$

Here we let

$$r = k/2h^2$$

instead of the usual value k/h^2.

It is shown in [11] that the local approximation of the difference equation (11.112) to the differential equation $u_t = u_{xx} + u_{yy}$ is of the same order in h and k as is the Crank-Nicolson difference equation.   On the other hand, since each step of the present procedure can be carried out explicitly, using the formulas given in Sec. 11.6, the amount of work required is much less than for the Crank-Nicolson method.   It is further shown in [11] that, for the case of the rectangle, the method is stable for any pair of values h and k.   It is interesting to note that the repeated use of either part of (11.112) alone would yield a process which could be unstable for some values of h and k.

As shown in [32], the fact that one is able to take large time steps with relatively little effort suggests that one could develop an efficient iterative procedure for solving the difference analogue of Laplace's equation.   As a matter of fact, since formulas analogous to (11.112) could be derived corresponding to the differential equation $u_t = L(u)$, where $L(u)$ is a more general elliptic operator, such a method could be, formally at least, applicable to a much wider class of elliptic equations.   If we replace $u(x,y,t)$ by $u^{(n)}(x,y)$, $u(x,y, t + k/2)$ by $u^{(n+\frac12)}(x,y)$, and $u(x,y, t + k)$ by $u^{(n+1)}(x,y)$, we get formula (11.46).   The method so obtained is frequently referred to as the *Peaceman-Rachford method* and also as the *alternating-direction implicit method*.   The former terminology seems preferable, since both the Peaceman-Rachford method and the Douglas-Rachford method are alternating-direction implicit methods.

Following an analysis similar to that given for the derivation of (11.112), we have for a single row iteration

$$\mu'_{p,q} = \frac{1 - 4r \sin^2 (q\pi h/2)}{1 + 4r \sin^2 (p\pi h/2)}$$

and for a single column iteration

$$\mu''_{p,q} = \frac{1 - 4r \sin^2 (p\pi h/2)}{1 + 4r \sin^2 (q\pi h/2)}.$$

For a double iteration we have

$$\mu_{p,q} = \frac{1 - 4r \sin^2 (q\pi h/2)}{1 + 4r \sin^2 (q\pi h/2)} \cdot \frac{1 - 4r \sin^2 (p\pi h/2)}{1 + 4r \sin^2 (p\pi h/2)}.$$

We note that in contrast to the situation for the forward difference method, all of the $\mu_{p,q}$ are less than one in absolute value for all r.   We note that even here, where we can safely take values of r as large as we please, we nevertheless cannot achieve arbitrarily rapid convergence merely by choosing r sufficiently large.   As described in Secs. 11.7 and 11.12, the convergence is accelerated by choosing a set of s different values of r so as approximately to minimize the expression

$$\max_{\substack{1 \le p \le M-1 \\ 1 \le q \le N-1}} \prod_{k=1}^{s} |\mu_{p,q}(r_k)|.$$

11.18 Estimation of Convergence Rates for Elliptic Problems

We have already seen how methods for solving parabolic partial differential equations often lead to iterative methods for solving difference-equation analogues of elliptic equations.   The methods considered in the preceding section led to methods of simultaneous displacements, in which new values obtained during an iteration are not used until after a complete iteration.   Such simultaneous-displacement methods can be associated with parabolic equations.   On the other hand, certain methods of successive displacements, such as the successive-overrelaxation method, can be associated with hyperbolic equations.   Furthermore, an analysis of such equations can often be used to provide information concerning the rate of convergence of the iterative method.

For example, let us consider a one-dimensional finite-difference analogue of the Dirichlet problem

$$u_i = \tfrac{1}{2}(u_{i-1} + u_{i+1}), \tag{11.113}$$

where u_0 and u_M are given.   Of course, this difference equation could very easily be solved analytically.   However, the analysis of the successive-overrelaxation method as applied to this problem is similar to that for more complicated problems.

The iterative formula for the successive-overrelaxation method is

$$u_i^{(n+1)} = \frac{\omega}{2}\,(u_{i+1}^{(n)} + u_{i-1}^{(n+1)}) - (\omega - 1)u_i^{(n)}. \tag{11.114}$$

We seek to obtain by a method which is a slight modification of that used by Garabedian [19] a related hyperbolic equation, the analysis of which will lead to an approximate formula for the optimum relaxation factor.

We let $u_i^{(n)} = u(x,t)$, $u_i^{(n+1)} = u(x, t + k)$, and $u_{i\pm1}^{(n)} = u(x \pm h, t)$. Equation (11.114) becomes

$$u(x, t + k) = \frac{\omega}{2}\,[u(x + h, t) + u(x - h, t + k)] - (\omega - 1)u(x,t). \tag{11.115}$$

Expanding by Taylor's theorem about (x,t), we get

$$u + ku_t + \frac{k^2}{2}u_{tt} + \cdots = \frac{\omega}{2}\left(u + hu_x + \frac{h^2}{2}u_{xx} + \cdots + u - hu_x \right.$$
$$\left. + ku_t + \frac{h^2}{2}u_{xx} - hku_{xt} + \frac{k^2}{2}u_{tt} + \cdots\right) - (\omega - 1)u.$$

Neglecting terms involving h^3, h^2k, hk^2, k^3, and higher-order terms, we have*

$$\left(ku_t + \frac{k^2}{2} u_{tt}\right)\left(1 - \frac{\omega}{2}\right) = \frac{\omega}{2}\left(h^2 u_{xx} - hk u_{xt}\right).$$

Dividing both sides by $hk\omega/2$ and letting $h/k = a$, we obtain

$$C\left(u_t + \frac{k}{2} u_{tt}\right) = a u_{xx} - u_{xt}, \tag{11.116}$$

where

$$C = \frac{2 - \omega}{\omega h}. \tag{11.117}$$

Introducing the new variable $s = t + (\frac{1}{2}a)x$ and letting $U(x,s) = u[x, s - (\frac{1}{2}a)x]$, we get

$$C\left(U_s + \frac{k}{2} U_{ss}\right) = a U_{xx} - \frac{1}{4a} U_{ss}. \tag{11.118}$$

Now, using the method of separation of variables, we let $U(x,s) = X(x)S(s)$, obtaining, upon substitution in (11.118),

$$a \frac{X''(x)}{X(x)} = \frac{(1/4a + Ck/2)S''(s) + CS'(s)}{S(s)}. \tag{11.119}$$

In the study of the convergence rate of the method defined by (11.114), it is sufficient to consider the difference $u_i^{(n)} - u_i$. Hence we may assume that $u_0^{(n)} = u_M^{(n)} = 0$ for all n or, equivalently, that $u(0,t) = u(1,t) = 0$ for all t. This implies that $X(0) = X(1) = 0$. Since both sides of (11.119) must be constant, we have $X(x) = \sin p\pi x, p = 1, 2, \ldots$. Moreover, we may let $S(s) = e^{-\beta s}$, where β satisfies

$$\left(\frac{1}{4a} + C\frac{k}{2}\right)\beta^2 - C\beta + a p^2\pi^2 = 0$$

or

$$\left(\frac{1}{4} + \frac{Ch}{2}\right)\left(\frac{\beta}{a}\right)^2 - C\left(\frac{\beta}{a}\right) + p^2\pi^2 = 0. \tag{11.120}$$

Solving for (β/a), we obtain

$$\frac{\beta}{a} = \frac{C \pm \sqrt{C^2 - p^2\pi^2(1 + 2Ch)}}{\frac{1}{2}(1 + 2Ch)}. \tag{11.121}$$

We assert that the rate of convergence for the method defined by (11.114) is determined by the smallest value which the real part of (β/a) can assume for all positive integral values of p. For on a single iteration

---

* Garabedian [19] neglected the terms involving k^2. The result obtained here agrees with Garabedian's result to a first-order approximation.

the error is reduced by a factor $e^{-\beta k} = e^{-(\beta/a)h}$. Thus, for given h, the larger this minimum value of (β/a), the faster will be the convergence rate. We seek to show that, to a first approximation, the optimum choice of C is π and the corresponding minimum value is 2π.

Let C_1 be the positive root of the quadratic equation

$$C_1{}^2 - \pi^2(1 + 2hC_1) = 0, \qquad (11.122)$$

which is given by

$$C_1 = h\pi^2 + \sqrt{h^2\pi^4 + \pi^2} = \pi + O(h). \qquad (11.123)$$

If $C = C_1$, then for $p \geq 1$, we have

$$\mathrm{Re}\left(\frac{\beta}{a}\right) = \frac{C_1}{\frac{1}{2}(1 + 2hC_1)} \doteq \frac{2\pi}{1 + 2hC_1} = 2\pi + O(h) \,.$$

Since $(d/dc)[C^2 - p^2\pi^2(1 + 2hC)] = 2(C - p^2\pi^2 h)$, it follows that this derivative is positive if $C \geq \pi$, $p = 1$, and if $h < 1/\pi$. For $C > C_1 > \pi$, it follows that $C^2 - \pi^2(1 + 2hC_1) > 0$. The roots of (11.120) for $p = 1$ are real, and the smaller is given by

$$\frac{\beta}{a} = \frac{\pi^2}{\frac{1}{2}[C + \sqrt{C^2 - p^2\pi^2(1 + 2Ch)}]} \leq 2\pi \,.$$

On the other hand, since the smaller root of (11.122) is negative, and since for very large values of C the function

$$g(C) = C^2 - \pi^2(1 + 2hC)$$

is positive, it follows that $g(C) \leq 0$ for $0 \leq C \leq C_1$. This being the case, the roots of (11.121) for $0 \leq C \leq C_1$ and for $p = 1$ are complex, and their real parts are given by

$$\mathrm{Re}\left(\frac{\beta}{a}\right) = \frac{C}{\frac{1}{2}(1 + 2Ch)} \leq 2C_1 = 2\pi + O(h) \,.$$

Thus, to a first approximation, one cannot do any better than to choose $C = \pi$. From (11.117), the corresponding value of ω is

$$\omega = \frac{2}{1 + \pi h} \,. \qquad (11.124)$$

As shown in Sec. 11.9, this agrees with the result obtained by the use of overrelaxation theory.

The preceding result can, of course, be derived either as a special case of the general theory of Sec. 11.9 or by direct use of the difference equation (11.115), using the method of separation of variables. This is true of two-dimensional as well as one-dimensional problems.

It is interesting to note that the new variable $s = t + \alpha x$ could be introduced directly into (11.115), with the result

$$U(x, s + k) = \frac{\omega}{2}[U(x + h, s + \alpha h) + U(x - h, s - \alpha h + k)]$$
$$- (\omega - 1)U(x,s). \quad (11.125)$$

Letting $\alpha = k/2h$, we obtain

$$U(x, s + k) = \frac{\omega}{2}\left[U\left(x + h, s + \frac{k}{2}\right) + U\left(x - h, s + \frac{k}{2}\right)\right]$$
$$- (\omega - 1)U(x,s). \quad (11.126)$$

We can then let $U(x,s) = \sin(p\pi x)e^{-\beta s}$, obtaining

$$e^{-\beta k} = \omega \cos(p\pi h)e^{-\beta k/2} - (\omega - 1). \quad (11.127)$$

Since $U(x,s) = \sin(p\pi x)e^{-\beta t - \alpha\beta x}$, it follows that in one time step (iteration) the error is reduced by a factor $\lambda = e^{-\beta k}$. Substituting in (11.127), we get

$$\lambda + \omega - 1 = \omega\mu\lambda^{\frac{1}{2}}, \quad (11.128)$$

where $\mu = \cos p\pi h$ is an eigenvalue for the Jacobi method. Since (11.128) is the basic relation between the eigenvalues of the successive-overrelaxation method and of the Jacobi method, the rest of the analysis is as given in Sec. 11.9.

Garabedian [19] applied his analysis to the 9-point difference-equation analogue of Laplace's equation:

$$u(x,y) = \frac{1}{20}\{4[u(x + h, y) + u(x - h, y) + u(x, y + h) + u(x, y - h)]$$
$$+ u(x + h, y + h) + u(x - h, y + h) + u(x + h, y - h)$$
$$+ u(x - h, y - h)\}.$$

In this case, although for rectangular regions the method of separation of variables can be used, the formulas for the eigenvalues which determine the convergence rate of the successive-overrelaxation method are very complicated and do not appear to have been successfully used.

By Garabedian's method, the optimum value of ω for a problem involving the unit square with mesh size h is given by

$$\omega = \frac{2}{1 + \sqrt{\dfrac{26}{25}}\,\pi h}$$

as compared with

$$\omega = \frac{2}{1 + \pi h}$$

for the 5-point formula.

In spite of the fact that the method described above is very useful in certain cases, considerable care must be exercised in its use. Thus, for instance, if we apply Richardson's iteration method to the difference equation (11.113), we get

$$u_i^{(n+1)} = u_i^{(n)} + r[u_{i+1}^{(n)} + u_{i-1}^{(n)} - 2u_i^{(n)}]. \tag{11.129}$$

As before, letting $u_i^{(n)} = u(x,t)$, $u_i^{(n+1)} = u(x, t + k)$, we have

$$u(x, t + k) = u(x,t) + r[u(x + h, t) + u(x - h, t) - 2u(x,t)]. \tag{11.130}$$

Using Taylor series expansions and neglecting terms involving k^2, h^3, and higher-order terms lead to

$$ku_t = rh^2 u_{xx}. \tag{11.131}$$

We next let $u(x,t) = T(t)X(x)$, where $T(t) = e^{-\beta t}$ and where we let $X(x) = \sin p\pi x$ (p an integer), in order that $u(0,t) = u(1,t) = 0$ for all t. We are led to the following result:

$$k\beta = rh^2 p^2 \pi^2.$$

Since the factor of reduction of the error for each time step (iteration) is

$$e^{-k\beta} = e^{-rh^2 p^2 \pi^2},$$

then the smallest value, corresponding to $p = 1$, is

$$e^{-rh^2\pi^2}.$$

According to this, one could obtain arbitrarily rapid convergence by choosing r sufficiently large.

On the other hand, we know that, with r substantially larger than $\frac{1}{2}$, the method defined by (11.129) will not even converge. In order to study this situation further, let us retain all terms in the Taylor expansions. By (11.115) we have

$$\sum_{m=1}^{\infty} \frac{k^m}{m!} \frac{\partial^m u}{\partial t^m} = 2r \sum_{m=1}^{\infty} \frac{h^{2m}}{(2m)!} \frac{\partial^{2m} u}{\partial x^{2m}}.$$

Letting $u = e^{-\beta t} \sin p\pi x$, we get

$$\sum_{m=1}^{\infty} \frac{k^m}{m!} (-\beta)^m = 2r \sum_{m=1}^{\infty} (-1)^m \frac{h^{2m}}{(2m)!} (p\pi)^{2m},$$

$$e^{-k\beta} - 1 = 2r(\cos p\pi h - 1) = -4r \sin^2 \frac{p\pi h}{2},$$

$$e^{-k\beta} = 1 - 4r \sin^2 \frac{p\pi h}{2}.$$

We remark that one could obtain this same result by substituting $u = e^{-\beta t} \sin p\pi x$ directly into (11.129).

Evidently, if r is substantially greater than $\frac{1}{2}$, the quantity $1 - 4r$ $\sin^2(p\pi h/2)$ is greater than one in modulus for some p, and the method may not converge. It is clear that the procedure based on the use of (11.131) is not applicable.

We note that the condition $r \leq \frac{1}{2}$ is just the condition which must be satisfied in order for (11.129), considered as a numerical procedure for solving the diffusion equation $u_t = u_{xx}$, to be stable. It is probably true that, before attempting to use the method of Garabedian, one should first determine limits on the iteration parameters based on stability considerations.

REFERENCES

1. A. C. Aitken, On the Iterative Solution of a System of Linear Equations, *Proc. Roy. Soc. Edinburgh, Sect. A*, vol. 63, pp. 52–60, 1950.

2. D. N. de G. Allen, "Relaxation Methods," McGraw-Hill Book Company, Inc., New York, 1954.

3. R. J. Arms, L. D. Gates, and B. Zondek, A Method of Block Iteration, *J. Soc. Indust. Appl. Math.*, vol. 4, pp. 220–229, 1956.

4. R. J. Arms and L. D. Gates, Jr., "The Computation of an Axially Symmetric Free Boundary Problem on NORC," part II, U.S. Naval Proving Ground Report 1533, Dahlgren, Va., April 5, 1957.

5. G. Birkhoff and R. S. Varga, Implicit Alternating Direction Methods, *Trans. Amer. Math. Soc.*, vol. 92, pp. 13–24, 1959.

6. G. Birkhoff and R. S. Varga, Reactor Criticality and Non-negative Matrices, *J. Soc. Indust. Appl. Math.*, vol. 6, pp. 354–377, 1958.

7. G. H. Bruce, D. W. Peaceman, H. H. Rachford, Jr., and J. D. Rice, Calculation of Unsteady-state Gas Flow through Porous Media, *Petroleum Trans. AIME*, vol. 198, pp. 79–92, 1953.

8. J. G. Charney and N. A. Phillips, Numerical Integration of the Quasi-geostrophic Equations for Barotropic and Simple Baroclinic Flows, *J. Meteorol.*, vol. 10, pp. 71–99, 1953.

9. R. Courant, K. Friedrichs, and H. Lewy, Über die partiellen Differenzengleichungen der mathematischen Physik, *Math. Ann.*, vol. 100, pp. 32–74, 1928.

10. J. Crank and P. Nicolson, A Practical Method for Numerical Evaluation of Solutions of Partial Differential Equations of the Heat-conduction Type, *Proc. Cambridge Philos. Soc.*, vol. 43, pp. 50–67, 1947.

11. J. Douglas, Jr., On the Numerical Integration of $\dfrac{\partial^2 u}{\partial x^2} + \dfrac{\partial^2 u}{\partial y^2} = \dfrac{\partial u}{\partial t}$ by Implicit Methods, *J. Soc. Indust. Appl. Math.*, vol. 3, pp. 42–65, 1955.

12. J. Douglas, Jr., and H. Rachford, On the Numerical Solution of Heat Conduction Problems in Two and Three Space Variables, *Trans. Amer. Math. Soc.*, vol. 82, pp. 421–439, 1956.

13. J. Douglas, Jr., On the Relation between Stability and Convergence in the Numerical Solution of Linear Parabolic and Hyperbolic Differential Equations, *J. Soc. Indust. Appl. Math.*, vol. 4, pp. 20–37, 1956.

14. L. W. Ehrlich, A Numerical Method of Solving a Heat Flow Problem with Moving Boundary, *J. Assoc. Comput. Mach.*, vol. 5, pp. 161–176, 1958.

15. G. Forsythe, Solving Linear Algebraic Equations Can Be Interesting, *Bull. Amer. Math. Soc.*, vol. 59, pp. 299–329, 1953.

16. S. Frankel, Convergence Rates of Iterative Treatments of Partial Differential Equations, *Math. Tables Aids Comput.*, vol. 4, pp. 65–75, 1950.

17. B. Friedman, "The Iterative Solution of Elliptic Difference Equations," A.E.C. Research and Development Report NYO-7698, Institute of Mathematical Sciences, New York University, June 1, 1957.

18. G. Frobenius, Über Matrizen aus nicht negativen Elementen, *Sitzber. Akad. Wiss. Berlin,* pp. 456–477, 1912.

19. P. R. Garabedian, Estimation of the Relaxation Factor for Small Mesh Size, *Math. Tables Aids Comput.*, vol. 10, pp. 183–185, 1956.

20. H. Geiringer, "On the Solution of Systems of Linear Equations by Certain Iteration Methods," Reissner Anniversary Volume, pp. 365–393, University of Michigan Press, Ann Arbor, Mich., 1949.

21. S. Geršgorin, Fehlerabschätzung für das Differenzenverfahren zur Lösung partieller Differentialgleichungen, *Z. Angew. Math. Mech.*, vol. 10, pp. 373–382, 1930.

22. P. Greebler, "TRIXY: A Computer Program for Multigroup Nuclear Reactor Calculations in Three-space Dimensions," Report KAPL-1549, Knolls Atomic Power Laboratory, General Electric Co., Schenectady, N.Y., Aug. 1, 1956.

23. F. John, On Integration of Parabolic Equations by Difference Methods, *Comm. Pure Appl. Math.*, vol. 5, pp. 155–211, 1952.

24. M. L. Juncosa and D. Young, On the Order of Convergence of Solutions of a Difference Equation to a Solution of the Diffusion Equation, *J. Soc. Indust. Appl. Math.*, vol. 1, pp. 111–135, 1953.

25. M. L. Juncosa and D. Young, On the Convergence of a Solution of a Difference Equation to a Solution of the Equation of Diffusion, *Proc. Amer. Math. Soc.*, vol. 5, pp. 168–174, 1954.

26. M. L. Juncosa and D. Young, On the Crank-Nicolson Procedure for Solving Parabolic Partial Differential Equations, *Proc. Cambridge Philos. Soc.*, vol. 53, pp. 448–461, 1957.

27. W. Kahan, The Rate of Convergence of the Extrapolated Gauss-Seidel Iteration, abstract of paper presented at the Conference on Matrix Computations, Wayne State University, Detroit, Sept. 4, 1957.

28. C. Lanczos, Solution of Systems of Linear Equations by Minimized Iterations, *J. Res. Nat. Bur. Standards*, vol. 49, pp. 33–53, 1952.

29. P. D. Lax and R. D. Richtmyer, Survey of Stability of Linear Finite Difference Equations, *Comm. Pure Appl. Math.*, vol. 9, pp. 267–293, 1956.

30. W. W. Leutert, On the Convergence of Unstable Approximate Solutions of the Heat Equation to the Exact Solution, *J. Math. Phys.*, vol. 30, pp. 245–251, 1952.

31. G. G. O'Brien, M. A. Hyman, and S. Kaplan, A Study of the Numerical Solution of Partial Differential Equations, *J. Math. Phys.*, vol. 29, pp. 223–251, 1951.

32. D. W. Peaceman and H. H. Rachford, Jr., The Numerical Solution of Parabolic and Elliptic Differential Equations, *J. Soc. Indust. Appl. Math.*, vol. 3, pp. 28–41, 1955.

33. L. F. Richardson, The Approximate Arithmetical Solution by Finite Differences of Physical Problems Involving Differential Equations, with Application to the Stresses in a Masonry Dam, *Philos. Trans. Roy. Soc. London, Ser. A*, vol. 210, pp. 307–357, 1910.

34. V. Romanovsky, Recherches sur les chaînes de Markoff, *Acta Math.*, vol. 66, pp. 147–251, 1936.

35. P. C. Rosenbloom, The Difference Equation Method for Solving the Dirichlet Problem, National Bureau of Standards Applied Mathematics Series, vol. 18, pp. 231–237, 1952.

36. J. Sheldon, On the Numerical Solution of Elliptic Difference Equations, *Math. Tables Aids Comput.*, vol. 9, pp. 101–112, 1955.

37. G. Shortley, Use of Tschebyscheff-polynomial Operators in the Numerical Solution of Boundary-value Problems, *J. Appl. Phys.*, vol. 24, pp. 392–396, 1953.

38. R. V. Southwell, "Relaxation Methods in Theoretical Physics," Oxford University Press, New York, 1946.

39. R. H. Stark, Rates of Convergence in Numerical Solution of the Diffusion Equation, *J. Assoc. Comput. Mach.*, vol. 3, pp. 29–40, 1956.

40. E. Stiefel, Recent Developments in Relaxation Techniques, in "Proceedings of the International Congress of Mathematicians," vol. I, pp. 384–391, North-Holland Publishing Co., Amsterdam, 1954.

41. L. H. Thomas, Elliptic Problems in Linear Difference Equations over a Network, Watson Scientific Computing Laboratory, Columbia University, New York, Sept. 12, 1949.

42. J. Todd, A Direct Approach to the Problem of Stability in the Numerical Solution of Partial Differential Equations, *Comm. Pure Appl. Math.*, vol. 9, pp. 597–612, 1956.

43. R. S. Varga, "Numerical Solution of the Two-group Diffusion Equation in $x - y$ Geometry," Report WAPD-159, Bettis Plant, Westinghouse Electric Corp., Pittsburgh, August, 1956.

44. R. S. Varga, P-cyclic Matrices: A Generalization of the Young-Frankel Successive Overrelaxation Method, *Pacific J. Math.*, vol. 9, pp. 617–628, 1959.

45. E. L. Wachspress and G. J. Habetler, An Alternating–direction-implicit Iteration Technique. *J. Soc. Indust. Appl. Math.*, vol. 8, pp. 403–424, 1960.

46. E. L. Wachspress, "CURE: A generalized Two-space-dimension Multigroup Coding for the IBM-704," Report KAPL-1724, Knolls Atomic Power Laboratory, General Electric Co., Schenectady, N.Y., Apr. 30, 1957.

47. J. L. Walsh and D. Young, On the Accuracy of the Numerical Solution of the Dirichlet Problem by Finite Differences, *J. Res. Nat. Bur. Standards*, vol. 51, pp. 343–363, 1953.

48. J. L. Walsh and D. Young, On the Degree of Convergence of Solutions of Difference Equations to the Solution of the Dirichlet Problem, *J. Math. Phys.*, vol. 33, pp. 80–93, 1954.

49. J. L. Walsh and D. Young, Lipschitz Conditions for Harmonic and Discrete Harmonic Functions, *J. Math. Phys.*, vol. 36, pp. 138–150, 1957.

50. C. H. Warlick, Convergence Rates of Numerical Methods for Solving $\dfrac{\partial^2 u}{\partial x^2} + \dfrac{k}{\rho}\dfrac{\partial u}{\partial \rho} + \dfrac{\partial^2 u}{\partial \rho^2} = 0$, M.A. thesis, University of Maryland, College Park, Md., 1955.

51. W. Wasow, On the Truncation Error in the Solution of Laplace's Equation by Finite Differences, *J. Res. Nat. Bur. Standards*, vol. 48, pp. 345–348, 1952.

52. W. Wasow, The Accuracy of Difference Approximations to Plane Dirichlet Problems with Piecewise Analytic Boundary Values, *Quart. Appl. Math.*, vol. 15, pp. 53–63, 1957.

53. D. Young, Iterative Methods for Solving Partial Difference Equations of Elliptic Type, doctoral thesis, Harvard University, Cambridge, Mass., 1950.

54. D. Young and C. H. Warlick, "On the Use of Richardson's Method for the Numerical Solution of Laplace's Equation on the ORDVAC," Ballistic Research Laboratories Memorandum Report 707, Aberdeen Proving Ground, Maryland, July, 1953.

55. D. Young, Iterative Methods for Solving Partial Difference Equations of Elliptic Type, *Trans. Amer. Math. Soc.*, vol. 76, pp. 92–111, 1954.

56. D. Young, On Richardson's Method for Solving Linear Systems with Positive Definite Matrices, *J. Math. Phys.*, vol. 32, pp. 243–255, 1954.

57. D. Young, Ordvac Solutions of the Dirichlet Problem, *J. Assoc. Comput. Mach.*, vol. 2, pp. 137–161, 1955.

58. D. M. Young, Jr., L. D. Gates, Jr., R. J. Arms, D. F. Eliezer, "The Computation of an Axially Symmetric Free Boundary Problem on NORC," U.S. Naval Proving Ground Report 1413, Dahlgren, Va., Dec. 16, 1955.

59. D. Young and H. Shaw, "Ordvac Solutions of $\dfrac{\partial^2 u}{\partial x^2} + \dfrac{\partial^2 u}{\partial y^2} + \dfrac{k}{y}\dfrac{\partial u}{\partial y} = 0$ for Boundary Value Problems and Problems of Mixed Type," Interim Technical Report 14, Office of Ordnance Research Contract DA-36-034-ORD-1486, University of Maryland, College Park, Md., February, 1956.

60. D. Young and L. Ehrlich, "On the Numerical Solution of Linear and Nonlinear Parabolic Equations on the Ordvac," Interim Technical Report 18, Office of Ordnance Research Contract DA-36-034-ORD-1486, University of Maryland, College Park, Md., February, 1956.

61. D. Young, On the Solution of Linear Systems by Iteration, in American Mathematical Society, "Numerical Analysis: Proceedings of Symposia in Applied Mathematics—Volume VI," J. H. Curtiss, ed., McGraw-Hill Book Company, Inc., New York, 1956.

62. G. G. Bilodeau, W. R. Cadwell, J. P. Dorsey, J. G. Fairey, and R. S. Varga, "PDQ: An IBM-704 Code to Solve the Two-dimensional Few-group Neutron-diffusion Equations," Report WAPD-TM-70, Bettis Plant, Westinghouse Electric Corp., Pittsburgh, August, 1957.

63. M. Hestenes and W. Karush, A Method of Gradients for the Calculation of the Characteristic Roots and Vectors of a Real Symmetric Matrix, *J. Res. Nat. Bur. Standards*, vol. 47, pp. 45–61, 1951.

64. E. H. Cuthill and R. S. Varga, A Method of Normalized Block Iteration, *J. Assoc. Comput. Mach.*, vol. 6, pp. 236–244, 1959.

65. P. Laasonen, On the Truncation Error of Discrete Approximations to the Solutions of Dirichlet Problems in a Domain with Corners, *J. Assoc. Comput. Mach.*, vol. 5, pp. 32–38, 1958.

12

Numerical Methods for Integral Equations

HANS F. BÜCKNER

MATHEMATICS RESEARCH CENTER
UNITED STATES ARMY
UNIVERSITY OF WISCONSIN

12.1 Some Examples of Integral Equations; Classification

The study of integral equations originated in the nineteenth century. Their practical application and numerical methods for solving the equations are much younger; most of this work has been done in the last decades, and more research is still to come. In modern perspective, integral equations appear as a special case of the problems in functional analysis. This is not to the disadvantage of the numerical analyst. The methods of functional analysis facilitate both the analysis and design of numerical procedures. For instance, the analogue of the familiar Newton process is important for the solution of nonlinear integral equations. (See Chap. 14 and Kantorovitch [61].)

Here we are concerned with linear integral equations. The following examples are to serve the purpose of a first orientation.

(a) Cascade Flow

We consider the plane flow of an incompressible fluid through a cascade of congruent profiles. The contours of the profiles in the complex plane of $z = x + iy$ are denoted by C_n (Fig. 12.1), where n runs through all positive and negative integers. The contours are simple; they do not intersect with one another, and they are so arranged that a shift of C_0 by nli produces C_n. The complex points ζ on the contour C_0 shall be related to the arc length s by means of a function $\zeta = f(s)$, which we assume to have continuous derivatives up to the second order. Any function $w(z)$, holomorphic in the domain

439

outside the contours, with period li, bounded and continuously approaching boundary values on the contours, can be represented by

$$w(z) = w_0 - \frac{1}{2li} \oint_{C_0} \left[\coth \frac{\pi}{l} (\zeta - z) \right] w(\zeta) \, d\zeta, \qquad z \text{ not on } C_n, \quad (12.1)$$

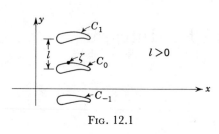

FIG. 12.1

with w_0 as an arbitrary constant. Formula (12.1) is a consequence of Cauchy's integral formula applied to one contour in the image plane $Z = \exp(2\pi z/l)$. We interpret $w(z) = u - iv$ as the complex velocity of a field of plane flow with u as the component in the x direction and v as the component in the y direction. Relation (12.1) can be rewritten as

$$w(z) = w_0 - \frac{1}{2li} \int_{C_0} \coth \frac{\pi}{l} (\zeta - z) \cdot [\gamma(s) - i\delta(s)] \, ds, \quad (12.2)$$

with
$$\gamma(s) = \operatorname{Re} [f'(s)w(\zeta)], \qquad \delta(s) = \operatorname{Im} [f'(s)w(\zeta)]. \quad (12.3)$$

The quantity $\gamma(s)$ is the velocity component tangent to C_0; $\delta(s)$ is the velocity component normal to C_0. If the contours are to be streamlines, $\delta(s)$ must vanish, and if z approaches a point $\tau = f(t)$ on C_0, the well-known Plemelj formula yields

$$\tfrac{1}{2}\gamma(t) = f'(t)w_0 - \frac{1}{2li} \int_{C_0} \left[\coth \frac{\pi}{l} (\zeta - \tau) \right] \gamma(s) \, ds. \quad (12.4)$$

This is a condition on the component $\gamma(s)$, and the problem of finding a flow field $w(z)$ through the cascade involves solving (12.4) for γ. We call (12.4) an integral equation for the unknown function γ; since the integrand of (12.4) is a linear function of γ, we speak of a linear integral equation. We still have to explain the concept of the integral involved. In (12.1) the integral can be interpreted as a Riemann or as a Lebesgue integral; both mean the same in the case (12.1), where the integrand is a continuous function. In general, we adhere to the concept of the Lebesgue integral. But (12.4) requires more explanation because of the singularity of the integrand at $\zeta = \tau$. Let us exclude from the integration that portion of C_0 for which $|\zeta - \tau| < \epsilon$ and let us denote the integral so obtained by $J(t,\epsilon)$. Now we go to the limit $\epsilon \to 0$. If the limit $J(t)$ of $J(t,\epsilon)$ exists, we define $J(t)$ as the integral in (12.4). $J(t)$ is known as the Cauchy principal value. This value exists if

$\gamma(s)$ satisfies a Hölder condition on C_0. Quite generally, this condition means

$$|F(P) - F(P')| < A \, |P - P'|^{\mu}, \qquad 0 < \mu \leq 1, \qquad P,P' \in S \quad (12.4')$$

with regard to a function $F(P)$ defined on a set S of the euclidean space E_n, with $|P - P'|$ standing for the distance of the points P,P'; here A and μ are constants.

Let us now split (12.4) into real and imaginary parts. Setting

$$-\frac{1}{li} f'(t) \coth \frac{\pi}{l} (\zeta - \tau) = K(t,s) + iL(t,s), \qquad (12.5)$$

$$2w_0 f'(t) = g(t) + ih(t), \qquad (12.6)$$

we obtain

$$\gamma(t) = \int_{C_0} K(t,s)\gamma(s) \, ds + g(t), \qquad (12.7)$$

$$0 = \int_{C_0} L(t,s)\gamma(s) \, ds + h(t). \qquad (12.7')$$

These are two linear integral equations for the unknown function $\gamma(s)$. It can be shown that they are equivalent to each other. This interesting fact can be related to the regular flow fields which Eq. (12.2) defines in the simply connected *interiors* of the contours C_n. Relation (12.7) means that the flow field inside C_0 has a vanishing tangential component along C_0; (12.7') states that the inside field has a vanishing normal component on C_0. A vanishing tangential component implies a vanishing interior flow field, and so does a vanishing normal component. Hence (12.7) and (12.7') mean the same.

The so-called kernels $K(t,s)$ and $L(t,s)$ exhibit the following features: $K(t,s)$ is continuous; $L(t,s)$ admits the split

$$L(t,s) = \frac{1}{\pi(s - t)} + H(t,s) \qquad (12.8)$$

with a continuous function H. Because of the first term in (12.8), the integral equation (12.7') is called singular. We do not go into more detail.

The preceding examples (12.7) and (12.7') have been given for two reasons. They show an equivalence of certain "singular" and "regular" integral equations. They also demonstrate that boundary-value problems of partial differential equations such as the calculation of flow fields can be reduced in dimension to problems involving the boundary only. The more difficult boundary-value problems of elasticity can be handled in a similar vein, as can be seen from Muskhelishvili's books [25, 26].

(b) Renewal Theory of Statistics

In an electronic device with a large number of tubes of the same type but of different age, tube failures will occur, and failing tubes will be replaced by new ones. Let $f(t)$ be the relative rate of tubes failing at age t. We want the total relative rate $r(t)$ of failing tubes at time $t > 0$. The function $r(t)$ satisfies

$$r(t) = g(t) + \int_0^t f(t - s)r(s) \, ds. \tag{12.9}$$

This expresses the fact that renewals of tubes apply to both the original ones (g) and to tubes installed at former times $s > 0$ (see Feller [14]). Relation (12.9) is a linear integral equation for the unknown function $r(t)$. The interval of integration depends on t; this is the most significant difference between (12.9) and (12.7). The t dependence of the interval of integration is typical for certain initial-value problems.

Classification of Integral Equations

If the unknown function appears under the integral sign only, we speak of an integral equation of the first kind. Equation (12.7′) is of this type. If the unknown function also stands outside the integral, as in (12.7) and in (12.9), we say that the integral equation is of the second kind. From now on we write the second kind in the form

$$y(s) = \lambda \int_a^b K(s,t)y(t) \, dt + f(s), \tag{12.10}$$

with s,t as real variables and a,b ($a < b$) as finite limits of the interval of integration. The unknown function is $y(s)$; $K(s,t), f(s)$ are given; λ is a parameter. All these quantities may assume complex values. Furthermore, we confine $f(s)$ to the class $L_2(a,b)$ and $K(s,t)$ to the class $L_2(D)$, where D stands for the square $a < s, t < b$. We look for solutions $y(s)$ of the class $L_2(a,b)$. Under these restrictions, Eq. (12.10) will be referred to as the *Fredholm integral equation*. This covers the case (12.7). If the kernel $K(s,t)$ in (12.10) vanishes for $t > s$, we may write

$$y(s) = \lambda \int_a^s K(s,t)y(t) \, dt + f(s); \tag{12.10′}$$

this particular case is known as the *Volterra integral equation*. For reasons which are given later, the parameter λ plays no essential role in (12.10′); therefore this equation is usually written without the parameter λ. The Volterra equation appears very often with a "difference" kernel $K(s,t) = F(s - t)$; Eq. (12.9) comes into this category.

We write integral equations of the first kind in the form

$$\int_a^b K(s,t)y(t)\ dt = f(s);\qquad (12.11)$$

many important equations of this type go with a singular kernel of the form

$$K(s,t) = \frac{c}{s-t} + H(s,t),\qquad c = \text{const};\qquad (12.12)$$

the function $H(s,t)$ is "less" singular than the first term in (12.12); very often it is continuous in the open square $a < s,\ t < b$. The integral in (12.11) is to be taken as the Cauchy principal value.

The main subject of this chapter is the numerical solution of Fredholm integral equations. However, a few remarks about singular integral equations of the first kind are given in the next section.

In general, the numerical methods are explained without proof of their validity, for which the reader is referred to the literature.

12.2 Integral Equations of the First Kind

We consider the singular type (12.11), (12.12). Sometimes it is useful to look for an equivalent equation of the second kind and to attack it by numerical methods. An example is Eq. (12.7') with its equivalent (12.7). As another example, we take

$$\frac{1}{2\pi}\int_{-1}^1 \left[\frac{1}{s-t} + H(s,t)\right]y(t)\ dt = f(s)\qquad (12.13)$$

under the restriction that $f(s)$ and $H(s,t)$ satisfy Hölder conditions in their closed domains of definition. Introducing

$$g(x) = \frac{1}{2\pi}\int_{-1}^1 H(x,s)y(s)\ ds,\qquad (12.14)$$

we rewrite (12.13) as follows:

$$\frac{1}{2\pi}\int_{-1}^1 \frac{y(t)\ dt}{s-t} = f(s) - g(s).\qquad (12.15)$$

Following Schmeidler [37], we write the solution to (12.15) in the form

$$y(t) = \frac{\Gamma}{\pi}Q(t) - \frac{1}{\pi}Q(t)\int_{-1}^1 \frac{f(x) - g(x)}{(t-x)Q(x)}\ dx,\qquad Q(t) = (1 - t^2)^{-\frac{1}{2}}$$
$$(12.16)$$

where Γ is an arbitrary constant. Relation (12.16) can be given the form

$$y(t) = \int_{-1}^{1} L(t,s) y(s) \, ds + h(t), \qquad (12.17)$$

with

$$h(t) = \frac{\Gamma}{\pi} Q(t) - \frac{1}{\pi} Q(t) \int_{-1}^{1} \frac{f(x)}{(t-x)Q(x)} \, dx, \qquad (12.18)$$

$$L(t,s) = \frac{1}{2\pi^2} Q(t) \int_{-1}^{1} \frac{H(x,s)}{(t-x)Q(x)} \, dx. \qquad (12.19)$$

The further transformation

$$y = zQ^{\frac{1}{2}} \qquad (12.20)$$

results in a Fredholm integral equation for $z(t)$. Some direct treatments of singular integral equations of the first kind have been suggested by various authors. Berg [3] deals with methods of iteration. Another direct approach uses the Hilbert space H of the real- or complex-valued functions of $L_2(a,b)$ with the scalar product

$$(f,g) = \int_{a}^{b} f(s)\bar{g}(s) \, ds, \qquad \bar{g} = \text{conjugate complex value of } g, \quad (12.21)$$

and defines the integral operations

$$\int_{a}^{b} K(s,t) y(t) \, dt = Ky, \qquad \int_{a}^{b} \overline{K(t,s)} y(t) \, dt = K^{*}y \qquad (12.22)$$

for sufficiently smooth functions $y \in H$; this definition is extended to the other elements of H by a process of closure. The definition has to satisfy certain conditions: $Ky, K^{*}y$ must be elements of H; K and K^{*} must be linear operations, that is, in the case of K,

$$K(\alpha_1 y_1 + \alpha_2 y_2) = \alpha_1 K y_1 + \alpha_2 K y_2 \qquad (12.23)$$

for any two constants α_1, α_2; and lastly

$$(Kf,g) = (f, K^{*}g). \qquad (12.24)$$

Schmeidler [37] proves that a necessary and sufficient condition for the possibility of defining $Ky, K^{*}y$ this way is the existence of two complete and orthonormal sets of functions $\varphi_1, \varphi_2, \ldots$ and $\psi_1, \psi_2, \ldots$ of H for which $K\varphi_i$ and $K^{*}\psi_i$ can be defined as elements of H in accordance with (12.24) and such that

$$|(Kf,g)| \leq M \|f\| \cdot \|g\|, \qquad \|f\| = (f,f)^{\frac{1}{2}}, \qquad (12.25)$$

for any two linear combinations

$$f = \sum_{k=1}^{n} c_k \varphi_k, \qquad g = \sum_{k=1}^{n} d_k \psi_k \qquad (12.26)$$

with M independent of n. Orthonormality means

$$(\varphi_i, \varphi_k) = \delta_{ik} = \text{Kronecker's symbol}, \qquad (12.27)$$

and completeness requires

$$f = 0 \qquad \text{if } (f, \varphi_k) = 0 \text{ for all } k. \qquad (12.28)$$

If the two systems exist, the general definition of Ky, K^*y is by

$$Ky = \sum_{n=1}^{\infty} (y, \varphi_n) K\varphi_n, \qquad K^*y = \sum_{n=1}^{\infty} (y, \psi_n) K^*\psi_n. \qquad (12.29)$$

The definition implies that K is bounded; that is,

$$\|Ky\| \le M \|y\|, \qquad M \text{ independent of } y. \qquad (12.30)$$

The smallest possible M is called the norm of K and denoted by $\|K\|$. K and K^* have the same norm. The integral equation (12.11), now written as

$$Ky = f, \qquad (12.31)$$

is treated by means of the following infinite system of linear equations:

$$\sum_{j=1}^{\infty} K_{ij} y_j = f_i, \qquad i = 1, 2, \ldots, \qquad (12.32)$$

where

$$K_{ij} = (K\varphi_j, \psi_i), \qquad f_i = (f, \psi_i), \qquad y_j = (y, \varphi_j). \qquad (12.33)$$

Equation (12.31) admits a solution $y \in H$ if and only if (12.32) admits a solution $y_1, y_2, \ldots$ with a convergent sum

$$\sum_{k=1}^{\infty} |y_k|^2. \qquad (12.34)$$

The numerical treatment of (12.31) can be achieved by solving the finite system

$$\sum_{j=1}^{n} K_{ij} y_j = f_i, \qquad i = 1, 2, \ldots, n, \qquad (12.35)$$

for the unknowns y_j and by using

$$Y_n = \sum_{j=1}^{n} y_j \varphi_j \qquad (12.36)$$

as an approximation to y. Here is the place to mention that Eq. (12.7′) was originated by Isay [17] and that his way of numerically solving it is based on (12.35).

Equation (12.13) for polynomials $H(s,t)$ has been treated in similar vein. To this end, (12.13) is transformed by the substitution $s = \cos s'$, $t = \cos t'$, and Fourier expansions are used in order to construct a solution. For details the reader is referred to Reissner [33] and Weissinger [50].

It is not necessary to work with orthonormal systems of functions φ_i. Sometimes it is quite useful to select a set of functions $u_1, u_2, \ldots$ for which the operations Ku_n can be carried out in closed form. One approximates f by a linear combination

$$f \approx \sum_{k=1}^{n} c_k v_k, \qquad v_k = Ku_k, \tag{12.37}$$

and takes $\sum_{k=1}^{n} c_k u_k$ as an approximation to y.

12.3   Theorems and Formulas on Fredholm Integral Equations

In the case of Fredholm integral equations the operations (12.22) are Lebesgue integrals; with respect to the Hilbert space H, as introduced in the preceding section, the operations Ky, K^*y satisfy (12.23), (12.24), (12.30). In addition, they are completely continuous, which means that K, for example, transforms any infinite sequence $f_1, f_2, \ldots, f_n, \ldots$ of elements of H with uniformly bounded norms $\|f_n\|$ into a sequence $Kf_n = g_n$ such that a convergent subsequence g_{n_i} exists; that is, an element g of H exists such that

$$\lim_{n_i \to \infty} \|g - g_{n_i}\| = 0. \tag{12.38}$$

The theory of completely continuous operators is well developed; we refer the reader to the excellent book by Riesz and Sz.-Nagy [35]. We quote some of the already classical results on Fredholm integral equations (12.10), and from here on we sometimes write these equations in the form

$$(I - \lambda K)y = f, \tag{12.39}$$

where I stands for the unit operator $Iy = y$.

(a) Fredholm's Alternative

For a given λ, either the equations $(I - \lambda K)y = f$ and $(I - \bar{\lambda}K^*)z = g$ have unique solutions y, z, or the homogeneous equations $(f = 0, g = 0)$ have nontrivial solutions. In the latter case the number of linearly independent solutions is finite and the same for both equations. If the homogeneous equations have nontrivial solutions, the inhomogeneous equations admit solutions for special elements f, g only. Necessary and sufficient for the existence of a solution is that f be orthogonal to all solutions of $(I - \bar{\lambda}K^*)z = 0$ and that g be orthogonal to all solutions of $(I - \lambda K)y = 0$.

(b) Eigenvalues, Eigenelements

Nontrivial solutions of $(I - \lambda K)y = 0$ exist for an at most enumerable set of values $\lambda_1, \lambda_2, \ldots$ of the parameter λ. These cannot accumulate to a finite point of the complex λ plane. The values λ are called the eigenvalues of the operator K, and the corresponding nontrivial solutions of the homogeneous equation are known as eigenelements or eigenfunctions. If λ is an eigenvalue of K, $\bar{\lambda}$ is an eigenvalue of K^* and vice versa. The Volterra integral equation (12.10') has no eigenvalues.

(c) The Operator $K(\lambda)$ and the Neumann-Liouville Series

The product KL of two integral operators K, L is defined by $(KL)y = K(Ly)$; in the case $L = K$ one writes $KK = K^2$, $KK^2 = K^3$, etc. The product of completely continuous integral operators is also a completely continuous integral operator. If λ is not an eigenvalue of K, the solution to (12.39) can be written as

$$y = [I + \lambda K(\lambda)]f, \tag{12.40}$$

with $K(\lambda)$ standing for a completely continuous integral operator. We have $K(0) = K$. With reference to another value μ of the parameter which is not an eigenvalue, the relation

$$K(\lambda) - K(\mu) = (\lambda - \mu)K(\lambda)K(\mu) = (\lambda - \mu)K(\mu)K(\lambda) \tag{12.41}$$

holds. For sufficiently small values of $|\lambda|$, the operator $K(\lambda)$ admits the representation by the so-called Neumann-Liouville series

$$K(\lambda) = \sum_{n=1}^{\infty} \lambda^{n-1}K^n, \tag{12.42}$$

which converges in the sense $\left\| K(\lambda) - \sum_{n-1}^{m} \lambda^{n-1}K^n \right\| \to 0$ when $m \to \infty$. A sufficient condition of convergence is $\|\lambda K\| < 1$; more precisely, convergence takes place for $|\lambda| < |\lambda_1|$ where λ_1 denotes an eigenvalue with smallest modulus. For $0 < r < |\lambda_1|$ a number R independent of n exists such that

$$\|K^n\| \leq Rr^{1-n}; \tag{12.43}$$

for continuous kernels $K(s,t)$, the kernel $K_n(s,t)$ of K^n satisfies

$$|K_n(s,t)| \leq R'r^{1-n} \tag{12.43'}$$

with a number R' not depending on s,t and n (see [4], [5]). Equations (12.43) and (12.43′) can be used as a basis for the development of iterative methods.

(d) Operators of Finite Rank

Kernels of the form

$$K(s,t) = \sum_{k=1}^{n} u_k(s)v_k(t) \tag{12.44}$$

are called *degenerate* or *of finite rank*. There is no lack of generality in assuming that the functions $u_1, u_2, \ldots, u_n$, as well as $v_1, v_2, \ldots, v_n$, are linearly independent. Solutions of (12.39) with (12.44) have the form $y = f + c_1 u_1 + c_2 u_2 + \cdots + c_n u_n$, with constant coefficients c_k. These are determined by the following set of linear equations:

$$c_k - \lambda \sum_{i=1}^{n} c_i(v_k, \bar{u}_i) = \lambda(v_k, f), \qquad k = 1, 2, \ldots, n. \tag{12.45}$$

This problem is in the realm of matrix algebra.

(e) Approximation of Operators

Any completely continuous integral operator K can be approximated by a suitable operator L of finite rank such that the norm $\|K - L\|$ is below a prescribed quantity $\epsilon > 0$. This approximation is of practical importance; it provides the basis for designing numerical methods. One of these methods is as follows.

(f) The Procedure by Erhard Schmidt

Let L be of finite rank and such that $\|\lambda M\| < 1$ with $M = K - L$. Equation (12.39) can be reduced to

$$y = [I + \lambda M(\lambda)]f + Ny, \qquad N = [I + \lambda M(\lambda)]L. \tag{12.46}$$

$M(\lambda)$ can be represented by the Neumann-Liouville series; the operator N is of finite rank; hence solving (12.46) amounts to solving a system (12.45).

Note. G. Kron's widely publicized method of network tearing is in essence a special application of Schmidt's procedure. Let us write

$$A = I - \lambda K, \qquad B = I - \lambda M, \qquad B^{-1} = I + \lambda M(\lambda), \qquad L = B - A,$$

and

$$Ay = f, \qquad By = f + (B - A)y; \qquad y = B^{-1}f + B^{-1}(B - A)y;$$

the last relation is identical with (12.46). The given problem requires the inversion of the operator A in order to find $y = A^{-1}f$; Schmidt selects an operator B which offers two advantages, namely:

1. The inversion of B is easier than the inversion of A in the sense that B^{-1} admits a convergent Neumann-Liouville series.

2. The operator $B^{-1}(B - A)$ is degenerate.

In the method of network tearing, the operators A, B are nonsingular $n \times n$ matrices. The matrix B is more easily inverted than A; the matrix $B^{-1}(B - A) = C$ has a rank r smaller than n. This is in accordance with advantages 1 and 2. In order to make use of $r < n$, one may set $C = ST$, where S has r columns and n rows and T has r rows and n columns. The solution of the auxiliary system $y = g + Cy$ with $g = B^{-1}f$ is achieved by introducing the column vector $z = Ty$ of r components, by solving $z = Tg + TSz$ for z, and finally by $y = g + Sz$. Actually, the preceding steps have nothing to do with networks; what makes certain linear networks a specialty is the fact that the selection of B is easy and that the split $C = ST$ is also found in an easy way.

(g) Splits of K and of $K(\lambda)$

With reference to any eigenvalue of K, say λ_1, K can be split into two operators A, B such that

$$K = A + B, \qquad AB = BA = 0, \tag{12.47}$$

where A is of finite rank with λ_1 as the only eigenvalue, whereas B has the same eigenvalues as K but not λ_1. The split implies

$$K(\lambda) = A(\lambda) + B(\lambda), \qquad A(\lambda)B(\lambda) = B(\lambda)A(\lambda) = 0; \tag{12.48}$$

$B(\lambda_1)$ exists; $A(\lambda)$ has the form

$$A(\lambda) = \sum_{i=1}^{\nu} A_i(\lambda - \lambda_1)^{-i}, \tag{12.49}$$

where $A_1, A_2, \ldots, A_\nu$ are integral operators of finite rank. The operator $A = A(0)$ can be given the special form

$$Au = \sum_{i,k=1}^{\rho} a_{ik}\varphi_i(u, \psi_k), \qquad a_{ii} = \frac{1}{\lambda_1}, \tag{12.50}$$

where the constant coefficients a_{ik} form a matrix of Jordan canonical form and the elements φ_i, ψ_k of H form a biorthonormal system; that is, $(\varphi_i, \psi_k) = \delta_{ik}$.

(h) Operator Polynomials

Let $f(x) = f_0 + f_1 x + \cdots + f_n x^n$ be any polynomial. With respect to the operator K, we define $f(K) = f_0 I + f_1 K + \cdots + f_n K^n$ as another operator. It is easily seen that $f(x) + g(x) = h(x)$ leads to $f(K) + g(K) = h(K)$ for any two polynomials f, g. Likewise, $f(x)g(x) = h(x)$ results in $f(K)g(K) = h(K)$.

If λ is an eigenvalue of K, we also write $\kappa = 1/\lambda$; κ will be called a characteristic value of K. We rewrite the eigenvalue problem in the form $Ky = \kappa y$. This form makes it possible to cover the case $\kappa = 0$. $Ky = 0$ can admit a finite or an infinite number of linearly independent solutions y. It follows from $Ky = \kappa y$ that $f(K)y = f(\kappa)y$; if, vice versa,

$$f(K)z = \mu z, \qquad z \neq 0, \tag{12.51}$$

then
$$\mu = f(\kappa), \tag{12.52}$$

with κ as a suitable characteristic value of K.

12.4 Hermitian Operators

If $K = K^*$, the operator K is called *hermitian*. K has at least one eigenvalue; all eigenvalues are real. Eigenelements of different eigenvalues are orthogonal to one another. One finds $\nu = 1$ in (12.49). Let us order the positive and negative characteristic values of K in sequences

$$\kappa_1, \kappa_2, \ldots, \kappa_n, \ldots; \qquad \kappa_{-1}, \kappa_{-2}, \ldots, \kappa_{-n}, \ldots$$

of decreasing modulus such that κ_n stands as often in the sequence as there are linearly independent eigenelements. The eigenelements shall be $y_1, y_2, \ldots, y_n, \ldots$ and $y_{-1}, y_{-2}, \ldots, y_{-n}, \ldots$, respectively. Without loss of generality it can be assumed that all eigenelements form an orthonormal system. The set of eigenelements of characteristic values different from zero is complete if $Ky = 0$ has the trivial solution only. For any positive integer n and any element u of H, Hilbert's fundamental formula

$$(K^n u, u) = \sum_k |(u, y_k)|^2 \kappa_k{}^n \tag{12.53}$$

holds; this implies, for $n = 1$,

$$\begin{aligned}
\kappa_1 &= \max (Ku, u), \quad \text{with} \quad \|u\| = 1; \\
\kappa_{-1} &= \min (Ku, u) \quad \text{with} \quad \|u\| = 1.
\end{aligned} \tag{12.54}$$

Maximum and minimum are attained for eigenfunctions of κ_1 and κ_{-1}, respectively. The other values κ_n can be characterized as solutions of the following minimax problem (Courant [12]). Let v_1, $v_2, \ldots, v_r$ be elements of H and confine u to those elements which satisfy

$$\|u\| = 1 \qquad \text{and} \qquad (u, v_i) = 0 \qquad \text{for } i = 1, 2, \ldots, r.$$

By variation of u, we define

$$F_+(v_1, v_2, \ldots, v_r) = \sup (Ku, u), \qquad F_-(v_1, v_2, \ldots, v_r) = \sup [-(Ku, u)]$$

as functionals of the v_i; these functionals give rise to

$$\kappa_{r+1} = \min_{v_i} F_+, \qquad \kappa_{-r-1} = \min_{v_i} -F_-. \qquad (12.55)$$

The kernel $K(s,t;\lambda)$ of $K(\lambda)$ admits the expansion

$$K(s,t;\lambda) = K(s,t) + \lambda \sum_k \frac{y_k(s)\bar{y}_k(t)}{\lambda_k(\lambda_k - \lambda)}. \qquad (12.56)$$

The split (12.47) with the characteristic value μ results in

$$A(s,t) = \mu \sum_{\kappa_i = \mu} y_i(s)\bar{y}_i(t). \qquad (12.57)$$

Special hermitian operators are those with a real kernel $K(s,t) = K(t,s)$. Their eigenfunctions can be taken as real functions. In some important applications one meets kernels $L(s,t) = p(t)K(s,t)$, where K is real and symmetric in s and t, the function p being nonnegative. The operation Ly can be linked to a hermitian one by means of

$$p^{\frac{1}{2}}(s) \int_a^b L(s,t)y(t)\, dt = \int_a^b p^{\frac{1}{2}}(s)p^{\frac{1}{2}}(t)K(s,t)z(t)\, dt, \qquad z = p^{\frac{1}{2}}y. \quad (12.58)$$

12.5 Inclusion Theorems for Hermitian Operators

Theorem 12.1. *For $U = (Ku,u)$ with $\|u\| = 1$, each of the real x sets $x - U \geq 0$, $x - U \leq 0$ contains at least one characteristic value of K. If U is not a characteristic value, then each of the sets $x - U > 0$, $x - U < 0$ contains at least one characteristic value of K.*

Because of the importance of this theorem for practical applications, we shall prove it.

Proof. The theorem is trivial for $(K - UI)u = 0$; if $(K - UI)u \neq 0$, we distinguish the following subcases:

(i) K has eigenvalues of both signs; then $\kappa_1 > U > \kappa_{-1}$, from (12.54), and the theorem is already proved.

(ii) K has eigenvalues of one sign only, say positive ones. $(K - UI)u \neq 0$ implies $Ku \neq 0$ and $(Ku,Ku) = (K^2u,u) > 0$. It follows from (12.53), $n = 2$, that $(u, y_k) \neq 0$ for at least one index k, and therefore $U > 0$. We find that $x - U > 0$ contains κ_1; if there is an infinite number of characteristic values of K, they accumulate at zero, and $x - U < 0$ contains an infinite number of them; if there is a finite number of characteristic values of K only, then $\kappa = 0$ must be one of them, and this one belongs to $x - U < 0$. This completes the proof. In the case of K having negative eigenvalues only, the reasoning is analogous.

With respect to any element $u \in H$ with the norm $|u| = 1$, we introduce the so-called Schwarz constants

$$a_0 = (u,u) = 1, \qquad a_n = (K^n u, u), \qquad n > 1. \qquad (12.59)$$

These constants are real. We take a system of *real* coefficients f_0, $f_1, \ldots, f_n$ such that

$$\sum_{k=0}^{n} f_k a_k = 0 \qquad (12.60)$$

and set up the polynomial $f(x) = f_0 + f_1 x + \cdots + f_n x^n$; with respect to $f(x)$, we may state the following theorem.

Theorem 12.2. *The polynomial $f(x)$ has at least one real zero. Each of the real x sets $f(x) \geq 0, f(x) \leq 0$ contains at least one characteristic value of K; if $f(K)u \neq 0$, nonempty sets $f(x) > 0, f(x) < 0$ exist; each of them contains at least one characteristic value of K.*

Proof. If $f(K)u = 0$, it follows from what has been stated about (12.52) that a characteristic value κ of K exists such that $f(\kappa) = 0$. In this case the theorem is trivial. If $f(K)u \neq 0$, we apply Theorem 12.1 to the hermitian integral operator $L = g(K)$, where $g(x) = f(x) - f_0$. We find $(Lu,u) = \sum_{k=1}^{n} a_k f_k = -f_0$; hence each of the real y sets $y + f_0 > 0$, $y + f_0 < 0$ contains at least one characteristic value of L. The characteristic values of L have the form $g(\kappa)$, where κ runs through the characteristic values of K. There exist two characteristic values κ' and κ'' of K such that $g(\kappa') + f_0 = f(\kappa') > 0; g(\kappa'') + f_0 = f(\kappa'') < 0$ (Q.E.D.).

In what follows, any polynomial $f(x)$ with real coefficients, satisfying (12.60), will be called an inclusion polynomial. The condition (12.60) can be written as

$$(f(K)u,u) = 0. \qquad (12.60')$$

If $f(K)u \neq 0$, we speak of a proper inclusion polynomial. If $f(K)u = 0$, we call $f(x)$ an improper inclusion polynomial. If $f(x)$ and $g(x)$ are inclusion polynomials with respect to u, then $af(x) + bg(x)$, with any two real coefficients a, b, is an inclusion polynomial. If no improper polynomial $f(x) \not\equiv 0$ exists, we say that u has infinite degree with respect to K. If improper polynomials $f(x) \not\equiv 0$ exist, there is one of minimum degree m; disregarding a constant factor, this "minimum polynomial" is unique. We call m the degree of u with respect to K.

Let us assume that the Schwarz constants $a_0, a_1, \ldots, a_{2n-2}$ admit a nontrivial solution of the following equations:

$$a_k f_0 + a_{k+1} f_1 + \cdots + a_{k+n-1} f_{n-1} = 0, \qquad k = 0, 1, \ldots, n - 1. \qquad (12.61)$$

Then both the polynomial $F_{n-1} = f_0 + f_1 x + \cdots + f_{n-1} x^{n-1}$ and the products $x^k F_{n-1}$, with $k = 1, 2, \ldots, n - 1$, are inclusion polynomials.

Any linear combination of them with real combination coefficients is an inclusion polynomial; hence F_{n-1}^2 is an inclusion polynomial. But

$$(F_{n-1}^2(K)u,u) = \|F_{n-1}(K)u\|^2 = 0 \qquad \text{and therefore} \qquad F_{n-1}(K)u = 0.$$
$$(12.62)$$

The case (12.61) then implies that u has a degree less than n. From now on, we assume u to have degree $m \geq n$. Then the polynomial

$$\phi_n(x) = \begin{vmatrix} 1 & x & \cdots & x^n \\ a_0 & a_1 & \cdots & a_n \\ a_1 & a_2 & \cdots & a_{n+1} \\ \cdots\cdots\cdots\cdots\cdots\cdots\cdots \\ a_{n-1} & a_{n-2} & \cdots & a_{2n-1} \end{vmatrix} \qquad (12.63)$$

has proper degree n. Obviously ϕ_n, $x^k\phi_n$, with $k \leq n - 1$, are inclusion polynomials. Any polynomial $g(x)$ with real coefficients and with degree less than n gives rise to an inclusion polynomial $g(x)\phi_n$. The polynomials $\phi_0, \phi_1, \ldots$ are orthogonal (see Szegö [45]), and they have real and distinct zeros only. If ϕ_n is a proper inclusion polynomial with zeros $x_1 < x_2 < \cdots < x_n$, then the intervals $(-\infty, x_1)$, (x_1, x_2), ..., (x_n, ∞) contain characteristic values of K. This can be proved by considering the polynomials $g(x)\phi_n$ with g as a divisor of ϕ_n (see [5]).

The preceding results seem to have been originated by Wielandt. In 1950 the present writer discussed the results with Wielandt, who then stated that his earlier work on hermitian matrices had led him to the inclusion polynomials. But the polynomials ϕ_n also show up in papers by Lanczos [19, 20, 21]. In 1954 Vorobyov [60] published results about using the polynomials ϕ_n for the approximate calculation of the characteristic values of hermitian operators.

Special inclusion polynomials are of the type

$$f(x) = f_k x^k + f_{k+1} x^{k+1} + f_{k+2} x^{k+2}.$$

These lead to the following special inclusion theorem.

Theorem 12.3. *If k is even, the two numbers*

$$P = \text{real} \qquad and \qquad Q = (a_k - Pa_{k+1})/(a_{k+1} - Pa_{k+2}),$$
$$if \ a_{k+1} - Pa_{k+2} \neq 0,$$

bracket at least one eigenvalue of K.

A special case of this theorem minimizes $|P - Q|$; the result is

$$P, Q = a_{k+1}/a_{k+2} \pm d \qquad \text{where } d^2 = a_k/a_{k+2} - (a_{k+1}/a_{k+2})^2. \quad (12.64)$$

The analogue of (12.64) for differential operators was found by Weinstein. Wielandt found the same result for hermitian matrices.

Many more results about the inclusion of characteristic values are available. The reader is referred to [5].

12.6 The Classical Iteration

Many iterative methods, which have been designed either to determine the eigenvalues and eigenelements of an integral operator K or to approximate the solution or solutions of the equation $(I - \lambda K)y = f$, derive a sequence of elements u_n of H from an initial element u_0 by means of polynomials $q_n(x)$ of degree n, such that

$$u_n = q_n(K)u_0. \tag{12.65}$$

The iteration involves in particular the elements

$$v_n = K^n u_0, \tag{12.66}$$

which we consider first. The split (12.47) with respect to λ_1 implies

$$K^n = A^n + B^n. \tag{12.67}$$

Let λ_1 be the only eigenvalue of smallest modulus. Application of (12.43) with respect to B gives

$$\lambda_1^{-n}(K^n - A^n)u_0 \to 0 \qquad \text{when } n \to \infty; \tag{12.68}$$

hence in the case $Au_0 \neq 0$ the asymptotic behavior of the sequence (12.66) is displayed by the sequence

$$w_n = A^n u_0. \tag{12.69}$$

The study of (12.69) is in the realm of matrix iteration because of the finite rank of A [see (12.50)]. The minimum polynomial of the matrix (a_{ik}) of coefficients in (12.50) implies a corresponding relation

$$(A - \lambda_1 I)^r = 0; \tag{12.70}$$

consequently

$$\sum_{k=0}^{r} \binom{r}{k}(-\lambda_1)^k w_{n-k} = 0. \tag{12.71}$$

This relation holds approximately when v_i is substituted for w_i; the error of the approximation goes to zero when $n \to \infty$. This provides the basis for finding information about A by means of the sequence (12.66). In the important case $r = 1$ the functions v_n, v_{n+1} will become proportional to each other as $n \to \infty$. The proportionality constant is λ_1. So far as the inhomogeneous equation $(I - \lambda K)y = f$ for $|\lambda| < |\lambda_1|$ is concerned, it can be solved by the iteration

$$u_{n+1} = \lambda K u_n + f. \tag{12.72}$$

The error is

$$u_{n+1} - y = \lambda K(u_n - y) = (\lambda K)^{n+1}(u_0 - y); \tag{12.73}$$

Eqs. (12.68) and (12.69) imply

$$\|u_n - y\| \to 0 \qquad \text{when } n \to \infty. \tag{12.74}$$

This holds in the sense of norm convergence. A stronger result can be obtained for continuous kernels, where the functions $u_{n+1}(s) - y(s)$ converge uniformly to zero for $a \le s \le b$.

In the special case $u_0 = f$ the iteration leads to

$$u_n = \sum_{i=0}^{n} \lambda^i K^i f, \tag{12.75}$$

which means that u_n is a partial sum of the solution y due to (12.40) and (12.42).

A limit case of the iteration appears for $\lambda = \lambda_1$, with f assumed to admit a solution of the integral equation. Convergence takes place for $Af = 0$ and $u_0 = f$. The functions u_n converge to the solution of

$$(I - \lambda_1 B)y = f. \tag{12.76}$$

One of the best-known examples is furnished by the limit case $l = \infty$ of the integral equation (12.7), which goes with the kernel

$$K(t,s) = -\frac{1}{\pi} \frac{\partial}{\partial n_s} \log r_{st}, \tag{12.77}$$

with r_{st} denoting the distance of the points s, t and with n_s standing for the inner normal at point s. All eigenvalues are real; $\lambda_1 = 1$ is the smallest in modulus, and the kernel $A(s,t)$ of A in (12.50) takes the form $A(s,t) = \varphi_1(s)$. The integral operator is also related to integral equations of Dirichlet's problem for the exterior of C_0 as well as of conformal mapping of the interior of C_0 onto the interior of the unit circle. The iteration (12.75) for this example has been widely explored, in particular by Warschawski [49] and through computational experiments by Todd and Warschawski [46]. Since the rate of convergence is $|\lambda_1/\lambda_2|$, where λ_2 is next to λ_1 in modulus, bounds for λ_2 have been given, especially for nearly circular contours; the papers cited also give estimates of the error of iteration.

Iteration in the case $\lambda = \lambda_1$ with the kernel (12.77) can also be carried out in the following way. We modify the integral equation by writing

$$y(t) = \int_{C_0} [K(t,s) - 1]y(s)\,ds + \Gamma + g(t), \qquad \Gamma = \int_{C_0} y(s)\,ds. \tag{12.78}$$

The new kernel $K(t,s) - 1$ has lost the eigenvalue $\lambda_1 = 1$; it still has all the other ones of $K(t,s)$. Therefore the method (12.72) will work; the constant Γ can be fixed arbitrarily. The modification (12.78) and other ones have been designed by Wielandt in order to overcome the restriction $|\lambda| < |\lambda_1|$ (see [54, 5]).

12.7 Iteration Polynomials

We return to the more general sequence (12.65); in particular we discuss the sequence $w_0 = 0$,

$$w_n = q_{n-1}(\lambda K)f, \qquad n = 1, 2, \ldots; q_{n-1} = \text{polynomial of degree } n - 1. \tag{12.79}$$

We introduce the error

$$w_n - y = -p_n(\lambda K)y, \qquad p_n(x) = 1 + (x - 1)q_{n-1}(x). \tag{12.80}$$

The special case $p_n = x^n$ characterizes the iteration of the preceding section.   A refined iteration is due to Wiarda [53].   He sets

$$w_{n+1} = \theta w_n + (1 - \theta)\lambda K w_n + (1 - \theta)f \tag{12.81}$$

with a suitable constant θ.   We find

$$w_{n+1} - y - [\theta + (1 - \theta)\lambda K](w_n - y), \tag{12.82}$$

and the polynomial $p_n(x)$ is

$$p_n(x) = [\theta + (1 - \theta)x]^n. \tag{12.83}$$

Wiarda investigated the sequence (12.81) for the case of a real and symmetric kernel.   It was shown by Bückner that the error converges to zero for any integral operator K and for any f if

$$|\theta| < 1 \qquad \text{and} \qquad |\theta + (1 - \theta)\lambda/\lambda_\nu| < 1, \qquad \nu = 1, 2, \ldots. \tag{12.84}$$

The proof uses (12.43′) as a tool.   The more general iteration method

$$w_{n+1} = [\theta_{n+1}I + \lambda(1 - \theta_{n+1})K]w_n + (1 - \theta_{n+1})f, \qquad \theta_{k+\rho} = \theta_k, \tag{12.85}$$

with an integer $\rho > 1$, has the polynomial

$$p_n(x) = \prod_{i=1}^{n} [\theta_i + (1 - \theta_i)x]. \tag{12.86}$$

The sequence (12.85) converges for

$$|p_\rho(0)| < 1, \qquad |p_\rho(z_k)| < 1, \qquad z_k = \lambda/\lambda_k, k = 1, 2, \ldots. \tag{12.87}$$

If λ is not an eigenvalue, parameters $\theta_1, \theta_2, \ldots, \theta_\rho$ can always be found to enforce (12.87).   In the case of real eigenvalues the special case

$$\left. \begin{aligned} w_1 &= (1 - \alpha)w_0 + \lambda\alpha K w_0 + \alpha f \\ w_2 &= (1 + \alpha)w_0 - \lambda\alpha K w_0 - \alpha f \end{aligned} \right\} \qquad \rho = 2 \tag{12.88}$$

leads to convergence for

$$|1 - \alpha^2| < 1, \qquad |1 - \alpha^2(1 - z_k{}^2)| < 1. \tag{12.89}$$

With a sufficiently small value of $|\alpha|$, convergence can always be enforced.

All these methods have been extended by Schönberg [38, 39] to bounded operators K in Hilbert and Banach spaces. He also found that an expansion of $(1 - z)^{-1}$ in polynomials of z, which converges uniformly in a simply connected domain of the complex z plane such that the values λ/λ_i are in the domain and the point $z = 1$ outside, implies a convergent expansion of $(I - \lambda K)^{-1} = I + \lambda K(\lambda)$ when λK is substituted for z. In the same vein, Bellman [2] has shown that regular summation methods of the geometric series of $(1 - z)^{-1}$ apply equally to the Neumann-Liouville series. His publication is concerned with an hermitian operator.

Schönberg's results provide the basis for very general iterative methods. One may generalize (12.71) by setting

$$w_{n+1} = (1 - \theta_{n+1})\lambda K w_n + t_{n+1} w_n + (\theta_{n+1} - t_{n+1})w_{n-1} + (1 - \theta_{n+1})f \tag{12.90}$$

with suitable coefficients θ_n, t_n. This iteration appears in the above-mentioned papers by Lanczos. Stiefel [44] writes $L = I - \lambda K$, introduces the residuals $r_n = f - L w_n$, and sets

$$r_n = P_n(L)f; \tag{12.91}$$

the polynomial $P_n(x)$ is related to $p_n(x)$ by $P_n(x) = p_n(1 - x)$. Assuming that the characteristic values of L are real, positive, and within an interval (u',b'), he recommends using the polynomials

$$P_n(x) = \frac{\cos nt}{\cosh nz}, \qquad \cos t = \frac{b' + a' - 2x}{b' - a'}, \qquad \cosh z = \frac{b' + a'}{b' - a'}. \tag{12.92}$$

They have the property $P_n(0) = 1$; among all polynomials of this property, the polynomials (12.92) have the least maximum absolute value in the interval (a',b'), which makes them Chebyshev polynomials in a generalized sense. Therefore the choice (12.92) admits an optimum liquidation of the residuals. The reduction of the residuals goes with the order $P_n \sim 2e^{-nz}$ for large values of n. The coefficients of (12.90) can be found from the recurrence relation of the polynomials P_n. Stiefel discusses in detail some numerical aspects of the method with regard to the kernel (12.77).

This is not the end of possible iterative methods. Wagner and Samuelson have reported on certain modifications of the preceding methods; Lonseth has given another survey of iteration methods, together with computational experiments. Weissinger has found a general criterion of convergence, related to operator equations defined for abstract sets. The quadratically convergent iteration method of Schulz, suggested for matrix problems, can be extended to integral equations. The reader is referred to the bibliography at the end of this chapter.

The sequence (12.65) can also be used to obtain information about A in the split (12.47), in particular with respect to eigenvalues other than λ_1. The polynomials $q_n(x)$ may be so chosen that, with respect to a certain characteristic value κ of K, $q_n(\kappa)$ prevails over the values of q_n for the other characteristic values. This can be done on the basis of a first guess on κ; if λ_1 is already known, the polynomials will be chosen such that $q_n(\kappa_1) = 0$, and the iteration will lead to information about another characteristic value. The special methods mentioned above have been adapted and used to this purpose for both integral and matrix operators.

In the case of hermitian operators, polynomial iteration for the purpose of finding eigenelements overlaps with the use of inclusion polynomials. Some typical results for the asymptotic behavior of functions of the Schwarz constants a_n may be mentioned. The ratios $\mu_n = a_{n-1}/a_n$ converge to an eigenvalue, say λ_1. The convergence involves $|\mu_{2n-1}| > |\lambda_1|$; if K is definite, we even have $|\mu_n| > |\lambda_1|$. In any case the inequality $|\mu_{2n-1}| > |\mu_{2n}|$, due to Grammel, holds. The numbers $\mu_1\mu_2 \geq \mu_3\mu_4 \geq \cdots$ are upper bounds of $\lambda_1{}^2$, as has been pointed out by Collatz [11]. Also due to Collatz is the sequence

$$Q_n = \mu_n \frac{\mu_{n-1} - \lambda_2}{\mu_n - \lambda_2} \tag{12.93}$$

which for a positive definite K with λ_1 as the smallest eigenvalue and λ_2 as the second smallest eigenvalue, converges to λ_1 *from below*. This can be generalized. The λ_2 in (12.93) can be replaced by R_n, provided that

$$\mu_n < R_n < \lambda_2, \qquad \frac{\mu_{n-1} - \mu_n}{R_n - \mu_n} \to 0 \qquad \text{as} \qquad n \to \infty \tag{12.94}$$

(see Bückner [5]). All these and other general results can be easily proved by means of the inclusion theorems mentioned above.

Quite another method of calculating the eigenvalues larger than λ_1 in modulus has been suggested by Wielandt [55]. He uses an approximation λ^* to a higher eigenvalue and iterates by solving the equation $(I - \lambda^*K)w_n = w_{n-1}$.

12.8 Analogy Methods

The numerical computation of the integral Ky goes in general with a rule of numerical quadrature of the type

$$\int_a^b g(t)\, dt \doteq \sum_{i=1}^n p_i g_i, \qquad g_i = g(x_i), \qquad (12.95)$$

with certain weights $p_1, p_2, \ldots, p_n$ and certain abscissas $a \le x_1 < x_2 < \cdots < x_n \le b$.

By such a rule the Fredholm integral equation turns approximately into the following set of simultaneous equations:

$$\sum_{k=1}^n (\delta_{ik} - \Lambda p_k K_{ik}) F_k = f_i, \qquad K_{ik} = K(x_i, x_k), \qquad i = 1, 2, \ldots, n \tag{12.96}$$

with the quantities F_i as approximations to $y(x_i)$ and with Λ replacing the parameter λ. The treatment of (12.96) in the homogeneous case $f_i \equiv 0$ will furnish approximations to the eigenvalues of K as well as to the eigenfunctions. In the inhomogeneous case one will obtain an approximation F_i to $y(x_i)$ of a solution y.

In the case of a real, symmetric, and continuous kernel $K(s,t)$ and for equidistant abscissas $x_k = a + kh$, $h = (b - a)/n = p_k$, Hilbert has shown that the suitably ordered zeros $\Lambda_i^{(n)}$ of det $(\delta_{ik} - \Lambda p_k K_{ik})$ converge toward eigenvalues λ of K as $n \to \infty$.

With the aid of the new abscissas $\xi_0 = a$,

$$\xi_k = a + P_n(b - a) \sum_{i=1}^k p_i, \qquad P_n^{-1} = \sum_{i=1}^n p_i, \tag{12.97}$$

and of the orthogonal set of functions

$$u_k(s) = 1 \quad \text{for} \quad \xi_{k-1} \le s < \xi_k, \qquad u_k = 0 \quad \text{elsewhere}, \tag{12.98}$$

one may introduce

$$f_n(s) = \sum_{i=1}^n f_i u_i(s), \qquad F_n(s) = \sum_{i=1}^n F_i u_i(s), \tag{12.99}$$

$$K_n(s,t) = P_n^{-1}(b - a)^{-1} \sum_{i,k=1}^n K_{ik} u_i(s) u_k(t).$$

The set (12.96) is equivalent to the integral equation

$$F_n(s) - \Lambda \int_a^b K_n(s,t) F_n(t)\, dt = f_n(s), \tag{12.100}$$

which has a kernel of finite rank. It is natural to assume that

$$r_n(g) = \sum_{i=1}^n p_i g_i - \int_a^b g\, ds \to \infty \qquad \text{as} \qquad n \to \infty \tag{12.101}$$

for continuous functions $g(s)$ if the quadrature rule is defined for all n.

It has been proved [5, 7] that

$$\lim K_n(s,t) = K(s,t), \qquad \lim f_n(s) = f(s) \qquad (12.102)$$

in the sense of uniform convergence if $f(s)$ and $K(s,t)$ are continuous. It has also been shown, under the same assumptions on f and K, that $F_n(s)$ converges uniformly to the solution y of $(I - \Lambda K)y = f$ if Λ is not an eigenvalue of K. Furthermore, the suitably ordered eigenvalues of $K_n(s,t)$ converge to the eigenvalues of K, and a similar result holds for the eigenfunctions of $K_n(s,t)$. The rate of convergence of the approximation depends on the rate of convergence of (12.101).

The choice of the rule (12.95) depends essentially on features of regularity of $f(s)$ and of $K(s,t)$. If both functions are continuous, but do not possess continuous derivatives, it does not help much to apply any rule with higher precision than the one investigated by Hilbert. If, on the other hand, $f(s)$ and $K(s,t)$ are analytic with respect to their variables, then higher precision rules should be employed. Nyström has reported on the application of the Gaussian rule to an integral equation with the kernel (12.77) related to an ellipse as a contour. For the same kernel Weddle's rule has been found satisfactory by Todd and Warschawski [46]. Prager used a five-ordinate Chebyshev rule in the same case.

Nyström [28–31] suggested adapting the rule to the kernel $K(s,t)$. More precisely, for given abscissas x_k, Nyström calculates the integrals

$$\int_a^b K(x_i,t)t^m \, dt, \qquad m = 0, 1, \ldots, n - 1.$$

The function $y(t)$ is approximated by its interpolation polynomial with ordinates $y(x_k)$ at the prescribed abscissas. Fox and Goodwin [15] use the trapezoidal rule, solve (12.96), then calculate an error term of the rule from this first approximation, and throw the error back into the system in order to calculate a correction to the first approximation.

Volterra equations have been treated in a similar way. Huber [16] transforms the Volterra equation by approximating $y(t)$ by a polygon function; the abscissas are equidistant. Wagner [47, 48] uses parabolic interpolation with respect to equidistant abscissas.

In certain cases, $K(s,t)$ has continuous partial derivatives in t up to a certain order r, whereas the derivative of order $(r + 1)$ jumps at $t = s$. This happens to certain homogeneous integral equations which represent vibration problems of one space dimension. The kernel K is related to or identical with the Green function of an ordinary differential equation under boundary conditions. A higher-precision integration rule for functions $g(t)$, which have continuous derivatives up to order $(r + 1)$, can be used if the system (12.96) is modified in the form

$$\sum_{k=1}^{n} [(1 + \Lambda d_i)\, \delta_{ik} - \Lambda p_k K_{ik}] F_k = 0. \tag{12.96'}$$

The term d_i depends on the jump of $\partial^{r+1} K / \partial t^{r+1}$.

In the case of hermitian operators K, error bounds of the method (12.96) for the approximations to the characteristic values have been found by Wielandt [59]. He assumes $\sum_{i=1}^{n} p_i = b - a$ and an ordering of the characteristic values of K and K_n in the sense

$$\kappa_1 \geq \kappa_2 \geq \cdots \geq 0, \qquad \kappa_{-1} \leq \kappa_{-2} \leq \cdots \leq 0,$$
$$\kappa_1' \geq \kappa_2' \geq \cdots \geq 0. \qquad \kappa_{-1}' \leq \kappa_{-2}' \leq \cdots \leq 0,$$

respectively. The error bounds are of the type $|\kappa_i - \kappa_i'| \leq M$, with M independent of i. The basic approach to these results uses the new concept of *an hermitian kernel $G(s,t)$ allowing an integration rule S.* This means that the approximation by means of (12.96) gives the correct characteristic values of $G(s,t)$. It is proved that a rule S, applied to K, admits the error bound

$$|\kappa_i' - \kappa_i| \leq \|K - G\|, \tag{12.103}$$

where G can be *any* hermitian operator allowing S. In practical applications, G is constructed as an operator of finite rank, and an upper bound M for $\|K - G\|$ is established. A typical example refers to the case of equal weights and equidistant abscissas, which we mentioned before. Assuming a Lipschitz condition $|K_{ik} - K(s,t)| \leq L[p(s) + p(t)]$, with $p(s) = s - x_k$ for $x_k \leq s < x_{k+1}$, Wielandt finds

$$|\kappa_i - \kappa_i'| < CL/n, \qquad C = \tfrac{1}{2} + \sqrt{\tfrac{1}{3}}. \tag{12.104}$$

This is also the best result for a given Lipschitz constant L; that is, C cannot be replaced by a smaller constant. Other examples refer to the trapezoidal rule, the central-point rule, the Simpson rule, and the Gaussian method.

12.9 Approximation of y by a Linear Combination of Given Functions

The method described in Sec. 12.2 by (12.35), (12.36) can also be applied to Fredholm integral equations. So far, it has been customary to work with only one complete system $u_1, u_2, \ldots$ of linearly independent functions of H. One may approximate a solution y of either the homogeneous or inhomogeneous integral equation by a linear combination

$$v = c_1 u_1 + c_2 u_2 + \cdots + c_n u_n. \tag{12.105}$$

For the integral equation $(I - \lambda K)y = f$, the method leads to the residual

$$r_n = f - (I - \lambda K)v = f - \sum_k c_k (I - \lambda K)u_k. \qquad (12.106)$$

The coefficients c_k can be determined from n conditions to be satisfied by r_n. Dealing with a continuous kernel and continuous functions f, u_k, one could apply the so-called method of collocation, which requires that the function r_n vanish at n prescribed abscissas. Another approach requires

$$(u_i, r_n) = 0 \qquad \text{for } i = 1, 2, \ldots, n. \qquad (12.107)$$

This leads to the equations

$$\sum_k [(u_i, u_k) - (u_i, \lambda K u_k)]\bar{c}_k = (u_i, f) \qquad (12.108)$$

Equation (12.108) can be used for both the inhomogeneous equation $(I - \lambda K)y = f$ and the eigenvalue problem $(I - \lambda K)y = 0$.

The selection of the functions $u_1, u_2, \ldots$ is of special importance. Very often orthonormal systems are used, especially systems with sin functions or systems of polynomials. In the case of a positive definite hermitian integral operator, Enskog [13] has suggested solving the inhomogeneous equation (λ not an eigenvalue) for $0 < \lambda < \lambda_1$, by means of functions u_i, which satisfy

$$(u_i, u_k) - \lambda(u_i, K u_k) = \delta_{ik}. \qquad (12.109)$$

In this case the solution of (12.108) is simply $\bar{c}_i = (u_i, f)$.

For some problems involving the inhomogeneous equation one may follow the pattern of relaxation. One starts with u_1 as a guess for y, calculates $(I - \lambda K)u_1 = w_1$, minimizes $g = f - cw_1$ by a choice of the constant c, and uses cu_1 as first approximation to y; thereafter a correction is determined by treating $(I - \lambda K)z = g$ in the same manner.

It can be shown that the system (12.108) is equivalent to an integral equation

$$(I - \lambda L)v = f_n, \qquad (12.110)$$

where f_n may be regarded as an approximation to f, and L as an approximation to K; L is of finite rank, related to the functions u_k. We found the same phenomenon in the preceding section on the analogy methods [see Eq. (12.100)]. This brings us to the more general method of perturbation where the operator K is considered as a function of a parameter ϵ such that

$$K(\epsilon) = K_0 + \epsilon K_1 + \epsilon^2 K_2 + \cdots, \qquad (12.111)$$

with operators K_0, K_1, ... not depending on ϵ. This covers the case

(12.110) with $\epsilon = 1$, $K_0 = L$, $K_1 = K - L$, $K_2 = 0$, $K_3 = 0, \ldots$. To solve $(I - \lambda K(\epsilon))y = f$, one sets

$$y = y_0 + \epsilon y_1 + \epsilon^2 y_2 + \cdots, \qquad (12.112)$$

and the functions y_k are determined by the algorithm

$$(I - \lambda K_0)y_n = K_1 y_{n-1} + K_2 y_{n-2} + \cdots + K_n y_0, \qquad n \geq 1;$$
$$(I - \lambda_0 K_0)y_0 = f. \qquad (12.113)$$

The eigenvalue problem $[I - \lambda K(\epsilon)]y = 0$ is treated by starting with a solution of the eigenvalue problem of K_0. Let it be $(\kappa_0 I - K_0)y_0 = 0$. Then a characteristic value $\kappa(\epsilon)$ and an eigenfunction $y(\epsilon)$ are wanted which admit the expansions

$$\kappa(\epsilon) = \kappa_0 + \kappa_1 \epsilon + \cdots, \qquad y = y_0 + y_1 \epsilon + \cdots. \quad (12.114)$$

A set of recursion formulas for the determination of κ_n and y_n can be set up. In the case where $K(\epsilon)$ and $K_0, K_1, \ldots$ are hermitian and where κ_0 is a single characteristic value of K_0, we assume that $y(\epsilon)$ and y_0 satisfy the following normalizing conditions:

$$\| y(\epsilon)\| = 1, \qquad (y_0, y_n) = \text{real} \qquad \text{for } n = 1, 2, \ldots. \quad (12.115)$$

The operator K_0 admits the split (12.48), $K_0 = A + B$ with respect to K_0. Writing

$$R = (\kappa_0 I - B)^{-1}(I - \kappa_0^{-1} A) \qquad (12.116)$$

and $\quad z_1 = K_1 y_0,$

$$z_n = K_n y_0 + (K_1 - \kappa_1 I)y_{n-1} + \cdots + (K_{n-1} - \kappa_{n-1} I)y_1,$$
$$n = 2, 3, \ldots, \quad (12.117)$$

the recursion formulas are

$$\kappa_n = (z_n, y_0), \qquad (12.118)$$
$$y_1 = R z_1,$$
$$y_n = -\tfrac{1}{2}[(y_1, y_{n-1}) + (y_2, y_{n-2}) + \cdots + (y_{n-1}, y_1)] + R z_n,$$
$$n = 2, 3, \ldots. \quad (12.119)$$

These formulas were first presented by Rellich [34], who established a general theory of the perturbation of operators in a Hilbert space. His fundamental results include the case of multiple characteristic values, of convergence of the series (12.114), and of error bounds for the remainder terms of the series, if the calculation is carried to κ_n, y_n only. His theory has been simplified by Sz.-Nagy, who also improved the error bounds [27]. More work on error bounds has been done by Schröder [40].

Although Rellich established the existence of eigenelements according to (12.114), he also pointed out that there may be irregular eigenvalues of $K(\epsilon)$ which cannot be found by (12.114).

Example. For $\epsilon < 0$, the kernel

$$K(s,t;\epsilon) = \min\,(s,t) - st/(1 + \epsilon), \qquad a = 0,\, b = 1,\, |\epsilon| < 1,$$

has an eigenvalue $\lambda^*(\epsilon)$, satisfying $\tanh \sqrt{-\lambda^*} = -\epsilon\sqrt{-\lambda^*}$. One finds $\lambda^* \to -\infty$ when $\epsilon \to 0$; neither λ^* nor $1/\lambda^*$ is expandable into a power series of ϵ, converging in some neighborhood of $\epsilon = 0$.

REFERENCES

1. H. Bateman, Numerical Solution of Linear Integral Equations, *Proc. Roy. Soc. London. Ser. A*, vol. 100, pp. 441–449, 1922.

2. R. Bellman, Note on Summability of Formal Solutions of Linear Integral Equations, *Duke Math. J.*, vol. 17, pp. 53–55, 1950.

3. L. Berg, Lösungsverfahren für singuläre Integralgleichungen, *Math. Nachr.*, vol. 14, pp. 193–212, 1955.

4. H. Bückner, A Special Method of Successive Approximations for Fredholm Integral Equations, *Duke Math. J.*, vol. 15, pp. 197–206, 1948.

5. H. Bückner, "Die praktische Behandlung von Integralgleichungen. Ergebnisse der angewandten Mathematik, Bd. 1," Springer-Verlag, Berlin, 1952.

6. H. Bückner, Ein unbeschränkt anwendbares Iterationsverfahren für Fredholmsche Integralgleichungen, *Math. Nachr.*, vol. 2, pp. 304–313, 1949.

7. H. Bückner, Konvergenzuntersuchungen bei einem algebraischen Verfahren zur näherungsweisen Lösung von Integralgleichungen, *Math. Nachr.*, vol. 3, pp. 358–372, 1950.

8. G. F. Carrier, On the Determination of the Eigenfunctions of Fredholm Equations, *J. Math. Phys.*, vol. 27, pp. 82–83, 1948.

9. L. Collatz, Einschliessungssatz für die Eigenwerte von Integralgleichungen, *Math. Z.*, vol. 47, pp. 395–398, 1941.

10. L. Collatz, "Numerische Behandlung von Differentialgleichungen," chap. 5, Springer-Verlag, Berlin, 1951.

11. L. Collatz, Schrittweise Näherungen bei Integralgleichungen und Eigenwertschranken, *Math. Z.*, vol. 46, pp. 692–708, 1940.

12. R. Courant and D. Hilbert, "Methoden der mathematischen Physik," 2d ed., vol. I, pp. 96–133, Springer-Verlag, Berlin, 1931.

13. D. Enskog, Kinetische Theorie der Vorgänge in mässig verdünnten Gasen, dissertation, Uppsala, Sweden, 1917.

14. W. Feller, On the Integral Equation of Renewal Theory, *Ann. Math. Statist.*, vol. 12, pp. 243–267, 1941.

15. L. Fox and E. T. Goodwin, The Numerical Solution of Nonsingular Integral Equations, *Philos. Trans. Roy. Soc. London. Ser. A*, vol. 245, no. 902, pp. 501–534.

16. A. Huber, Eine Näherungsmethode zur Auflösung Volterrascher Integralgleichungen, *Monatsh. Math. Phys.*, vol. 47, pp. 240–246, 1939.

17. W. H. Isay, Beitrag zur Potentialstroemung durch axiale Schaufelgitter, *Z. Angew. Math. Mech.*, pp. 397–409, 1953.

18. W. M. Kincaid, Numerical Methods for Finding Characteristic Roots and Vectors of Matrices, *Quart. Appl. Math.*, vol. 5, pp. 320–345, 1947.

19. C. Lanczos, An Iteration Method for the Solution of the Eigenvalue Problem of Linear Differential and Integral Operators, *J. Res. Nat. Bur. Standards*, vol. 45, p. 255, 1950.

20. C. Lanczos, Chebyshev Polynomials in the Solution of Large-scale Linear Systems, *Proc. Assoc. Comput. Mach.*, p. 124, 1953.

21. C. Lanczos, Solution of Systems of Linear Equations by Minimized Iterations, *J. Res. Nat. Bur. Standards*, vol. 49, p. 33, 1952.

22. N. J. Lehmann, Beiträge zur numerischen Lösung linearer Eigenwertprobleme, *Z. Angew. Math. Mech.*, vol. 29, pp. 341–356, 1949; vol. 30, pp. 1–16, 1950.

23. A. T. Lonseth, Approximate Solutions of Fredholm Type Integral Equations, *Bull. Amer. Math. Soc.*, vol. 60, pp. 415–430, 1954.

24. F. Lösch, Zur praktischen Berechnung der Eigenwerte linearer Integralgleichungen, *Z. Angew. Math. Mech.*, vol. 24, pp. 35–41, 1944.

25. N. I. Muskhelishvili, "Singular Integral Equations," P. Noordhoff, N.V., Groningen, Netherlands, 1953 (2d Russian ed., Moscow, 1946).

26. N. I. Muskhelishvili, "Some Basic Problems of the Mathematical Theory of Elasticity," P. Noordhoff, N.V., Groningen, Netherlands, 1953 (1st Russian ed., Leningrad, 1933).

27. B. Sz.-Nagy, Perturbations des transformations autoadjointes dans l'espace de Hilbert, *Comment. Math. Helv.*, vol. 19, pp. 347–366, 1946–1947.

28. E. J. Nyström, Über die praktische Auflösung von linearen Integralgleichungen mit Anwendungen auf Randwertaufgaben der Potentialtheorie, *Soc. Sci. Fenn. Comment. Phys-Math.*, vol. 4, no. 15, 1928.

29. E. J. Nyström, Über die praktische Auflösung von Integralgleichungen, *Soc. Sci. Fenn. Comment. Phys.-Math.*, vol. 5, no. 5, 1929.

30. E. J. Nyström, Über die praktische Auflösung von Integralgleichungen mit Anwendungen auf Randwertaufgaben, *Acta Math.*, vol. 54, pp. 185–204, 1930.

31. E. J. Nyström, Zur numerischen Lösung von Randwertaufgaben bei gewöhnlichen Differentialgleichungen, *Acta Math.*, vol. 76, pp. 157–184, 1944.

32. W. Prager, Die Druckverteilung an Körpern in ebener Potentialströmung, *Phys. Z.*, vol. 29, pp. 865–869, 1928.

33. E. Reissner, Solution of a Class of Singular Integral Equations, *Bull. Amer. Math. Soc.*, vol. 51, pp. 920–922, 1945.

34. F. Rellich, Störungstheorie der Spektralzerlegung, Fünf Mitteilungen, in particular, I. Mitteilung, *Math. Ann.*, vol. 113, pp. 600–619, 1936; IV. Mitteilung, *Math. Ann.*, vol. 117, pp. 356–382, 1940; V. Mitteilung, *Math. Ann.*, vol. 118, pp. 462–484, 1942.

35. F. Riesz and B. Sz.-Nagy, "Leçons d'Analyse Fonctionelle," Académie des Sciences de Hongrie, Budapest, 1952.

36. P. A. Samuelson, Rapidly Converging Solutions to Integral Equations, *J. Math. Phys.*, vol. 31, pp. 276–286, 1953.

37. W. Schmeidler, "Integralgleichungen mit Anwendungen in Physik und Technik," vol. I, "Lineare Integralgleichungen," vol. XXII, "Mathematik und ihre Anwendungen in Physik und Technik," Akademische Verlagsgesellschaft, Leipzig, 1950.

38. M. Schönberg, Sur la méthode d'iteration de Wiarda et Bückner pour la résolution de l'équation de Fredholm, I, *Acad. Roy. Belg. Bull. Cl. Sci.*, ser. 37, vol. 5, pp. 1141–1156, 1951.

39. M. Schönberg, Sur la méthode d'iteration de Wiarda et Bückner pour la résolution de l'équation de Fredholm, II, *Acad. Roy. Belg. Bull. Cl. Sci.*, ser. 38, vol. 5, pp. 154–167, 1952.

40. J. Schröder, Fehlerabschätzungen zur Störungsrechnung bei linearen Eigenwertproblemen, dissertation, Hannover, Germany, 1952.

41. G. Schulz, Iterative Berechnung der reziproken Matrix, *Z. Angew. Math. Mech.*, vol. 13, pp. 57–59, 1933.

42. E. Schwerin, Über Transversalschwingungen von Stäben veränderlichen Querschnitts, *Z. Techn. Phys.*, vol. 8, pp. 264–271, 1927.

43. H. A. Schwarz, "Gesammelte mathematische Abhandlungen," vol. I, pp. 241–265, Springer-Verlag, Berlin, 1890.

44. E. Stiefel, On Solving Fredholm Integral Equations, *J. Soc. Indust. Appl. Math.*, pp. 63–85, 1956.

45. G. Szegö, "Orthogonal Polynomials," American Mathematical Society Colloquium Publications, vol. 123, p. 26, 1939.

46. J. Todd and S. E. Warschawski, On the Solution of the Lichtenstein-Gershgorin Integral Equation in Conformal Mapping, II; Computational Experiments, in J. Todd, ed., "Experiments in the Computation of Conformal Maps," National Bureau of Standards Applied Mathematics Series, vol. 42, 1955.

47. C. Wagner, On the Solution of Fredholm Integral Equations of Second Kind by Iteration, *J. Math. Phys.*, vol. 30, pp. 23–30, 1951.

48. C. Wagner, On the Numerical Evaluation of Fredholm Integral Equations with the Aid of the Liouville-Neumann Series, *J. Math. Phys.*, vol. 30, pp. 232–234, 1952.

49. S. E. Warschawski, On the Solution of the Lichtenstein-Gershgorin Integral Equation in Conformal Mapping, I: Theory, in J. Todd, ed., "Experiments in the Computation of Conformal Maps," National Bureau of Standards Applied Mathematics Series, vol. 42, 1955.

50. J. Weissinger, Ein Satz über Fourierreihen und seine Anwendung auf die Tragflügeltheorie, *Math. Z.*, vol. 47, pp. 16–33, 1940.

51. J. Weissinger, Zur Theorie und Anwendung des Iterationsverfahrens, *Math. Nachr.*, vol. 8, pp. 193–212, 1952.

52. E. T. Whittaker, On the Numerical Solution of Integral Equations, *Proc. Roy. Soc. London. Ser. A*, vol. 94, pp. 367–383, 1918.

53. G. Wiarda, "Integralgleichungen unter besonderer Berücksichtigung der Anwendungen," p. 126, Teubner, Leipzig, 1930.

54. H. Wielandt, Das Iterationsverfahren bei nicht selbstadjungierten linearen Eigenwertaufgaben, *Math. Z.*, vol. 50, pp. 93–143, 1944.

55. H. Wielandt, Bestimmung höherer Eigenwerte durch gebrochene Iteration, AVA-Bericht B44/J37, 1944 (unpublished).

56. H. Wielandt, Die Einschliessungssätze von Eigenwerten normaler Matrizen, *Math. Ann.*, vol. 121, pp. 234–241, 1948.

57. H. Wielandt, Ein Ansatz von L. Schwarz zur Lösung singulärer Integralgleichungen, 1. Art., AVA-Bericht B44/J22, 1944 (unpublished).

58. H. Wielandt, Einschliessung von Eigenwerten Hermitescher Matrizen nach dem Abschnittsverfahren, *Arch. Math.*, vol. 5, pp. 108–114, 1955.

59. H. Wielandt, Error Bounds for Eigenvalues of Symmetric Integral Equations, in American Mathematical Society, "Numerical Analysis: Proceedings of Symposia in Applied Mathematics—Volume VI," J. H. Curtiss, ed., pp. 261–282, McGraw-Hill Book Company, Inc., New York, 1956.

60. J. V. Vorobyov, Orthogonal Operator Polynomials and Methods to Approximately Determine the Spectrum of Linear and Bounded Operators, *Uspekhi Mat. Nauk*, vol. 9, pp. 83–90, 1954 (in Russian).

61. L. V. Kantorovitch, Functional Analysis and Applied Mathematics, *Uspekhi Mat. Nauk*, vol. 3, pp. 89–185, 1948; there is a translation by C. D. Benster, in G. E. Forsythe, ed., *Nat. Bur. Standards Report* 1509, 1952.

Recent Literature

Among the recent books and papers which are particularly relevant are the following:

62. "Symposium on the Numerical Treatment of Ordinary Differential Equations, Integral and Integro-differential Equations." Proceedings of the Rome Symposium (20–24 September 1960) Organized by the Provisional International Computation Center, Birkhauser Verlag, Basel, Stuttgart, 1960.

63. S. G. Mikhlin, "Integral Equations," Pergamon Press, London, 1957.

64. F. G. Tricomi, "Integral Equations," Interscience Publishers, Inc., New York, 1957.

65. E. Martensen, Berechnung der Druckverteilung an Gitterprofilen in ebener Potentialstromüng mit einer Fredholmschen Integralgleichung, *Arch. Rational Mech. Anal.*, vol. 3, pp. 235–270, 1959. (This paper is related to the equation (12.7), as is [32] also.)

13

Errors of Numerical Approximation for Analytic Functions

PHILIP J. DAVIS

NATIONAL BUREAU OF STANDARDS

13.1 Introduction

It has become traditional in works on numerical methods to express errors committed in the use of approximate formulas of integration, differentiation, interpolation, etc., in terms of the higher derivatives of the function operated upon.   The error consists of two parts: (1) a multiplicative constant which depends solely on the numerical rule employed and (2) a higher derivative $f^{(n)}(\xi)$ evaluated at some intermediate point of the interval I.   In some cases, the error is given by an expression of the form $c_1 f^{(n)}(\xi) + c_2 f^{(m)}(\eta)$.   In most cases, the exact value of ξ will be unknown, and the estimate $\max_{\xi \in I} |f^{(n)}(\xi)|$ is employed instead.   Such expressions of error are valid for the class of real functions which are sufficiently differentiable and therefore possess wide applicability.   On the other hand, they have several drawbacks.   In the first place, since the error term of different rules may contain different orders of derivatives, the respective accuracy of the rules may not be compared on a common basis.   Secondly, data on the higher derivatives may be unavailable or may be difficult to obtain.   Such will be the case, for example, in operating with functions which are given in closed form but which are highly composite—for example, $f(x) = [1 + (1 + e^{x^2})^{1/2}]^{1/2}$.

In the present discussion we derive a complex-variable method for estimating errors which arise when approximation rules are applied to analytic functions.   In contrast to the usual real-variable methods, this method does not involve the use of the higher derivatives of the function but requires instead a knowledge of the size of the function in the complex plane.   It is therefore of practical value in dealing with functions of the type described above.   That such estimates are, in principle, possible for

468

analytic functions can be seen from Cauchy's inequality

$$|f^{(n)}(t)| \leq \text{const} \max_{z \in C} \left| \frac{f(z)}{(z - t)^{n+1}} \right|, \tag{13.1}$$

which gives us information about the size of the derivatives of an analytic function in terms of its boundary values.

We derive our estimates of error by introducing a Hilbert space of analytic functions and using the Riesz representation of bounded linear functionals. The error $E(f)$ committed in the use of formulas of numerical approximation applied to f may be estimated in the form $|E(f)| \leq \sigma_E \|f\|$. This estimate is a Schwarz inequality. The quantity σ_E is the norm of the error functional; it depends solely on the approximation rule employed and is independent of the particular function operated upon. The quantity $\|f\|$ is the norm of f in the Hilbert space and may be estimated from a knowledge of the values of the function in the complex plane. Having precomputed σ_E, we need only estimate $\|f\|$ in order to obtain the error in any specific instance.

13.2 Essentials of the Method

Let B designate a bounded region lying in the plane of the complex variable $z = x + iy$. By $L^2(B)$, we mean the class of functions which are single-valued regular analytic in B and are such that

$$\iint_B |f(z)|^2 \, dx \, dy < \infty. \tag{13.2}$$

The class $L^2(B)$ has been studied extensively. For the fundamentals of this theory, see Bergman [2]. We note in particular that, if $f(z)$ is regular in the closure of B, then (13.2) holds. The positive square root of the quantity (13.2) is termed the *norm* of f over $L^2(B)$ and is designated by $\|f\|$ or $\|f\|_B$. That is,

$$\|f\|_B = \left[\iint_B |f(z)|^2 \, dx \, dy \right]^{1/2} \qquad f \in L^2(B). \tag{13.3}$$

If a region G satisfies $G \subseteq B$ and if $f \in L^2(B)$, it is clear that $f \in L^2(G)$ and that

$$\|f\|_G \leq \|f\|_B. \tag{13.4}$$

The principal features of the class $L^2(B)$ are as follows. We introduce the integral

$$\iint_B f(z)\overline{g(z)} \, dx \, dy = (f,g) \qquad f, g \in L^2(B), \tag{13.5}$$

as an inner product. The class $L^2(B)$ possesses complete orthonormal systems $\{\zeta_n(z)\}$ in the sense of (13.5). Every function of the class can be expanded in a Fourier series

$$f(z) = \sum_{n=0}^{\infty} a_n \zeta_n(z), \tag{13.6}$$

wherein

$$a_n = (f, \zeta_n) \qquad (n = 0, 1, \ldots). \tag{13.7}$$

The convergence of (13.6) is uniform and absolute in every closed subregion of B. Moreover, we have

$$\| f \|^2 = \sum_{n=0}^{\infty} |a_n|^2. \tag{13.8}$$

The bilinear series $\sum_{n=0}^{\infty} \zeta_n(z) \overline{\zeta_n(w)}$ converges for $z, w \in B$ to a function $K_B(z, \bar{w})$, which is called the Bergman kernel function of B and which possesses the characteristic reproducing property $(f(z), K_B(z, \bar{w})) = f(w)$ for all $f \in L^2(B)$. For simply connected regions B with a Jordan boundary, there exists a complete orthonormal set of polynomials $\{p_n(z)\}$.

Let E be a bounded linear functional over $L^2(B)$; its norm may be obtained in the following way. Let $\zeta_n(z)$, $n = 0, 1, \ldots$, be a complete orthonormal system for $L^2(B)$. Then it may be shown that

$$\|E\|^2 = \sum_{n=0}^{\infty} |E(\zeta_n)|^2. \tag{13.9}$$

This may be expressed in the alternative but equivalent form

$$\|E\|^2 = E_z E_{\bar{w}} K_B(z, \bar{w}), \tag{13.10}$$

where the subscripts on the E mean that the functional operation is to be carried out on the variable indicated. We have, then, for all $f \in L^2(B)$,

$$|E(f)| \le \|E\| \, \|f\|, \tag{13.11}$$

with the equality sign attained for some $f \in L^2(B)$.

If z_k designates a fixed point in the interior of B and if I designates a closed interval lying in the interior of B, then the expressions $f^{(n)}(z_k)$, $n = 0, 1, \ldots$, and $\int_I f(z) \, dz$ represent bounded linear functionals over $L^2(B)$. Consider next some typical error expressions which occur in numerical analysis. For instance,

$$E_1(f) = \int_I f(z) \, dz - \sum_{k=1}^{n} a_k f(z_k)$$

is a quadrature error,

$$E_2(f) = f'(z_0) - \sum_{k=1}^{n} a_k f(z_k)$$

is an error in a differentiation formula, and

$$E_3(f) = f(z_0) - \sum_{k=1}^{n} a_k f(z_k)$$

is an error in an interpolation or extrapolation.   In view of the above remark, and subject to those restrictions on the location of z_k and I, the errors E that arise are bounded linear functionals over $L^2(B)$.   We are therefore in a position to apply the inequality (13.11).

We should like next to develop some practical error estimates for analytic functions.   Let us assume that we are dealing with the fixed interval $[-1, +1]$.   If $f(z)$ is analytic in the closed interval, then it also is analytic in a certain region D of the z plane which contains $[-1, +1]$ in its interior.   If B designates a closed region with $[-1, +1] \subset B \subset D$, then $f(z) \in L^2(B)$.   Of course, if we want to deal with the family of all functions which are analytic on $[-1, +1]$, we cannot fix a B beforehand but must have available a family of B's which collapse to $[-1, +1]$.

Now, there are two cases in which the orthonormal polynomials over B have a simple structure.   They are the circle and the ellipse, and in view of the preceding remark, we reject the former in favor of the latter.

To discuss the case of the ellipse, it is best to assume that it has been

TABLE 13.1   GEOMETRIC QUANTITIES FOR ELLIPSES

a	b	ρ	$(\pi ab)^{1/2}$
1.01	.1418	1.3266	.6607
1.02	.2010	1.4908	.8026
1.03	.2468	1.6302	.8936
1.04	.2857	1.7574	.9661
1.05	.3202	1.8773	1.0277
1.10	.4583	2.4282	1.2584
1.15	.5679	2.9511	1.4324
1.20	.6633	3.4720	1.5814
1.25	.7500	4.0000	1.7162
1.30	.8307	4.5397	1.8420
1.40	.9798	5.6634	2.0759
1.50	1.1180	6.8541	2.2953
1.75	1.4361	10.1515	2.8099
2.00	1.7321	13.9282	3.2989
2.50	2.2913	22.9565	4.2421
3.00	2.8284	33.9706	5.1631
4.00	3.8730	61.9839	6.9763
5.00	4.8990	97.9898	8.7723

placed in a normalized position. Let an ellipse, therefore, have its major axis along the x axis and its foci at the points $(-1,0)$ and $(1,0)$. Let a and $b = (a^2 - 1)^{1/2}$ designate its semimajor and semiminor axes, respectively, and let the quantity $\rho = \rho(a)$ be defined by

$$\rho = (a + b)^2, \qquad a = \tfrac{1}{2}(\rho^{1/2} + \rho^{-1/2}), \qquad b = \tfrac{1}{2}(\rho^{1/2} - \rho^{-1/2}). \quad (13.12)$$

This ellipse will be designated by $\mathscr{E}_\rho$. For values of $\rho > 1$, these ellipses form a confocal family and collapse to the segment $[-1,+1]$ as $\rho \to 1$. Table 13.1 gives the values of the geometric quantities b and ρ for a number of selected values of a.

We introduce the Chebyshev polynomials of the second kind by means of the definition

$$U_n(z) = (1 - z^2)^{-1/2} \sin\left[(n + 1) \arccos z\right] \qquad (n = 0, 1, \ldots). \quad (13.13)$$

It can then be shown that the polynomials

$$p_n(z) = 2(n + 1)^{1/2} \pi^{-1/2} (\rho^{n+1} - \rho^{-n-1})^{-1/2} U_n(z) \qquad (n = 0, 1, \ldots) \quad (13.14)$$

form a complete orthonormal system for $L^2(\mathscr{E}_\rho)$.

13.3   Quadrature Errors for $L^2(\mathscr{E}_\rho)$

The program outlined in the previous section has been carried out to a considerable extent for quadrature errors.

In conformity with the above normalization, we assume that the integration to be performed is over the interval $[-1,1]$. The case of an arbitrary interval may be handled by means of an appropriate linear transformation (see Sec. 13.6). An arbitrary $(N + 1)$-point quadrature formula is given by

$$\int_{-1}^{+1} f(x)\, dx \doteq \sum_{k=0}^{N} a_k f(\lambda_k) = R(f), \quad (13.15)$$

where λ_k are certain abscissas lying in $[-1,1]$ and a_k are the associated weights. The error $E = E(f)$ involved in the rule R is

$$E(f) = \int_{-1}^{1} f(x)\, dx - R(f). \quad (13.16)$$

If $f(x)$ is analytic on $[-1,1]$, then it is clear that for some value of $\rho > 1$, f may be continued analytically so as to be regular in the closed ellipse $\mathscr{E}_\rho$. Such an $f(z)$ is therefore of class $L^2(\mathscr{E}_\rho)$ and may be expanded in a series of Chebyshev polynomials

$$f(z) = \sum_{n=0}^{\infty} a_n p_n(z), \qquad \sum_{n=0}^{\infty} |a_n|^2 = \|f\|^2 < \infty, \quad (13.17)$$

which converges uniformly and absolutely in the interior of $\mathscr{E}_\rho$. Applying the operator E to (13.17), we obtain

$$E(f) = \sum_{n=0}^{\infty} a_n E(p_n). \tag{13.18}$$

Let us now write

$$\sigma_R{}^2 = \sum_{n=0}^{\infty} |E(p_n)|^2; \tag{13.19}$$

then, in view of (13.8) and (13.9), there is obtained

$$|E(f)| \le \sigma_R \|f\|. \tag{13.20}$$

The quantity σ_R, which is the norm over $L^2(\mathscr{E}_\rho)$ of the bounded linear functional E, depends only on the ellipse $\mathscr{E}_\rho$ and the quadrature rule R; but is independent of f, and may therefore be computed once for all. Using (13.19) and (13.14), we have

$$\sigma_R{}^2 = \frac{4}{\pi} \sum_{n=0}^{\infty} (n+1) \frac{|E[U_n(z)]|^2}{\rho^{n+1} - \rho^{-n-1}}. \tag{13.21}$$

We have, moreover,

$$U_n(z) = (n+1)^{-1} T'_{n+1}(z) \qquad (n = 0, 1, \ldots), \tag{13.22}$$

where $T_n(z)$ designates the Chebyshev polynomials of the first kind defined by

$$T_n(z) = \cos (n \arccos z) \qquad (n = 0, 1, \ldots). \tag{13.23}$$

Therefore,

$$\int_{-1}^{+1} U_n(x)\, dx = \frac{1}{n+1} [T_{n+1}(1) - T_{n+1}(-1)] = \frac{1}{n+1} [1 + (-1)^n]. \tag{13.24}$$

If quantities τ_n are defined by

$$\tau_n = 0, \qquad n \text{ odd}, \tag{13.25}$$

$$\tau_n = \frac{2}{n+1}, \qquad n \text{ even},$$

then we have

$$\sigma_R{}^2 = \frac{4}{\pi} \sum_{n=0}^{\infty} \frac{n+1}{\rho^{n+1} - \rho^{-n-1}} \left[\tau_n - \sum_{k=0}^{N} a_k U_n(\lambda_k) \right]^2. \tag{13.26}$$

Table 13.2 lists the values of σ corresponding to the trapezoidal, the Simpson, the Weddle, and the Gaussian 2-, 3-, 7-, 10-, and 16-point formulas and for a range of values of the parameter ρ. These values were computed from (13.26) on the National Bureau of Standards Eastern Automatic Computer (SEAC).

TABLE 13.2 VALUES OF σ_R†

R / a	Trapezoidal	Simpson	Weddle	Gauss 2-pt.	Gauss 3-pt.	Gauss 7-pt.	Gauss 10-pt.	Gauss 16-pt.
1.01	1.216 (1)	4.048 (0)	1.237 (0)	1.184 (0)	9.512 (−1)	4.060 (−1)	2.050 (−1)	4.737 (−2)
1.02	6.007 (0)	1.995 (0)	5.835 (−1)	7.710 (−1)	5.790 (−1)	1.670 (−1)	5.997 (−2)	6.900 (−3)
1.03	3.962 (0)	1.309 (0)	3.585 (−1)	5.834 (−1)	4.109 (−1)	8.521 (−2)	2.346 (−2)	1.580 (−3)
1.04	2.941 (0)	9.632 (−1)	2.449 (−1)	4.696 (−1)	3.115 (−1)	4.846 (−2)	1.066 (−2)	4.572 (−4)
1.05	2.329 (0)	7.550 (−1)	1.774 (−1)	3.912 (−1)	2.453 (−1)	2.952 (−2)	5.236 (−3)	1.538 (−4)
1.1	1.110 (0)	3.339 (−1)	5.318 (−2)	1.989 (−1)	9.843 (−2)	4.284 (−3)	3.573 (−4)	2.197 (−6)
1.15	7.064 (−1)	1.935 (−1)	2.181 (−2)	1.211 (−1)	4.959 (−2)	9.913 (−4)	4.608 (−5)	8.820 (−7)
1.2	5.059 (−1)	1.255 (−1)	1.045 (−2)	8.033 (−2)	2.805 (−2)	2.931 (−4)	8.363 (−6)	6.037 (−9)
1.25	3.865 (−1)	8.682 (−2)	5.518 (−3)	5.628 (−2)	1.708 (−2)	1.015 (−4)	1.829 (−6)	5.644 (−10)
1.3	3.075 (−1)	6.272 (−2)	3.125 (−3)	4.097 (−2)	1.097 (−2)	3.933 (−5)	5.007 (−7)	7.234 (−11)
1.4	2.105 (−1)	3.574 (−2)	1.162 (−3)	2.355 (−2)	5.054 (−3)	7.475 (−6)	4.909 (−8)	1.882 (−12)
1.5	1.539 (−1)	2.208 (−2)	4.969 (−4)	1.461 (−2)	2.592 (−3)	1.812 (−6)	6.620 (−9)	8.074 (−14)
1.75	8.271 (−2)	8.228 (−3)	8.824 (−5)	5.467 (−3)	6.553 (−4)	9.380 (−8)	1.071 (−10)	1.238 (−16)
2.0	5.084 (−2)	3.725 (−3)	2.237 (−5)	2.479 (−3)	2.166 (−4)	8.749 (−9)	3.869 (−12)	6.699 (−19)
2.5	2.382 (−2)	1.067 (−3)	2.836 (−6)	7.107 (−4)	3.768 (−5)	2.063 (−10)	2.037 (−14)	1.760 (−21)
3.0	1.320 (−2)	4.002 (−4)	6.064 (−7)	2.668 (−4)	9.558 (−6)	1.092 (−11)	3.325 (−16)	2.736 (−25)
4.0	5.344 (−3)	8.896 (−5)	6.443 (−8)	5.899 (−5)	1.165 (−6)	1.200 (−13)	6.018 (−19)	1.342 (−29)
5.0	2.688 (−3)	2.822 (−5)	1.244 (−8)	1.908 (−5)	2.345 (−7)	3.867 (−15)	4.909 (−21)	7.011 (−33)

† Values in the parentheses indicate the power of 10 by which the tabulated values should be multiplied.

13.4 On the Error Estimate (13.20)

The inequality (13.20) allows us to estimate quadrature errors from a table of values of σ and form an estimate of the norm $\| f \|$. Let us assume that we are dealing with a fixed rule R with error E. The value of the parameter ρ is at our disposal to a certain extent. For functions $f(x)$ which are analytic on $[-1,1]$, there will be a range of values of ρ, $1 < \rho < \rho^* \leq \infty$, for which $f(z) \in L^2(\mathscr{E}_\rho)$. For each such ρ, the inequality (13.20) is valid. To exhibit the dependence of (13.20) on ρ, we should write

$$|E(f)| \leq \sigma_R(\rho) \, \|f\|_{\mathscr{E}_\rho}, \qquad 1 < \rho < \rho^*. \tag{13.20'}$$

Now $\|f\|_{\mathscr{E}_\rho} = 0$ when $\rho = 1$ and increases as ρ increases. On the other hand, $\sigma_R(\rho)$ decreases as ρ increases. Hence, the best estimate will occur for some intermediate value of ρ. The inequality (13.20') can therefore be improved by writing

$$|E(f)| \leq \min_{1 < \rho < \rho^*} \sigma_R(\rho) \, \|f\|_{\mathscr{E}_\rho}. \tag{13.27}$$

Let the rule R, as well as the ellipse $\mathscr{E}_\rho$, be fixed. Then the inequality (13.20') is a best possible one in the following sense: there exist functions g of class $L^2(\mathscr{E}_\rho')$ such that

$$|E(g)| = \sigma_R(\rho) \, \|g\|_{\mathscr{E}_\rho}. \tag{13.28}$$

In general, of course, the error will be less. There are two additional facts which, in the practical carrying out of this method, tend to diminish the precision of the method. The first is that the exact minimum in (13.27) is difficult to ascertain, so that what one does is simply to take the minimum of a finite number of such values. The second is that the norm of f cannot be computed exactly except in the simplest cases, so that an appropriate upper bound must be used. The net effect of all this is to replace the right-hand side of (13.27) with a less precise upper bound, but one which is much more readily ascertained.

13.5 Methods for Estimating $\| f \|$

It appears, then, that the principal task confronting the numerical analyst when using the present method is that of estimating the norm $\| f \|$ over some ellipse $\mathscr{E}_\rho$. In this section we explain a number of devices which may be useful for this purpose. By the very definition (13.3), we have

$$\|f\|_{\mathscr{E}_\rho}^2 = \iint_{\mathscr{E}_\rho} |f(z)|^2 \, dx \, dy, \tag{13.29}$$

and it may be possible in certain simple cases to evaluate (13.29) directly.

If $f(z)$ is continuous in the closed ellipse $\bar{\mathscr{E}}_\rho$ and if we set

$$M_\rho = \max_{z\epsilon\bar{\mathscr{E}}_\rho} |f(z)|, \tag{13.30}$$

then we have, from (13.29),

$$\|f\|^2_{\mathscr{E}_\rho} \leq M_\rho^2 \iint_{\mathscr{E}_\rho} dx\, dy, \tag{13.31}$$

so that

$$\|f\|_{\mathscr{E}_\rho} \leq \sqrt{\pi ab}\, M_\rho, \tag{13.32}$$

where the quantities a and b are related to ρ by means of (13.12). The quantity M_ρ or an upper bound for it can, in many cases, be obtained by algebraic manipulation. It may be more convenient to replace $\mathscr{E}_\rho$ by some circle containing it, say the circle C_a:

$$|z| \leq a = \frac{\rho + 1}{2\rho^{1/2}}.$$

We then have

$$\|f\|_{\mathscr{E}_\rho} < \|f\|_{C_a} \leq a\sqrt{\pi} \max_{|z| \leq a} |f(z)|, \tag{13.33}$$

assuming that $f(z)$ is regular in $\bar{C}_a$.

If $f(z)$ is of class $L^2(C_a)$ and its Taylor expansion is known:

$$f(z) = \sum_{n=0}^{\infty} \alpha_n z^n, \tag{13.34}$$

then it can be shown that we have

$$\|f\|^2_{C_a} = \pi a^2 \sum_{n=0}^{\infty} \frac{|\alpha_n^2|\, a^{2n}}{n + 1}, \tag{13.35}$$

which is an exact evaluation of the middle term of the inequality (13.33). The quantity $\|f\|_{\mathscr{E}_\rho}$ may itself be expressed as an infinite series involving the Taylor coefficients α_n, but such expressions are more cumbersome and consequently less useful.

It should be pointed out that in cases of great complexity, there is always the possibility of obtaining M_ρ directly by evaluating $|f(z)|$ along the boundary of $\mathscr{E}_\rho$ on a sufficiently dense set of points. Despite the loss of accuracy involved in combining (13.20) and (13.32), errors obtained in this way will, in general, be better than those obtained by using the conventional real-variable error expressions and estimating the derivatives which occur there by means of Cauchy's inequality. This can be explained by the fact that the real-variable expressions must be valid for a wider class of functions.

13.6   The Case of an Arbitrary Interval

The quantities of Tables 13.1 and 13.2 refer to the interval $[-1,1]$. The case of an arbitrary interval $[a,b]$ is dealt with by means of the linear transformation

$$x = \frac{2w}{b-a} - \frac{b+a}{b-a},$$

$$w = \frac{b-a}{2} x + \frac{b+a}{2},$$

(13.36)

which carries the interval $a \leq w \leq b$ into $-1 \leq x \leq 1$. Let the rule E^* be given on $[a,b]$ as follows:

$$E^*(f) = \int_a^b f(w)\, dw - \sum_{k=0}^N a_k f(\lambda_k).$$

(13.37)

The analogous rule on $[-1,1]$ is given by

$$E(f) = \int_{-1}^{+1} f(x)\, dx - \sum_{k=0}^N \frac{2}{b-a} a_k f\left(\frac{2\lambda_k}{b-a} - \frac{b+a}{b-a}\right)$$

(13.38)

and is known by the same name.   If $f(w)$ is analytic on $[a,b]$, then

$$g(x) = f\left(\frac{b-a}{2} x + \frac{b+a}{2}\right)$$

(13.39)

is analytic on $[-1,1]$, and setting

$$x_k = \frac{2\lambda_k}{b-a} - \frac{b+a}{b-a},$$

we have

$$E^*(f) = \int_a^b f(w)\, dw - \sum_{k=0}^N a_k f(\lambda_k)$$

$$= \frac{b-a}{2}\left[\int_{-1}^{+1} g(x)\, dx - \sum_{k=0}^N a_k g(x_k)\frac{2}{b-a}\right],$$

(13.40)

so that from (13.40), (13.39), and (13.38),

$$E^*(f) = \frac{b-a}{2} E(g).$$

(13.41)

Thus, $$|E^*(f)| = \frac{b-a}{2} |E(g)| \leq \frac{b-a}{2} \sigma_R(\rho)\, \|g\|_{\mathscr{E}_\rho}.$$

(13.42)

The $\sigma_R(\rho)$ are the tabulated values (Table 13.2) in the $z = x + iy$ plane, and $\|g\|_{\mathscr{E}_\rho}$ also refers to this plane.

13.7 Examples

1. Estimate the error E incurred in evaluating $\int_0^1 \exp(e^x)\,dx$ by Weddle's rule.   From (13.39) we have

$$g(z) = \exp[e^{(z+1)/2}],$$

which is an entire function of z and is therefore of class $L^2(\mathscr{E}_\rho)$ for all $\rho > 1$.   Now,

$$|\exp[e^{(z+1)/2}]| = \exp\{\mathrm{Re}[e^{(z+1)/2}]\} = \exp[e^{(x+1)/2}\cos y/2].$$

Thus on $\mathscr{E}_\rho$ we have

$$|\exp[e^{(z+1)/2}]| \leq \exp[e^{(a+1)/2}].$$

By (13.42) and (13.32) we have

$$|E| < \tfrac{1}{2}(\pi ab)^{1/2}\exp[e^{(a+1)/2}]\sigma_W \qquad (W = \text{Weddle}). \quad (13.43)$$

According to (13.20′), the estimate (13.43) is valid for all $a > 1$.   Of the values tabulated, the right-hand member of (13.43) is minimized for $a = 2.5$ and yields

$$|E| < \tfrac{1}{2}(4.242)(315.7)(2.836 \times 10^{-6}) = .0019. \quad (13.44)$$

In the above work, the norm of $\exp[e^{(z+1)/2}]$ has been estimated crudely, and a number of improvements suggest themselves.   Thus, for instance,

$$|\exp[e^{(z+1)/2}]| < \exp[e^{(x+1)/2}],$$

and since this last function is concave upward, we have

$$\exp[e^{(x+1)/2}] \leq \tfrac{1}{2}\{\exp[e^{(a+1)/2}] + \exp[e^{(-a+1)/2}]\}$$

$$+ \frac{x}{2a}\{\exp[e^{(a+1)/2}] - \exp[e^{(-a+1)/2}]\}, \qquad -a \leq x \leq a. \quad (13.45)$$

It is now easily verified that for arbitrary A, B, C,

$$\iint\limits_{\mathscr{E}_\rho}(Ax + By + C)^2\,dx\,dy = \pi ab\left(\frac{A^2a^2}{4} + \frac{B^2b^2}{4} + C^2\right), \quad (13.46)$$

so that we have

$$|E| < \tfrac{1}{2}(\pi ab)^{1/2}\left(\frac{A^2a^2}{4} + C^2\right)^{1/2}\sigma_W \quad (13.47)$$

where
$$A = \frac{1}{2a}\{\exp[e^{(a+1)/2}] - \exp[e^{(-a+1)/2}]\},$$
$$C = \tfrac{1}{2}\{\exp[e^{(a+1)/2}] + \exp[e^{(-a+1)/2}]\}. \quad (13.48)$$

For $a = 2.5$, we have $A = 162.82$, $C = 158.65$, so that

$$|E| < \tfrac{1}{2}(4.2421)(160.6)(2.836 \times 10^{-6}) = .00097 \qquad (13.49)$$

A conventional estimate of error using the formula

$$|E| \leq \max_{0 \leq \xi \leq 1}\left[\frac{h^7}{140}\, f^{(6)}(\xi) + \frac{9h^9}{1400}\, f^{(8)}(\xi)\right], \qquad f(x) = \exp(e^x),$$

yielded the value $E \leq .006$.

2. Estimate the error E incurred in evaluating $\int_3^4 \Gamma(w)\, dw$ by means of the 7-point Gaussian rule. This is a case in which conventional methods cannot be used, owing to the lack of information about the higher derivatives of the integrand. Transferring to the interval $[-1,1]$, we must consider the function $g(z) = \Gamma[\tfrac{1}{2}(z + 7)]$. This function is regular in $|z| < 7$; hence we may take a in the range $1 < a < 7$. Now,

$$|\Gamma(x + iy)| \leq \Gamma(x) \qquad \text{for } x > 0,$$

so that

$$|g(z)| = |\Gamma[\tfrac{1}{2}(x + 7) + \tfrac{1}{2}iy]| \leq \Gamma[\tfrac{1}{2}(x + 7)].$$

By the concavity of the Γ function,

$$|g(z)| \leq \max\{\Gamma[\tfrac{1}{2}(a + 7)], \Gamma[\tfrac{1}{2}(-a + 7)]\}, \qquad z \in \mathscr{E}_\rho.$$

Thus we have, from (13.42) and (13.32),

$$|E| < \tfrac{1}{2}(\pi ab)^{1/2} \max\{\Gamma[\tfrac{1}{2}(a + 7)], \Gamma[\tfrac{1}{2}(-a + 7)]\}\, \sigma_{G_7(a)}$$
$$(G_7 = \text{Gauss 7-point}). \quad (13.50)$$

The selection $a = 5.0$ yields

$$|E| \leq \tfrac{1}{2}(8.772)(120)(3.867 \times 10^{-15}) = 2.04 \times 10^{-12}. \quad (13.51)$$

For a further example of the utility of the method, the reader is referred to Henrici [6].

13.8 Quadrature Schemes

One theoretical question which can be treated by the methods outlined in Secs. 13.2 and 13.3 is that of the convergence of a scheme of quadratures of the form

$$\int_{-1}^{+1} f(x)\, dx \doteq \sum_{k=0}^{n} a_{nk} f(\lambda_{nk}) = Q_n(f), \qquad (13.52)$$

when applied to certain distinguished classes of analytic functions on $[-1, +1]$. The question of the convergence of $Q_n(f)$ to the integral in (13.52) has been solved completely by Pólya [12] for the case in which f is selected from the class of continuous functions. There seems to be less discussion of the problem when f is selected from the class of analytic functions on $[-1, +1]$ or from certain of its subclasses.

We say that the quadrature scheme (13.52) converges *uniformly in* $L^2(B)$ if, having been given an $\epsilon > 0$, there is an $n_0 = n_0(\epsilon)$ such that, for all $f \in L^2(B)$ and $n \geq n_0$, we have

$$\left| \int_{-1}^{+1} f(x)\, dx - \sum_{k=0}^{n} a_{nk} f(\lambda_{nk}) \right| \leq \epsilon \, \|f\|. \qquad (13.53)$$

Theorem 13.1. *A condition necessary and sufficient in order that the quadrature scheme* (13.52) *converge uniformly in* $L^2(B)$ *is that*

$$\lim_{n \to \infty} \|E_n\|^2 = \lim_{n \to \infty} E_{nz} E_{n\bar{w}} K_B(z, \bar{w}) = 0. \qquad (13.54)$$

Proof. Suppose that (13.54) holds. Then, given an $\epsilon > 0$, we can find an $n_0(\epsilon)$ such that $\|E_n\| \leq \epsilon$ for all $n \geq n_0(\epsilon)$. Hence, by (13.11), the inequality (13.53) must hold. Conversely, suppose that (13.53) holds. For each n, it is possible to find a nontrivial function $f_n(z) \in L^2(B)$ such that

$$|E_n(f_n)| = \|E_n\| \, \|f_n\|. \qquad (13.55)$$

By (13.53), given an $\epsilon > 0$, we may find an $n = n_0(\epsilon)$ such that for all $n \geq n_0(\epsilon)$ and for all $f \in L^2(B)$ we have $|E_n(f)| \leq \epsilon \, \|f\|$. Hence, in particular, for the f_n of (13.55),

$$\|E_n\| \, \|f_n\| = |E_n(f_n)| \leq \epsilon \, \|f_n\|. \qquad (13.56)$$

Therefore (13.54) must follow.

We note that, in view of (13.9), the condition (13.54) can, in principle, be converted into a necessary and sufficient condition on the weights a_{nk} and abscissas λ_{nk}.

Corollary. *From* (13.21), *a condition necessary and sufficient in order that the quadrature scheme* (13.53) *converge uniformly in* $L^2(\mathscr{E}_\rho)$ *is that*

$$\lim_{n \to \infty} \frac{4}{\pi} \sum_{k=0}^{\infty} (k+1) \frac{|E_n(U_k)|^2}{\rho^{k+1} - \rho^{-k-1}} = 0. \qquad (13.57)$$

13.9 Interpolatory Quadrature

An important class of quadrature schemes is formed by those which are of interpolatory type. For such quadratures we have

$$Q_n(f) = \int_{-1}^{+1} f(x)\, dx, \qquad (13.58)$$

whenever f is a polynomial of degree not larger than n. If the scheme is of interpolatory type, then (13.57) becomes

$$\lim_{n \to \infty} \frac{4}{\pi} \sum_{k=n+1}^{\infty} (k+1) \frac{|E_n(U_k)|^2}{\rho^{k+1} - \rho^{-k-1}} = 0. \qquad (13.59)$$

In view of the inequalities

$$\rho^{-1}\rho^{-k} \le (\rho^{k+1} - \rho^{-k-1})^{-1} \le (\rho - \rho^{-1})^{-1}\rho^{-k} \qquad (\rho > 1), \quad (13.60)$$

condition (13.59) is equivalent to

$$\lim_{n \to \infty} \sum_{k=n+1}^{\infty} (k+1) \frac{|E_n(U_k)|^2}{\rho^k} = 0. \qquad (13.61)$$

With τ_k given by (13.25), then (13.61) becomes

$$\lim_{n \to \infty} \sum_{k=n+1}^{\infty} (k+1) \left[\tau_k - \sum_{j=0}^{n} a_{nj} U_k(\lambda_{nj}) \right]^2 \rho^{-k} = 0. \qquad (13.62)$$

The following sufficient condition for the uniform convergence in $L^2(\mathscr{E}_\rho)$ of an interpolatory quadrature scheme can now be obtained.   Set

$$M_n = \sum_{j=0}^{n} |a_{nj}|, \qquad (13.63)$$

and observe that for real abscissas λ in $[-1,+1]$ we have

$$|U_k(\lambda)| \le k + 1. \qquad (13.64)$$

Then, using (13.25) and (13.63), for fixed $\rho > 1$ we get

$$\sum_{k=n+1}^{\infty} (k+1) \left[\tau_k - \sum_{j=0}^{\infty} a_{nj} U_k(\lambda_{nj}) \right]^2 \rho^{-k} \le \sum_{k=n+1}^{\infty} (k+1)$$

$$\times [\tau_k + (k+1)M_n]^2 \rho^{-k} \le 4 \sum_{k=n+1}^{\infty} [(k+1)\rho^k]^{-1}$$

$$+ 4M_n \sum_{k=n+1}^{\infty} (k+1)\rho^{-k} + M_n^2 \sum_{k=n+1}^{\infty} (k+1)^3 \rho^{-k}$$

$$< o(1) + C_1 M_n n \rho^{-n} + C_2 M_n^2 n^3 \rho^{-n} \qquad (n \to \infty),$$

$$(13.65)$$

where C_1 and C_2 are two positive constants which may depend on ρ but are independent of n.   Thus, we have the following result:

Theorem 13.2.   *Let*

$$\lim_{n \to \infty} M_n n^{3/2} \rho^{-n/2} = 0. \qquad (13.66)$$

Then an interpolatory quadrature scheme converges uniformly in $L^2(\mathscr{E}_\rho)$.
Pólya ([12], p. 285) has remarked that, if

$$\lim_{n \to \infty} (M_n)^{1/n} = 1, \qquad (13.67)$$

then an interpolatory quadrature scheme converges for all functions which are analytic in the closed basic interval. Under hypothesis (13.67), we have

$$M_n = (1 + \epsilon_n)^n, \qquad \epsilon_n \to 0,$$

so that (13.66) holds with all $\rho > 1$. Thus, under Pólya's hypothesis, we see that the convergence is also uniform in every $L^2(\mathscr{E}_\rho)$, $\rho > 1$.

13.10   Newton-Cotes Quadrature

We turn now to a specific quadrature scheme on $[-1, +1]$, namely, the Newton-Cotes scheme.   In this scheme, we have

$$Q_n(f) = a_{n0}f(-1) + a_{n1}f(-1 + 2/n) + a_{n2}f(-1 + 4/n) + \cdots$$
$$+ a_{nn}f(1) \qquad (n = 1, 2, \ldots), \quad (13.68)$$

where the Cotes numbers a_{nk} have been determined so that

$$Q_n(f) = \int_{-1}^{+1} f \, dx$$

holds for an arbitrary polynomial of degree $\leq n$. We have now the following estimate due to Ouspensky [11] (Ouspensky's basic interval is $[0,1]$):

$$a_{nk} = -\frac{2}{n(\log n)^2}\binom{n}{k}\left[\frac{(-1)^k}{k} + \frac{(-1)^{n-k}}{n-k}\right](1 + \eta_{nk}), \quad (13.69)$$

where $\eta_{nk} \to 0$ as $n \to \infty$ uniformly for $k = 1, 2, \ldots, n - 1$ and

$$a_{n0} = a_{nn} = \frac{2}{n \log n}(1 + \epsilon_n), \qquad \epsilon_n \to 0. \quad (13.70)$$

Thus,

$$M_n = \sum_{j=0}^{\infty} |a_{nj}| \leq \frac{4(1 + \delta_n)}{n(\log n)^2}\sum_{k=1}^{n-1}\binom{n}{k} + \frac{4}{n \log n}(1 + \epsilon_n), \quad (13.71)$$

where we have written $\eta_{nk} < \delta_n$ $(k = 1, 2, \ldots, n - 1)$, $\delta_n \to 0$.   Hence,

$$M_n \leq \frac{4(1 + \delta_n)2^n}{n(\log n)^2} + \frac{4}{n \log n}(1 + \epsilon_n). \quad (13.72)$$

Condition (13.66) now holds with $\rho^{1/2} > 2$.   We have therefore arrived at the following result:

Theorem 13.3.   *The Newton-Cotes quadrature scheme converges uniformly in $L^2(\mathscr{E}_\rho)$ whenever $\rho > 4$.*

Investigation of the convergence of the Newton-Cotes quadrature scheme has an interesting history which is worth retelling here.   Stieltjes, in 1884, first proved the convergence of the Gauss mechanical quadrature for the class of Riemann integrable functions and, in a letter to Hermite, raised the question of the convergence of the Newton-Cotes scheme.   In

1925 Ouspensky [11] arrived at the asymptotic result (13.69) and, from the growth of Cotes numbers, concluded only that the Newton-Cotes scheme is devoid of practical value.   In 1933 Pólya [12] showed that this scheme is not valid for all continuous functions and, indeed, is not valid for the class of analytic functions.   Pólya's counterexample, referred to the interval $[-1, +1]$, is

$$f(w) = -\sum_{k=4}^{\infty} a^{k!} \frac{\sin k! \, [(w+1)/2]}{\cos \pi [(w+1)/2]} \qquad (\tfrac{1}{2} < a < 1), \qquad (13.73)$$

for which the Newton-Cotes scheme diverges.   The functions $f(w)$ are regular in the strip

$$|\mathrm{Im}(w)| < \frac{-2 \log a}{\pi} \qquad (13.74)$$

and have a natural boundary along the sides of the strip.   The widest such strip must be less than

$$|\mathrm{Im}(w)| < \frac{2 \log 2}{\pi} = .4412.$$

The function (13.73) cannot, therefore, be continued analytically to $\mathscr{E}_{\rho=4}$, for which the semiminor axis is $b = .7500$.   Therefore, Theorem 13.3 rehabilitates the Newton-Cotes quadrature scheme for functions which are regular over a sufficiently large portion of the complex plane.

REFERENCES

1. S. Bergman, Sur les fonctions orthogonales de plusieurs variables complexes avec les applications à la théorie des fonctions analytiques, *Mém. Sci. Math.*, fasc. CVI, Gauthier-Villars, Paris, 1947.

2. S. Bergman, "Kernel Functions and Conformal Mapping," Mathematical Surveys, no. 5, American Mathematical Society, Providence, R.I., 1950.

3. P. Davis, Errors of Numerical Approximation for Analytic Functions, *J. Rational Mech. Anal.*, vol. 2, pp. 303–313, 1953.

4. P. Davis, On a Problem in the Theory of Mechanical Quadratures, *Pacific J. Math.*, vol. 5, supplement 1, pp. 669–674, 1955.

5. P. Davis and P. Rabinowitz, On the Estimation of Quadrature Errors for Analytic Functions, *Math. Tables Aids Comput.*, vol. 8, pp. 193–203, 1954.

6. P. Henrici, Application of Two Methods of Numerical Analysis to the Computation of the Reflected Radiation of a Point Source, *J. Washington Acad. Sci.*, vol. 45, pp. 38–45, 1955.

7. C. Lanczos, Introduction, "Tables of Chebyshev Polynomials," National Bureau of Standards Applied Mathematics Series vol. 9, 1952.

8. L. F. Meyers and A. Sard, Best Approximate Integration Formulas, *J. Math. Phys.*, vol. 29, pp. 118–123, 1950.

9. Z. Nehari, "Conformal Mapping," McGraw-Hill Book Company, Inc., New York, 1952.

10. S. M. Nikolsky, Concerning Estimation for Approximate Quadrature Formulas, *Uspekhi Mat. Nauk*, vol. 5, pp. 165–177, 1950 (in Russian).

11. J. Ouspensky, Sur les valeurs asymptotiques des coefficients de Cotes, *Bull. Amer. Math. Soc.*, vol. 31, pp. 145–156, 1925.

12. G. Pólya, Über die Konvergenz von Quadraturverfahren, *Math. Z.*, vol. 37, pp. 264–286, 1933.

13. A. Sard, Best Approximate Integration Formulas, *Amer. J. Math.*, vol. 71, pp. 80–91, 1949.

14. G. Szegö, "Orthogonal Polynomials," Colloquium Publications, vol. 23, American Mathematical Society, Providence, R.I., 1959.

14

Numerical Analysis and Functional Analysis

HENRY A. ANTOSIEWICZ

PROFESSOR OF MATHEMATICS

UNIVERSITY OF SOUTHERN CALIFORNIA

LOS ANGELES

WERNER C. RHEINBOLDT

DIRECTOR, COMPUTER SCIENCE CENTER

UNIVERSITY OF MARYLAND

COLLEGE PARK, MARYLAND

BASIC CONCEPTS

In the first part of the chapter, Secs. 14.1 to 14.3, we state the fundamental concepts which we require later. For all details and further information we refer to the books on functional analysis (e.g. [2, 9, 11, 12, 14]) listed in the bibliography following Sec. 14.3.

14.1 Metric Spaces

A set $\mathfrak{X}$ is called a metric space if for every two elements x, y of $\mathfrak{X}$ there is defined a real-valued function $\rho(x, y)$, called the distance between x and y, which has these properties:

(i) $\quad \rho(x, y) = 0 \quad$ if and only if $x = y$;

(ii) $\quad \rho(x, y) \leq \rho(z, x) + \rho(z, y) \quad$ for any three elements x, y, z.

It follows that $\rho(x, y) \geq 0$ and $\rho(x, y) = \rho(y, x)$; hence the triangle axiom (ii) becomes $\rho(x, y) \leq \rho(x, z) + \rho(z, y)$.

In a metric space $\mathfrak{X}$ the set of points $x \in \mathfrak{X}$ with $\rho(x, x_0) < r$ is called the (open) sphere $S(x_0, r)$ of center $x_0(\in \mathfrak{X})$ and radius $r(>0)$. A set $M \subset \mathfrak{X}$ is said to be open if every $x \in M$ is the center of some (open) sphere contained in $\mathfrak{X}$. This definition of open sets introduces a topology in $\mathfrak{X}$ under which $\mathfrak{X}$ becomes a normal Hausdorff space.

A sequence $\{x_n\}$, $x_n \in \mathfrak{X}$, converges to a point $x \in \mathfrak{X}$ if $\rho(x_n, x) \to 0$

as $n \to \infty$; we write $x_n \to x$ as $n \to \infty$. A sequence $\{x_n\}$, $x_n \in \mathfrak{X}$, is called a Cauchy sequence if $\rho(x_n, x_m) \to 0$ as n, $m \to \infty$. Clearly, if $x_n \to x$ as $n \to \infty$, then $\{x_n\}$ is a Cauchy sequence, but every Cauchy sequence $\{x_n\}$ need not converge to a point $x \in \mathfrak{X}$.

A metric space $\mathfrak{X}$ is said to be complete if every Cauchy sequence in $\mathfrak{X}$ converges to a point of $\mathfrak{X}$.

Example. The field of real (or complex) numbers considered as metric space with $\rho(x, y) = |x - y|$ is a complete metric space.

A metric space $\mathfrak{X}$ is separable if there exists a countable set which is dense in $\mathfrak{X}$, that is, whose (topological) closure is $\mathfrak{X}$.

Let $\mathfrak{X}$, $\mathfrak{Y}$ be two metric spaces, distinct or not, with metrics $\rho_{\mathfrak{X}}$, $\rho_{\mathfrak{Y}}$, respectively. A single-valued function $y = T(x)$ with domain $\mathfrak{D} \subset \mathfrak{X}$ and range $\mathfrak{R} \subset \mathfrak{Y}$ is called an operator (or mapping) from $\mathfrak{D}$ onto $\mathfrak{R}$ or, simply, an operator from $\mathfrak{D}$ into $\mathfrak{Y}$; that is, to every $x \in \mathfrak{D}$ there corresponds a unique $y \in \mathfrak{R}$, and every $y \in \mathfrak{R}$ is the image of at least one $x \in \mathfrak{D}$. If $\mathfrak{S} \subset \mathfrak{R}$, then the set of points $x \in \mathfrak{D}$ for which $T(x) \subset \mathfrak{S}$ is called the inverse image of $\mathfrak{S}$ and is denoted by $T^{-1}(\mathfrak{S})$. The operator is said to be one-to-one if $\mathfrak{S} = T(\mathfrak{U})$ implies $\mathfrak{U} = T^{-1}(\mathfrak{S})$ for every $\mathfrak{U} \subset \mathfrak{D}$.

If $y = T(x)$ is a one-to-one operator from $\mathfrak{D} \subset \mathfrak{X}$ onto $\mathfrak{R} \subset \mathfrak{Y}$, there exists a unique single-valued function $x = T^{-1}(y)$, called the inverse operator to $y = T(x)$, with domain $\mathfrak{R}(\subset \mathfrak{Y})$ and range $\mathfrak{D}(\subset \mathfrak{X})$ such that $T[T^{-1}(y)] = y$ for every $y \in \mathfrak{R}$, and $T^{-1}[T(x)] = x$ for every $x \in \mathfrak{D}$.

The operator $y = T(x)$ from $\mathfrak{D} \subset \mathfrak{X}$ into $\mathfrak{Y}$ is continuous at $x_0 \in \mathfrak{D}$ if to every $\epsilon > 0$ there corresponds a $\delta(\epsilon) > 0$ such that $\rho_{\mathfrak{Y}}[T(x), T(x_0)] < \epsilon$ for all $x \in \mathfrak{D}$ with $\rho_{\mathfrak{X}}(x, x_0) < \delta$ or, equivalently, if $x_n \to x_0$ implies $T(x_n) \to T(x_0)$. If $y = T(x)$ is continuous at every $x \in \mathfrak{D}$, it is said to be continuous on $\mathfrak{D}$.

14.2 Linear Spaces

A set $\mathfrak{X}$ with at least two distinct elements is a linear (vector) space (or linear system or module) over the field of complex (real) numbers if its elements admit of two operations, called addition and scalar multiplication, such that

1. $\mathfrak{X}$ is an abelian group with respect to addition.
2. Scalar multiplication has these properties:
   a. To every complex (real) number α and every $x \in \mathfrak{X}$ there corresponds a unique $\alpha x = x \alpha \in \mathfrak{X}$.
   b. $(\alpha + \beta)x = \alpha x + \beta x$, $(\alpha \beta)x = \alpha(\beta x)$ for every complex (real) α, β and every $x \in \mathfrak{X}$.
   c. $\alpha(x + y) = \alpha x + \alpha y$ for every complex (real) α and every $x, y \in \mathfrak{X}$.
   d. $1 \cdot x = x$ for every $x \in \mathfrak{X}$.

The points of a linear system are usually called vectors.

A set of n vectors $x_i \in \mathfrak{X}$ is said to be linearly independent if $\sum_{i=1}^{n} \alpha_i x_i = 0$ implies $\alpha_i = 0$ for all i; otherwise, the n vectors are said to be linearly dependent. If $\mathfrak{X}$ contains a linearly independent set of n vectors and every system of $(n + 1)$ vectors is linearly dependent, then $\mathfrak{X}$ has dimension n. If n is not finite, $\mathfrak{X}$ is said to be of infinite dimension.

A linear subspace M of a linear space $\mathfrak{X}$ is a set $M \subset \mathfrak{X}$ such that, if x, y belong to M, then $\alpha x + \beta y \in M$ for every complex (real) α, β.

A linear space $\mathfrak{X}$ is called a normed linear space if to every $x \in \mathfrak{X}$ there corresponds a real number $\|x\|$, the norm of x, with these properties:

(i) $\|x\| \geq 0$ and $\|x\| = 0$ if and only if $x = 0$,

(ii) $\|\alpha x\| = |\alpha| \, \|x\|$,

(iii) $\|x + y\| \leq \|x\| + \|y\|$.

If the distance between x and y is defined by $\rho(x, y) = \|x - y\|$, then $\mathfrak{X}$ becomes a metric space.

A complex (real) linear space $\mathfrak{X}$ is called an inner-product space if for every two vectors x, y of $\mathfrak{X}$ there is defined a complex-valued (real-valued) function (x, y) called the inner product of x and y, such that

(i) $(x, y) = \overline{(y, x)}$

(ii) $(\alpha x + \beta y, z) = \alpha(x, z) + \beta(y, z)$ for every x, y, z of $\mathfrak{X}$ and every complex (real) α, β.

(iii) $(x, x) \geq 0$ and $(x, x) = 0$ if and only if $x = 0$.

If $\mathfrak{X}$ is an inner-product space, then $\|x\| = +\sqrt{(x, x)}$ is a norm for $\mathfrak{X}$; this follows from the Schwarz inequality $|(x, y)|^2 \leq (x, x)(y, y)$.

A normed linear space $\mathfrak{X}$ which is complete is called a Banach space. An inner-product space $\mathfrak{X}$ which is complete under the norm $\|x\| = +\sqrt{(x, x)}$ is called a Hilbert space.

Example. The n-dimensional euclidean space is a Hilbert space. The set l_p of all complex sequences $\{\alpha_n\}$ such that $\sum_{1}^{\infty} |\alpha_n|^p < \infty$ for some $p \in [1, \infty)$ is a Banach space under the norm

$$\|\{\alpha_n\}\| = \left[\sum_{1}^{\infty} |\alpha_n|^p \right]^{1/p}.$$

Let $\mathfrak{X}$, $\mathfrak{Y}$ be linear spaces. An operator $y = A(x)$ from $\mathfrak{D} \subset \mathfrak{X}$ into $\mathfrak{Y}$ is said to be linear if $\mathfrak{D}$ is a linear subspace of $\mathfrak{X}$ and if $A(\alpha x + \beta y) = \alpha A(x) + \beta A(y)$ for every x, y of $\mathfrak{D}$ and every complex (real) α, β. It follows that the range $\mathfrak{R}$ of A is a linear subspace of $\mathfrak{Y}$. If $\mathfrak{Y}$ is the field of complex (real) numbers, a linear operator $y = A(x)$ from a linear space $\mathfrak{X}$ into $\mathfrak{Y}$ is often called a linear functional.

A linear operator A from a normed linear space $\mathfrak{X}$ into a normed linear space $\mathfrak{Y}$ is bounded if $\|A(x)\| \le M \|x\|$ for all $x \in \mathfrak{X}$. The number $\|A\| = \sup\{\|Ax\|, \|x\| \le 1\}$ is defined as the norm of A. A linear operator from a normed linear space $\mathfrak{X}$ into a normed linear space $\mathfrak{Y}$ is continuous on $\mathfrak{X}$ if and only if it is bounded.

Example. Let E_m be the linear space of real m-dimensional column vectors x. A linear operator $y = A(x)$ from E_m into itself is defined by a system of linear equations

$$\eta_i = \sum_{k=1}^{m} a_{ik}\xi_k, \qquad i = 1, \ldots, m,$$

and hence is known once the $m \times m$ matrix (a_{ik}) is given. If E_m is normed by the l_1 norm

$$\|x\| = \sum_{1}^{m} |\xi_k|, \qquad \text{then} \qquad \|A\| = \max_k \sum_i |a_{ik}|;$$

if E_m is normed by the l_∞ norm

$$\|x\| = \max_i |\xi_i|, \qquad \text{then} \qquad \|A\| = \max \sum_k |a_{ik}|.$$

If E_m is given the usual euclidean l_2 norm

$$\|x\| = \left(\sum_{1}^{m} |\xi_k|^2\right)^{1/2}, \qquad \text{then} \qquad \|A\| \le \left(\sum_{i,k} |a_{ik}|^2\right)^{1/2}.$$

Let $\mathfrak{X}$ be a (real) Banach space and $\mathfrak{X}^*$ the set of bounded linear functions from $\mathfrak{X}$ to the real field E_1. Under the ordinary definition of addition and real scalar multiplication, $\mathfrak{X}^*$ becomes a linear space. In fact, if the norm of $x^* \in \mathfrak{X}^*$ is defined by $\|x^*\| = \sup\{|x^*(x)|, \|x\| \le 1\}$, $\mathfrak{X}^*$ can be shown to be a (real) Banach space, called the adjoint (or conjugate) space of $\mathfrak{X}$.

Let $\mathfrak{X}$ be a Hilbert space and A a linear operator from a set $\mathfrak{D}$ dense in $\mathfrak{X}$ into $\mathfrak{X}$. The (Hilbert space) adjoint A^* of A is defined as follows: the domain of A^* is the set of all $y^* \in \mathfrak{X}$ for which there exists an $x^* \in \mathfrak{X}$ such that

$$(Ax, y^*) = (x, x^*) \qquad \text{for all } x \in \mathfrak{D}.$$

The vector x^*, which is unique, is then the image of y^* under the adjoint operator A^*; that is, $x^* = A^*(y^*)$. Clearly, A^* is a linear operator from $\mathfrak{X}$ into itself.

If $\mathfrak{X} = E_m$ and A is the linear operator given by the matrix (a_{ik}), the adjoint A^* is defined by the transposed matrix (a_{ki}). Observe that $(Ax, y) = (x, A^*y)$ for all x, y of E_m.

A linear operator A defined on a domain $\mathfrak{D}$ dense in a Hilbert space $\mathfrak{X}$ is called self-adjoint if the domain of its adjoint A^* is $\mathfrak{D}$ and $A(x) = A^*(x)$ for every $x \in \mathfrak{D}$. As in matrix theory, a self-adjoint operator A is positive if $(Ax, x) > 0$ for every $x \in \mathfrak{D}$, $x \ne 0$, and positive definite if $(Ax, x) \ge \mu(x, x)$ for every x where $\mu > 0$.

A linear operator A with domain $\mathfrak{D}$ in a normed linear space $\mathfrak{X}$ and range in a normed linear space $\mathfrak{Y}$ has an inverse A^{-1} provided $A(x) = 0$ if and only if $x = 0$. Clearly A^{-1} is a linear operator. Moreover, A^{-1} exists and is bounded if and only if a constant $\mu > 0$ can be found such that $\|A(x)\| \geq \mu \|x\|$ for every $x \in \mathfrak{D}$; the supremum of admissible μ is $\|A^{-1}\|^{-1}$.

Let $\mathfrak{X}$ be a Banach space and A a linear operator from $\mathfrak{X}$ into itself. If $\|A\| < 1$, then $(I - A)^{-1}$ exists (I being the identity operator) and has domain $\mathfrak{X}$, and $\|(I - A)^{-1}\| \leq (1 - \|A\|)^{-1}$.

14.3 Gateaux and Fréchet Differentials

Let $\mathfrak{X}$, $\mathfrak{Y}$ be real normed linear spaces and $y = T(x)$ a (linear or non-linear) operator with domain $\mathfrak{D} \subset \mathfrak{X}$ and range $\mathfrak{R} \subset \mathfrak{Y}$; to avoid trivialities, it is assumed that $\mathfrak{D}$ has a nonempty interior. Let x_0 be an interior point of $\mathfrak{D}$ and let $h \in \mathfrak{X}$ be arbitrary. Then $x_0 + th \in \mathfrak{D}$ for small enough (real) t, say $|t| < \epsilon(x_0,h)$. If the limit

$$\delta T(x_0,h) = \lim_{t \to 0} \frac{1}{t} [T(x_0 + th) - T(x_0)]$$

exists, it is called the Gateaux differential of T at x_0 with increment h. If T has a Gateaux differential at x_0 for every increment $h \in \mathfrak{X}$, then T is said to be Gateaux-differentiable or, simply, G-differentiable at x_0; and if T is G-differentiable at every x_0 of an open set $\mathfrak{D}_0 \subset \mathfrak{D}$, it is called G-differentiable on $\mathfrak{D}_0$.

Example. Let $\mathfrak{X}$ be the ordinary euclidean (ξ_1,ξ_2) plane and $\mathfrak{Y}$ the real line. Then $\eta = F(\xi_1,\xi_2)$ is G-differentiable at a point (ξ_1',ξ_2') of an open set $\mathfrak{D} \in \mathfrak{X}$ if

$$\delta F(v,h) = \lim_{t \to 0} \frac{1}{t} [F(\xi_1' + th_1, \xi_2' + th_2) - F(\xi_1',\xi_2')]$$

exists for every $h = (h_1,h_2) \in \mathfrak{X}$. This is equivalent to requiring that the directional derivative of $F(\xi_1,\xi_2)$ exists at (ξ_1',ξ_2') for every direction vector $h \in \mathfrak{X}$.

If $\delta T(x_0,h)$ exists, so does $\delta T(x_0,\alpha h)$ for any (real) α and

$$\delta T(x_0,\alpha h) = \alpha\, \delta T(x_0,h).$$

If T_1, T_2 have a G differential at x_0 with increment h, so has $T = \alpha T_1 + \beta T_2$ for any real α, β and

$$\delta T(x_0,h) = \alpha\, \delta T_1(x_0,h) + \beta\, \delta T_2(x_0,h).$$

The G differential $\delta T(x_0,h)$ is not necessarily linear in h, and even if it is, it need not be continuous in h. If T is G-differentiable on an open set $\mathfrak{D}_0 \subset \mathfrak{D}$ such that $\delta T(x_0,h)$ is continuous in x at some $x_0 \in \mathfrak{D}$ for every fixed $h \in \mathfrak{X}$, then $\delta T(x_0,h)$ is linear in h.   In this case, $\delta T(x_0,h) = A(h)$, where A is a linear operator from $\mathfrak{X}$ into $\mathfrak{Y}$.   At times $A(h)$ is called the G derivative of T at x_0.

T is said to be Fréchet-differentiable or, simply, F-differentiable at an interior point $x_0 \in \mathfrak{D}$ if it has a G differential $\delta T(x_0,h)$ which is linear and continuous in h and if

$$\lim_{h \to 0} \frac{1}{\|h\|} \, \| T(x_0 + h) - T(x_0) - \delta T(x_0,h) \| = 0.$$

$\delta T(x_0,h)$ is then called the Fréchet differential of T at x_0 with increment h.   If T is F-differentiable at every point of an open set $\mathfrak{D}_0 \subset \mathfrak{D}$, it is called F-differentiable on $\mathfrak{D}_0$.

The correspondence between $h \in \mathfrak{X}$ and the F differential $\delta T(x_0,h)$ is by definition a bounded linear operator A_{x_0} depending on $x_0 \in \mathfrak{D}$.   The correspondence between $x_0 \in \mathfrak{D}$ and A_{x_0} is an operator from $\mathfrak{D}$ into the normed linear space $\mathfrak{E}(\mathfrak{X}, \mathfrak{Y})$ of bounded linear operators from $\mathfrak{X}$ to $\mathfrak{Y}$; this operator is called the Fréchet or, simply, the F derivative T' of T.

If T is F-differentiable at $x_0 \in \mathfrak{D}$, then T is continuous at x_0.   If T_1, T_2 are F-differentiable at $x_0 \in \mathfrak{D}$, so is $T = \alpha T_1 + \beta T_2$ for any real α, β, and

$$T' = \alpha T_1' + \beta T_2'.$$

If T is F-differentiable on an open convex set $\mathfrak{D}_0 \subset \mathfrak{X}$, then

$$\| T(x + h) - T(x) \| \leq \|h\| \sup \{\| T'(x + th)\|, 0 \leq t \leq 1\}$$

so long as $x \in \mathfrak{D}_0$ and $x + h \in \mathfrak{D}_0$.

A linear operator A is F-differentiable only if it is defined and bounded on $\mathfrak{X}$.   If A' exists, $A'(x) = A$, so that A' is defined on $\mathfrak{X}$ also.

If an operator T on $\mathfrak{D}$ to $\mathfrak{Y}$ is F-differentiable on $\mathfrak{D}_0 \subset \mathfrak{D}$, then T' may be F-differentiable on some set $\mathfrak{D}_1 \subset \mathfrak{D}_0$.   In this case the F derivative of T' is called the second F derivative of T and denoted by T''; it is an operator from $\mathfrak{D}_1$ into the normed linear space of bounded linear operators from $\mathfrak{X}$ into $\mathfrak{E}(\mathfrak{X}, \mathfrak{Y})$.

If T is twice F-differentiable on an open convex set $\mathfrak{D}_1 \subset \mathfrak{X}$, then

$$\| T(x + h) - T(x) - T'(x)h \| \leq \tfrac{1}{2} \|h\|^2 \sup \{\| T''(x + th)\|, 0 \leq t \leq 1\}$$

so long as $x \in \mathfrak{D}_1$ and $x + h \in \mathfrak{D}_1$.

REFERENCES

1. S. Banach, "Théorie des Opérations Linéaires," vol. 1, Monografje Matematyczne, Warsaw, 1932.

2. M. Day, "Normed Linear Spaces," Springer-Verlag, Berlin, 1958.

3. N. Dunford and J. T. Schwartz, "Linear Operators," vol. I: "General Theory," Interscience Publishers, Inc., New York, 1958.

4. M. Fréchet, La notion de différentielle dans l'analyse générale, *Ann. École Norm. Sup.*, ser. 3, vol. 42, pp. 293–323, 1925.

5. R. Gateaux, Fonctions d'une infinité des variables independantes, *Bull. Soc. Math. France*, vol. 47, pp. 70–96, 1919.

6. R. Gateaux, Sur les fonctionelles continues et les fonctionelles analytiques, *Bull. Soc. Math. France*, vol. 50, pp. 1–21, 1922.

7. L. M. Graves, Riemann Integration and Taylor's Theorem in General Analysis, *Trans. Amer. Math. Soc.*, vol. 29, pp. 163–177, 1927.

8. L. M. Graves and T. H. Hildebrandt, Implicit Functions and Their Differentials in General Analysis, *Trans. Amer. Math. Soc.*, vol. 29, pp. 127–153, 1927.

9. E. Hille and R. S. Phillips, "Functional Analysis and Semigroups," American Mathematical Society Colloquium Publications, vol. 31 (in particular, chaps. 3, 26), New York, 1957.

10. L. V. Kantorovich, Functional Analysis and Applied Mathematics, *Uspekhi Mat. Nauk*, vol. 3, no. 6, pp. 89–185, 1948; translation by C. D. Benster, National Bureau of Standards Report 1509, G. E. Forsythe, ed., 1952.

11. L. A. Lusternik and W. I. Sobolew, "Elemente der Funktionalanalysis," Akademie-Verlag G.m.b.H., Berlin, 1955.

12. F. Riesz and B. Sz.-Nagy, "Functional Analysis," Frederick Ungar Publishing Co., New York, 1955.

13. M. H. Stone, "Linear Transformations in Hilbert Space," American Mathematical Society Colloquium Publications, vol. 15, New York, 1932.

14. A. E. Taylor, "Introduction to Functional Analysis," John Wiley & Sons, Inc., New York, 1958.

15. M. A. Zorn, Gateaux Differentiability and Essential Boundedness, *Duke Math. J.*, vol. 12, pp. 579–583, 1945.

16. M. A. Zorn, Derivatives and Fréchet Differentials, *Bull. Amer. Math. Soc.*, vol. 52, pp. 133–137, 1946.

SUCCESSIVE APPROXIMATIONS

We prove here the central-fixed-point theorem on successive approximation and show that many of the iteration procedures found in nearly every branch of applied mathematics are merely applications of this theorem. Our presentation is intended to point out the power of the basically simple theorem and to indicate at the same time its limitations. We do not aim at the most general treatment possible.

14.4 The General Theorem

Let $\mathfrak{X}$ be a complete metric space with metric ρ and T an operator with domain $\mathfrak{D}$ and range in $\mathfrak{X}$ such that for all x, y in $\mathfrak{D}$

$$\rho[T(x), T(y)] \leq \alpha\rho(x,y)$$

where $0 < \alpha < 1$. Such an operator is called a contracting operator (or mapping); it is obviously continuous on $\mathfrak{D}$.

Theorem 14.1. *Let $x_0 \in \mathfrak{D}$ be selected such that the closed sphere $\bar{S}(x_0, r)$ of center x_0 and radius $r \geq (1 - \alpha)^{-1}\rho[x_0, T(x_0)]$ is contained in $\mathfrak{D}$ and define*

$$x_{n+1} = T(x_n), \qquad n = 0, 1, 2, \ldots .$$

Then $\{x_n\}$ converges to a point $x^* \in \bar{S}(x_0,r)$, which is the unique solution [in $\bar{S}(x_0,r)$] of the equation $x = T(x)$.

Proof. We show first that $x_n \in \bar{S}(x_0,r)$ for all integers $n \geq 0$. This is clear for $n = 0$; since, for every integer $k \geq 1$,

$$\rho(x_{k+1},x_k) = \rho[T(x_k),T(x_{k-1})] \leq \alpha\rho(x_k,x_{k-1}) \leq \cdots \leq \alpha^k(1-\alpha)r < r;$$

it follows by induction that

$$\rho(x_{n+1},x_0) \leq \sum_0^n \rho(x_{k+1},x_k) \leq (1-\alpha)r \sum_0^n \alpha^k = (1-\alpha^{n+1})r < r.$$

Further, for any integer $p \geq 1$,

$$\rho(x_n,x_{n+p}) \leq \sum_{k=1}^p \rho(x_{n+k-1},x_{n+k}) \leq \alpha^n(1-\alpha^p)(1-\alpha)^{-1}\rho[x_0,T(x_0)]$$
$$\leq \alpha^n(1-\alpha^p)r,$$

which shows that $\{x_n\}$ is a Cauchy sequence. Since $\mathfrak{X}$ is complete, $x_n \to x^*$ as $n \to \infty$ and, evidently, $x^* \in \bar{S}(x_0,r)$. Moreover, for any $n \geq 1$,

$$\rho(x^*,T(x^*)) \leq \rho(x^*,x_n) + \rho[x_n,T(x^*)]$$
$$= \rho(x^*,x_n) + \rho[T(x_{n-1}),T(x^*)]$$
$$\leq \rho(x^*,x_n) + \alpha\rho(x^*,x_{n-1}),$$

so that, as $n \to \infty$, $\rho[x^*,T(x^*)] = 0$, which implies $x^* = T(x^*)$. If $y \neq x^*$ were another solution of $x = T(x)$, then $\rho(x^*,y) = \rho[T(x^*),T(y)] \leq \alpha\rho(x^*,y)$, whence $\rho(x^*,y) = 0$, which is absurd.

Remark. A bound for the error at the nth iteration is

$$\rho(x_n,x^*) \leq \alpha(1-\alpha)^{-1}\rho(x_{n-1},x_n),$$

which follows from

$$\rho(x_n,x_{n+p}) \leq \sum_1^p \rho(x_{n+k-1},x_{n+k}) \leq \alpha(1-\alpha^p)(1-\alpha)^{-1}\rho(x_{n-1},x_n)$$

on letting $p \to \infty$.

14.5 Solution of Systems of Equations

Let $\mathfrak{X}$ be the linear space E_m of real m-dimensional column vectors x metricized by one of the following norms:

(i) l_1 norm: $\|x\| = \sum_1^m |\xi_k|.$

(ii) l_2 norm: $\|x\| = \left(\sum_1^m |\xi_k|^2\right)^{1/2}.$

(iii) l_∞ norm: $\|x\| = \max_k |\xi_k|.$

Under each norm, E_m is complete.   Let

$$x = T(x)$$

be given, where T is a vector function defined on a set $\mathfrak{D} \subset E_m$ whose components $\tau_k(\xi_1, \ldots, \xi_m)$ satisfy on $\mathfrak{D}$ Lipschitz conditions

$$|\tau_k(\xi_1, \ldots, \xi_m) - \tau_k(\eta_1, \ldots, \eta_m)| \leq \sum_{j=1}^{m} \mu_{kj} |\xi_j - \eta_j| \qquad (k = 1, \ldots, m)$$

To solve this equation on $\mathfrak{D}$ by iteration in "total steps"

$$x_{n+1} = T(x_n)$$

starting from an x_0 chosen according to Theorem 14.1, we introduce the "comparison" matrix $M = (\mu_{ij})$, $1 \leq i, j \leq m$, and the vector function $\alpha(x)$ defined by $\alpha_k(x) = |\xi_k|$, $k = 1, \ldots, m$.

Interpreting $x \leq y$ to mean, as usual, $\xi_k \leq \eta_k$ for each $k = 1, 2, \ldots, m$, we can then write the Lipschitz conditions in the form

$$\alpha[T(x) - T(y)] \leq M\alpha(x - y),$$

whence, for each of the three norms indicated above,

$$\|T(x) - T(y)\| = \|\alpha[T(x) - T(y)]\| \leq \|M\alpha(x - y)\|$$
$$\leq \|M\| \, \|\alpha(x - y)\| = \|M\| \, \|x - y\|,$$

since, obviously, $\|\alpha(x)\| = \|x\|$ always.   Therefore,

$$\|M\| \leq \mu < 1$$

is sufficient for the convergence of the successive approximations.   Thus, we obtain for the three norms three (sufficient) conditions for convergence and these error estimates:

(i) l_1 norm:

$$\|M\| = \mu_1 = \max_k \sum_{i=1}^{m} |\mu_{ik}| < 1,$$

$$\sum_{k=1}^{m} |\xi_k^{(n)} - \xi_k^*| \leq \frac{\mu_1}{1 - \mu_1} \sum_{k=1}^{m} |\xi_k^{(n)} - \xi_k^{(n-1)}|.$$

(ii) l_2 norm:

$$\|M\| \leq \mu_2 = \left(\sum_{i,j=1}^{m} |\mu_{ij}|^2 \right)^{1/2} < 1,$$

$$\left\{ \sum_{k=1}^{m} [\xi_k^{(n)} - \xi_k^*]^2 \right\}^{1/2} \leq \frac{\mu_2}{1 - \mu_2} \left\{ \sum_{k=1}^{m} [\xi_k^{(n)} - \xi_k^{(n-1)}]^2 \right\}^{1/2}.$$

(iii) l_∞ norm:

$$\|M\| = \mu_\infty = \max_i \sum_{k=1}^m |\mu_{ik}| < 1,$$

$$\max_i |\xi_i^{(n)} - \xi_i^*| \le \frac{\mu_\infty}{1 - \mu_\infty} \max_i |\xi_i^{(n)} - \xi_i^{(n-1)}|.$$

To solve the equation $x = T(x)$ by iteration in "single steps"

$$\xi_k^{(n+1)} = \tau_k[\xi_1^{(n+1)}, \ldots, \xi_{k-1}^{(n+1)}, \xi_k^{(n)}, \ldots, \xi_m^{(n)}], \qquad k = 1, \ldots, m,$$

we define the vector function S with components

$$\eta_k = \sigma_k(x) = \tau_k(\eta_1, \ldots, \eta_{k-1}, \xi_k, \ldots, \xi_m) \qquad (k = 1, 2, \ldots, m).$$

The single-step iteration formulas can then be written as

$$x_{n+1} = S(x_n), \qquad n = 1, 2, \ldots.$$

We now split the comparison matrix $M = M' + M''$, where

$$M' = (m'_{ij}) \qquad \text{with} \qquad m'_{ij} = \begin{cases} 0 & \text{for } i \le j \\ \mu_{ij} & \text{for } i > j \end{cases}$$

and

$$M'' = (m''_{ij}) \qquad \text{with} \qquad m''_{ij} = \begin{cases} \mu_{ij} & \text{for } i \le j \\ 0 & \text{for } i > j \end{cases}.$$

Then the Lipschitz condition assumes the form

$$\alpha[S(x) - S(y)] \le M'\alpha[S(x) - S(y)] + M''\alpha(x - y).$$

Since M' is lower triangular, the matrix $I - M''$ is clearly nonsingular, and hence $N = (I - M')^{-1}M''$ is defined everywhere; moreover, $Nx \ge 0$ for $x \ge 0$, since $\mu_{ij} \ge 0$ for $1 \le i, j \le m$. Thus,

$$\alpha[S(x) - S(y)] \le N\alpha(x - y),$$

whence for each of the three norms

$$\|S(x) - S(y)\| = \|\alpha[S(x) - S(y)]\| \le \|N\alpha(x - y)\| \le \|N\| \, \|\alpha(x - y)\|$$
$$= \|N\| \, \|x - y\|.$$

Therefore, the condition

$$\nu = \|N\| < 1$$

suffices for the convergence of the iteration, provided the initial approximation is selected according to Theorem 14.1.

If $\|M'\| < 1$, then $\|N\| \le \|M'\| \, (1 - \|M'\|)^{-1}$; if, moreover, $\|M'\| + \|M''\| < 1$, then this inequality may be extended to $\|N\| \le \|M''\| \, (1 - \|M'\|)^{-1} \le \|M'\| + \|M''\|$. These estimates are rough; for details we refer to [8, 9]. For the l_∞ norm of E_m an exact evaluation of

$\|N\|$ was first given by Mehmke and Nekrasov [10]; see also Sassenfeld [11], who proceeds as follows:

Let e denote the vector in E_m whose components are all 1, so that $\|e\| = 1$. Since $Nx \geq 0$ for $x \geq 0$, it follows that $Ne \geq N\alpha(x) \geq N(x)$ if $\|x\| \leq 1$, whence

$$\|N\| = \|Ne\| = \max n_i.$$

where $n_1 = \sum_1^n \mu_{ik}$, $\quad n_j = \sum_1^{j-i} \mu_{ik} n_k + \sum_1^m \mu_{ik} \quad$ for $2 \leq j \leq m - 1,$

and $$n_m = \sum_1^{m-1} \mu_{mk} n_k + \mu_{mm}.$$

14.6 Systems of Integral Equations

The previous results carry over without essential changes to an m-dimensional system of Fredholm integral equations

$$x(t) = z(t) + \lambda \int_a^b \kappa[t,s,x(s)] \, ds$$

over a finite interval $[a,b]$.   Here λ is a parameter, and κ is assumed to be continuous in its variables on some set $\mathfrak{D}$ and to satisfy uniformly a Lipschitz condition in x.   We omit the details.

In the case of a Volterra equation of the second kind,

$$x(t) = z(t) + \lambda \int_a^t \kappa[t,s,x(s)] \, ds,$$

the situation is somewhat different.   For the sake of simplicity, let us restrict ourselves to a single equation—$x(t)$ a scalar function—and assume that $\kappa(t,s,u)$ is continuous on the box

$$|t - a| \leq \delta_0, \qquad |s - a| \leq \delta_0, \qquad |u| \leq \delta_1,$$

and satisfies there the Lipschitz condition

$$|\kappa(t,s,u) - \kappa(t,s,v)| \leq \mu \, |u - v|$$

uniformly in t and s.   Let $\mathfrak{C}$ be the normed linear space of (real) continuous functions $x(t)$ on the interval $[a - \delta_0, a + \delta_0]$ with norm $\|x\| = \max_t |x(t)|$ and define

$$T(x) = z(t) + \int_a^t \kappa[t,s,x(s)] \, ds$$

on the sphere in $\mathfrak{C}$ with center at the origin and radius δ_1.   Thus, for $t \geq a$,

$$|T(x) - T(y)| = \left| \int_a^t \{\kappa[t,s,x(s)] - \kappa[t,s,y(s)]\} \, ds \right| \leq \mu \int_a^t |x(s) - y(s)| \, ds$$

Hence, taking norms and writing $J(x) = \int_a^t x(s) \, ds$, we find

$$\| T(x) - T(y) \| = \max_t | T(x) - T(y) |$$

$$\leq \mu \max_t J(|x - y|) \leq \mu \, \|J\| \, \|x - y\|,$$

and it is easy to see that $\|J\| = \delta_0$. Therefore,

$$\| T(x) - T(y) \| \leq \mu \delta_0 \, \|x - y\|,$$

so that $\mu \delta_0 < 1$ is sufficient, by Theorem 14.1, for the convergence of the iteration $x_{n+1} = T(x_n)$ to the (unique) solution $x = T(x)$, provided, of course, that $x_0(t)$ is chosen suitably.

This result is not so satisfactory as the analogous result for Fredholm equations. One reason for this is the fact that in the case of linear Volterra equations the iterations are known to converge no matter what initial approximation is chosen. Theorem 14.1 has been generalized [2, 5–8] so as to include this particular case as well as other similar ones. These generalizations consist mainly in the introduction of metric spaces in which the distance between two points is no longer a nonnegative real number but rather an element of a certain type of partially ordered set.

14.7 Boundary-value Problems

Consider the boundary-value problem

$$F_1[x, y, \ldots, y^{(n)}] = F_2[x, y, \ldots, y^{(m)}] \qquad (0 \leq m \leq n - 1),$$

$$U_j[y] \equiv U_j[y(a_1), \ldots, y^{(n-1)}(a_1), \ldots, y(a_r), \ldots, y^{(n-1)}(a_r)] = 0$$
$$(j = 1, \ldots, n),$$

where the constants $a_1, \ldots, a_r$ are given, and suppose that the reduced problem

$$F_1[x, y, \ldots, y^{(n)}] = r(x), \qquad U_j[y] = 0 \qquad (j = 1, \ldots, n)$$

has for any given continuous $r(x)$ a unique solution that can be determined explicitly. Then the following iteration procedure can be set up:

$$F_1[x, y_{k+1}, \ldots, y^{(n)}_{k+1}] = F_2[x, y_k, \ldots, y^{(m)}_k] \qquad (k = 0, 1, \ldots.),$$
$$U_j[y_{k+1}] = 0 \qquad (j = 1, \ldots, m),$$

starting from a function $y_0(x)$ which is of class $\mathfrak{C}^m$ on the interval considered and satisfies $U_j[y_0] = 0$. Schröder [7] determined conditions for convergence under the assumptions that

$$F_1[x, y, \ldots, y^{(n)}] = \sum_{i=1}^{n} g_i(x) y^{(i)},$$

where $g_n(x) > 0$ and $g_i(x)$, $1 \leq i \leq n$, is continuous on the compact interval $[a,b]$, and

$$U_j[y] = \sum_{i=1}^{n-1} [\alpha_{ji} y^{(i)}(a) + \beta_{ji} y^{(i)}(b)] - c_j \qquad (j = 1, 2, \ldots, n).$$

We do not describe his results here but, rather, restrict ourselves to discussing the special case

$$y'' + f(x,y,y') = 0, \qquad y(0) = c_1, \qquad y(1) = c_2,$$

which was treated first by Picard [4] and later by Lettenmeyer [3], Collatz [1], and also Schröder [7]; our treatment follows Collatz.

Suppose $f(x,y,p)$ is continuous on $x \in [0,1]$, $|y| \leq \delta_1$, $|p| \leq \delta_2$ and satisfies there

$$|f(x,y,p) - f(x,y^*,p^*)| \leq \mu_1 |y - y^*| + \mu_2 |p - p^*|$$

uniformly in x.   Let

$$g(x,\xi) = \begin{cases} x(1 - \xi) & (0 \leq x \leq \xi \leq 1) \\ \xi(1 - x) & (0 \leq \xi \leq x \leq 1) \end{cases}$$

be Green's function of the reduced problem $y'' = 0, y(0) = y(1) = 0$. Then the solution of the given problem may be written in the form

$$y(x) = c_1 + (c_2 - c_1)x + \int_0^1 g(x,\xi) f[\xi, y(\xi), y'(\xi)] \, d\xi$$

with $$y'(x) = c_2 - c_1 + \int_0^1 g_x(x,\xi) f[\xi, y(\xi), y'(\xi)] \, d\xi,$$

where $$g_x(x,\xi) = \begin{cases} 1 - \xi & (0 \leq x \leq \xi \leq 1) \\ -\xi & (0 \leq \xi \leq x \leq 1). \end{cases}$$

The iteration to be studied is

$$y_{k+1}(x) = c_1 + (c_2 - c_1)x + \int_0^1 g(x,\xi) f[\xi, y_k(\xi), y_k'(\xi)] \, d\xi,$$

$$y_{k+1}'(x) = c_2 - c_1 + \int_0^1 g_x(x,\xi) f[\xi, y_k(\xi), y_k'(\xi)] \, d\xi,$$

with suitably chosen $y_0(x)$.   The results of the general theory of successive approximations for Fredholm integral equations are not applicable here because $g_x(x,\xi)$ is not a continuous function of x.

We introduce the linear space $\mathfrak{C}^1[0,1]$ of real functions of class $\mathfrak{C}^1$ on $[0,1]$ and define on it the norm

$$\|y\| = \max_{x \in [0,1]} [\mu_1 |y(x)| + \mu_2 |y'(x)|] \, \tau^{-1}(x),$$

where $\tau(x)$ is some positive continuous function on $[0,1]$. It can be shown that $\mathfrak{C}^1[0,1]$ is complete under this norm. The operator

$$T(y) = c_1 + (c_2 - c_1)x + \int_0^1 g(x,\xi)\, f\,[\xi, y(\xi), y'(\xi)]\, d\xi$$

from the set $\mathfrak{D} \subset \mathfrak{C}^1[0,1]$ of functions $y(x)\,(\in \mathfrak{C}^1[0,1])$, with $|y(x)| \leq \delta_1$, $|y'(x)| \leq \delta_2$ on $[0,1]$ into $\mathfrak{C}^1[0,1]$, satisfies the inequality

$$\| T(x) - T(y^*)\| \leq \alpha \,\|y - y^*\|,$$

where

$$\alpha = \max_{x \in [0,1]} \tau^{-1}(x)\left[\mu_1 \int_0^1 |g(x,\xi)|\,\tau(\xi)\, d\xi + \mu_2 \int_0^1 |g_x(x,\xi)|\,\tau(\xi)\, d\xi\right].$$

Hence, $\alpha < 1$ is required in order that the iterations converge.   Clearly, the estimation of α depends on the choice of the weight function $\tau(x)$.
  For $\tau(x) \equiv 1$ we find

$$\alpha_0 = \max_{x \in [0,1]} \tau^{-1}(x)\int_0^1 |g(x,\xi)|\,\tau(\xi)\, d\xi = \tfrac{1}{8},$$

$$\alpha_1 = \max_{x \in [0,1]} \tau^{-1}(x)\int_0^1 |g_x(x,\xi)|\,\tau(\xi)\, d\xi = \tfrac{1}{2},$$

so that $\alpha \leq \tfrac{1}{2}(\tfrac{1}{4}\mu_1 + \mu_2)$.   For larger values of μ_2 Collatz [1] proposes to use

$$\tau(x) = 1 - \tfrac{1}{4}(15 - \sqrt{33})x(1 - x) = 1 - 2.314x(1 - x),$$

which yields $\alpha \leq \beta(\tfrac{1}{2}\mu_1 + \mu_2)$, where $\beta = \tfrac{1}{48}(9 + \sqrt{33}) = .3072$.
The range of permissible μ_1, μ_2 values for these two estimates is shown in Fig. 14.1 (see also [7]).

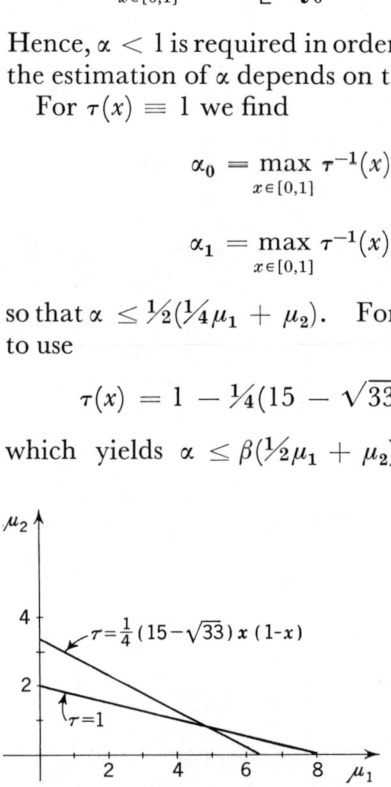

FIG. 14.1

The estimations of α depend, of course, also on the constants μ_1, μ_2, which depend themselves on the domain $\mathfrak{D} \subset \mathfrak{C}^1[0,1]$ on which the operator T is defined.   This domain is not known a priori.   It is often very useful to start with a relatively rough estimate for $\mathfrak{D}$ and refine this estimate in the course of the iteration process after more insight into the problem has been gained.   As an example, consider this problem (see [1]):

$$y'' - yy' + 6x = 0, \qquad y(0) = y(1) = 0.$$

Here the iterations become

$$y_{k+1}(x) = \int_0^1 g(x,\xi)[6\xi - y_k(\xi)y_k'(\xi)] \, d\xi,$$

where $g(x,\xi)$ is Green's function, as before. Selecting as domain $\mathfrak{D}_0$: $[0,1]$, $|y| \leq 1$, $|y'| \leq 3$, we find $\mu_1 = 3$, $\mu_2 = 1$, so that with $\tau(x) \equiv 1$ the norm is simply

$$\|y\| = \max_{x\in[0,1]} [3\,|y(x)| + |y'(x)|].$$

Hence $\alpha \leq \frac{3}{8} + \frac{1}{2} = \frac{7}{8} < 1$. The "natural" initial approximation would be $y_0(x) \equiv 0$, which would yield $y_1(x) = x - x^3$; yet this initial approximation does not satisfy the conditions of Theorem 14.1, since the sphere

$$\|y - y_0\| = \|y\| \leq \frac{1}{1 - \alpha} \|y_1 - y_0\| = 8 \|x - x^3\| = 16$$

is not contained in $\mathfrak{D}_0$. However, $y_1(x) = x - x^2$ is an admissible initial approximation for which $y_2(x) = \frac{1}{210}(202x - 175x^3 - 42x^5 + 15x^7)$; this is seen from the inequalities

$$|y_1(x) - y_2(x)| \leq .0075, \qquad |y_1'(x) - y_2'(x)| \leq .0382,$$

which give $\|y_2 - y_1\| \leq .0607$, so that $\|y - y_1\| \leq 8 \|y_2 - y_1\| \leq .4856$. Therefore, the iterations $\{y_k(x)\}$ converge to the unique solution $y^*(x)$ of the boundary-value problem in the sphere $\|y - y_1\| \leq .4856$.

For $y_2(x)$ we obtain the error estimates

$$\|y_2 - y^*\| \leq \frac{\alpha}{1 - \alpha} \|y_2 - y_1\| \leq .4249,$$

which means that

$$|y_2(x) - y^*(x)| \leq .142, \qquad |y_2'(x) - y^{*'}(x)| \leq .425$$

and hence

$$|y^*(x)| \leq .535, \qquad |y^{*'}(x)| \leq 2.463.$$

Thus, our first estimate of the domain $\mathfrak{D}_0$ may now be improved to

$$\mathfrak{D}_1\colon [0,1], \qquad |y| \leq .535, \qquad |y'| \leq 2.463.$$

This changes the norm in $\mathfrak{C}^1[0,1]$ to

$$\|y\| = \max_{x\in[0,1]} [2.463\,|y(x)| + .535\,|y'(x)|]$$

$[\tau(x) \equiv 1$ again] and the convergence factor to

$$\alpha = \frac{2.463}{8} + \frac{.535}{2} = .576.$$

Note the considerable improvement in α.

We now repeat the previous considerations to obtain a better estimate for $\|y_2 - y_1\|$, which, in turn, permits us to refine our estimate of the domain again.   The third step yields $\mu_1 = 2.110$, $\mu_2 = .409$, the norm

$$\|y\| = \max_{x \in [0.1]} [2.110 |y(x)| + .409 |y'(x)|],$$

and the improved convergence factor $\alpha = .469$.   Hence, we find, similarly as above,

$$|y_2(x) - y_2^*(x)| \leq .01, \qquad |y_2'(x) - y_2^{*\prime}(x)| \leq .052.$$

These bounds are rather remarkable in that they refer to only the second iterate.

Observe that we did not use explicitly Green's function here because the particular form of the equation $y'' - yy' + 6x = 0$ implies that all iterates will be polynomials in x provided the initial approximation $y_0(x)$ is a polynomial.   Thus, the iteration scheme can be modified to

$$y''_{k+1} = y_k y'_k - 6x, \qquad y_{k+1}(0) = y_{k+1}(1) = 0.$$

Collatz [1] showed that estimates for the convergence factor can be obtained also in more general cases without explicit knowledge of Green's function.

REFERENCES

1. L. Collatz, Einige Anwendungen funktionalanalytischer Methoden in der praktischen Analysis, *Z. Angew. Math. Phys.*, vol. 4, pp. 327–357, 1953.

2. L. Kantorovich, The Method of Successive Approximations for Functional Equations, *Acta Math.*, vol. 71, pp. 63–97, 1939.

3. F. Lettenmeyer, Über die von einem Punkt ausgehenden Integralkurven einer Differentialgleichung 2. Ordnung, *Deutsche Math.*, vol. 7, pp. 56–74, 1944.

4. E. Picard, "Traité d'Analyse," III, Gauthier-Villars, Paris, 1908.

5. J. Schröder, Das Iterationsverfahren bei allgemeinerem Abstandsbegriff, *Math. Z.*, vol. 66, pp. 111–116, 1956.

6. J. Schröder, Nichtlineare Majoranten beim Verfahren der schrittweisen Näherung, *Arch. Math.*, vol. 7, pp. 471–484, 1956.

7. J. Schröder, Neue Fehlerabschätzungen für verschiedene Iterationsverfahren, *Z. Angew. Math. Mech.*, vol. 36, pp. 168–181, 1956.

8. J. Weissinger, Über das Iterationsverfahren, *Z. Angew. Math. Mech.*, vol. 31, pp. 245–246, 1951.

9. J. Weissinger, Zur Theorie und Anwendung des Iterationsverfahrens, *Math. Nachr.*, vol. 8, pp. 193–212, 1952.

10. R. Mehmke and P. A. Nekrasov, Auflösung eines linearen Systems von Gleichungen durch successive Annäherung, *Mat. Sb.*, vol. 16, pp. 437–459, 1892.

11. H. Sassenfeld, Ein hinreichendes Konvergenzkriterium und eine Fehlerabschätzung für die Iteration in Einzelschritten bei linearen Gleichungen, *Z. Angew. Math. Mech.*, vol. 31, pp. 92–94, 1951.

CONJUGATE-DIRECTION METHODS AND THE METHOD OF STEEPEST DESCENT

This section deals with certain iteration methods for solving the equation $Ax = 0$ where A is a linear, self-adjoint, positive definite operator from a Hilbert space $\mathfrak{H}$ into itself. All considerations are based on the well-known observation that most linear problems in analysis may be reduced to the variational problem of finding extrema for quadratic functionals.

14.8 Principal Theorems

Let A be a linear, self-adjoint, positive definite operator with domain $\mathfrak{D}$ in a Hilbert space $\mathfrak{H}$ and range $\mathfrak{R} \subset \mathfrak{H}$. Then there exists an $m > 0$ such that $(Ax,x) \geq m(x,x)$ for all x in $\mathfrak{D}$, and hence A has a continuous inverse A^{-1} whose domain is $\mathfrak{R}$ and range $\mathfrak{D}$. Thus, for any given $v \in \mathfrak{R}$ the equation

$$Ax = v$$

has a unique solution $u = A^{-1}v \in \mathfrak{D}$. If $x \in \mathfrak{D}$ is an approximation to u, we call $r = v - Ax$ the residual of x and call $y = u - x$ the error of x. The functional

$$F(x) = (y,r) = (u - x, A(u - x))$$

is referred to as the error functional. For any $x \in \mathfrak{D}$ and any $h \in \mathfrak{H}$, we have $\delta F(x,h) = -2(A(u - x),h) = -2(r,h)$, whence, by Schwarz's inequality,

$$\sup \{|\delta F(x,h)|, \|h\| = 1\} = 2\|r\|.$$

Therefore, we speak of r also as the **gradient** of $F(x)$ at x.

Theorem 14.2. *Let $\mathfrak{B}$ be a linear subspace of $\mathfrak{D}$ and $x_0 \in \mathfrak{D}$. Then*

$$F(x_0) \leq F(x_0 + z)$$

for all $z \in \mathfrak{B}$ if and only if the gradient r_0 of $F(x)$ at x_0 satisfies $(r_0,z) = 0$ on $\mathfrak{B}$. Hence, in particular, $F(x_0) \leq F(x)$ for all $x \in \mathfrak{D}$ if and only if $Ax_0 = v$.

Proof. The sufficiency part follows on observing that, for any nonzero $z \in \mathfrak{B}$,

$$F(x_0 + z) - F(x_0) = (z,Az) - 2(r_0,z),$$

whence, if $(r_0,z) = 0$ on $\mathfrak{B}$, then $F(x_0 + z) - F(x_0) > 0$. If $F(x_0) \leq F(x_0 + z)$ for all $z \in \mathfrak{B}$, then

$$F(x_0) - F(x_0 + tz) = 2t(r_0,z) - t^2(z,Az) \leq 0$$

for $z \in \mathfrak{B}$ and sufficiently small $|t| < \epsilon(x_0,z)$. Thus, the function

$F(x_0) - F(x_0 + tz)$ has a relative maximum at $t = 0$, and this implies $(r_0, z) = 0$.

In particular, if $\mathfrak{B} = \mathfrak{D}$ and $z = u - x_0$, then

$$0 = (r_0, u - x_0) = (A(u - x_0), u - x_0) \geq m(u - x_0, u - x_0),$$

which is possible only if $x_0 = u$, that is, if $Ax_0 = v$.

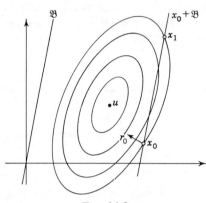

FIG. 14.2

This theorem admits a simple geometric interpretation when $\mathfrak{D} = \mathfrak{H}$ and $\mathfrak{H}$ is the euclidean plane. Then $F(x) = $ const defines a family of ellipses with center $u \, (= A^{-1}v)$, and the gradient of $F(x)$ at x has the direction of the normal to the ellipse through x. The linear subspace $\mathfrak{B}$ is a straight line through the origin. It is clear that on $x_0 + \mathfrak{B}$ there is always an interval $[x_0, x_1]$ on which $F(x) \leq F(x_0)$ unless $x_0 + \mathfrak{B}$ is tangent to the ellipse through x_0, that is, orthogonal to r_0.

Theorem 14.3.   *Let $\mathfrak{B}$ be a closed linear subspace of $\mathfrak{D}$.   There exists a unique x_0 minimizing $F(x)$ on $\mathfrak{B}$ for which $r_0 \equiv A(u - x_0)$ satisfies $(r_0, z) = 0$ on $\mathfrak{B}$.*

Proof.   Since A is positive definite, inf $\{F(x), x \in \mathfrak{B}\} = \gamma > 0$.   Let $\{x_n\}$ be a sequence of points $x_n \in \mathfrak{B}$ such that $\gamma_n = F(x_n) \to \gamma$ as $n \to \infty$.   Then $F(x_n + tz) \geq \gamma$ for any real t and $z \in \mathfrak{B}$, which implies

$$(z, A(u - x_n))^2 \leq (\gamma_n - \gamma)(z, Az)$$

For $z = x_n - x_m$, $m \neq n$, this yields

$$(\gamma_m - \gamma_n) + (\gamma_n - \gamma) \geq (x_n - x_m, A(x_n - x_m)),$$

whence, by the positive definiteness of A, $\{x_n\}$ is a Cauchy sequence. Since $\mathfrak{H}$ is complete and $\mathfrak{B}$ closed, there is an $x_0 \in \mathfrak{B}$ such that $x_n \to x_0$ as $n \to \infty$.   Now, for any $z \in \mathfrak{B}$,

$$|(r_0, z)| = |(A(u - x_0), z)| \leq |(A(u - x_n), z)| + |(A(x_n - x_0), z)|$$
$$\leq |(A(u - x_n), z)| + \|Az\| \, \|x_n - x_0\|,$$

and since the right-hand side tends to zero as $n \to \infty$, this shows that $(r_0, z) = 0$.   Therefore, by Theorem 14.2, $F(x_0) \leq F(z)$ for all $z \in \mathfrak{B}$, that is, $F(x_0) = \gamma$.

Suppose $\mathfrak{B}$ contains an $x' \neq x_0$ for which also $F(x') \leq F(z)$ for any $z \in \mathfrak{B}$.   Then, by Theorem 14.2, $(A(u - x'), z) = 0$, whence

$(A(x_0 - x'), z) = 0$ for all $z \in \mathfrak{B}$. If $z = x_0 - x'$, this contradicts the positive definiteness of A. Hence x_0 is unique.

Theorem 14.4. *Let* $\{\mathfrak{B}_n\}$ *be an expanding sequence of closed linear subspaces* $\mathfrak{B}_n \subset \mathfrak{D}$ *covering* $\mathfrak{D}$, *and let* $\{x_n\}$ *be the sequence of points such that* $x_n \in \mathfrak{B}_n$ *and* $F(x_n) = \min \{F(x), x \in \mathfrak{B}_n\}$. *Then* $r_n \equiv A(u - x_n)$ *satisfies* $(r_n, z) = 0$ *on* $\mathfrak{B}_n$ *for each* n, *and* $x_n \to u$ *as* $n \to \infty$ *(in the norm topology)*.

Proof. The first assertion follows trivially from Theorem 14.3. The proof of the second assertion parallels the proof of Theorem 14.3. Since $F(x_1) \geq F(x_2) \geq \cdots \geq 0$, there is a $\gamma \geq 0$ such that $F(x_n) \to \gamma$ as $n \to \infty$. Hence, as before, $(z, A(u - x_n))^2 < [F(x_n) - \gamma](z, Az)$ for $z \in \bigcup_1^\infty \mathfrak{B}_n$, so that for $z = x_n - x_m$, $m \neq n$,

$$[F(x_m) - \gamma] + [F(x_n) - \gamma] \geq (x_n - x_m, A(x_n - x_m)),$$

which shows, by the positive definiteness of A, that $\{x_n\}$ is a Cauchy sequence. Thus, $x_n \to x_0 \in \mathfrak{H}$ as $n \to \infty$. Given $z \in \bigcup_1^\infty \mathfrak{B}_n$, there is a smallest integer $n = n_0(z)$ such that $z \in \mathfrak{B}_{n_0}$. Then $(z, A(u - x_n)) = 0$ for $n \geq n_0$, or $(Az, u - x_n) = 0$ for $n \geq n_0$, and this implies, by continuity, that $(Az, u - x_0) = 0$ for every $z \in \bigcup_1^\infty \mathfrak{B}_n$. From the self-adjointness of A follows $u - x_0 \in \mathfrak{D}$ $\left(\text{since } \bigcup_1^\infty \mathfrak{B}_n = \mathfrak{D}\right)$.

We have yet to show that $x_0 = u$. This follows because, as we have just shown, $u - x_0 \in \mathfrak{D}$, and so

$$(u - x_0, A(u - x_0)) = 0,$$

which means that

$$A(u - x_0) \in \mathfrak{D}'.$$

The positiveness of A implies $u = x_0$ as required.

The preceding theorems may be extended to more general classes of operators (see, e.g., [4, 5]). Our presentation follows that of [4], except that our proofs are based on ideas due to Friedrichs [1, 2].

14.9   Conjugate-direction Methods

The method of expanding subspaces, though not immediately usable for practical applications as outlined above, forms the basis of many numerical methods. For the discussion of some of these methods, we assume now that A is defined on the entire space $\mathfrak{H}$ and hence necessarily bounded; that is, $0 < m(x, x) \leq (Ax, x) \leq M(x, x)$ for all $x \neq 0$ in $\mathfrak{H}$. This restriction may be removed to a certain extent (see [4, 7]). We also make the assumption that $\mathfrak{H}$ is separable; it guarantees the existence of at least one linearly independent sequence $\{p_n\}$, $p_n \in \mathfrak{H}$, such that the finite-dimensional and hence closed linear subspaces $\mathfrak{B}_n$ spanned by $\{p_0, \ldots, p_{n-1}\}$ form an expanding sequence with $\overset{\infty}{\underset{1}{\bigcup}} \mathfrak{B}_n = \mathfrak{H}$.

To apply Theorem 14.4, we must compute $x_n \in \mathfrak{B}_n$ for each $n \geq 1$, such that $F(x_n) = \min \{F(x), x \in \mathfrak{B}_n\}$. This is trivial for x_1, because, by Theorem 14.3, $(A(u - x_1), p_0) = (v - Ax_1, p_0) = 0$; hence, since $x_1 = \mu p_0$, we have $x_1 = [(v,p_0)/(Ap_0,p_0)]p_0$. In general, we shall have $x_n = \sum_{k=0}^{n-1} \mu_{nk} p_k$, where the coefficients depend on n. This raises the question whether conditions upon the sequence $\{p_n\}$ can be found under which, for each n, $x_{n+1} = x_n + \alpha_n p_n$ so that $x_n = \sum_{k=0}^{n-1} \alpha_k p_k$, with coefficients α_k independent of n. For, in this case, if x_n has been found, Theorem 14.3 yields, for x_{n+1}, the equation $(A(u - x_{n+1}), p_n) = 0$, from which we obtain immediately $x_{n+1} = x_n + [(r_n,p_n)/(Ap_n,p_n)]p_n$, with $r_n = v - Ax_n$. Hence, the sequence $\{x_n\}$ can be determined simply by the iteration

$$x_0 = 0, \qquad x_{n+1} = x_n + \frac{(r_n,p_n)}{(Ap_n,p_n)} p_n \qquad (n \geq 0).$$

An answer to the question raised is given by the following two lemmas.

Lemma 14.1. *Let $\{x_n\}$, $x_n \in \mathfrak{B}_n$ be such that $F(x_n) = \min \{F(x), x \in \mathfrak{B}_n\}$. If for each n, $x_n = \sum_{k=0}^{n-1} \alpha_k p_k$, where the coefficients are independent of n, then for each $k \geq 0$, either*

$$(Ap_k, p_j) = 0 \qquad for\ j = 0, \ldots, k - 1$$

and

$$\alpha_k = \frac{(r_k, p_k)}{(Ap_k, p_k)} \qquad where\ r_k = v - Ax_k$$

or

$$(r_k, p_k) = 0 \qquad and \qquad \alpha_k = 0.$$

Proof. Since $x_{k+1} = x_k + \alpha_k p_k$, $r_{k+1} - r_k = -\alpha_k Ap_k$, and hence, for $j = 0, \ldots, k$, $(r_{k+1}, p_j) - (r_k, p_j) = -\alpha_k(Ap_k, p_j)$. Thus, by Theorem 14.3, $\alpha_k = (r_k, p_k)/(Ap_k, p_k)$ and $\alpha_k(Ap_k, p_j) = 0$ for $j = 0, \ldots, k - 1$. Therefore, either $(Ap_k, p_j) = 0$ for $j = 0, \ldots, k - 1$ or $\alpha_k = 0$; that is, $(r_k, p_k) = 0$.

Lemma 14.2. *Let $\{p_n\}$, $p_n \in \mathfrak{H}$, be a linearly independent sequence, $\{\mathfrak{B}_n\}$ the sequence of subspaces $\mathfrak{B}_n \subset \mathfrak{H}$ spanned by $\{p_0, \ldots, p_{n-1}\}$ such that $\overset{\infty}{\underset{1}{\bigcup}} \mathfrak{B}_n = \mathfrak{B}$. Let*

$$x_0 = 0, \qquad x_{n+1} = x_n + \frac{(r_n, p_n)}{(Ap_n, p_n)} p_n, \qquad n \geq 0,$$

where $r_n = v - Ax_n$. *If either* $(r_n, p_n) = 0$ *or* $(Ap_n, p_k) = 0$ *for* $k = 0, \ldots,$
$n - 1$, *then* x_n *is such that* $F(x_n) = \min \{F(x), x \in \mathfrak{B}_n\}$ *and* $x_n \to u$ *as*
$n \to \infty$ (*in the norm topology*).

Proof. Note first that $(r_n, p_k) = 0$ for $k = 0, 1, \ldots, n - 1$. This
follows readily by induction. Hence, for any $x = \sum_{k=0}^{n-1} \xi_k p_k$, we find that
$(r_n, x - x_n) = 0$, whence, by Theorem 14.2, $F(x_n) \leq F(x)$. Thus
$F(x_n) = \min \{F(x), x \in \mathfrak{B}_n\}$. Theorem 14.4 implies $x_n \to u$ as $n \to \infty$.

Several remarks concerning Lemma 14.2 are in order. In the first
place, observe that the condition $(r_n, p_n) = 0$ implies $x_{n+1} = x_n$, so that
the minimum of $F(x)$ in $\mathfrak{B}_n$ is also the minimum in $\mathfrak{B}_{n+1} \subset \mathfrak{B}_n$. This
happens, for example, when $x_n = u$. If $\mathfrak{H}$ is finite-dimensional, then the
iteration always converges in finitely many steps. Except for this
particular case, however, the occurrence of any repetitive steps $x_{n+1} = x_n$
is undesirable. Hence those vectors $\{p_n\}$ will be of importance for which
$(Ap_n, p_k) = 0$ for $k = 0, \ldots, n - 1$. Then, for every n and $k = 0, \ldots,$
$n - 1$,

$$(r_n, p_n) = (r_k, p_n) + (r_n - p_k, p_n) = (r_k, p_n) - \sum_{j=k}^{n-1} \alpha_j(Ap_j, p_n) = (r_k, p_n),$$

so that

$$\alpha_n = \frac{(r_k, p_n)}{(Ap_n, p_n)} \qquad \text{for } k = 0, \ldots, n - 1.$$

Secondly, the requirement in Lemma 14.2 that the iteration start
with $x_0 = 0$ can be easily removed. For, if $x_0 \neq 0$, we need consider
only the problem $Ax = v - Ax_0 = \hat{v}$; the iteration $\hat{x}_0 = 0, \hat{x}_{n+1} = \hat{x}_n + [(\hat{r}_n, p_n)/(Ap_n, p_n)]p_n$ converges then to the solution $\hat{u} = u - x_0$.

We combine these remarks with Lemma 14.2 in the following
theorem.

Theorem 14.5. *Let* $\{p_n\}$, $p_n \in \mathfrak{H}$, *be a linearly independent sequence so
chosen that* $(p_i, Ap_k) = 0$ *for* $i \neq k$ *and that the subspaces* $\mathfrak{B}_n \subset \mathfrak{H}$ *spanned by*
$\{p_0, \ldots, p_{n-1}\}$ *satisfy* $\bigcup_1^\infty \mathfrak{B}_n = \mathfrak{H}$. *Then, for any* $x_0 \in \mathfrak{H}$, *the sequence* $\{\alpha_n\}$
defined by $x_{n+1} = x_n + \alpha_n p_n$, $n \geq 0$, *where* $\alpha_n = (r_n, p_n)/(Ap_n, p_n)$ *converges
to the unique solution* u *of* $Ax = v$. *Moreover,* x_n *minimizes* $F(x)$ *on the line*
$x = x_{n-1} + \alpha p_{n-1}$ *as well as on the plane* $x = x_0 + \mathfrak{B}_n = \Big\{x \in \mathfrak{H}, x = x_0 +$
$\sum_{k=0}^{n-1} \xi_k p_k\Big\}$. *The vectors* $r_n = v - Ax_n$ *satisfy* $r_{n+1} = r_n - \alpha_n Ap_n$, *and*

$$(r_n, p_k) = 0, \qquad (r_n, p_n) = (r_k, p_n) \qquad (k = 0, 1, \ldots, n - 1).$$

Hence also

$$\alpha_n = \frac{(r_k, p_n)}{(Ap_n, p_n)} \qquad \text{for } k = 0, \ldots, n - 1.$$

The iteration described in Theorem 14.5 has been called by Hestenes and Stiefel [5, 6, 9, 10] an iteration by the method of conjugate directions.

14.10   Error Estimates and Rates of Convergence

For any given iteration by the method of conjugate directions, the error function $F(x)$ decreases at each step.   However, it cannot be computed without knowledge of the desired solution.   Estimates for its magnitude are given by the following theorems.

Theorem 14.6.   *Let* $y = u - x$ *be the error for any* $x \in \mathfrak{H}$ *and* $r = v - Ax$. *If* $\mu(z) = (Az,z)/(z,z)$ *for* $z \in \mathfrak{H}$, *then*

(i) $$\mu(y) \leq \mu(r),$$

(ii) $$(r,r)/\mu(r) \leq F(x) \leq (r,r)/\mu(y),$$

(iii) $$\|r\|/\mu(r) \leq \|y\| \leq \|r\|/\mu(y).$$

Proof.   There exists a unique positive self-adjoint operator B such that $B^2 = A$.   Schwarz's inequality yields $(Bz,BAz)^2 \leq (z,Az)(Az,A^2z)$ and $(z,Az)^2 \leq (z,z)(Az,Az)$ whence

$$\frac{(z,Az)}{(z,z)} \leq \frac{(Az,Az)}{(z,Az)} \leq \frac{(Az,A^2z)}{(Az,Az)}.$$

For $z = y$, this gives (i) and (ii).   From $F(x) = (y,Ay) = (y,r) \leq \|y\| \|r\|$ follows (iii).

Theorem 14.7.   *Let* $\{x_n\}$ *be defined as in Theorem 14.5, let* $y_n = u - x_n$ *and* $r_n = v - Ax_n$.   *Then*

(i) $$F(x_n) \leq \left(1 - \sigma_{n-1}\frac{m}{M}\right)F(x_{n-1}),$$

(ii) $$(y_n,y_n) \leq \frac{1}{m}\left(1 - \sigma_{n-1}\frac{m}{M}\right)F(x_{n-1}),$$

(iii) $$(r_n,r_n) \leq M\left(1 - \sigma_{n-1}\frac{m}{M}\right)F(x_{n-1}),$$

where $\sigma_n = (r_n,p_n)^2/[(r_n,r_n)(p_n,p_n)] \leq 1$ *and* m, M *are the lower and upper bounds of* A, *respectively.*

Proof.   Let $\mu(z) = (Az,z)/(z,z)$, $\nu(z) = (A^{-1}z,z)/(z,z)$ for $z \in \mathfrak{H}$, so that $0 < m \leq \mu(z) \leq M$, $0 < 1/M \leq \nu(z) \leq 1/m$.   An easy computation yields

$$\frac{F(x_n) - F(x_{n+1})}{F(x_n)} = \frac{\sigma_n}{\mu(p_n)\nu(r_n)},$$

whence (i) follows directly.   (ii) and (iii) follow from (i) on using

$$F(x_{n+1}) \geq m(y_{n+1},y_{n+1}), \qquad F(x_{n+1}) \geq \frac{1}{M}(r_{n+1},r_{n+1}).$$

Theorem 14.7 shows that the best possible choice for the sequence $\{p_n\}$ would be that for which $\sigma_n = 1$ whatever n; this, however, occurs only when p_n and r_n are linearly dependent for each n. Iteration methods with this choice of the sequence $\{p_n\}$ are the so-called steepest-descent methods (see Sec. 14.13).

14.11   The Conjugate-gradient Method

All conjugate-direction methods assume that there is given a linearly independent sequence $\{p_n\}$, $p_n \in \mathfrak{H}$, such that the vectors p_n are mutually A-orthogonal, that is, $(Ap_i, p_k) = 0$ for $i \neq k$, and that $\bigcup_1^\infty \mathfrak{B}_n = \mathfrak{H}$ where $\mathfrak{B}_n \subset \mathfrak{H}$ is the subspace spanned by $\{p_0, \ldots, p_{n-1}\}$. From any linearly independent sequence $\{u_n\}$, $u_n \in \mathfrak{H}$, one can construct, by a straight-forward adaptation of the Gram-Schmidt orthonormalization process, a linearly independent sequence $\{p_n\}$, $p_n \in \mathfrak{H}$, of mutually A-orthogonal vectors:

$$p_0 = \eta_0 u_0, \qquad p_n = \eta_n u_n - \eta_n \sum_0^{n-1} \frac{(u_n, Ap_k)}{(p_k, Ap_k)} p_k \qquad (n \geq 1),$$

where $\eta_n \neq 0$ are normalization factors; and it is clear that the subspace $\mathfrak{B}'_n$ spanned by $\{u_0, \ldots, u_{n-1}\}$ is $\mathfrak{B}_n$ and that $\bigcup_1^\infty \mathfrak{B}_n = \mathfrak{H}$ if and only if $\bigcup_1^\infty \mathfrak{B}'_n = \mathfrak{H}$. Thus, if an initial approximation $x_0 \in \mathfrak{H}$ to the solution u of $Ax = v$ is known, a natural choice for the sequence $\{u_n\}$ will be

$$u_0 = r_0 \equiv v - Ax_0, \qquad u_n = A^n r_0, \qquad (n \geq 1),$$

provided it can be shown to be linearly independent and such that $\bigcup_1^\infty \mathfrak{B}'_n = \mathfrak{H}$. No necessary and sufficient conditions on A appear to be known which ensure the existence of vectors r_0 for which the sequence $\{u_n\}$ has the required properties. Therefore, x_0 must be assumed to be such that these requirements on $\{u_n\}$ are met. The A-orthogonalization process then yields

$$p_0 = \eta_0 r_0, \qquad p_n = \eta_n A^n r_0 - \eta_n \sum_0^{n-1} \frac{(A^n r_0, Ap_k)}{(p_k, Ap_k)} p_k, \qquad (n \geq 1).$$

It is natural to expect that a conjugate-direction method using this sequence $\{p_n\}$ and starting from x_0 as the initial approximation will lead to good results. This is indeed so [10, 11]; yet in many applications this advantage would hardly outweigh the amount of work involved in such a procedure.

Hestenes and Stiefel [6] observed that by a judicious selection of the normalization factors η_n in $\{p_n\}$ the iterations involved in the A-orthogonalization process assume the same simple form as the iteration in a conjugate-direction method.   This is their conjugate-gradient method.

Note first that p_n appears as a formal polynomial in A so that the equation $(Ap_i, p_k) = 0$ for $i \neq k$ of A orthogonality becomes an orthogonality relation between such polynomials.   Just as for scalar orthogonal polynomials, it can be shown that any three consecutive polynomials p_{n+1}, p_n, p_{n-1} are connected by a linear relation.   In fact, we find

$$p_0 = \eta_0 r_0, \qquad p_{n+1} = \gamma_n(Ap_n - \delta_n p_n - \epsilon_n p_{n-1}) \qquad (n \geq 1),$$

where

$$\gamma_n = \frac{\eta_{n+1}}{\eta_n}, \qquad \delta_n = \frac{(Ap_n, Ap_n)}{(p_n, Ap_n)}, \qquad \epsilon_0 = 0, \qquad \epsilon_n = \frac{(Ap_n, Ap_{n-1})}{(p_{n-1}, Ap_{n-1})}.$$

Now the conjugate-direction method using $\{p_n\}$ and starting from x_0 yields

$$x_{n+1} = x_n + \alpha_n p_n, \qquad \alpha_n = \frac{(r_n, p_n)}{(Ap_n, p_n)} \qquad (n \geq 0),$$

$$r_{n+1} = r_n - \alpha_n Ap_n, \qquad (r_n, p_k) = 0 \qquad (k = 0, \ldots, n-1).$$

Choosing $\eta_0 = 0$ and $\gamma_n = -\alpha_n$, we obtain, after a simple calculation,

$$p_{n+1} = -\alpha_n Ap_n + (1 - \beta_n)p_n + \beta_{n-1}p_{n-1} \qquad (n \geq 0),$$

where $\qquad \beta_{-1} = 0, \qquad \beta_n = \frac{(r_{n+1}, Ap_n)}{(p_n, Ap_n)} \qquad (n \geq 0),$

and since $p_1 = r_1 - \beta_0 p_0$, we have, by induction,

$$p_n = r_n - \beta_{n-1}p_{n-1} \qquad (n \geq 0).$$

Theorem 14.8.   *Let $x_0 \in \mathfrak{H}$ be given and suppose that $\{A^n r_0\}$, $r_0 = v - Ax_0$, is a linearly independent sequence such that $\bigcup_1^\infty \mathfrak{B}_n = \mathfrak{H}$, where $\mathfrak{B}_n$ is the subspace spanned by $\{r_0, Ar_0, \ldots, A^{n-1}r_0\}$.   Define $p_0 = r_0$ and*

$$x_{n+1} = x_n + \alpha_n p_n, \qquad r_{n+1} = r_n - \alpha_n Ap_n, \qquad p_{n+1} = r_{n+1} - \beta_n p_n$$
$$(n \geq 0)$$

where $\qquad \alpha_n = \frac{(r_n, p_n)}{(p_n, Ap_n)}, \qquad \beta_n = \frac{(r_{n+1}, Ap_n)}{(p_n, Ap_n)}.$

Then $x_n \to u$ as $n \to \infty$ (in the norm topology) where u is the (unique) solution

of $Ax = v$. *Moreover,* x *minimizes* $F(x)$ *on* $\mathfrak{B}_n$ *on the line* $x = x_{n-1} + \alpha p_{n-1}$
as well as on the plane $x = x_0 + \sum_0^{n-1} \xi_k p_k$.

For a detailed discussion of the properties of the conjugate-gradient method, which would lead us too far here, we refer to [5, 6]. We mention only the following relation, which we state without proof.

Lemma 14.3. *Consider the conjugate-gradient method of Theorem 14.8. Then*

(i) $\qquad\qquad (r_i, r_k) = 0 \qquad for\ i \neq k\ and\ for\ k = 0, 1, \ldots, n,$

(ii) $\qquad\qquad (p_n, r_k) = (r_n, r_n),$

(iii) $\qquad\qquad p_n = (r_n, r_n) \sum_{i=k}^{n} \frac{1}{(r_i, r_k)} r_i,$

(iv) $\qquad\qquad (p_n, p_k) = \dfrac{(r_n, r_n)}{(r_k, r_k)} (p_k, p_k).$

Moreover, $\quad \alpha_n = \dfrac{(r_n, r_n)}{(p_n, A p_n)} \quad$ *and* $\quad \beta_n = -\dfrac{(r_{n+1}, r_{n+1})}{(r_n, r_n)} \quad$ *for* $n \geq 0$.

It follows that $\alpha_n \neq 0$ and hence that $x_{n+1} \neq x_n$ if and only if $r_n \neq 0$. Thus, if $r_{n_0} = 0$, then $x_{n_0} = u$, and $r_n = p_n = 0$ and $x_n = u$ for $n \geq n_0$, so that the process stops. This shows that, if $\mathfrak{H}$ is N-dimensional, the conjugate-gradient method terminates with $x_N = u$.

As mentioned before (see p. 506), the error function $F(x)$ is decreased at each step in any conjugate-direction method. This, however, does not imply in general that also the error vectors $y_n = u - x_n$ or the residual vectors $r_n = v - A x_n$ are decreased at each step (see [6]). The next theorem shows that for the conjugate-gradient method the sequence $\{\|y_n\|\}$ always decreases monotonically.

Theorem 14.9. *Let* $\mathfrak{C}_n$ *be the convex closure of* $x_0, \ldots, x_n$; *that is,*

$$\mathfrak{C}_n = \left\{ x \in \mathfrak{H},\ x = \sum_{k=0}^{n} \xi_k x_k,\ \xi_k \geq 0,\ \sum_0^n \xi_k = 1 \right\}.\quad \textit{Then}\ x_n \in \mathfrak{C}_n\ \textit{minimizes}$$

$\|u - x\|$ *on* $\mathfrak{C}_n$.

Proof. For any $x \in \mathfrak{C}_n$ we have $x_n - x = \sum_0^{n-1} \hat{\xi}_k p_k$, where $\hat{\xi}_k \geq 0$, and since $(p_k, p_i) \geq 0$ for $i = 0, \ldots, k-1$, it follows readily that $(u - x_n, x_n - x) \geq 0$. Hence $\|u - x\|^2 - \|u - x_n\|^2 \geq 0$ for $x \in \mathfrak{C}_n$.

14.12   Rate of Convergence

For the conjugate-gradient method the estimates of Theorem 14.9 can be improved as follows.

Theorem 14.10.   *Let $\{x_n\}$, $\{r_n\}$ be defined as in Theorem 14.8 and let $y_n = u - x_n$, $n \geq 0$.   Then*

(i) $$F(x_n) \leq \delta F(x_{n-1}) \leq \delta^n F(x_0),$$

(ii) $$(y_n, y_n) \leq \frac{1}{m} \delta F(x_{n-1}) \leq \frac{1}{m} \delta^n F(x_0),$$

(iii) $$(r_n, r_n) \leq \frac{1}{M} \delta F(x_{n-1}) \leq \frac{1}{M} \delta^n F(x_0),$$

where $\delta = 1 - m/M$ and m, M are the lower and upper bounds of A, respectively.

Proof.   In the notation of the proof of Theorem 14.7 we find, after a slight reduction,

$$\frac{F(x_{n+1})}{F(x_n)} = 1 - \frac{\alpha_n}{\nu(r_n)}$$

and $$\frac{1}{M} \leq \frac{1}{\mu(r_n)} \leq \alpha_n \leq \frac{1}{\mu(p_n)} \leq \frac{1}{m}.$$

Hence $F(x_{n+1})/F(x_n) \leq 1 - m/M$.   Since

$$(p_n, p_n) = (r_n, r_n) + \beta_{n-1}^2 (p_{n-1}, p_{n-1}) \geq (r_n, r_n),$$

equality is possible only if $\beta_{n-1} = 0$ or $p_{n-1} = 0$.   The first alternative arises if $r_n = 0$, that is, if the iteration terminates; the second is impossible so long as the iteration progresses.   Thus $\sigma_n < 1$, which improves the estimate of Theorem 14.7.

14.13   The Method of Steepest Descent

The rate of convergence of a conjugate-direction method is best (see p. 507) if the sequence $\{p_n\}$ is so chosen that $p_n = r_n$ for every n. This is done in the method of steepest descent.   However, Theorem 14.5 no longer applies, since, in general, the relations $(Ar_i, r_k) = 0$ for $i \neq k$ do not hold.

Let us first make the following observation.   If $x_0 \in \mathfrak{H}$ is an approximation to the solution u of $Ax = v$ and if

$$x_{n+1} = x_n + \alpha_n r_n, \qquad r_n = v - Ax_n \qquad (n \geq 0),$$

where $\{\alpha_n\}$ is some sequence of constants, then x_{n+1} lies at each step in the direction which maximizes the change of the error function $F(x)$.   This follows from the fact that the differential $\delta F(x_n, h)$ assumes its maximum over all unit vectors $h \in \mathfrak{H}$ for $h = \|r_n\|^{-1} r_n$.   Hence, in order to minimize $F(x)$ in going from x_n to x_{n+1}, we must choose α_n such that

$$(v - A(x_n + \alpha_n r_n), \alpha_n r_n) = 0,$$

that is, $\alpha_n = (r_n,r_n)/(Ar_n,r_n)$. This is the sequence $\{\alpha_n\}$ used in the method of steepest descent (which also explains its name). Observe that $F(x)$ is not minimized on a sequence of expanding subspaces as it is in any conjugate-direction method.

Theorem 14.11. *For any $x_0 \in \mathfrak{H}$ the sequence $\{x_n\}$ defined by*

$$x_{n+1} = x_n + \frac{(r_n,r_n)}{(Ar_n,r_n)}\, r_n, \qquad r_n = v - Ax_n \qquad (n \geq 0)$$

converges (in the norm topology) to the (unique) solution u of $Ax = v$. Moreover, x_n minimizes $F(x)$ on the line $x = x_{n-1} + \alpha r_{n-1}$. The rate of convergence is given by

$$(y_n,y_n) \leq \frac{1}{m}\left(\frac{M-m}{M+m}\right)^{2n} F(x_0), \qquad y_n = u - x_n,$$

where m,M are the lower and upper bounds of A, respectively.

Proof. We readily find

$$F(x_{n+1}) \leq \left(1 - \frac{m}{M}\right)F(x_n) \leq \left(1 - \frac{m}{M}\right)^{n+1} F(x_0) \qquad (n \geq 0),$$

whence $\qquad (y_n,y_n) \leq \dfrac{1}{m}F(x_n) \leq \dfrac{1}{m}\left(1 - \dfrac{m}{M}\right)^n F(x_0).$

This implies $x_n \to u$ as $n \to \infty$. To obtain the estimate for the rate of convergence, we use with $x = r_n$ the inequality $(x,x)^2 \leq (Ax,x)(A^{-1}x,x)$ $\leq [(m+M)^2/4mM](x,x)^2$ proved in [3] for any $x \in \mathfrak{H}$.

Theorem 14.11 has been extended by Kantorovich [7] to more general operators A, particularly to self-adjoint semibounded operators. Another extension, due to Rosenbloom [12], uses in place of the polygonal paths a continuous path of steepest descent defined by a differential equation.

REFERENCES

1. K. Friedrichs, Spektraltheorie halbbeschränkter Operatoren, *Math. Ann.*, vol. 109, pp. 465–487, 685–713, 1934.

2. K. Friedrichs, Spektraltheorie halbbeschränkter Operatoren, *Math. Ann.*, vol. 110, pp. 777–779, 1935.

3. W. Greub and W. Rheinboldt, On a Generalization of an Inequality of L. V. Kantorovich, *Proc. Amer. Math. Soc.*, vol. 10, pp. 407–415, 1959.

4. R. M. Hayes, Iterative Methods of Solving Linear Problems on Hilbert Space, in O. Taussky, ed., "Contributions to the Solution of Systems of Linear Equations and the Determination of Eigenvalues," National Bureau of Standards Applied Mathematics Series, vol. 39, pp. 71–104, 1954.

5. M. R. Hestenes, The Conjugate Gradient Method for Solving Linear Systems, in American Mathematical Society, "Numerical Analysis: Proceedings of Symposia in Applied Mathematics—Volume VI," J. H. Curtiss, ed., McGraw-Hill Book Company, Inc., New York, 1956.

6. M. R. Hestenes and E. Stiefel, Methods of Conjugate Gradients for Solving Linear Systems, *J. Res. Nat. Bur. Standards*, vol. 49, p. 409, 1952.

7. L. V. Kantorovich, 1948 (see reference following Sec. 14.3).

8. F. Riesz and B. Sz.-Nagy, 1955 (see reference following Sec. 14.3).

9. E. Stiefel, Über einige Methoden der Relaxationsrechnung, *Z. Angew. Math. Phys.*, vol. 3, pp. 1–33, 1952.

10. E. Stiefel, Relaxationsmethoden bester Strategie zur Lösung linearer Gleichungssysteme, *Comment. Math. Helv.*, vol. 29, pp. 157–179, 1955.

11. E. Stiefel, Kernel Polynomials in Linear Algebra and Their Numerical Applications, in "Further Contributions to the Solution of Simultaneous Linear Equations and the Determination of Eigenvalues," National Bureau of Standards Applied Mathematics Series, vol. 49, pp. 1–22, 1958.

12. P. C. Rosenbloom, The Method of Steepest Descent, in American Mathematical Society, "Numerical Analysis: Proceedings of Symposia in Applied Mathematics—Volume VI," J. H. Curtiss, ed., pp. 127–176, McGraw-Hill Book Company, Inc., New York, 1956.

NEWTON'S METHOD

In Secs. 14.14 and 14.15 we discuss Newton's method for solving a linear or nonlinear equation $F(x) = 0$ when F is an operator from a Banach space $\mathfrak{B}_1$ to a Banach space $\mathfrak{B}_2$. The principal theorem on the convergence of the method for this general case parallels the well-known classical result for scalar equations. Our presentation does not include the recent generalizations of Altman [1–7], Schröder [19], and Collatz [9], for which we refer to the original papers cited.

14.14   The General Theorem

Let $\mathfrak{B}_1$, $\mathfrak{B}_2$ be Banach spaces and let F be an operator with domain $\mathfrak{D} \subset \mathfrak{B}_1$ and range in $\mathfrak{B}_2$. If F is F-differentiable on a neighborhood (in $\mathfrak{D}$) of a point $x_0 \in \mathfrak{D}$, we denote by f_0 the bounded linear operator $F'(x_0)$ and by f_0^{-1} its inverse $[F'(x_0)]^{-1}$, if it exists.

Theorem 14.12.   *Let $x_0 \in \mathfrak{D}$ be selected such that the following conditions hold:*

(i) *There exists a sphere $S(x_0, r_0)$ on which F is twice F-differentiable and $\|F''(x)\| \leq K$.*

(ii) *The bounded linear operator $f_0 = F'(x_0)$ maps $S(x_0, r_0)$ onto $\mathfrak{B}_2$ and has a bounded inverse f_0^{-1} on $\mathfrak{B}_2$ such that $\|f_0^{-1}\| \leq \beta_0$, $\|f_0^{-1}[F(x_0)]\| \leq \eta_0$.*

(iii) *The constant $h_0 = \beta_0 \eta_0 K$ satisfies $h_0 \leq \frac{1}{2}$ and*

$$(1/h_0)(1 - \sqrt{1 - 2h_0})\eta_0 < r_0.$$

Then the sequence $\{x_n\}$ defined by

$$x_{n+1} = x_n - f_n^{-1}[F(x_n)], \qquad n \geq 0,$$

exists for all n and converges to a solution $u \in S(x_0, r_0)$ of $F(x) = 0$.

The rate of convergence is given by

$$\|u - x_n\| \le 2^{-(n-1)}(2h_0)^{2^{n-1}}\eta_0.$$

Moreover, u is unique in every closed sphere $\bar{S}(x_0,r) \subset S(x_0,r_0)$ *with* $r < (1/h_0)(1 + \sqrt{1 - 2h_0})\eta_0$.

Proof. Clearly, x_1 is defined and $\|x_1 - x_0\| \le \eta_0 < r_0$; hence there is a sphere $S(x_1,r_1) \subset S(x_0,r_0)$ on which (i) holds. By (ii) and the mean-value theorem (see p. 490), $\|f_0^{-1}(f_0 - f_1)\| \le h_0 < 1$, so that the linear bounded operator $g(x) = x - f_0^{-1}[f_0(x) - f_1(x)]$ has an inverse g^{-1} with $\|g^{-1}\| \le (1 - h_0)^{-1}$ (see p. 489).

Obviously, $f_0[g(x)] = f_1(x)$ and $(f_0 g)^{-1} = g^{-1}f_0^{-1}$, so that f_1^{-1} exists and is bounded. Hence (ii) is satisfied for x_1 with $\beta_1 = \beta_0/(1 - h_0)$. To find a bound for $\|f_1^{-1}[F(x_1)]\|$, we consider $G_0(x) = x - f_0^{-1}[F(x)]$, for which $G_0(x_0) = x_1$ and $G_0'(x_0)h = 0$ for $h \in \mathfrak{B}_1$. Since $f_0^{-1}[F(x_1)] = G_0(x_0) - G_1(x_1) + G_0'(X_0)(x_1 - x_0)$, we obtain $\|f_0^{-1}[F(x_1)]\| \le \frac{1}{2}h_0\eta_0$, whence $\|f_1^{-1}[F(x_1)]\| \le \|g^{-1}\| \|f_0^{-1}[F(x_1)]\| \le h_0\eta_0/[2(1 - h_0)]$. Thus, we can take $\eta_1 = h_0\eta_0/[2(1 - h_0)]$. Now we easily verify (iii) with $h_1 = \beta_1\eta_1 K$ and $r_1 = (1/h_1)(1 - \sqrt{1 - 2h_1})\eta_1 + \epsilon$, where $\epsilon > 0$ is such that $S(x_0,r_0) \supset S(x_1,r_1) \supset \bar{S}(x_1, r_1 - \epsilon)$.

It follows by induction that the sequence $\{x_n\}$ is well defined and that each x_n satisfies conditions (i) to (iii) with constants β_n, η_n, h_n, which are related by the equations

$$\beta_n = \frac{\beta_{n-1}}{1 - h_{n-1}}, \qquad \eta_n = \frac{1}{2}\frac{h_{n-1}\eta_{n-1}}{1 - h_{n-1}}, \qquad h_n = \frac{1}{2}\frac{h_{n-1}^2}{(1 - h_{n-1})^2}.$$

Hence, a simple reduction shows that

$$h_n \le \frac{1}{2}(2h_0)^{2^n}, \qquad \eta_n \le 2^{-n}(2h_0)^{2^n-1}\eta_0.$$

Since $\|x_{n+1} - x_n\| \le \eta_n$, it follows that $\|x_{n+p} - x_n\| \le 2\eta_n$, and so $\{x_n\}$ converges to a point $u \in \mathfrak{B}_1$ for which $\|u - x_n\| \le 2\eta_n$. This implies $\|u - x_0\| \le (1/h_0)(1 - \sqrt{1 - 2h_0})\eta_0$; that is, $u \in S(x_0,r_0)$ by the last inequality in (iii). Indeed, u is a solution of $F(x) = 0$ because

$$F'(x_2)(x_{n+1} - x_n) + F(x_n) = 0$$

for each n and hence $\|F(x_n)\| \le [\|F'(x_0)\| + r_0 K] \|x_{n+1} - x_n\|$.

The uniqueness of u in every sphere $\bar{S}(x_0,r) \subset S(x_0,r)$ with $r < (1/h_0)(1 + \sqrt{1 - 2h_0})\eta_0$ is proved by contradiction. If $\hat{u} \ne u$ were another solution in $\bar{S}(x_0,r)$, then $\|\hat{u} - x_0\| = (\theta/h_0)(1 + \sqrt{1 - 2h_0})\eta_0$, where $0 \leq \theta < 1$, and $G_0(\hat{u}) = \hat{u}$. Similarly as before, we obtain $\|\hat{u} - x_1\| \leq (\theta^2/h_1)(1 + \sqrt{1 - 2h_1})\eta_1$ and, by induction,

$$\|\hat{u} - x_n\| \leq \frac{\theta^{2n}}{h_n}(1 + \sqrt{1 - 2h_n})\eta_n \leq \frac{2\theta^{2n}}{\beta_n K} \leq \frac{2\theta^{2n}}{\beta_0 K}.$$

Then $\|\hat{u} - x_n\| \to 0$ as $n \to \infty$, which is absurd, since $x_n \to u$ as $n \to \infty$. This completes the proof (see also [11–15, 16]).

There are several remarks that must be made.

Remark 1.   The estimate $\|f_0^{-1}[F(x_0)]\| \leq \eta_0$ in (ii) may be written in the form $\|x_1 - x_0\| \leq \eta_0$, which is frequently more convenient to use.   Also, it can be replaced by the estimate $\|F(x_0)\| \leq \eta_0'$, whence $\|f_0^{-1}[F(x_0)]\| \leq \beta_0 \eta_0' = \eta_0$.

Remark 2.   Putting $\rho_{1,2} = (1/h_0)(1 \pm \sqrt{1 - 2h_0})\eta_0$, observe that $S(x_0, \rho_2) \subset \bar{S}(x_0, 2\eta_0) \subset S(x_0, \rho_1)$.   Hence the second condition in (iii) may be replaced by the weaker requirement $S(x_0, r_0) > \bar{S}(x_0, 2\eta_0)$.   The sequence $\{x_n\}$ then converges to a solution u of $F(x) = 0$, which is unique in $\bar{S}(x_0, 2\eta_0)$.

Remark 3.   Condition (iii) and the radius ρ_1 for the sphere $\bar{S}(x_0, \rho_1)$ in which uniqueness holds are best possible, as the following example shows. With $\mathfrak{B}_1 = \mathfrak{B}_2 = \mathfrak{R}$ and $F(x) = \frac{1}{2}x^2 - x + h$, we find for $x_0 = 0$ that $\beta_0 = K = 1$, $\eta_0 = h_0 = h$.   Clearly, $u = 1 \pm \sqrt{1 - 2h}$ exists only if $h_0 = h \leq \frac{1}{2}$; the smaller root lies on the boundary of $S(x_0, \rho_2)$, the larger on the boundary of $S(x_0, \rho_1)$.

Remark 4.   At each step we are required to find $f_n^{-1}[F(x_n)]$ or, equivalently, to solve $F'(x_u)(x_n - x_{n+1}) = F(x_n)$, which may present considerable difficulties.   Then the following theorem is of importance for applications.

Theorem 14.13.   *Let condition* (i), (ii) *of Theorem* 14.15 *be satisfied, and suppose* (iii) *that* $h_0 = \beta_0\eta_0 K < \frac{1}{2}$ *and* $(1/h_0)(1 - \sqrt{1 - 2h_0})\eta_0 < r_0$. *Then the sequence* $\{x_n\}$ *defined by*

$$x_{n+1} = x_n - f_0^{-1}[F(x_n)], \qquad n \geq 0,$$

exists for all n *and converges to a solution* $u \in S(x_0, \mu\eta_0)$ *of* $F(x) = 0$, *where* $\mu = 1 - \sqrt{1 - 2h_0}$ (<1).   *Moreover, the rate of convergence is given by*

$$\|u - x_n\| \leq \mu^{n-1} \|x_1 - x_0\|.$$

The proof is entirely analogous to that of Theorem 14.12.

14.15   Solution of Scalar Equations

We apply first Theorem 14.12 to the case of a single scalar equation $F(x) = 0$ where F is defined and real-valued on some bounded interval $I_0 = (x_0 - r_0, x_0 + r_0)$.

Theorem 14.14.   *Let $x_0(\in I_0)$ be selected such that the following conditions hold:*

(i) *F has a continuous second derivative $F''(x)$ on I_0 such that $|F''(x)| \le K$.*
(ii) *$F'(x_0) \ne 0$.*
(iii) *$h_0 = K\,|F(x_0)|\,[|F'(x_0)|]^{-2}$ satisfies $h_0 \le \frac{1}{2}$ and*

$$(1 - \sqrt{1 - 2h_0})\,|F(x_0)|\,[|F'(x_0)|]^{-1} < r_0.$$

Then the sequence $\{x_n\}$ defined by

$$x_{n+1} = x_n - F(x_n)[F'(x_n)]^{-1}, \qquad n \ge 0,$$

converges to the unique solution u of $F(x) = 0$ for which

$$|u - x_0| \le \frac{1}{K}\,(1 - \sqrt{1 - 2h_0})\,|F'(x_0)|.$$

Let us now consider a system of m equations,

$$f_k(\xi_1, \ldots, \xi_m) = 0, \qquad k = 1, 2, \ldots, m,$$

defined on some domain of $\Re^m$.   We denote by $J(x)$ the Jacobian matrix $\left(\dfrac{\partial f_i}{\partial \xi_k}\right)$ at the point $x = (\xi_1, \ldots, \xi_m)$, if it exists.   In terms of the l_∞ norm on $\Re^m$, Theorem 14.12 can be stated as follows.

Theorem 14.15.   *Let $x_0 = (\xi_1{}^0, \ldots, \xi_m{}^0)$ be selected such that the following conditions hold:*

(i) *The functions f_k have continuous second-order partial derivatives on $Q(x_0, r_0) = \{x \in \Re^m;\ |\xi_k - \xi_k{}^0| < r_0,\ 1 \le k \le m\}$ such that $\left|\dfrac{\partial^2 f_i}{\partial \xi_j\,\partial \xi_k}\right| \le K,\ 1 \le i, j, k \le m$, on $Q(x_0, r_0)$.*

(ii) *Let $J(x_0) \ne 0$ and $|f_k(\xi_1{}^0, \ldots, \xi_m{}^0)| \le \eta_0$ for $1 \le k \le m$, and*

$$\max_i \sum_1^m \left|\left(\frac{\partial \xi_i}{\partial f_k}\right)\right|_{x=x_0} \le \beta_0.†$$

(iii) *The constant $h_0 = \beta_0{}^2 \eta_0 K m^2$ satisfies $h_0 \le \frac{1}{2}$ and*

$$(1/h_0)(1 - \sqrt{1 - 2h_0})\beta_0\eta_0 < r_0.$$

Then the sequence x_n of vectors $x_n = (\xi_1{}^n, \ldots, \xi_m{}^n)$ defined by

$$x_{n+1} = x_n - J^{-1}(x_n)f(x_n),$$

where $f(x_n) = [f_1(\xi_1{}^n, \ldots, \xi_m{}^n), \ldots, f_m(\xi_1{}^n, \ldots, \xi_m{}^n)]$, converges to the unique solution $u = (u_1, \ldots, u_m)$ of $f(x) = 0$, for which

$$|u_k - \xi_k{}^0| \le \frac{1}{h_0}\,(1 - \sqrt{1 - 2h_0})\beta_0\eta_0, \qquad k = 1, 2, \ldots, m.$$

† The inverse of $J(x_0)$ is denoted by $J^{-1}(x_0) = \left(\left(\dfrac{\partial \xi_i}{\partial f_k}\right)\Big|_{x=x_0}\right)$.

Using the euclidean norm $\|x\|^2 = \left(\sum_{k=1}^{m} \xi_k{}^2\right)^{\frac{1}{2}}$ on $\mathfrak{R}^m$, we obtain the following formulation.

Theorem 14.15′. *Let* $x_0 = (\xi_1{}^0, \ldots, \xi_m{}^0)$ *be selected such that the following conditions hold:*

(i) *The functions* f_k *have continuous second-order partial derivatives on*

$$S(x_0, r_0) = \{x \in \mathfrak{R}^m : \|x\| < r_0\} \text{ such that } \sum_{i,j,k}\left(\frac{\partial^2 f_i}{\partial \xi_j\, \partial \xi_k}\right)^2 \leq K^2 \text{ on } S(x_0, r_0).$$

(ii) $\text{Det } [J(x_0)] \neq 0$, $\|J^{-1}(x_0)f(x_0)\| \leq \eta_0$, *and* $\sum_{i,k}\left[\left(\frac{\partial \xi_i}{\partial f_k}\right)\Big|_{x=x_0}\right]^2 \leq \beta_0{}^2.$

(iii) *The constant* $h_0 = \beta_0 \eta_0 K$ *satisfies* $h_0 \leq \frac{1}{2}$ *and*

$$(1/h_0)(1 - \sqrt{1 - 2h_0})\eta_0 < r_0.$$

Then the sequence $\{x_n\}$ *of vectors* $x_n = (\xi_1{}^n, \ldots, \xi_m{}^n)$ *defined by*

$$x_{n+1} = x_n - J^{-1}(x_n)f(x_n),$$

where $f(x_n) = [f_1(\xi_1{}^n, \ldots, \xi_m{}^n), \ldots, f_m(\xi_1{}^n, \ldots, \xi_m{}^n)]$, *converges to the unique solution* $u = (u_1, \ldots, u_m)$ *of* $f(x) = 0$, *for which*

$$\|u - x_0\| \leq \frac{1}{h_0}(1 - \sqrt{1 - 2h_0})\eta_0.$$

There is an interesting example due to Kantorovich [11] for which Theorem 14.15′ guarantees the convergence of Newton's process and the conditions of Theorem 14.15 are not satisfied. For examples and applications to integral equations, we refer to [11].

In a series of papers [2–7], Altman extended Newton's method to the case in which $F'(x_0)$ has no inverse; he also showed [7] that the Newton iteration for $F(x) = \|Ax - v\|$ is identical with the iteration by steepest descent for solving the linear equation $Ax = v$. This yields a generalization of the method of steepest descent to nonlinear equations. Other extensions are due to Schröder [19] and Collatz [9].

REFERENCES

1. M. Altman, A Generalization of Newton's Method, *Bull. Acad. Polon. Sci. Cl. III*, vol. 3, p. 189, 1955.

2. M. Altman, On the Approximate Solution of Non-linear Functional Equations, *Bull. Acad. Polon. Sci. Cl. III*, vol. 5, pp. 457–460, 1957.

3. M. Altman, Concerning Approximate Solutions of Non-linear Functional Equations, *Bull. Acad. Polon. Sci. Cl. III*, vol. 5, pp. 461–465, 1957.

4. M. Altman, On Approximate Solution of Operator Equations in Hilbert Space, *Bull. Acad. Polon. Sci. Cl. III*, vol. 5, p. 605, 1957.

5. M. Altman, Concerning the Approximate Solutions of Operator Equations in Hilbert Space, *Bull. Acad. Polon. Sci. Cl. III*, vol. 5, p. 711, 1957.

6. M. Altman, On the Generalization of Newton's Method, *Bull. Acad. Polon. Sci. Cl. III*, vol. 5, p. 789, 1957.

7. M. Altman, Connection between the Method of Steepest Descent and Newton's Method, *Bull. Acad. Polon. Sci. Cl. III*, vol. 5, pp. 1031–1036, 1957.

8. R. G. Bartle, Newton's Method in Banach Spaces, *Proc. Amer. Math. Soc.*, vol. 6, pp. 827–831, 1955.

9. L. Collatz, Näherungsverfahren höherer Ordnung für Gleichungen in Banach Räumen, *Arch. Rational Mech. Anal.*, vol. 2, pp. 66–75, 1958.

10. L. V. Kantorovich, The Method of Successive Approximations for Functional Equations, *Acta Math.*, vol. 71, pp. 63–97, 1939.

11. L. V. Kantorovich, 1948 (see reference following Sec. 14.3).

12. L. V. Kantorovich, On Newton's Method, *Trudy Mat. Inst. Steklov.*, vol. 28, pp. 104–144, 1949.

13. L. V. Kantorovich, The Principle of Majorants and Newton's Method, *Dokl. Akad. Nauk SSSR*, n.s., vol. 76, pp. 17–20, 1951.

14. L. V. Kantorovich, Some Further Applications of the Principle of Majorants, *Dokl. Akad. Nauk SSSR*, n.s., vol. 80, pp. 849–852, 1951.

15. L. V. Kantorovich, Some Further Applications of the Newton Approximation Method for Functional Equations, *Vestnik Leningrad Univ.*, vol. 7, pp. 68–103, 1957.

16. I. P. Mysovski, Concerning the Question of Convergence of Newton's Method, *Trudy Mat. Inst. Steklov.*, vol. 28, pp. 104–144, 1949.

17. A. Ostrowski, Konvergenzdiskussion und Fehlerabschätzung für die Newtonsche Methode bei Gleichungssystemen, *Comment. Math. Helv.*, vol. 9, pp. 79–103, 1936.

18. A. Ostrowski, Über die Konvergenz und die Abrundungsfestigkeit des Newtonschen Verfahrens, *Rec. Math. Moscou*, vol. 2, pp. 1073–1094, 1937.

19. J. Schröder, Über das Newtonsche Verfahren, *Arch. Rational Mech. Anal.*, vol. 1, pp. 154–180, 1957.

15

Discrete Variable Problems

MARSHALL HALL, Jr.

PROFESSOR OF MATHEMATICS

CALIFORNIA INSTITUTE OF TECHNOLOGY

15.1 Some Properties of Block Designs

The theorems on block designs which are stated in this section provide sufficient background for the two following sections. Proofs are not given, but references are provided at the end of the section for the reader who wishes to know the proofs.

An incomplete balanced block design (or more briefly, a block design) is an arrangement of objects into sets (or blocks) in the following way:

1. There are b blocks, each containing k distinct objects.

2. There are v objects, and each object occurs in r distinct blocks.

3. Each unordered pair of objects a_i, a_j occurs together in exactly λ of the b blocks.

There are two obvious relations on the five parameters:

$$bk = vr,$$
$$r(k - 1) = \lambda(v - 1). \tag{15.1}$$

The first of these counts the total number of occurrences of objects in blocks, there being, on the one hand, b blocks each containing k objects and, on the other hand, v objects each occurring in r blocks. For the second relation we count the number of pairs containing a specified object, say a_1. On the one hand, a_1 occurs in r blocks, and in each of these is paired with the remaining $(k - 1)$ objects. On the other hand, a_1 is to be paired λ times with each of the remaining $(v - 1)$ objects.

We say that a block design is *symmetric* if $b = v$, $k = r$, in which case the second relation takes the form

$$k(k - 1) = \lambda(v - 1). \tag{15.2}$$

With a block design D we may associate its *incidence matrix* A defined in the following way. The objects are numbered from 1 to v, a_i, $i = 1, \ldots,$ v, and the blocks numbered from 1 to b, B_j, $j = 1, \ldots, b$. An incidence number a_{ij} is defined by

$$
\begin{aligned}
a_{ij} &= +1 \qquad \text{if } a_i \in B_j, \\
a_{ij} &= 0 \qquad \text{if } a_i \notin B_j.
\end{aligned}
\tag{15.3}
$$

Then the incidence matrix A is the $v \times b$ matrix of the incidence numbers

$$
A = (a_{ij}) \qquad i = 1, \ldots, v; j = 1, \ldots, b.
\tag{15.4}
$$

The following relation on the incidence matrix is fundamental:

$$
AA^T = \begin{pmatrix}
r & \cdot & \cdot & \cdot & \cdot & \lambda \\
\cdot & r & & & & \cdot \\
\cdot & & \cdot & & & \cdot \\
\cdot & & & \cdot & & \cdot \\
\cdot & & & & \cdot & \cdot \\
\lambda & \cdot & \cdot & \cdot & \cdot & r
\end{pmatrix} = B,
\tag{15.5}
$$

where B is the $v \times v$ matrix with r down the main diagonal and λ off the main diagonal. This is easily seen for, with $AA^T = B$, an element b_{ij} of B is the inner product of the ith and jth rows of A. Thus b_{ii} is the inner product of the ith row with itself, and the ith row consists of 0s and 1s, the 1s giving the occurrences of object a_i in blocks. But since a_i is in r blocks, the number of 1s in the row is r. This gives $b_{ii} = r$. For b_{ij}, $j \neq i$, in calculating the inner product of the ith and jth rows of A, we have a sum of b products, each of which is zero, except for those t's for which $a_{it} = +1$ and $a_{jt} = +1$—in other words, those t's for which both objects, a_i and a_j, are in block B_t. But this happens exactly λ times, and so $b_{ij} = \lambda$.

It is easy to evaluate the determinant of B, and this is

$$
\det B = (r - \lambda)^{v-1}[(v - 1)\lambda + r].
\tag{15.6}
$$

If we had $r = \lambda$, then every object would be paired with every other object in every occurrence, and this can happen only in the trivial case in which $k = v$ and every block contains all the objects. Hence $r > \lambda$, and so B is nonsingular, whence, since A is a $v \times b$ matrix, from considerations of rank it follows that

$$
b \geq v.
\tag{15.6'}
$$

For the incidence matrix A of a symmetric design, more than (15.5) is true. We have, in fact,

$$AA^T = A^T A = (k - \lambda)I + \lambda S = B, \qquad AS = SA = kS, \qquad (15.7)$$

where S is the $v \times v$ matrix consisting entirely of 1s. The relation $A^T A = B$ for a symmetric design means that the dual of a symmetric design, obtained by interchanging the roles of object and block, is also a design with the same parameters as the original (but not in general isomorphic to the original). In particular, for a symmetric design any two blocks have λ objects in common. Hence, from a symmetric design we may, by deleting a block B and the objects in it, obtain a smaller, nonsymmetric design, called the *residual design*. Also, the objects in B as they appear in the remaining blocks will themselves form a design, called the *derived design*. Thus in the following design, with $v = b = 25$, $r = k = 9$, $\lambda = 3$, if we delete the block $17, \ldots, 25$ and its objects elsewhere, we obtain the residual design with objects $1, \ldots, 16$ with parameters $v = 16$, $b = 24$, $r = 9$, $k = 6$, $\lambda = 3$. The objects $17, \ldots, 25$ in the first 24 blocks form the derived design with $v = 9$, $b = 24$, $r = 8$, $k = 3$, $\lambda = 2$.

$$v = b = 25, \qquad r = k = 9, \qquad \lambda = 3$$

1	2	5	6	11	12	17	20	23		2	4	5	7	14	16	18	20	25
1	2	9	10	15	16	17	21	25		5	6	9	10	13	14	17	18	19
1	2	7	8	13	14	17	22	24		5	7	9	11	13	15	20	21	22
3	4	7	8	9	10	17	20	23		5	8	9	12	13	16	23	24	25
3	4	11	12	13	14	17	21	25		7	8	11	12	15	16	17	18	19
1	3	5	7	10	12	18	21	24		6	8	10	12	14	16	20	21	22
1	3	9	11	14	16	18	22	23		6	7	10	11	14	15	23	24	25
1	3	6	8	13	15	18	20	25
2	4	6	8	9	11	18	21	24
2	4	10	12	13	15	18	22	23
3	4	5	6	15	16	17	22	24
1	4	5	8	10	11	19	22	25
1	4	9	12	14	15	19	20	24
1	4	6	7	13	16	19	21	23
2	3	6	7	9	12	19	22	25
2	3	10	11	13	16	19	21	24
2	3	5	8	14	15	19	21	23

$$(15.8)$$

$$17 \quad 18 \quad 19 \quad 20 \quad 21 \quad 22 \quad 23 \quad 24 \quad 25$$

For a fuller account of this part of the theory, see Mann [4]. But given a design with the parameters of a residual design, it is not always possible to adjoin a block and its objects to obtain a symmetric design. The following design is an example due to Bhattacharya [5]:

$$v = 16, \qquad b = 24, \qquad r = 9, \qquad k = 6, \qquad \lambda = 3$$

1	2	7	8	14	15	1	4	7	8	11	16
3	5	7	8	11	13	2	4	8	10	12	14
2	3	8	9	13	16	5	6	8	10	15	16
3	5	8	9	12	14	1	6	8	10	12	13
1	6	7	9	12	13	1	2	3	11	12	15
2	5	7	10	13	15	2	6	7	9	14	16
3	4	7	10	12	16	1	4	5	13	14	16
3	4	6	13	14	15	2	5	6	11	12	16
4	5	7	9	12	15	1	3	9	10	15	16
2	4	9	10	11	13	4	6	8	9	11	15
3	6	7	10	11	14	1	5	9	10	11	14
1	2	3	4	5	6	11	12	13	14	15	16

(15.9)

In this example it is clearly impossible to adjoin a further block and nine further objects in such a way as to obtain a symmetric design with $v = b = 25$, $r = k = 9$, $\lambda = 3$, since, as indicated by the underlines, two blocks contain the four objects 1, 6, 12, 13 in common, and this is impossible in a symmetric design with $\lambda = 3$.

There are many things we should like to know about block designs. Fundamentally, we should like to know for which parameters v, b, r, k, λ satisfying (15.1) a design exists, how many designs exist if there are any, and what can be said about the structure or automorphisms of such systems.   A symmetric design with $\lambda = 1$ is a finite projective plane, and writing $k - \lambda = n$, we have the parameters $v = b = n^2 + n + 1$, $r = k = n + 1, \lambda = 1$.   Finite planes are known to exist whenever n is a prime or prime power, but no finite plane has as yet been found with n an integer, not a prime or prime power.

Chowla and Ryser [1] have shown that a necessary condition for the existence of a symmetric design is that (1) if v is even, then $n = k - \lambda$ must be a square, or (2) if v is odd, the diophantine equation

$$x^2 = (k - \lambda)y^2 + (-1)^{(v-1)/2} \lambda z^2 \tag{15.10}$$

must have a nonzero solution in integers.   This and some similar non-existence theorems are based on the Hasse-Minkowski theory of the rational equivalence of quadratic forms.

A further type of theoretical approach is due to Connor [2].   Equation (15.5) for the incidence matrix is equivalent to the following representation of quadratic forms:

$$L_1^2 + \cdots + L_b^2 = r(x_1^2 + \cdots + x_v^2) + 2\lambda \sum_{i<j} x_i x_j, \tag{15.11}$$

where

$$L_j = \sum_{i=1}^{v} a_{ij}x_i \qquad \text{for each } j = 1, \dots, b$$

and the a_{ij} are the elements of the incidence matrix.   If we specify some of the blocks, say $B_1, \dots, B_t$, then, writing Q for the right-hand side of (15.11), we have

$$Q^* = Q - L_1^2 - \cdots - L_t^2 = L_{t+1}^2 + \cdots + L_b^2. \qquad (15.12)$$

Hence Q^* must be a semidefinite form if it is to be possible to complete the design by finding $L_{t+1}, \dots, L_b$.   Connor has found a test for Q^* of the following type.   Let S_{ju} be the number of elements common to blocks B_j and B_u, $j, u = 1, \dots, t$; then put $c_{jj} = (r - k)(r - \lambda)$, $c_{ju} = \lambda k - rS_{ju}$ $(j \neq u)$.   Then a necessary condition that it be possible to complete $B_1, \dots, B_t$ to a full design is that

$$\det |C_{ju}| \geq 0. \qquad (15.13)$$

This relation is a consequence of the fact that Q^* must be semidefinite. Connor gives somewhat more than (15.13), but this is the main conclusion.

It may happen that a block design possesses an automorphism.   Thus the following design,

$$v = b = 13, \qquad r = k = 4, \qquad \lambda = 1$$

0	1	3	9
1	2	4	10
2	3	5	11
3	4	6	12
4	5	7	0
5	6	8	1
6	7	9	2
7	8	10	3
8	9	11	4
9	10	12	5
10	11	0	6
11	12	1	7
12	0	2	8,

(15.14)

clearly has the automorphism of order 13, $x \to x + 1$, where the objects are regarded as residues modulo 13.   In general, we may have a symmetric design whose objects may be regarded as the residues modulo v where $x \to x + 1$ is an automorphism cyclic of order v on both the objects and the blocks.   Such a design is completely determined by a single block, and, say, above 2, 3, 5, 11 (mod 13) determines the entire design.

The property of k residues modulo v, $a_1, \ldots, a_k$ (mod v) determining such a design is the following: every residue $d \not\equiv 0$ (mod v) has exactly λ representations in the form

$$d \equiv a_i - a_j \ (\text{mod } v), \tag{15.15}$$

where a_i and a_j are in the set $a_1, \ldots, a_k$ (mod v), called a *difference set* of k residues modulo v.

We say that a residue t prime to v is a *multiplier* of the difference set if $x \to tx$ (mod v) is an automorphism of the design; or, what is the same thing, *for an appropriate s, $ta_1, ta_2, \ldots, ta_k$ (mod v) are $a_1 + s, \ldots, a_k + s$ (mod v) in some order*.

The multipliers of a difference set form a multiplicative group modulo v. Every known difference set possesses some multiplier different from the identity modulo v, and there is some evidence that this may be universally true. A theorem on the existence of multipliers is the following, whose proof may be found in [3].

Theorem. *If $a_1, \ldots, a_k$ (mod v) are a difference set and if p is a prime dividing $k - \lambda$ such that $p \nmid v$ and $p > \lambda$, then p is a multiplier of the difference set.*

REFERENCES

1. S. Chowla and H. J. Ryser, Combinatorial Problems, *Canad. J. Math.*, vol. 2, pp. 93–99, 1950.

2. W. S. Connor, Jr., On the Structure of Balanced Incomplete Block Designs, *Ann. Math. Statist.*, vol. 23, pp. 57–71, 1952.

3. M. Hall, Jr., and H. J. Ryser, Cyclic Incidence Matrices, *Canad. J. Math.*, vol. 4, pp. 495–502, 1951.

4. H. B. Mann, "Analysis and Design of Experiments," Dover Publications, New York, 1949.

5. K. N. Bhattacharya, A New Balanced Incomplete Block Design, *Science and Culture*, vol. 9, p. 508, 1944.

15.2 Systematic Search for Block Designs

In a projective plane of order 8 there are $8 + 1 = 9$ points on every line and 9 lines through every point. There are, in all, 73 points and 73 lines. This is the symmetric block design with $v = b = 73$, $k = r = 9$, and $\lambda = 1$.

Let A, B, C be the vertices of a triangle in a plane of order n. Call AB the line at infinity L_∞, AC the line $x = 0$, and BC the line $y = 0$. Label the $(n - 1)$ remaining lines through A as $x = 1$, $x = 2$, $\ldots$, $x = n - 1$ in any order and label the $(n - 1)$ remaining lines through B as $y = 1$, $\ldots$, $y = n - 1$ in any order. A point P not on L_∞ will then lie on a unique line $x = a$ and a unique line $y = b$. Then assign to P the coordinates (a, b).

The $(n - 1)$ lines through $C = (0,0)$, apart from AC and BC, will intersect each of $x = 1, \ldots, x = n - 1$ once and each of $y = 1, \ldots, y = n - 1$ once. Such a line L will intersect L_∞ in some infinite point and will also contain $(0,0)$ and $(n - 1)$ points (i,j), where i and j take values 1 to $n - 1$. With L, associate the permutation

$$\begin{pmatrix} 0, & 1, \ldots, & n - 1 \\ 0, & a_1, \ldots, & a_{n-1} \end{pmatrix}$$

if $(0,0), (1,a_1), \ldots, (n - 1, a_{n-1})$ are the finite points of L. The second rows of the $(n - 1)L$'s give the array

$$\begin{array}{lllll}
0 & a_{11}, & a_{12}, & \ldots, & a_{1,n-1} \\
0 & a_{21}, & a_{22}, & \ldots, & a_{2,n-1} \\
\cdot & \cdots & \cdots & \cdots & \cdots \\
0 & a_{n-1,1}, & a_{n-1,2}, & \ldots, & a_{n-1,n-1},
\end{array} \qquad (15.16)$$

and this (deleting the 0s) will be a Latin square of order $n - 1$; that is, every digit $1, \ldots, n - 1$ occurs exactly once in each row and exactly once in each column.

We may start a search for planes of order 8 by taking a list of 7×7 Latin squares. To within equivalence for geometric purposes, there are 147 such squares, of which 146 were listed by Norton [5]. Sade [6] found an omission and verified that, with this square added, Norton's list is complete. Indeed, it is necessary to investigate only 100 of the 147 squares, since these are listed in terms of the number of *intercalates*, an intercalate being a subarray of the type

$$\begin{array}{ccccc}
a & \cdot & \cdot & \cdot & \cdot & b \\
\cdot & & & & \cdot \\
\cdot & & & & \cdot \\
\cdot & & & & \cdot \\
\cdot & & & & \cdot \\
\cdot & & & & \cdot \\
b & \cdot & \cdot & \cdot & \cdot & a \, ,
\end{array} \qquad (15.17)$$

and a simple argument shows that for an appropriate choice of A, B, C in the plane we shall find a square with at most 12 intercalates. Thus we need examine only squares 1 to 99 of Norton's list and the omission found by Sade.

All 100 squares used in the search can be normalized, so that the first two lines of (15.16) read

$$\begin{array}{cccccccc}
0 & 1 & 2 & 3 & 4 & 5 & 6 & 7 \\
0 & 2 & 3 & 4 & 5 & 6 & 7 & 1.
\end{array} \qquad (15.18)$$

Thus the 100 squares consist of these two and a further set of five lines. An attempt to add further lines of a plane to each of these 100 starts was made in the summer of 1955 on SWAC. We already have the first line of (15.18) as a line through $(1,1)$. There will be in addition the known lines $x = 1$ and $y = 1$ and six further lines of the following form:

$$
\begin{array}{cccccccc}
X & 1 & 3 & X & X & X & X & X \\
X & 1 & X & 4 & X & X & X & X \\
X & 1 & X & X & 5 & X & X & X \\
X & 1 & X & X & X & 6 & X & X \\
X & 1 & X & X & X & X & 7 & X \\
X & 1 & X & X & X & X & X & X.
\end{array}
\tag{15.19}
$$

Here the first five are the lines joining $(1,1)$ to the points $(2,3)$, $(4,5)$, $(5,6)$, and $(6,7)$ of the second line of (15.18), and these are, of course, distinct lines, since no line of (15.19) may intersect the second line of (15.18) twice. The sixth line of (15.19) is, of course, the unique line through $(1,1)$ parallel to 0 2 3 4 5 6 7 1. If we succeed in finding the lines (15.19), we may then add further lines through $(2,3)$, these being of the form

$$
\begin{array}{cccccccc}
X & X & 3 & X & 4 & X & X & X \\
X & X & 3 & X & X & 5 & X & X \\
X & X & 3 & X & X & X & 6 & X \\
X & X & 3 & X & X & X & X & 7 \\
X & X & 3 & X & X & X & X & X.
\end{array}
\tag{15.20}
$$

The first four of these are the lines through $(2,3)$ intersecting the first line of (15.19) in $(4,4)$, $(5,5)$, $(6,6)$, and $(7,7)$, and the last is the parallel. For only the first of the 100 squares was it possible to add all 11 lines of (15.19) and (15.20), and in this case there were only four ways in which this could be done. The rest of the work was easily done by hand, two of the four answers being impossible to complete and the other two both leading to the same plane, this being the known desarguesian plane of order 8 and by this study shown to be unique. The criterion for acceptability of a line is, of course, that it should not have as many as two points in common with any previous line. Thus for a line

$$
\begin{pmatrix}
0 & 1 & 2 & 3 & 4 & 5 & 6 & 7 \\
a_0 & a_1 & a_2 & a_3 & a_4 & a_5 & a_6 & a_7
\end{pmatrix},
$$

the a's must be $0, \ldots, 7$ in some order, and this sequence of eight numbers may not agree in more than one position with any line already taken.

Let us illustrate the nature of the search with square 70:

$$
\begin{array}{cccccccc}
0 & 1 & 2 & 3 & 4 & 5 & 6 & 7 \\
0 & 2 & 3 & 4 & 5 & 6 & 7 & 1 \\
0 & 3 & 4 & 2 & 1 & 7 & 5 & 6 \\
0 & 4 & 7 & 6 & 2 & 1 & 3 & 5 \\
0 & 5 & 1 & 7 & 6 & 2 & 4 & 3 \\
0 & 6 & 5 & 1 & 7 & 3 & 2 & 4 \\
0 & 7 & 6 & 5 & 3 & 4 & 1 & 2.
\end{array}
$$

There are 21 ways of adding the lines (15.19) to square 70.   These are as follows:

70.1:
```
6 1 3 2 7 0 4 5
5 1 6 4 2 7 0 3
3 1 7 0 5 4 2 6
4 1 5 7 0 6 3 2
2 1 4 5 6 3 7 0
7 1 0 6 3 2 5 4
```

70.6:
```
6 1 3 7 2 4 5 0
5 1 7 4 3 0 2 6
7 1 6 0 5 2 3 4
2 1 4 5 7 6 0 3
4 1 0 2 6 3 7 5
3 1 5 6 0 7 4 2
```

70.2:
```
2 1 3 5 7 0 4 6
7 1 6 4 2 3 5 0
6 1 7 2 5 4 0 3
3 1 4 7 0 6 2 5
5 1 0 6 3 2 7 4
4 1 5 0 6 7 3 2
```

70.7:
```
6 1 3 7 2 0 5 4
5 1 0 4 6 7 3 2
3 1 7 0 5 4 2 6
2 1 4 5 7 6 0 3
4 1 5 6 3 2 7 0
7 1 6 2 0 3 4 5
```

70.3:
```
6 1 3 5 2 7 0 4
2 1 7 4 6 3 5 0
7 1 0 6 5 4 2 3
5 1 4 7 0 6 3 2
4 1 5 0 3 2 7 6
3 1 6 2 7 0 4 5
```

70.8:
```
4 1 3 0 6 7 2 5
5 1 7 4 3 2 0 6
7 1 0 6 5 3 4 2
2 1 4 5 7 6 3 0
6 1 5 2 0 4 7 3
3 1 6 7 2 0 5 4
```

70.4:
```
4 1 3 5 7 2 0 6
5 1 0 4 6 7 3 2
6 1 7 2 5 3 4 0
7 1 4 0 3 6 2 5
2 1 5 6 0 4 7 3
3 1 6 7 2 0 5 4
```

70.9:
```
5 1 3 6 0 7 4 2
7 1 5 4 3 2 0 6
6 1 7 0 5 4 2 3
2 1 4 5 7 6 3 0
4 1 0 2 6 3 7 5
3 1 6 7 2 0 5 4
```

70.5:
```
4 1 3 0 6 7 2 5
3 1 6 4 7 2 5 0
6 1 4 7 5 0 3 2
5 1 7 2 3 6 0 4
2 1 5 6 0 4 7 3
7 1 0 5 2 3 4 6
```

70.10:
```
4 1 3 6 7 0 5 2
5 1 7 4 3 2 0 6
7 1 6 2 5 3 4 0
3 1 4 7 0 6 2 5
6 1 5 0 2 4 7 3
2 1 0 5 6 7 3 4
```

70.11: 5 1 3 6 7 0 4 2   70.16: 4 1 3 0 6 7 2 5

70.11:	5	1	3	6	7	0	4	2
	7	1	6	4	5	4	0	3
	6	1	7	2	5	4	0	3
	3	1	4	7	0	6	2	5
	4	1	5	0	3	2	7	6
	2	1	0	5	6	7	3	4

70.16:	4	1	3	0	6	7	2	5
	3	1	6	4	7	2	5	0
	7	1	0	6	5	3	4	2
	5	1	7	2	3	6	0	4
	6	1	4	5	2	0	7	3
	2	1	5	7	0	4	3	6

70.12:	6	1	3	2	7	0	4	5
	7	1	0	4	6	3	5	2
	2	1	6	0	5	7	3	4
	4	1	7	5	0	6	2	3
	5	1	4	6	3	2	7	0
	3	1	5	7	2	4	0	6

70.17:	5	1	3	6	7	0	4	2
	2	1	5	4	6	7	3	0
	3	1	0	7	5	4	2	6
	7	1	4	5	2	6	0	3
	4	1	6	2	0	3	7	5
	6	1	7	0	3	2	5	4

70.13:	5	1	3	6	7	0	4	2
	6	1	7	4	3	2	5	0
	2	1	6	0	5	7	3	4
	7	1	4	5	0	6	2	3
	4	1	0	2	6	3	7	5
	3	1	5	7	2	4	0	6

70.18:	4	1	3	5	7	2	0	6
	2	1	5	4	6	7	3	0
	6	1	7	0	5	4	2	3
	7	1	0	2	3	6	4	5
	5	1	4	6	0	3	7	2
	3	1	6	7	2	0	5	4

70.14:	6	1	3	5	2	7	4	0
	5	1	7	4	6	3	0	2
	7	1	6	2	5	0	3	4
	3	1	4	7	0	6	2	5
	4	1	5	0	3	2	7	6
	2	1	0	6	7	4	5	3

70.19:	4	1	3	5	7	2	0	6
	6	1	5	4	0	7	3	2
	7	1	0	6	5	4	2	3
	5	1	7	2	3	6	4	0
	2	1	4	0	6	3	7	5
	3	1	6	7	2	0	5	4

70.15:	6	1	3	2	7	4	0	5
	5	1	0	4	6	7	3	2
	2	1	7	0	5	3	4	6
	7	1	4	5	0	6	2	3
	4	1	5	6	3	2	7	0
	3	1	6	7	2	0	5	4

70.20:	4	1	3	6	7	0	5	2
	6	1	5	4	2	7	0	3
	7	1	6	0	5	2	3	4
	5	1	4	7	3	6	2	0
	3	1	0	2	6	4	7	5
	2	1	7	5	0	3	4	6

70.21:	6	1	3	2	7	4	0	5
	7	1	5	4	6	0	3	2
	4	1	6	0	5	7	2	3
	3	1	0	7	2	6	5	4
	5	1	4	6	3	2	7	0
	2	1	7	5	0	3	4	6

If we now endeavor to add the lines of (15.20) to 70.1, the first set of lines (15.19), we find exactly two possibilities for lines of the form

$$X\ X\ 3\ X\ 4\ X\ X\ X,$$

and for each of these one line of the form $X\ X\ 3\ X\ X\ 5\ X\ X$. The two cases are

$$
\begin{array}{cccccccc}
5 & 6 & 3 & 7 & 4 & 1 & 2 & 0 \\
7 & 4 & 3 & 1 & 6 & 5 & 0 & 2
\end{array}
\qquad
\begin{array}{cccccccc}
1 & 5 & 3 & 6 & 4 & 7 & 2 & 0, \\
7 & 4 & 3 & 1 & 6 & 5 & 0 & 2.
\end{array}
$$

In neither case is it possible to add a line of the form $X\ X\ 3\ X\ X\ X\ 6\ X$, and thus 70.1 cannot be completed to a plane. The other starts go out in much the same way.

It is worth noting that it was found by hand computation that the starts would go through the lines (15.19) in some quantity, the average being around 20 cases for each square. But it never appeared possible to add more than two or three more lines. A machine program for adding more than the 11 lines would have been much harder to write and harder to get onto SWAC, which has only 256 words of high-speed memory. And as matters turned out, the amount left to hand computation was very small. Thus in this case, as in many others, the right proportion of hand and machine calculation provided by far the most satisfactory solution.

The program contained two main subroutines, the first the calculation of the lines (15.19) the second those of (15.20). Each of these was sufficiently long so that it was necessary to store one on the drum while the other was being used, but the number of completions of lines (15.19) was sufficiently small (as remarked above, about 20 for each run) so that the time consumed by transfers onto and off the drum was negligible.

Each digit was added singly. The method is best explained by an illustration. Suppose that, in adding the lines (15.19), we have the line

$$
\begin{array}{cccccccc}
6 & 1 & 3 & 2 & 7 & 0 & 4 & 5 \\
X_1 & 1 & X_3 & 4 & X_5 & X_6 & X_7 & X_8.
\end{array}
$$

We add $X_3, X_5, X_6, X_7, X_8, X_1$ in this order, since X_1 is the least restricted digit. Suppose that we have also taken $X_3 = 6$.

$$
\begin{array}{cccccccc}
6 & 1 & 3 & 2 & 7 & 0 & 4 & 5 \\
X_1 & 1 & 6 & 4 & X_5 & X_6 & X_7 & X_8.
\end{array}
$$

To find X_5, we construct a little table of digits which may be used as X_5. Here $X_5 \neq 1, 6, 4$, the digits already used in the line. Also, $X_5 \neq 7$, the digit above it, since we may not have two lines of the form

$X\,1\,X\,X\,7\,X\,X\,X$. We also look at a catalogue made from square 70 and indicating exclusions and find

$$
\begin{array}{ccccccccccccccccc}
X & 1 & X & X & 4 & X & X & X = 0 & 1 & 2 & 3 & 4 & 5 & 6 & 7 \\
X & X & 6 & X & 3 & X & X & X = 0 & 7 & 6 & 5 & 3 & 4 & 1 & 2 \\
X & X & X & 4 & 5 & X & X & X = 0 & 2 & 3 & 4 & 5 & 6 & 7 & 1.
\end{array}
$$

Hence we have $X_5 \neq 4, 3, 5$. The combined exclusions are $X_5 \neq 1, 3, 4, 5, 6, 7$. Thus X_5 may be 0 or 2, and we represent this information positionally using 8 bits of a word, these being in this case

$$1 \quad 0 \quad 1 \quad 0 \quad 0 \quad 0 \quad 0 \quad 0.$$

The 1s are in positions 0 and 2, which indicate that these digits are permissible. The 0s indicate that the remaining digits may not be used. These bits are computed by Boolean operations, since it will be noted that 4 has been excluded twice as a possibility for X_5. A shift to the left, with testing for overflow, indicates which is the smallest available digit. This is then used (here the zero) and the value then discarded, but remaining values are retained to be used on a backtrack. Going forward, we recompute the exclusions. Thus, if another value is used for X_3, we recompute the exclusions for X_5 even though some of these remain valid—for example, $X_5 \neq 4, 5$.

A flow chart of the program is given in [4, p. 191].

A block design with $k = 3$, $\lambda = 1$ is called a *Steiner triple system*. The systems with $v = 15$ were sought by systematic search. The full set of parameters is $b = 35$, $v = 15$, $r = 7$, $k = 3$, $\lambda = 1$.

One such system is the following:

```
1  2  3
1  4  5    2  4  6    3  4 10
1  6  7    2  5  8    3  5  7
1  8  9    2  7  9    3  6 11   4  7 12   5  6 14   6  8 12   7  8 11
1 10 11    2 10 12    3  8 15   4  8 13   5  9 10   6  9 15   7 10 15
1 12 13    2 11 14    3  9 13   4  9 14   5 11 13   6 10 13   7 13 14
1 14 15    2 13 15    3 12 14   4 11 15   5 12 15   8 10 14   9 11 12.
```

Suppose that, in constructing such a system, we have taken all triples involving 1, 2, and 3, say as above. We then construct a 15 × 15 table showing which objects have appeared with which. Thus 4 has appeared with 1, 2, 3, 5, 6, 10. Hence the triples to be with 4 will be of the form

$$
\begin{array}{ccc}
4 & X_1 & X_2 \\
4 & X_3 & X_4 \\
4 & X_5 & X_6 \\
4 & X_7 & X_8,
\end{array}
$$

where $X_1, \ldots, X_8$ are 7, 8, 9, 11, 12, 13, 14, 15 in some order. The order of these four triples is immaterial, and so we may take $X_1 = 7$ without loss of generality. For X_2 we may take any one of 8, 9, 11, 12, 13, 14, 15 which has not already appeared with 7. We begin by taking the smallest, $X_2 = 8$. Next X_3 is taken as the smallest value not used, then, in turn, X_5 and X_7. We continue until we reach a conflict; then we backtrack, using the next higher value. We give the initial steps:

```
4  X  X      4  7  X      4  7  8      4  7  8      4  7  8
4  X  X      4  X  X      4  X  X      4  9  X      4  9  11
4  X  X      4  X  X      4  X  X      4  X  X      4  X  X
4  X  X      4  X  X      4  X  X      4  X  X      4  X  X
```

```
      4  7   8      4  7   8                   4  7   8
      4  9  11      4  9  11                   4  9  11
      4 12   X      4 12  13   (conflict)      4 12  14   (conflict)
      4  X   X      4  X   X                   4  X   X
```

```
            4  7   8      4  7   8      4  7   8
            4  9  11      4  9  11      4  9  11
            4 12  15      4 12  15      4 12  15
            4  X   X      4 13   X      4 13  14.
```

This gives a set of permissible triples with 4, which is then stored, and the process continues with 5 and these triples. Backtracking to the 4s later on, we backtrack to

```
4   7   8
4   9  11
4  12   X
4   X   X
```

but find that all values have been used with 12. We now backtrack further to

```
4   7   8
4   9   X
4   X   X
4   X   X
```

and proceed to

```
4   7   8
4   9  12
4   X   X
4   X   X.
```

An attempt was made to restrict the initial starts as much as possible, so as to avoid duplication, without, of course, missing any possible system.

The triples with 1 may trivially be taken as above. Then with 2 there are only four essentially different possibilities:

	A			B			C			D	
2	4	6	2	4	6	2	4	6	2	4	6
2	5	7	2	5	7	2	5	8	2	5	8
2	8	10	2	8	15	2	7	9	2	7	10
2	9	11	2	9	10	2	10	12	2	9	12
2	12	14	2	11	12	2	11	14	2	11	14
2	13	15	2	13	14	2	13	15	2	13	15

For A there are three sets of four triples of the form $(1,a,b)$, $(1,c,d)$, $(2,a,c)$, $(2,b,d)$. This A type is called a *triple tetrad* (the term is due to Cole [7]). B has one such set and is called a *single tetrad*. C has two sets of the form $(1,a,b)$, $(1,c,d)$, $(1,e,f)$, $(2,a,c)$, $(2,b,e)$, $(2,d,f)$ and is called a *hexad*. D has no combination of interlocking triples short of the full subsystem [excluding $(1,2,3)$] and is called a *duodecad*. Thus, attempts to limit duplication were made primarily in terms of triples involving 3.

Despite attempts to eliminate duplication, several thousand complete solutions were found. The problem then was to determine which were isomorphic. For this J. D. Swift used two ingenious programs. The set of all triples involving two letters i and j will have one of the four patterns A, B, C, D listed above, and the type of the pattern will be unchanged by substitution. Thus the set of all patterns A, B, C, D is an invariant of the system. There will be $(15 \cdot 14)/2 = 105$ such patterns A, B, C, D, and a necessary condition for the isomorphism of two systems is that they both have the same number of A's, B's, C's, and D's. (The system given as an example has only C's and D's.) A first program calculated the patterns A, B, C, D, and it was found that there were in all 80 different sets of such patterns. A second program took a single system from one of the 80 sets and tried to set up an isomorphism with the remaining systems in that set. This succeeded in every case, and so it was shown that there are exactly 80 Steiner triple systems of order 15. These had been listed by hand previously by White, Cole, and Cummings [7] and by Fisher [1]. All 80 systems were obtained by Cole and his co-workers, but it was not clear that their methods were exhaustive. Indeed, their long monograph uses several methods, and most of the methods used are certainly not exhaustive. Fisher used an exhaustive method but in fact obtained only 79 of the 80 systems, missing the one listed here.

Let us turn to the search for difference sets (see [2]) carried out on SWAC. We seek k residues modulo v,

$$a_1, a_2, \ldots, a_k \ (\text{mod } v)$$

such that every residue $d \neq 0 \pmod{v}$ has exactly λ representations into the form

$$a_i - a_j \equiv d \pmod{v}.$$

Here we have the relation

$$k(k - 1) = (v - 1).$$

We take $k < v/2$ (as we may, since the complement of a difference set is also a difference set). The range $3 \leq k \leq 50$ was studied, and this involved 268 choices of parameters. Of these choices 101 correspond to no design, because of the criteria of Chowla and Ryser, and thus a fortiori to no difference set. Of the remaining 167, difference sets were found in 46 cases, and in only 12 cases does the existence of a difference set remain undecided.

A variety of hand procedures made it possible to find some difference sets and show in other cases that none existed. But in a number of cases searches were carried out well beyond the scope of hand calculation. Every case treated on the machine involved a situation in which there was a multiplier and in which some block was fixed by the multiplier. We illustrate the general method with an example.

$$v = 121, \qquad k = 40, \qquad \lambda = 13.$$

Here 3 divides $n = k - \lambda = 27$ and can be shown to be a multiplier fixing a block. Hence the residues of the difference set occur in sets left unchanged by multiplication by 3. A first program on SWAC calculates these sets. In this case we have the following sets:

A	0
B	11, 33, 44, 55, 99
C	22, 66, 77, 88, 110
$R1$	1, 3, 9, 27, 81
$R2$	4, 12, 36, 108, 82
$R3$	5, 15, 45, 14, 42
$R4$	16, 48, 23, 69, 86
$R5$	20, 60, 59, 56, 47
$R6$	25, 75, 104, 70, 89
$R7$	26, 78, 113, 97, 49
$R8$	31, 93, 37, 111, 91
$R9$	34, 102, 64, 71, 92
$R10$	38, 114, 100, 58, 53
$R11$	67, 80, 119, 115, 103

$N1$	2, 6, 18, 54, 41
$N2$	7, 21, 63, 68, 83
$N3$	8, 24, 72, 95, 43
$N4$	10, 30, 90, 28, 84
$N5$	13, 39, 117, 109, 85
$N6$	17, 51, 32, 96, 46
$N7$	19, 57, 50, 29, 87
$N8$	35, 105, 73, 98, 52
$N9$	40, 120, 118, 112, 94
$N10$	61, 62, 65, 74, 101
$N11$	76, 107, 79, 116, 106

In the second SWAC program, an initial set is taken, differences are tallied, then a further set is taken, and new differences are computed and tallied.   If any difference occurs more than λ times, the last set added is discarded, together with the differences it contributed, and then a further set is tried.   After several hours' running on the machine, three solutions were found, of which two were isomorphic, but the run was stopped since it appeared that it would take perhaps a hundred hours to make the complete run.   At this stage it was decided to examine the situation by hand.   Considering the difference set modulo 11, let us suppose that b_0 residues are congruent to 0 (mod 11).   The residues 1, 3, 4, 5, 9 (quadratic residues) will occur equally often, say x times, and the residues 2, 6, 7, 8, 10 (quadratic nonresidues) will occur equally often, say y times. Then we have two relations:

$$a_0 + 5x + 5y = 40,$$
$$a_0(x + y) + 2x^2 + 5xy + 2y^2 = 143.$$

The first of these says merely that $k = 40$.   The second counts differences congruent to 1 (mod 11), and each of 11 such residues modulo 121 must occur 13 times.   The solutions of these equations are

$a_0 = 0,$	$x = 5,$	$y = 3,$	$a_0 = 0,$	$x = 3,$	$y = 5;$
$a_0 = 1,$	$x = 5,$	$y = 2,$	$a_0 = 1,$	$x = 2,$	$y = 5.$

Hence, multiplying the difference set by a suitable value, we may assume $x = 5$; that is, the difference set includes exactly five of the sets $R1, \ldots, R11$.   Moreover, these sets, under multiplication by quadratic residues modulo 121, are permuted in a cycle of length 11.   This gives us, to within isomorphism,

$$\frac{1}{11} \cdot \frac{11 \cdot 10 \cdot 9 \cdot 8 \cdot 7}{1 \cdot 2 \cdot 3 \cdot 4 \cdot 5} = 42 \text{ ways}$$

of choosing these sets.   With 42 separate starts, each start went through very quickly on the machine, and a total of four nonisomorphic solutions were found.   These are as follows:

$$v = 121, \qquad k = 40, \qquad \lambda = 13$$

1.   1, 3, 4, 7, 9, 11, 12, 13, 21, 25, 27, 33, 34, 36, 39, 44, 55, 63, 64, 67, 68, 70, 71, 75, 80, 81, 82, 83, 85, 89, 92, 99, 102, 103, 104, 108, 109, 115, 117, 119.

2.   1, 3, 4, 5, 9, 12, 13, 14, 15, 16, 17, 22, 23, 27, 32, 34, 36, 39, 42, 45, 46, 48, 51, 64, 66, 69, 71, 77, 81, 82, 85, 86, 88, 92, 96, 102, 108, 109, 110, 117.

3.   1, 3, 4, 7, 8, 9, 12, 21, 24, 25, 26, 27, 34, 36, 40, 43, 49, 63, 64, 68, 70, 71, 72, 75, 78, 81, 82, 83, 89, 92, 94, 95, 97, 102, 104, 108, 112, 113, 118, 120.

4.   1, 3, 4, 5, 7, 9, 12, 14, 15, 17, 21, 27, 32, 36, 38, 42, 45, 46, 51, 53, 58, 63, 67, 68, 76, 79, 80, 81, 82, 83, 96, 100, 103, 106, 107, 108, 114, 115, 116, 119.

Of these solutions, the first represents the three spaces in a four-dimensional projective space over the field with three elements.   The other three do not do so (as is easily seen by checking the intersections of three sets) and so represent different designs.   It is not known whether or not 2, 3, and 4 represent the same or different designs.

REFERENCES

1. R. A. Fisher, An Examination of the Different Possible Solutions in a Problem of Incomplete Blocks, *Ann. Eugenics*, vol. 10, pp. 52–75, 1940.

2. M. Hall, Jr., A Survey of Difference Sets, *Proc. Amer. Math. Soc.*, vol. 7, pp. 975–986, 1956.

3. M. Hall, Jr., and J. D. Swift, Determination of Steiner Triple Systems of Order 15, *Math. Tables Aids Comput.*, vol. 9, pp. 146–156, 1955.

4. M. Hall, Jr., J. D. Swift, and R. J. Walker, Uniqueness of the Projective Plane of Order Eight, *Math. Tables Aids Comput.*, vol. 10, pp. 186–194, 1956.

5. H. W. Norton, the 7 × 7 Squares, *Ann. Eugenics*, vol. 9, pp. 269–307, 1939.

6. A. Sade, An Omission in Norton's List of 7 × 7 Squares, *Ann. Math. Statist.*, vol. 22, pp. 306–307, 1951.

7. A. S. White, F. N. Cole, and L. D. Cummings, Complete Classification of Triad Systems on Fifteen Elements, *Mem. Nat. Acad. Sci.*, vol. 14, 2d mem., 1925.

15.3   Suggested Numerical Analysis of Some Discrete Problems

Certain problems in group theory might profitably be attacked by machine methods.   We consider first the problem of investigating a group G generated by elements subject to certain relations.   Since the word problem for groups is unsolvable, it cannot be expected that all group problems of this type can be treated, but most problems which arise naturally can be expected to be within reason.   The main difficulty encountered is the sheer volume of the calculations involved, but this is the sort of work in which computing machines have made their greatest contribution. If such calculations were to be carried out, several questions would remain to be settled—mainly, how much of the intermediate work should be recorded and in what form the results should be given. But these issues are common in all numerical analysis.

Given a group G and a subgroup H, a procedure is given here (1) for finding generators for H in terms of generators for G and representatives of left cosets of H in G and (2) for expressing relations on the generators of G as relations on the generators of H. For example, if it is believed that G has a specific finite order, then we may choose H as a subgroup which will reduce to the identity if the hypothesis is correct. Or it may be to our advantage to choose some subgroup H which is believed to be of a relatively simple kind.

It is known [4] that a group G generated by a finite number of elements $a_1, \ldots, a_r$ in which $z^4 = 1$ for every $z \in g$ is finite and that there is a largest group $B(4,r)$ such that every other group with this property is a homomorplue image of it. Trivially, $B(4,1)$ is of order 4, and it is known that $B(4,2)$ is of order 2^{12}, but the order of $B(4,r)$ is not known in general. Calculation of, say, $B(4,3)$ should be of considerable value in determining this. The procedures are illustrated with $B(4,3)$ in mind.

Let H be a subgroup of a group G and let the following be the decomposition of G in terms of left cosets of H:

$$G = H \cdot 1 + Hx_2 + \cdots + Hx_m, \qquad x_1 = 1. \qquad (15.21)$$

For $g \in G$, let us define

$$\varphi(g) = x_i \qquad \text{if } g \in Hx_i. \qquad (15.22)$$

The notation $\bar{g} = x_i$ is sometimes used. We note that, if $g \in Hx_i$, then

$$g = hx_i, \qquad \text{where } h \in H, \qquad (15.23)$$

and consequently

$$g\varphi(g)^{-1} = h \in H. \qquad (15.24)$$

Theorem. *If G is generated by $a_1, a_2, \ldots, a_r$ and if (15.22) gives the decomposition of G into left cosets of H, then H is generated by $u_{ik} = x_i a_k \varphi(x_i a_k)^{-1}$, $i = 1, \ldots, n, k = 1, \ldots, r$.*

Corollary. *If G is generated by r elements and H is of index n in G, then H is generated by at most rn elements.*

Proof. Consider an arbitrary element h_0 of H. Then h_0 may be expressed in terms of the generators $a_1, \ldots, a_r$ of G in the form

$$h_0 = b_1 b_2 \cdots b_t, \qquad (15.25)$$

where each $b_i = a_j^{\epsilon}$, $\epsilon = \neq 1$ for some j. We certainly have

$$\varphi(1) = 1, \qquad \varphi(h_0) = 1, \qquad (15.26)$$

since by hypothesis $h_0 \in H$, and the identity has by convention been chosen as the representative of H. Then the following is an identical relation:

$$h_0 = \varphi(1)b_1\varphi(b_1)^{-1} \cdot \varphi(b_1)b_2\varphi(b_1b_2)^{-1} \cdot \varphi(b_1b_2) \cdots \varphi(b_1 \cdots b_{t-2})b_{t-1}$$
$$\times \varphi(b_1 \cdots b_{t-1})^{-1} \cdot \varphi(b_1 \cdots b_{t-1})b_t\varphi(b_1 \cdots b_t)^{-1} \qquad (15.27)$$

since between b_s and b_{s+1} we have inserted $\varphi(b_1 \cdots b_s)^{-1}\varphi(b_1 \cdots b_s) = 1$ and $\varphi(1) = 1$, $\varphi(b_1 \cdots b_t)^{-1} = \varphi(h_0)^{-1} = 1$. Thus we have expressed h_0 as a product of factors of the form

$$u = \varphi(b_1 \cdots b_{s-1})b_s\varphi(b_1 \cdots b_s)^{-1}. \qquad (15.28)$$

But if $b_s = a_k$ and $\varphi(b_1 \cdots b_{s-1}) = x_i$, then u in (15.28) is of the form $x_ia_k\varphi(x_ia_k)^{-1}$, whereas if $b_s = a_k^{-1}$ and $\varphi(b_1 \cdots b_s) = x_j$, then u in (15.28) is of the form $[x_ja_k\varphi(x_ja_k)^{-1}]^{-1}$. Thus h_0 is expressed in terms of elements $x_ia_k\varphi(x_ia_k)^{-1}$, and, by (15.24), we note that these are all in H.

It is natural to construct coset representatives for H from previously constructed representatives by adding on a generator a_k or its inverse a_k^{-1}. This kind of construction is always possible. More precisely, a set of elements S in a group is called a *Schreier system* if, whenever $x \in S$, $x = b_1 \cdots b_s$, each $b_i = $ some a_j^ϵ, $\epsilon = \pm 1$, then also $b_1 \cdots b_{s-1} \in S$. Coset representatives may always be taken as a Schreier system, and indeed if elements are ordered by length and by an alphabetical order for the same length, then, choosing the earliest element as representative for each coset, the coset representatives automatically form a Schreier system. With a Schreier system of representatives, there are various further results which hold for the generators of H. For example, if G is a free group, then the generators $u_{ik} \neq 1$ of H are free generators (see [1, 2, 3]).

Suppose that G is generated by elements a, b, c, and let H be the normal subgroup of index 8 such that G/H is the elementary abelian group of order 8. Let us take $1, a, b, c, ab, ac, bc, abc$ as coset representatives of H. We find the following 17 generators u for H:

x_i	x_ia	$\varphi(x_ia)$	$u = x_ia\varphi(x_ia)^{-1}$	
1	a	a	1	
a	a^2	1	a^2	
b	ba	ab	$bab^{-1}a^{-1}$	
c	ca	ac	$ca\,c^{-1}a^{-1}$	
ab	aba	b	$abab^{-1}$	(15.29a)
ac	aca	c	$acac^{-1}$	
bc	bca	abc	$bca\,c^{-1}b^{-1}a^{-1}$	
abc	$abca$	bc	$abca\,c^{-1}b^{-1}$	

x_i	x_ib	$\varphi(x_ib)$	$u = x_ib\varphi(x_ib)^{-1}$
1	b	b	1
a	ab	ab	1
b	b^2	1	b^2
c	cb	bc	$cbc^{-1}b^{-1}$
ab	ab^2	a	ab^2a^{-1}
ac	acb	abc	$acb\,c^{-1}b^{-1}a^{-1}$
bc	bcb	c	$bcbc^{-1}$
abc	$abcb$	ac	$abcbc^{-1}a^{-1}$

$$(15.29b)$$

x_i	x_ic	$\varphi(x_ic)$	$u = x_ic\varphi(x_ic)^{-1}$
1	c	c	1
a	ac	ac	1
b	bc	bc	1
c	c^2	1	c^2
ab	abc	abc	1
ac	ac^2	a	ac^2a^{-1}
bc	bc^2	b	bc^2b^{-1}
abc	abc^2	ab	$abc^2b^{-1}a^{-1}$

$$(15.29c)$$

We list the 17 generators and also their inverses by length and alphabetically for the same length:

α_1	a^2	α_1^{-1}	a^{-2}
α_2	b^2	α_2^{-1}	b^{-2}
α_3	c^2	α_3^{-1}	c^{-2}
α_4	$abab^{-1}$	α_8^{-1}	$aba^{-1}b^{-1}$
α_5	ab^2a^{-1}	α_5^{-1}	$ab^{-2}a^{-1}$
α_6	$acac^{-1}$	α_{11}^{-1}	$aca^{-1}c^{-1}$
α_7	ac^2a^{-1}	α_7^{-1}	$a\,c^{-2}a^{-1}$
α_8	$bab^{-1}a^{-1}$	α_4^{-1}	$b\,a^{-1}b^{-1}a^{-1}$
α_9	$bcbc^{-1}$	α_{12}^{-1}	$b\,c\,b^{-1}c^{-1}$
α_{10}	bc^2b^{-1}	α_{10}^{-1}	$b\,c^{-2}b^{-1}$
α_{11}	$cac^{-1}a^{-1}$	α_6^{-1}	$c\,a^{-1}c^{-1}a^{-1}$
α_{12}	$cbc^{-1}b^{-1}$	α_9^{-1}	$c\,b^{-1}c^{-1}b^{-1}$
α_{13}	$abc\,a\,c^{-1}b^{-1}$	α_{17}^{-1}	$a\,b\,c\,a^{-1}c^{-1}b^{-1}$
α_{14}	$abc\,b\,c^{-1}a^{-1}$	α_{16}^{-1}	$a\,b\,c\,b^{-1}c^{-1}a^{-1}$
α_{15}	$abc^2b^{-1}a^{-1}$	α_{15}^{-1}	$a\,b\,c^{-2}b^{-1}a^{-1}$
α_{16}	$acb\,c^{-1}b^{-1}a^{-1}$	α_{14}^{-1}	$a\,c\,b^{-1}c^{-1}b^{-1}a^{-1}$
α_{17}	$bc\,a\,c^{-1}b^{-1}a^{-1}$	α_{13}^{-1}	$b\,c\,a^{-1}c^{-1}b^{-1}a^{-1}$

$$(15.30)$$

The square of every element of G lies in H. In particular, let us express

$(a\,b^{-1}\,c)^2 = ab^{-1}\,c\,a\,b^{-1}\,c$ in terms of the α's. We proceed as follows:

$$
\begin{aligned}
ab^{-1}\,c\,a\,b^{-1}\,c &= (a\,b^{-1})(c\,ab^{-1}\,c) \\
&= (ab^{-2}\,a^{-1} \cdot ab)(c\,ab^{-1}\,c) \\
&= \alpha_5^{-1}(abc\,a)(b^{-1}\,c) \\
&= \alpha_5^{-1}(abca\,c^{-1}\,b^{-1} \cdot bc)(b^{-1}\,c^{-1}) \\
&= \alpha_5^{-1}\,\alpha_{13}(bcb^{-1})\,c^{-1} \\
&= \alpha_5^{-1}\,\alpha_{13}(bcb^{-1}\,c^{-1} \cdot c)\,c^{-1} \\
&= \alpha_5^{-1}\,\alpha_{13}\,\alpha_{12}^{-1}.
\end{aligned}
\tag{15.31}
$$

Hence $(ab^{-1}\,c)^2 = \alpha_5^{-1}\alpha_{13}\,\alpha_{12}^{-1}$, and if in G we have the relation

$$
(ab^{-1}\,c)^4 = 1, \tag{15.32}
$$

this becomes in H the relation

$$
(\alpha_5^{-1}\,\alpha_{13}\,\alpha_{12}^{-1})^2 = 1. \tag{15.32'}
$$

The procedure for converting used in (15.31) may be described in a form suitable for computers. The generators of H, the α_i, are first computed, and the α_i and their inverses are alphabetized and stored. We take an initial segment of $ab^{-1}c\,ab^{-1}\,c$ as long as possible, which is a coset representative (here only the letter a), and then also the succeeding letter, taking ab^{-1}. Since the added letter is an inverse, we look under the inverses of the α's for a (necessarily unique) word beginning this way. This is $\alpha_5^{-1} = ab^{-2}\,a^{-1}$. We follow this by correcting terms so that the value is unchanged; thus $ab^{-1} = ab^{-2}\,a^{-1} \cdot ab$. We then keep the α and proceed in the same way with the remaining letters; here $abcab^{-1}\,c = (abca)(b^{-1}\,c)$, since abc is a coset representative but $abca$ is not. The same procedure is followed here, and with another step the expression $\alpha_5^{-1}\,\alpha_{13}\,\alpha_{12}^{-1}$ is obtained.

This procedure, when coset representatives are as short as possible and form a Schreier system, will always give a shorter expression for an element of H in terms of the generators of H than its expression in terms of generators of G. Thus $ab^{-1}\,c\,ab^{-1}\,c$ is of length 6, and $\alpha_5^{-1}\,\alpha_{13}\,\alpha_{12}^{-1}$ is of length 3. If we are fortunate in our choice, we find an explicit form for the elements of H. A favorable case is, of course, that in which H turns out to be abelian.

Next we consider two ways in which numerical analysis can be applied to the study of block designs.

Extensive use of the criterion of Connor mentioned in Sec. 15.1 has not as yet been made. Consider the problem of constructing a design with parameters $b = 69, v = 46, r = 9, k = 6, \lambda = 1$. It is not known at present whether or not such a design exists. As mentioned in Sec.

15.1, if we have t initial trial blocks $B_1, \ldots, B_t$ and if $S_{ju}, j, u = 1, \ldots, t$, is the number of objects common to B_j and B_u, then putting

$$c_{jj} = (r - k)(r - \lambda), \qquad c_{ju} = \lambda k - r S_{ju} \qquad (j \neq u), \quad (15.33)$$

a necessary condition in order that it be possible to complete $B_1, \ldots, B_t$ to a full design is that

$$\det C_t = \det |c_{ju}| \geq 0. \qquad (15.34)$$

Hence, if we find that certain choices make $\det |c_{ju}| < 0$, we may exclude from consideration all sets of initial blocks of this kind. If this excludes a sufficient number of combinations, this may provide a method of building up the design by using only permissible combinations or, if everything is excluded, of showing that no such design exists.

For the particular design mentioned, since $\lambda = 1$, then $S_{ju}, j \neq u$ can have only the value 0 or 1. Here $c_{jj} = 24$, $c_{ju} = 6$ if $S_{ju} = 0$, and $c_{ju} = -3$ if $S_{ju} = 1$. We may divide out the common factor 3 of these numbers for purposes of testing (15.34). We thus consider determinants of symmetric matrices, diagonal elements being 8, off-diagonal elements being 2 for parallel blocks, -1 for intersecting blocks. Thus we find with all off-diagonal elements -1

$$\begin{vmatrix} 8 & -1 & \cdot & \cdot & \cdot & \cdot & \cdot & \cdot & \cdot & -1 \\ -1 & 8 & & & & & & & & \cdot \\ \cdot & & 8 & & & & & & & \cdot \\ \cdot & & & 8 & & & & & & \cdot \\ \cdot & & & & 8 & & & & & \cdot \\ \cdot & & & & & 8 & & & & \cdot \\ \cdot & & & & & & 8 & & & \cdot \\ \cdot & & & & & & & 8 & & \cdot \\ \cdot & & & & & & & & 0 & \cdot \\ -1 & \cdot & \cdot & \cdot & \cdot & \cdot & \cdot & \cdot & \cdot & 8 \end{vmatrix} = -9^9, \quad (15.35)$$

and so we cannot have 10 blocks each intersecting the other 9. Indeed, we can show that if 9 blocks intersect each other, a further block must intersect 6 of these and be parallel to the remaining 3.

If a large number of these determinants is evaluated, it is to be hoped that the information gained will be such as to indicate how to go about the construction of this design. Naturally it is to be wished that study of a particular design will suggest methods and theorems of general application.

A further attack on block designs is based on the theory of convex spaces.

In Sec. 15.1 it was noted that, if we take

$$L_j = \sum_{i=1} a_{ij} x_i, \qquad j = 1, \ldots, b, \qquad (15.36)$$

where $a_{ij} = 1$ if the ith object is in the jth block and $a_{ij} = 0$ if not, then

$$L_1^2 + \cdots + L_b^2 = Q = r(x_1^2 + \cdots + x_v^2) + 2\lambda \sum_{i<j} x_i x_j. \quad (15.37)$$

Here, if we make a trial for the first t blocks, we are assuming explicit values for $L_1, \ldots, L_t$, and we must have

$$\bar{Q} = Q - L_1^2 - \cdots - L_t^2 = L_{t+1}^2 + \cdots + L_b^2. \quad (15.38)$$

Connor's method depends on asserting that, if $L_{t+1}, \ldots, L_b$ exist in (15.38), then $\bar{Q}$ must be a positive semidefinite form. But even stronger statements may be made about $\bar{Q}$. We use the fact that $L_{t+1}, \ldots, L_b$, if they exist, will be linear forms with nonnegative coefficients. Hence Q must belong to the class T of quadratic forms which can be written as the sum of squares of nonnegative linear forms. Trivially, the class T consists of semidefinite forms with nonnegative coefficients. But the class T is even more restricted. For consider the form

$$\begin{aligned} Q &= x_1^2 + x_2^2 + x_3^2 + x_4^2 + x_5^2 + x_1 x_4 + x_1 x_5 + \tfrac{3}{2} x_2 x_3 + x_2 x_5 + x_3 x_4 \\ &= (x_4 + \tfrac{1}{2} x_1 + \tfrac{1}{2} x_3)^2 + (x_5 + \tfrac{1}{2} x_1 + \tfrac{1}{2} x_2)^2 \\ &\quad + \tfrac{1}{2}(x_1 - \tfrac{1}{2} x_2 - \tfrac{1}{2} x_3)^2 + \tfrac{5}{8}(x_2 + x_3)^2. \end{aligned} \quad (15.39)$$

From (15.39) it is clear that Q is positive semidefinite and has nonnegative coefficients. But Q does not belong to the class T of forms which are sums of squares of nonnegative linear forms. We shall assume that Q has such a representation and reach a contradiction. We assume

$$Q = \sum_{i=1}^{n} L_i^2, \qquad L_i \geq 0, \quad (15.40)$$

and we let the numbering in (15.40) be such that $L_1, \ldots, L_r$ are the linear forms

$$L = \cdots + u_2 x_2 + u_3 x_3 + \cdots,$$

in which both x_2 and x_3 have positive coefficients. In such an L the coefficients of x_1, x_4, and x_5 must be zero, since otherwise, in (15.40), we would get one of the terms $x_1 x_2$, $x_2 x_4$, $x_3 x_5$ with a positive coefficient contrary to the explicit form of Q in (15.39). Hence

$$L_1^2 + \cdots + L_r^2 = A x_2^2 + \tfrac{3}{2} x_2 x_3 + B x_3^2. \quad (15.41)$$

Thus (15.40) becomes

$$\begin{aligned} Q &= Q(x_1, x_2, x_3, x_4, x_5) \\ &= A x_2^2 + \tfrac{3}{2} x_2 x_3 + B x_3^2 + Q_1(x_1, x_2, x_3, x_4, x_5), \end{aligned} \quad (15.42)$$

where $Q_1 = L_{r+1}^2 + \cdots + L_n^2. \quad (15.43)$

If we now put $x_1 = \frac{1}{2}x_2 + \frac{1}{2}x_3$, $x_5 = -\frac{1}{2}x_1 - \frac{1}{2}x_2$, $x_4 = -\frac{1}{2}x_1 - \frac{1}{2}x_3$ in (15.40), then (15.41) is unaffected, and, by (15.39), Q reduces to $\frac{5}{8}(x_2 + x_3)^2$. Here (15.42) takes the form

$$\tfrac{5}{8}(x_2 + x_3)^2 = Ax_2{}^2 + \tfrac{3}{2}x_2x_3 + Bx_3{}^2 + Q_1(x_2, x_3), \quad (15.44)$$

and Q_1 is positive semidefinite. Thus $0 \le A \le \frac{5}{8}$, $0 \le B \le \frac{5}{8}$, and so

$$\tfrac{9}{4} - 4AB \ge \tfrac{36}{16} - \tfrac{25}{16} = \tfrac{11}{16}. \quad (15.45)$$

Thus the form on the right-hand side of (15.41) has a positive discriminant and is indefinite, conflicting with its expression as a sum of squares. We have been led to a conflict by the assumption that Q could be written as a sum of squares of nonnegative forms.

This example shows that the class T of quadratic forms which can be expressed as the sum of squares of nonnegative linear forms is more restricted than the intersection of the class D of semidefinite forms and the class $\bar{P}$ of forms with nonnegative coefficients. How are we to recognize and make use of this restriction? The theory of convex spaces gives us some information on this. With a quadratic form $Q(x_1, \ldots, x_n)$,

$$Q = \sum b_{ij}x_ix_j \quad (i, j = 1, \ldots, n; \; b_{ji} = b_{ij}), \quad (15.46)$$

we associate a point $B = (b_{11}, \ldots, b_{nn})$ in n^2-dimensional space, restricting ourselves to the linear subspace for which $b_{ij} = b_{ji}$. Here the class T is a convex cone, and the extreme points of T are merely the squares of nonnegative linear forms $(a_1x_1 + \cdots + a_nx_n)^2$, $a_i \ge 0$. The adjoint space T^* consists of all points $C(c_{11}, \ldots, c_{nn})$ with $c_{ij} = c_{ji}$ such that

$$\sum_{i,j} c_{ij}b_{ij} \ge 0 \quad (15.47)$$

for every $B \in T$. Since we know the extreme points of T, this means that

$$\sum_{i,j} c_{ij}a_ia_j \ge 0 \quad \text{for all } a_i \ge 0. \quad (15.48)$$

In other words, (15.48) says that T^* is the space of quadratic forms nonnegative for nonnegative arguments. A. Horn has shown that the spaces D of semidefinite forms and P of nonnegative forms are each their own adjoint. From the general theory of convex spaces, since $T \subseteq D \cap P$, it follows that $T^* \supseteq D \cup P$. Thus T^* contains all semidefinite forms and all nonnegative forms, but indeed T^* contains still further forms. The symmetric matrix

$$K = \begin{pmatrix} 1 & 1 & 1 & -1 & -1 \\ 1 & 1 & -1 & 1 & -1 \\ 1 & -1 & 1 & -1 & 1 \\ -1 & 1 & -1 & 1 & 1 \\ -1 & -1 & 1 & 1 & 1 \end{pmatrix} \quad (15.49)$$

corresponds to the form

$$K = x_1{}^2 + x_2{}^2 + x_3{}^2 + x_4{}^2 + x_5{}^2 + 2x_1x_2 + 2x_1x_3 - 2x_1x_4 - 2x_1x_5$$
$$- 2x_2x_3 + 2x_2x_4 - 2x_2x_5 - 2x_3x_4 + 2x_3x_5 + 2x_4x_5. \quad (15.50)$$

We may express K in two ways:

$$K = (x_1 + x_2 - x_3 - x_4 - x_5)^2 + 4x_1x_3 + 4(x_2 - x_3)x_4, \quad (15.51)$$
$$K = (x_1 - x_2 + x_3 - x_4 - x_5) + 4x_1x_2 + 4(x_3 - x_2)x_5. \quad (15.52)$$

For nonnegative x's we see from (15.51) that if $x_2 \geq x_3$, then $K \geq 0$, whereas, from (15.52), if $x_3 \geq x_2$, then $K \geq 0$. Hence in every case K is nonnegative for nonnegative arguments. Thus K is in T^*, and indeed Horn has shown that K is an extreme point of T^*. The form Q of (15.39) corresponds to the matrix

$$Q = \begin{pmatrix} 1 & 0 & 0 & \frac{1}{2} & \frac{1}{2} \\ 0 & 1 & \frac{3}{4} & 0 & \frac{1}{2} \\ 0 & \frac{3}{4} & 1 & \frac{1}{2} & 0 \\ \frac{1}{2} & 0 & \frac{1}{2} & 1 & 0 \\ \frac{1}{2} & \frac{1}{2} & 0 & 0 & 1 \end{pmatrix}. \quad (15.53)$$

If we calculate the inner product of the 25 dimensional vectors corresponding to K and Q, we find

$$(K,Q) = 5 - 2(\tfrac{1}{2} + \tfrac{1}{2} + \tfrac{3}{4} + \tfrac{1}{2} + \tfrac{1}{2}) = -\tfrac{1}{2}. \quad (15.54)$$

Hence, since K is a point of T^*, Q is *not* a point of T. This yields a new proof that Q is not a sum of squares of nonnegative linear forms. Thus a calculation of points $C = (c_{ij})$ of T^* gives the simple linear test (15.47) for determining whether a form is in T. Presumably extreme points of T^* such as K give the most effective tests. However, once points in T^* have been calculated, they may be tabulated in some permanent form and will thereafter be available to test large numbers of forms such as $\bar{Q}$ arising in (15.38). The test (15.47) is very simple to apply, once the points in T^* have been found.

REFERENCES

1. M. Hall, Jr., and T. Rado, On Schreier Systems in Free Groups, *Trans. Amer. Math. Soc.*, vol. 64, pp. 386–408, 1948.

2. M. Hall, Jr., Coset Representations in Free Groups, *Trans. Amer. Math. Soc.*, vol. 67, pp. 421–432, 1949.

3. M. Hall, Jr., Subgroups of Finite Index in Free Groups, *Canad. J. Math.*, vol. 1, pp. 187–191, 1949.

4. I. N. Sanov, Solution of Burnside's Problem for Exponent 4, *Leningrad State Univ. Ann.*, vol. 10, pp. 166–170, 1940.

16

Number Theory

HARVEY COHN

PROFESSOR OF MATHEMATICS

UNIVERSITY OF ARIZONA

OLGA TAUSSKY

RESEARCH ASSOCIATE

CALIFORNIA INSTITUTE OF TECHNOLOGY

SOME ILLUSTRATIVE COMPUTATIONS IN ALGEBRAIC NUMBER THEORY *by Harvey Cohn*

The object of the first part of this chapter, Secs. 16.1 to 16.3, is to focus attention on a special phase of integral numerical analysis [1], namely, algebraic-number-theory computations, in which a high degree of purity is preserved in machine work through two features: first, the machine serves as a "scientific instrument" rather than as a "tally sheet," participating in some of the intricacies of the theory [2]; second, the machine can use modular arithmetic [3] to treat irrationals exactly, without round-off. The subject matter is a little too specialized to be treated in detail or depth; we therefore restrict ourselves to illustrative samples.

16.1 Rational Primes

The best-known algebraic-number-theory computation is a seemingly integral one, namely, the testing of certain primes [4].

We might first digress briefly to note that the discovery of new primes is plagued by the disadvantage of diminishing returns, for the testing of a prime P by itself would involve in theory approximately $P^{1/2}$ trial divisions by potential divisors. The object of good machine practice is therefore not a tour de force of electronic reliability but the discovery of new infinite classes of prospective primes that can be tested more elegantly (in fewer steps).

Most of the very elegant tricks apply to relatively isolated cases. For instance, consider the rather crucial fact that 641 divides $2^{32} + 1$, first seen by Euler.   If one happens to notice that

$$641 = 640 + 1 = 5 \cdot 2^7 + 1$$
$$= 625 + 16 = 5^4 + 2^4,$$

then it is easily seen that

$$5 \cdot 2^7 + 1 \equiv 5^4 + 2^4 \equiv 0 \qquad (\text{mod } 641);$$

and thus, eliminating the symbol 5 between two congruences, we obtain $2^{32} + 1 \equiv 0$.   Actually, the number 641 was not too hard to locate, since it can be shown that the number $F = 2^{2^t} + 1$ has as its prime divisors only numbers $\equiv 1 \pmod{2^{t+2}}$.   Yet this is of little help in general, since the number of trials is now reduced only slightly, to the order $F^{1/2}/\log F$.   Such clever devices for the so-called Fermat primes F do not seem to generalize to machine programs very well [5].   A machine-type (but less interesting) criterion of primality is that $3^{(F-1)/2} \equiv -1 \pmod{F}$.   A variant of this test which is both complicated enough to require algebraic number theory and simple enough to be transparent will now be applied to a different set of primes.

The Mersenne primes are those primes $P = 2^p - 1$ where p is an odd prime.   The Lucas-Lehmer test [6] for primality is as follows: *define*

$$u_0 = 4, \qquad u_{n+1} = u_n{}^2 - 2; \qquad (16.1)$$

then P is prime if and only if

$$u_{p-2} \equiv 0 \qquad (\text{mod } P). \qquad (16.1a)$$

Now this criterion becomes algebraic rather than integral if we define

$$\omega_t = 2 \cos 2\pi/2^t,$$
$$\omega_2 = 2 \cos \pi/2 = 0 \qquad (16.2)$$

and note that as before

$$\omega_t = \omega_{t+1}^2 - 2. \qquad (16.2a)$$

Then ω_p corresponds to u_0 and ω_2 to u_{p-2}.   Thus the Lucas-Lehmer test states that P is prime if and only if, in some way, ω_p "represents" 4 (mod P).   We then look into this type of congruence more closely.

Specifically, we define an algebraic integer [7] as a number ω satisfying an irreducible monic equation in integral coefficients a_i, namely,

$$f(\omega) = \omega^n - a_1\omega^{n-1} + a_2\omega^{n-2} - \cdots + (-)^n a_n = 0. \quad (16.3)$$

Here the conjugate roots have as their product a_n, the *norm*, more generally denoted as $N(\omega) = a_n$. Easily, $N(\omega_1\omega_2) = N(\omega_1)N(\omega_2)$. We can then say that an algebraic integer ω is *represented* by an ordinary integer u (mod q) when

$$N(\omega - u) \equiv 0 \qquad (\text{mod } q). \tag{16.4}$$

Now it is not true that for every q there exists a u that will make (16.4) valid. Actually, in terms of the defining polynomial for ω, (16.4) states that

$$f(u) \equiv 0 \qquad (\text{mod } q) \tag{16.4a}$$

for any such u, so that there are at most n of them when q is prime. The proof goes precisely as in the case of "numerical" solutions of equations. Also, multiple roots can occur only when the "discriminant is 0" in the numerical case or only when q divides the discriminant, or the rational integer

$$D = \Pi[\omega^{(r)} - \omega^{(s)}]^2, \tag{16.5}$$

taken over distinct (unordered) pairs of conjugates of ω. Furthermore, in most of the cases under consideration the equation is *normal*; that is, every root is equal to some polynomial in rational coefficients of any one root. Thus for a normal algebraic integer, if the prime q does not divide the discriminant, then (16.5) has no roots or exactly n distinct roots.

Now let us apply this development to Mersenne primes. The induction of ω_t in (16.2) implies that $\omega_2 = 0$, $\omega_3 = 2^{1/2}$, $\omega_4 = (2 + 2^{1/2})^{1/2}$, until finally, for example,

$$\omega_p = \{2 + [2 + (2 + 2^{1/2})^{1/2}]^{1/2}\}^{1/2} \cdots \qquad (p - 2) \text{ radicals} \tag{16.6}$$

or conversely ω_p satisfies this equation of degree 2^{p-2}.

$$f_{p-2}(\omega) = \{[(\omega^2 - 2)^2 - 2]^2 - 2\}^2 - 2 = 0 \cdots \qquad (p - 2) \text{ squares.} \tag{16.7}$$

Thus we can easily see the *sufficiency* of the Lucas-Lehmer test for primality, once we notice that (16.7) is normal. This is seen by writing the 2^{p-2} roots as $\omega^{(r)} = 2 \cos 2\pi r/2^p$, where r is odd, $1 < r < 2^{p-1}$. Then, if s is another odd value and if $r \equiv ks$ (mod 2^p), we easily can express $\omega^{(r)} = \varphi[\omega^{(s)}]$, where $\cos k\theta = \varphi(\cos \theta)$ by a well-known trigonometric identity. Furthermore, it can be seen that D is an exact power of 2; in fact, writing $\omega^{(r)} = \exp 2\pi i r/2^p + \exp - 2\pi i r/2^p$, we can verify (see [8])

$$D = 2^{2^{p-1}(p-1)}. \tag{16.5a}$$

Suppose now the condition (16.1a) holds; then we show that P has no proper prime divisor q. For, if so, $f_{p-2}(u) \equiv 0$ (mod q) would have its full quota of 2^{p-2} distinct roots (by virtue of the presence of the *one* root $u \equiv 4$). Then 2^{p-2} [$= (P + 1)/4] \leq q$, and thus P must be a prime, since it could have no prime divisor $q \leq P^{1/2}$ as long as $P^{1/2} \leq (P + 1)/4$ (true when $P \geq 31$).

The sufficiency of the Lucas-Lehmer test is therefore established. Unfortunately the *necessity* goes too deeply into algebraic number theory to be appropriate here. We merely note in conclusion that this process has the order of log P steps, a considerable improvement [9] over $P^{1/2}$, and that, incidentally, the advantages of a binary machine become manifest when P is represented in digital notation.

16.2 Units

The elementary (rational) operations require the introduction, with ω, of the *field* $R(\omega)$, or the set of all quantities that are expressible as rational functions of ω with rational coefficients. The elements of $R(\omega)$ that are also algebraic integers are called *integers of the field* $R(\omega)$. They are not necessarily all expressible as a polynomial in ω with integers for coefficients, but for convenience we consider only fields $R(\omega)$ generated by an ω with this property. It can be verified, for instance, that for the quadratic field connected with $m^{1/2}$ we would have to take $\omega = m^{1/2}$ when $m \not\equiv 1 \pmod{4}$ and $\omega = (1 + m^{1/2})/2$ when $m \equiv 1 \pmod{4}$ (here m is square-free). Thus the equation in integers (for $m = 7$), $x^2 - 7y^2 = \pm A$, is the same as $N(\omega) = \pm A$ where $\omega = x + y \cdot 7^{1/2}$, an unknown field integer in $R(7^{1/2})$.

From the last illustration we can see the importance of a special class of algebraic integers known as *units* η with $N(\eta) = \pm 1$, since two solutions of $N(\xi) = \pm A$ might be trivially equivalent $(\eta \xi_1 = \xi_2)$.

The problem of finding units in an arbitrary field cannot be dismissed as purely mechanical, but the procedure is generally to search for a ξ_1, ξ_2 with $N(\xi_1) = N(\xi_2) = A$ and ask hopefully whether $\eta = \xi_1/\xi_2$ is an integer. Rationalizing the denominator by writing $\eta = [\xi_1 \xi_2' \cdots \xi_2^{(n)}]/[\xi_2 \xi_2' \cdots \xi_2^{(n)}]$, we see that, since the value of the denominator is $N(\xi_2) = A$, the problem is to show that the numerator is a polynomial in ω whose coefficients are all divisible [10] by A. In other words, the numerator can be calculated modulo A to see whether the coefficients are congruent to zero. In principle this is the same as asking whether ξ_1/ξ_2 *really* represents a zero division modulo p for any prime divisor p of A or whether cancellation (owing to units) forestalls this zero division.

A related problem consists of deciding whether or not one unit is a power of another (unknown) unit; that is, for a given η, can we write

$$\eta = \pm \eta_0^r \tag{16.8}$$

for an unknown η_0 and r? In practice the number of different values of r is limited by other conditions beyond this discussion; so we specialize to fixed r. For instance, consider the trial

$$\eta = 7 + 5 \cdot 2^{1/2} = (a + b \cdot 2^{1/2})^3 = \eta_0^3. \qquad (16.8a)$$

We first find a prime p (see [11]) for which $2^{1/2}$ represents an odd integer and for which the cube-root extraction is unique. We try $p = 23$, since $N(5 - 2^{1/2}) = 23$; so now $2^{1/2}$ represents 5 (mod 23). Then, if η_0 represents u_0 and η_0' represents u_0', we find that (16.8a) becomes

$$7 + 5 \cdot 5 \equiv u_0^3 \quad (\text{mod } 23),$$
$$7 - 5 \cdot 5 \equiv (u_0')^3, \qquad (16.8b)$$

and by primitive roots, for example, $u_0 \equiv +6$, $u_0' \equiv -4$.

Hence, solving in terms of the representation of η_0 as $a + b \cdot 2^{1/2}$, we find

$$a + b \cdot 5 \equiv 6 \ (\equiv u_0) \quad (\text{mod } 23),$$
$$a - b \cdot 5 \equiv -4 \ (\equiv u_0'), \qquad (16.8c)$$

and so $a = 1$, $b = 1$ (mod 23). If we try other acceptable moduli, like $47 = N(7 - 2^{1/2})$, we can use the Chinese remainder theorem to find that, in no time, a and b are determined modulo some enormous integer. Here we could either verify the natural guess

$$7 + 5 \cdot 2^{1/2} = (1 + 1 \cdot 2^{1/2})^3, \qquad (16.8d)$$

made on the basis of the residues of a and b, or use some (difficult) estimates on the a priori size of a and b to determine the actual values [12].

16.3 Unique Factorization

Now the significance of algebraic number theory lies in the fact that the integers of a field do not generally exhibit unique factorization. This became clear in the famous case in which Fermat's last theorem [13] was "solved" by Lamé, Cauchy, and others on the basis of such a false assumption. Specifically, if we consider indecomposables to mean algebraic integers of the field with no further factorizations (not using units), then we *cannot* assume that two factorizations of a number into indecomposables must match factor for factor (ignoring multiplications by units). Thus the primes of an algebraic number field are not the indecomposables but are specially contrived, so-called *ideal* numbers (which are too involved to discuss further here).

Thus, discussing this failure of unique factorization rather than the remedy, we might consider the field generated by $\omega = (-5)^{1/2}$. Here clearly

$$N[-4 + (-5)^{1/2}] = 21 \equiv 0 \quad (\text{mod } 7), \qquad (16.9)$$

or 4 represents ω (mod 7). Note that (16.9) gives a factorization of 21, irreconcilable with $3 \cdot 7$, although all four factors 3, 7, -4, $\pm(-5)^{1/2}$ are indecomposable (and no units exist to provide cross identifications).

Now it is true, more generally, that unique factorization in a normal field will *fail* if q is a modulus for which an algebraic integer is representable by an ordinary integer whereas *no* algebraic integer ω_q exists for which

$$q = N(\omega_q). \tag{16.10}$$

Here the electronic computer can be put to work contriving long series of fields and primes q for which (16.10) is manifestly impossible and hence for which unique factorization must fail [14].

In conclusion we might mention a more famous unsolved problem which should be amenable to further computation, namely, the proof or disproof of unique factorization in fields of the type $R(\omega_t)$, $\omega_t = 2 \cos 2\pi/2^t$. Now Reuschle's tabulation [15] of complex "primes" shows, among other things, that the unique factorization occurs when $t = 3$, 4 and is not contradicted by the inadequate evidence for $t = 5$, 6, 7. It turns out, as part of the theory, that it is only necessary to test those q which are congruent to ± 1 (mod 2^t) and lie below the quantity $D^{1/2}$[for D in (16.5a)]. The problem is also one of central interest since $R(\omega_3)$, $R(\omega_4)$, $R(\omega_5)$, . . . present an especially important example of a set of fields each of which is included in the next by (16.2a). Yet no progress has been made since 1875, although a general revival of computational interest seems clear from the current literature [16].

16.4 Notes

1. For a bibliography of immediately relevant material, see O. Taussky, Some Computational Problems in Algebraic Number Theory, in American Mathematical Society, "Numerical Analysis: Proceedings of Symposia in Applied Mathematics—Volume VI," J. H. Curtiss, ed., pp. 103–108, McGraw-Hill Book Company, Inc., New York, 1956 (see Secs. 16.5 to 16.10). For a more varied survey of computational work, see J. Todd, Motivations for Working in Numerical Analysis, in "Transactions of Symposium on Computing, Mechanics, Statistics, and Partial Differential Equations," pp. 97–116, Interscience Publishers, Inc., New York, 1955 (see Chap. 1).

2. Lest the reader underestimate the intricacies of tallying, he should consult E. Lehmer, Number Theory on the SWAC, in American Mathematical Society, "Numerical Analysis: Proceedings of Symposia in Applied Mathematics—Volume VI," J. H. Curtiss, ed., pp. 187–193, McGraw-Hill Book Company, Inc., New York, 1956.

3. The discussion in this chapter presupposes elementary congruence properties. See, for example, G. H. Hardy and E. M. Wright, "An Introduction to the Theory of Numbers," Oxford University Press, New York, 1954.

4. A recent picture of the "large-prime" competition as well as a fairly complete set of references can be found in R. M. Robinson, Mersenne and Fermat Numbers, *Proc. Amer. Math. Soc.*, vol. 5, pp. 842–846, 1954.

5. An effort to generalize this device (of Western) can be found in J. C. Morehead, Extension of the Sieve of Eratosthenes to Arithmetical Progressions and Applications, *Ann. Math.*, vol. 10, pp. 88–104, 1909.

6. See D. H. Lehmer, An Extended Theory of Lucas' Function, *Ann. Math.*, vol. 31, pp. 419–448, 1930.

7. The high degree of abstraction achieved by the algebraic theory of numbers produced a remoteness from the examination of integers.   For an earlier reference work, see H. Weber, "Lehrbuch der Algebra," II, Vieweg-Verlag, Brunswick, Germany, 1899.

8. See page 756 of the book by Weber referred to in [7].

9. A factor of log P must be applied to machine time, owing to the size of P in digits (and registers) needed for the calculations modulo P.

10. It is actually preferable to make A a prime p or power of a prime whenever convenient.   See H. Cohn and S. Gorn, A Computation of Cyclic Cubic Units, *J. Res. Nat. Bur. Standards*, vol. 59, pp. 155–168, 1957.

11. In this particular case the reader can check that $p \equiv -1$ (mod 3) is the condition that only one cube root in, say, each congruence (16.8b) exist.

12. A corresponding calculation of cyclic cubic units was made by H. P. F. Swinnerton-Dyer using an electronic computer, but the report of this study exists only in manuscript.

13. See G. E. Wahlin and H. S. Vandiver, "Algebraic Numbers," II, National Research Council Bulletin 62, 1928.   The work of the latter author in Fermat's last theorem presages more modern computational attitudes.

14. See H. Cohn, A Device for Generating Fields of Even Class Numbers, *Proc. Amer. Math. Soc.*, vol. 7, pp. 595–598, 1956.

15. See C. G. Reuschle, "Tafeln der Complexen Primzahlen welche aus Wurzeln der Einheit gebildet sind," Berlin, 1875.

16. For many illustrations of modern advanced computational techniques, see H. Hasse, Arithmetische Bestimmung von Grundeinheit und Klassenzahl in zyklischen kubischen und biquadratischen Zahlkörpern, *Abh. Deutsch. Akad. Wiss. Berlin. Math.-Nat. Kl.*, 1950.

SOME COMPUTATIONAL PROBLEMS IN ALGEBRAIC NUMBER THEORY* *by Olga Taussky*

16.5 Introduction

It is frequently claimed that many facts in ordinary number theory can be fully understood only through their generalization to algebraic number fields. A typical fact is the exceptional role played by the prime number 2 in many cases. However, in number fields one proves with ease that all numbers $1 - \zeta$ play an exceptional role when ζ is a

* This is an extended version of the article on pp. 187–193 of American Mathematical Society, "Numerical Analysis: Proceedings of Symposia in Applied Mathematics—Volume VI," J. H. Curtiss, ed., McGraw-Hill Book Company, Inc., New York, 1956.

root of unity.   Another example is the quadratic law of reciprocity, for which a really illuminating proof is found only by using number fields.   Also, the Fermat problem is frequently attacked via number fields.

However, the study of number theory in these fields provides its own difficulties and has still to deal with many open problems.   Progress is particularly hindered by the greatly increased difficulties of numerical examples in these fields, as compared to the rational field.

In this brief report concerning computational problems in algebraic number theory, only problems concerning the most fundamental concepts are mentioned.   A list of table work concerning algebraic number fields—there is not much of it—can be found in D. H. Lehmer [1]. Many other problems have come up (see, e.g., [2]).

16.6   Integral Bases

It is known that for fields of degree ≥ 3 an integral base cannot always be found which consists of the powers of a single algebraic integer only.   Although the existence of an integral base for any field is easily established, its construction presents difficulties (see, e.g., [3]).

16.7   Factorization of Rational Primes in Number Fields

An ordinary prime number p will, in general, not remain a prime number in a given algebraic number field F but will split up into a product of powers of prime ideals:

$$p = \mathfrak{p}_1^{e_1} \cdots \mathfrak{p}_r^{e_r}.$$

Apart from a finite number of primes p, namely, the divisors of the discriminant of F, we have $e_i = 1$.

The question is, What are the possible values of r and of the e_i? Further, since norm $\mathfrak{p}_i = p^{f_i}$, what are the f_i?   The laws which govern these numbers are not fully known in all fields.   However, a great number of important facts are known about them, and their structure is completely clarified in cyclotomic fields and their subfields.   Since the extensions of class-field theory to general algebraic extensions have not yet been able to clear up the decomposition laws of rational primes in arbitrary fields, special numerical work in this connection is very desirable.   Kuroda [4] has computed some results concerning nonabelian fields of degree 2^n.

Like many other computations in algebraic number theory, the splitting of rational primes can be treated by *rational* methods only.   This fact is very important if computation by automatic computing machinery is considered.   Only the knowledge of the irreducible polynomial $f(x)$, a zero of which generates the field in question, is needed; for the following facts hold for all but a finite number of primes [5].   Let

$$f(x) \equiv P_1^{e_1} \cdots P_r^{e_r} \qquad (\bmod p),$$

where P_i is an irreducible polynomial modulo p and $P_i \not\equiv P_k \ (\bmod p)$, $i \neq k$.   Then p splits up in the form

$$p = \mathfrak{p}_1^{e_1} \cdots \mathfrak{p}_r^{e_r},$$

where $\mathfrak{p}_i \neq \mathfrak{p}_k$.   If the degree of P_i is f_i, then norm $\mathfrak{p}_i = p^{f_i}$.

Ore [6, 7] extended the method just described to include all prime numbers by considering congruences modulo p^r where r is sufficiently large.

16.8   Units

Other important problems arise in connection with the units in fields. To find the units is not always easy.   The main problem is to find a set of base units.

In complex quadratic fields there are no units apart from roots of unity.   In real quadratic fields there is one base unit ϵ and all other units are of the form $\pm\epsilon^n$, $n = 0, \pm1, \pm2, \ldots$.   If d is the discriminant of the field, then the unit ϵ is of the form $(x + y\sqrt{d})/2$, where x, y are the smallest positive solutions of $(x^2 - dy^2)/4 = \pm1$.   There is a rational routine method for finding ϵ by means of continued fractions.

Let $p > 2$ be a prime number.   The base unit of the field generated by $\sqrt{p}$ can be put into the form $(t + u\sqrt{p})/2$.   Recently Ankeny, Artin, and Chowla [10] inquired whether $u \not\equiv 0(p)$.   They verified this for $p \equiv 5(8)$ and $p < 2000$.   This conjecture was later verified by K. Goldberg on SEAC up to $p < 100,000$.

A routine method for finding a unit in cyclic cubic fields which, together with its conjugates, generates all the units was given by Hasse [8].

Units in noncyclic cubic fields were treated by several authors (see [9], where more references can be found; see also [1]).

16.9   Ideal Classes and Class Numbers

Tables for the class numbers of real quadratic fields have been made by Ince [11] and for the cyclic cubic fields by Hasse [8].   Hasse has a routine method for finding the class numbers in cyclic cubic fields, but it is rather complicated.

If no routine method is aimed at, the work is sometimes simpler. A bound for the class number and a method for computing it are given by the following known theorem:

In each class there is an ideal whose norm does not exceed $\sqrt{|d|}$ where d is the discriminant of the field.

A sharper bound is $(4/\pi)^{r_2}(n!/n^n)\sqrt{|d|}$ (see [12]).   It is further known that

$$hK = \lim_{s\to 1} (s-1)\zeta(s),$$

where h is the class number, and

$$K = \frac{2^{r_1}(2\pi)^{r_2}}{w}\frac{R}{\sqrt{|d|}}.$$

Here R is the regulator of the field, d the discriminant, w the number of roots of unity, r_1 the number of real conjugate fields, $2r_2$ the number of complex ones, and

$$\zeta(s) = \sum \frac{1}{(\text{norm } \mathfrak{a})^s},$$

where $\mathfrak{a}$ runs through all ideals in the field.   (This sum converges for all $s > 1$.)

Further, there are many facts whose knowledge can cut down the work considerably in special cases.   Quite a number of facts are known about the class number in cyclotomic fields and their subfields.   These fields have been investigated more closely, partly because they are more accessible and partly because of their importance to the Fermat problem.   Many results concerning class numbers in these fields go back to Kummer and to H. Weber.   Later Furtwängler [13, 14] generalized some of their results; for example, he proved that the class number of the field generated by the l^rth root of unity is divisible by l if and only if the class number of the field generated by the lth root of unity is.   Further, let f, F be two subfields of the field of the l^rth root of unity and $f \subset F$.   He then proved that the class number of f divides that of F.   More recently a book by Hasse [15] appeared which is concerned with the class number in these fields and their largest real subfields.   It contains many new theorems and tables.

Scholz [16], Inaba [17], Taussky [18], and others studied the subfields of prime degree l of cyclotomic fields.   The subfield of degree l of the field generated by the pth root of unity [p a prime $\equiv 1(l)$] has a class number prime to l.   On the other hand, a subfield of degree l of the field generated by the p_1p_2th roots of unity has always a class number divisible by l if $p_1 \equiv 1(l)$, $p_2 \equiv 1(l)$ are two different primes and if the field is not contained in the field of the p_1th or the p_2th roots of unity.   The class number of such a field is not divisible by l^2 if one, at least, of the two congruences

$$x^l \equiv p_1(p_2), \qquad x^l \equiv p_2(p_1)$$

has no rational solutions.

An example of such a case is $l = 3, p_1 = 7, p_2 = 13$. This means that the class number of a cubic subfield of the field of the ninety-first root of unity (which is not a subfield of the field of the seventh or thirteenth root of unity) is divisible by 3 but not by 9. For one of these fields it will now be shown that its class number is actually 3.

It can easily be checked that

$$f(x) \equiv x^3 - 7 \cdot 13x + 3 \cdot 7 \cdot 13 = 0$$

has discriminant $11^2 \cdot 7^2 \cdot 13^2$ and that any of its roots θ defines a cyclic cubic field whose discriminant is $7^2 \cdot 13^2$. From a refinement of Minkowski's theory (see [19]; also [12], p. 452; for even sharper results, see [20]) it follows that for a cyclic cubic field with discriminant D there is in every ideal class an ideal $\mathfrak{a}$ such that

$$\text{norm } \mathfrak{a} \leq \tfrac{2}{9}\sqrt{D}.$$

In our case this gives norm $\mathfrak{a} \leq 20$. The prime numbers 3, 11, 19 split up into three factors in the field, while 2, 5, 17 remain prime numbers. It is therefore only necessary to examine in what classes the prime ideal factors of 3, 11, 19 lie. Since the class number is divisible by 3 but not by 9, only the class numbers 3, 6, 12, 15 come into question. The class numbers 6 and 15 are impossible, since in such a case the 2-class group or the 5-class group of the field would have to be cyclic. In this case let $\mathfrak{p}$ be a prime ideal belonging to a class of order 2 or 5. Let, for example, the 2-class group be cyclic. In this case we would have

$$\mathfrak{p}^s \sim \mathfrak{p}^a,$$

where s is a generating automorphism of the Galois group of the field and a is a rational integer. Hence

$$\mathfrak{p}^{s^3} \sim \mathfrak{p}^{a^3}.$$

This implies $a^3 \equiv 1(2)$, which implies $a \equiv 1(2)$. This means that $\mathfrak{p} \sim 1$. The same argument applies for the 5-class group.

In order to show that the class number 12 cannot occur, we prove that the prime numbers 3, 11, 19 are norms of numbers or that their third powers are. For this purpose we compute the norms of some numbers $x + y\theta$ by means of the formula

$$\text{norm } (x + y\theta) = x^3 - ax^2y + bxy^2 - cy^3$$

if

$$\theta^3 + a\theta^2 + b\theta + c = 0.$$

We obtain

$$\text{norm } (1 + \theta) = -3 \cdot 11^2,$$
$$\text{norm } (2 - \theta) = 3^2 \cdot 11,$$
$$\text{norm } (5 - \theta) = -3 \cdot 19,$$
$$\text{norm } (3 - \theta) = 3^3.$$

These facts imply that the class number of the field is 3.

A treatment by rational methods is also possible for the classes, at least in many cases [21–23]. If the field admits an integral base which consists of the powers of a single number, then there is a one-to-one correspondence between the ideal classes and the classes of $n \times n$ matrices $S^{-1}AS$, where A is a fixed matrix with $f(A) = 0$. The elements a_{ik}, s_{ik} in $A = (a_{ik})$, $S = (s_{ik})$ are rational integers, and S runs through all matrices with $|S| = \pm 1$.

In complex quadratic fields the class number exceeds unity, apart from a finite number of cases. This was conjectured by Gauss and proved by Heilbronn [25]. Heilbronn also proves, with Linfoot [26], that for $m > 163$ at most one further m is possible such that the field $F(\sqrt{m})$ has class number unity. It is still an open question whether there is a further m. Work by D. H. Lehmer [27] indicates that probably no further m exists. (For class numbers in noncyclic cubic fields, see again [1, 9]).

16.10 Principal Idealization

A rather complicated computation concerns the application of the following famous theorem of Hilbert (see [28], Theorem 94, Zahl-bericht). Let f be a field and F a relatively cyclic extension of relative degree l of f (l is a prime number). Let all prime ideals of f split up in F into different prime ideals. Then there exists an ideal in f which is not a principal ideal in f but which is principal in F. Further, that ideal in f lies in a class of order l, and the class number of f is divisible by l.

If the class group of f is cyclic, then there is no further problem, but if the class group has at least two base classes, then the following problem arises:

Given such an f and F, which class of f is the one that does go over into the principal class in F?

If f is a quadratic field $R(\sqrt{m})$ and $l = 2$, this is not too difficult. However, if $l = 3$, the difficulties increase. In the first place, one has to go a long way to find a field with a 3-class number ≥ 9 and a non-cyclic class group. The first imaginary quadratic field with this property is $F(\sqrt{-3,299})$. It has a 3-class number 27. A field with a 3-class number 9 and a noncyclic class group is $F(\sqrt{-4,027})$. For this problem, a rational method was also found to succeed (see [28, 29]).

REFERENCES

1. D. H. Lehmer, "Guide to Tables in the Theory of Numbers," National Research Council, Bulletin 105, Washington, D.C., 1941.
2. J. von Neumann and H. H. Goldstine, A Numerical Study of a Conjecture by Kummer, *Math. Tables Aids Comput.*, vol. 7, pp. 133–134, 1953.
3. M. Hall, Indices in Cubic Fields, *Bull. Amer. Math. Soc.*, vol. 43, pp. 104–108, 1937.
4. S. Kuroda, Über die Zerlegung rationaler Primzahlen in gewissen nicht-abelschen Körpern, *J. Math. Soc. Jap.*, vol. 3, pp. 148–156, 1951.
5. R. Dedekind, "Gesammelte mathematische Werke," vol. I, pp. 202–232, Vieweg-Verlag, Brunswick, Germany, 1930.
6. Ö. Ore, Über den Zusammenhang zwischen den definierenden Gleichungen und der Idealtheorie in algebraischen Zahlkörpern, I, *Math. Ann.*, vol. 96, pp. 313–352, 1927.
7. Ö. Ore, Über den Zusammenhang zwischen den definierenden Gleichungen und der Idealtheorie in algebraischen Zahlkörpern, II, *Math. Ann.*, vol. 97, pp. 569–598, 1927.
8. H. Hasse, Arithmetische Bestimmung von Grundeinheit und Klassenzahl in zyklischen kubischen und biquadratischen Zahlkörpern, *Abh. Deutsch. Akad. Wiss. Math.-Nat. Kl.* (Jahrgang 1948), no. 2, 1950.
9. J. W. S. Cassels, The Rational Solutions of the Diophantine Equation $Y^2 = X^3 - D$, *Acta Math.*, vol. 82, pp. 243–273, 1950.
10. N. C. Ankeny, E. Artin, and S. Chowla, The Class Number of Real Quadratic Number Fields, *Ann. of Math.*, vol. 56, pp. 479–493, 1952.
11. E. L. Ince, "Cycles of Reduced Ideals in Quadratic Fields," British Association for the Advancement of Science Mathematical Tables, vol. IV, 1934.
12. H. Hasse, "Zahlentheorie," Akademie-Verlag, Berlin, 1949.
13. P. Furtwängler, Über die Klassenzahlen Abelscher Zahlkörper, *J. Reine Angew. Math.*, vol. 134, pp. 91–95, 1908.
14. P. Furtwängler, Über die Klassenzahlen der Kreisteilungskörper, *J. Reine Angew. Math.*, vol. 140, pp. 29–32, 1914.
15. H. Hasse, "Über die Klassenzahl Abelscher Zahlkörper," Akademie-Verlag, Berlin, 1952.
16. A. Scholz, Zwei Bemerkungen zum Klassenkörperturm, *J. Reine Angew. Math.*, vol. 161, pp. 201–207, 1929.
17. E. Inaba, Über die Struktur der l-Klassengruppe zyklischer Zahlkörper vom Primzahlgrad l, *J. Fac. Sci. Imp. Univ. Tokyo*, vol. IV, no. 2, pp. 61–115, 1940.
18. O. Taussky, A Remark on Unramified Class Fields, *J. London Math. Soc.*, vol. 12, pp. 86–88, 1937.
19. H. Minkowski, Dichteste gitterförmige Lagerung kongruenter Körper, *Nachr. Ges. Wiss. Göttingen*, pp. 311–355, 1904.
20. H. Davenport, Note on the Product of Three Homogeneous Linear Forms, *J. London Math. Soc.*, vol. 16, pp. 98–101, 1941.
21. O. Taussky, On a Theorem of Latimer and MacDuffee, *Canad. J. Math.*, vol. 1, pp. 300–302, 1949.
22. O. Taussky, Classes of Matrices and Quadratic Fields, *Pacific J. Math.*, vol. 1, pp. 127–132, 1951.

23. O. Taussky, Classes of Matrices and Quadratic Fields, II, *J. London Math. Soc.*, vol. 27, pp. 237–239, 1952.

24. O. Taussky, On Matrix Classes Corresponding to an Ideal and Its Inverse, *Illinois J. Math.*, vol. 1, pp. 108–113, 1957.

25. H. Heilbronn, On the Class-number in Imaginary Quadratic Fields, *Quart. J. Math. Oxford Ser.*, vol. 5, pp. 150–160, 1934.

26. H. Heilbronn and E. H. Linfoot, On the Imaginary Quadratic Corpora of Class-number One, *Quart. J. Math. Oxford Ser.*, vol. 5, pp. 293–301, 1934.

27. D. H. Lehmer, On Imaginary Quadratic Fields Whose Class Number is Unity, *Bull. Amer. Math. Soc.*, vol. 39, p. 360, 1933.

28. D. Hilbert, "Gesammelte Abhandlungen," vol. I, Springer-Verlag, Berlin, 1932.

29. A. Scholz and Olga Taussky, Die Hauptideale der kubischen Klassenkörper imaginär quadratischer Zahlkörper: ihre rechnerische Bestimmung und ihr Einfluss auf den Klassenkörperturm, *J. Reine Angew. Math.*, vol. 171, pp. 19–41, 1934.

30. O. Taussky, Arnold Scholz zum Gedächtnis, *Math. Nachr.*, vol. 7, pp. 374–386, 1952.

31. W. E. H. Berwick, The Classification of Ideal Numbers that depend on a Cubic Irrationality, *Proc. London Math. Soc.*, vol. 12, pp. 393–429, 1913.

32. G. Beyer, Über eine Klasseneinteilung aller kubischen Restcharaktere, *Abh. Math. Sem. Univ. Hamburg*, vol. 19, pp. 115–116, 1954.

33. G. Bullig, Ein periodisches Verfahren zur Berechnung eines Systems von Grundeinheiten in den total reellen kubischen Körpern, *Abh. Math. Sem. Univ. Hamburg*, vol. 12, pp. 369–414, 1938.

34. H. Cohn, Periodic Algorithm for Cubic Forms, I, *Amer. J. Math.*, vol. 74, pp. 821–833, 1952.

35. H. Cohn, Periodic Algorithm for Cubic Forms, II, *Amer. J. Math.*, vol. 76, pp. 904–914, 1954.

36. H. Cohn, Numerical Study of Signature Rank of Cyclotomic Units, *Math. Tables Aids Comput.*, vol. 8, pp. 186–188, 1954.

37. H. Cohn, Some Experiments in Ideal Factorization on the MIDAC, *J. Assoc. Comput. Mach.*, vol. 2, pp. 111–116, 1955.

38. H. Cohn, Numerical Study of Quintics of Small Discriminant, *Comm. Pure Appl. Math.*, vol. 8, pp. 377–385, 1955.

39. H. Cohn, A Numerical Study of Dedekind's Cubic Class Number Formula, *J. Res. Nat. Bur. Standards*, vol. 59, pp. 265–271, 1957.

40. H. Cohn, A Computation of Some Bi-quadratic Class Numbers, *Math. Tables Aids Comput.*, vol. 12, pp. 213–217, 1958.

41. H. Cohn, Numerical Study of the Representation of a Totally Positive Quadratic Integer as the Sum of Quadratic Integral Squares, *Numer. Math.*, vol. 1, pp. 121–134, 1959.

42. H. Cohn and S. Gorn, A Computation of Cyclic Cubic Units, *J. Res. Nat. Bur. Standards*, vol. 59, pp. 155–168, 1957.

43. B. N. Delaunay and D. K. Faddeev, Theory of Irrationals of the Third Degree, *Trav. Inst. Stekloff*, vol. 11, 1940 (in Russian).

44. A. Fröhlich, A Remark on the Class Number of Abelian Fields, *J. London Math. Soc.*, vol. 29, p. 498, 1954.

45. A. Fröhlich, On the Absolute Class Group of Abelian Fields, *J. London Math. Soc.*, vol. 29, pp. 211–217, 1954.

46. A. Fröhlich, On a Method for the Determination of Class Number Factors in Number Fields, *Mathematika*, vol. 4, pp. 113–121, 1957.

47. S. Gorn, "A Computation with Algebraic Numbers," Ballistic Research Laboratories, Aberdeen Proving Ground, Report 963, 1955.

48. J. Hunter, The Minimum Discriminants of Cyclic Fields, *Proc. Glasgow Math. Assoc.*, vol. 3, pp. 57–67, 1957.

49. K. Iwasawa, On Some Invariants of Cyclotomic Fields, *Amer. J. Math.*, vol. 80, pp. 773–783, 1958.

50. E. Lehmer, On the Location of Gauss Sums, *Math. Tables Aids Comput.*, vol. 10, pp. 194–202, 1956.

51. A. Markoff, Sur les nombres entiers dépendents d'une racine cubique d'un nombre entier, *Mém. Acad. Imp. Sci. Petersbourg*, ser. 7, vol. 38, no. 9, 1882.

52. C. Meyer, "Die Berechnung der Klassenzahl abelscher Körper über quadratischen Zahlkörpern," Akademie-Verlag, Berlin, 1957.

53. T. Nagell,- Bemerkungen über numerisches Rechnen mit algebraischen Zahlen, *J. Reine Angew. Math.*, vol. 176, pp. 70–72, 1931.

54. L. Rédei, Die 2-Ringklassengruppe des quadratischen Zahlkörpers und die Theorie der Pellschen Gleichung, *Acta Math. Acad. Sci. Hungar.*, vol. 4, pp. 31–87, 1953.

55. H. P. F. Swinnerton-Dyer, Table for Class Number and Fundamental Unit for Cubic Cyclic Fields with Prime Conductor $f < 2800$, Obtained on EDSAC (Cambridge) by a Modification of the Method in Hasse [15], Using a Result of H. Heilbronn (unpublished).

56. L. Tornheim, Minimal Basis and Inessential Discriminant Divisors for a Cubic Field, *Pacific J. Math.*, vol. 5, pp. 623–631, 1955.

57. J. V. Uspensky, A Method of Finding Units in Cubic Orders of a Negative Discriminant, *Trans. Amer. Math. Soc.*, vol. 33, pp. 1–22, 1931.

58. J. von Neumann and B. Tuckerman, Continued Fraction Expansion of $2^{1/3}$, *Math. Tables Aids Comput.*, vol. 9, pp. 23–24, 1955.

17

Linear Estimation and Related Topics

MARVIN ZELEN*

MATHEMATICS RESEARCH CENTER

UNITED STATES ARMY

UNIVERSITY OF WISCONSIN

This chapter is concerned with: (1) the Gauss-Markoff theorem, (2) likelihood-ratio tests of linear hypothesis, (3) the distribution of quadratic forms and of the variance ratio, and (4) applications. These topics cover much of the theory in applied statistics and are the fundamental theorems on which the widely used analysis of variance is based.†

THE GAUSS-MARKOFF THEOREM

17.1 Preliminaries

Definition 17.1. Let y be a random variable having the distribution function $F(y)$, that is,

(i)	$0 \leq F(y) \leq 1,$
(ii)	$F(-\infty) = 0, \qquad F(+\infty) = 1,$
(iii)	$F(y)$ is nondecreasing,
(iv)	$F(y)$ is continuous on the right.

The expected value of the random variable y is defined by

$$E(y) = \mu = \int_{-\infty}^{\infty} y \, dF(y). \tag{17.1}$$

* This chapter was written when the author was at the National Bureau of Standards.

† *Added in Proof:* Since this article has been written two excellent books have been published which cover many of the topics discussed in this chapter. These are F. A. Graybill, "An Introduction to Linear Statistical Models," vol. I, McGraw-Hill Book Company, Inc., New York, 1961; and H. Scheffe, "The Analysis of Variance," John Wiley & Sons, Inc., New York, 1959.

Definition 17.2.   The variance of y is defined by

$$\sigma^2 = E(y - \mu)^2 = \int_{-\infty}^{\infty} (y - \mu)^2 \, dF(y). \tag{17.2}$$

Note that $\sigma^2 = E(y^2) - \mu^2$.

Definition 17.3.   Let y_i and y_j be random variables having the joint distribution $F(y_i, y_j)$.   Then the covariance between y_i and y_j is defined by

$$\sigma_{ij} = \operatorname{cov}(y_i, y_j) = E[(y_i - \mu_i)(y_j - \mu_j)]$$

$$= \int_{-\infty}^{\infty} \int_{-\infty}^{\infty} (y_i - \mu_i)(y_j - \mu_j) \, dF(y_i, y_j) \tag{17.3}$$

Note that $\sigma_{ij} = E(y_i y_j) - \mu_i \mu_j$.

Definition 17.4.   Let $Y' = (y_1, y_2, \ldots, y_n)$ be a vector of random variables and let $\mu' = (\mu_1, \mu_2, \ldots, \mu_n)$ where $\mu_i = E(y_i)$.   Then we write $\mu = E(Y)$.   Also, let $\sigma_{ii} = \sigma_i^2$ and V be the $n \times n$ matrix $V = (\sigma_{ij})$. V is termed the variance-covariance matrix of the vector Y and is defined by

$$\operatorname{var} Y = V = E[(Y - \mu)(Y - \mu)'] = E(YY') - \mu\mu'. \tag{17.4}$$

The following two lemmas will be useful in what follows.

Lemma 17.1.   *Let C be an $r \times n$ matrix.   Then*

(i) $$E(CY) = C\mu,$$

(ii) $$\operatorname{var} CY = CVC'.$$

Proof.   (i) follows directly from the definition of the expected value operator.   (ii) is proved as follows:

$$\operatorname{var} CY = E[(CY - C\mu)(CY - C\mu)']$$

$$= CE[(Y - \mu)(Y - \mu)']C' = CVC'.$$

An important case is that in which $C = (c_1, c_2, \ldots, c_n)$ is a $1 \times n$ vector and $V = \sigma^2 I$.   Then $\operatorname{var} CY = CC'\sigma^2 = \sigma^2 \sum_{i=1}^{n} c_i^2$.   Note also from (ii) that $E[(CY)(CY)'] = CVC' + (C\mu)(C\mu)'$.

Lemma 17.2.   *The expected value of the quadratic form $Y'AY$, where $A = (a_{ij})$ is an $n \times n$ matrix, is $E(Y'AY) = \mu'A\mu + \operatorname{tr} AV$, where $\operatorname{tr} AV$ denotes the trace of AV.*

Proof.   Since $Y'AY = \sum_i a_{ii} y_i^2 + \sum\sum_{i \neq j} a_{ij} y_i y_j$, we have

$$E(Y'AY) = \sum_i a_{ii} (\sigma_{ii} + \mu_i^2) + \sum\sum_{i \neq j} a_{ij} (\sigma_{ij} + \mu_i \mu_j)$$

$$= \sum\sum_{ij} a_{ij} \mu_i \mu_j + \sum\sum_{ij} a_{ij} \sigma_{ij}$$

$$= \mu'A\mu + \operatorname{tr} AV.$$

17.2   The Gauss-Markoff Theorem

The method of least squares has been in use now for over 150 years. It is now recognized that Gauss [4], in 1821 (collected works, 1873), placed this method on a sound theoretical basis without any assumptions that the random variables follow a normal distribution.   Gauss' contribution was somehow neglected until it was "rediscovered" by Markoff [6].   For a more detailed historical introduction, see Plackett [7].

Definition 17.5.   A function $f(Y)$ of the random vector Y is an unbiased estimate of a parameter θ if $E[f(Y)] = \theta$.   When such a function $f(Y)$ exists, then θ is called an estimable parameter.

Definition 17.6.   Let $l' = (l_1, l_2, \ldots, l_n)$ be a vector of constants. Then the linear function $L = l'Y$ is called the minimum variance unbiased estimate of θ if $E(L) = \theta$ and var $L = \min$ (among the class of all linear estimators).   Sometimes this estimate is called the "best estimate."

Theorem 17.1 (*The Gauss-Markoff theorem*).   *Let* $X = (X_{i\alpha})$, $i = 1, 2, \ldots, p$; $\alpha = 1, 2, \ldots, n$ *be a* $p \times n$ ($p \leq n$) *matrix of known constants with rank p and let* $\beta' = (\beta_1, \beta_2, \ldots, \beta_p)$ *be a vector of unknown parameters. Consider the* $1 \times n$ *vector of random variables* $Y' = (y_1, y_2, \ldots, y_n)$ *such that*

$$E(Y) = X'\beta,$$
$$\text{var } Y = \sigma^2 I. \tag{17.5}$$

Then the best estimate of any linear function $\theta = l'\beta$, $l' = (l_1, l_2, \ldots, l_n)$ *is obtained by substituting into θ the estimates $\hat{\beta}_i$ obtained by minimizing the sum of squares $S = (Y - X'\beta)'(Y - X'\beta)$ with respect to each β_i.   Furthermore, the solutions of the $\hat{\beta}$ are obtained by solving the set of p simultaneous equations*

$$a\hat{\beta} = XY, \tag{17.6}$$

where $a = XX'$.   [The set of equations (17.6) is usually termed the normal equations.]

Proof.   (i) Consider the linear function $\hat{\theta} = d'Y$, where d is determined by the conditions (17.5).   Since $\hat{\theta}$ is to be unbiased, we have $E(\hat{\theta}) = d'E(Y) = d'X'\beta = l'\beta$, which results in

$$d'X' = l' \quad \text{or} \quad Xd = l. \tag{17.7}$$

Using Lemma 17.1, var $\hat{\theta} = d'd\sigma^2$.   Thus we wish to minimize $d'd$ subject to the condition (17.7).   Using the method of Lagrange multipliers, let $Q = d'd - 2\lambda'(Xd - l)$, where $\lambda' = (\lambda_1, \lambda_2, \ldots, \lambda_p)$. Define the operator $\partial/\partial d$ by

$$\frac{\partial}{\partial d} = \left(\frac{\partial}{\partial d_1}, \frac{\partial}{\partial d_2}, \ldots, \frac{\partial}{\partial d_p} \right).$$

Then a necessary condition for Q to be a minimum is that $\partial Q/\partial d = 0$. This results in

$$\frac{\partial Q}{\partial d} = 2d' - 2\lambda'X = 0$$

or

$$d = X'\lambda. \tag{17.8}$$

Premultiplying (17.8) by X results in $Xd = a\lambda = l$, and thus, since $a = XX'$ is not singular,

$$\lambda = a^{-1}l. \tag{17.9}$$

Substituting (17.9) in (17.8) results in

$$d = X'a^{-1}l, \tag{17.10}$$

and since $\theta = d'Y$, we have

$$\theta = l'a^{-1}XY. \tag{17.11}$$

However, $E(\theta) = l'a^{-1}XE(Y) = l'\beta$. Therefore we can define $\hat{\beta}$ by

$$\hat{\beta} = a^{-1}XY, \tag{17.12}$$

and $\hat{\beta}$ will be an unbiased estimate of β. Premultiplying (17.12) by a results in the normal equations.

(ii) It remains to show that the same result is obtained if $S = (Y - X'\beta)'(Y - X'\beta)$ is minimized with respect to β. The necessary condition for S to be a minimum is that $\partial S/\partial \beta = 0$. Carrying out the differentiation results in

$$\frac{\partial S}{\partial \beta'} = -2X(Y - X'\beta) = 0,$$

which produces the normal equations. One can easily show that the solution of the normal equations results in minimum S by virtue of the identity

$$S = (Y - X'\hat{\beta})'(Y - X'\hat{\beta}) + \delta'a\delta \geq (Y - X'\hat{\beta})'(Y - X'\hat{\beta}),$$

where $\beta = \hat{\beta} + \delta$.

Corollary 1.

$$\operatorname{var} \hat{\beta} = a^{-1}\sigma^2.$$

Proof. Since $\hat{\beta} = a^{-1}XY$, we have, using Lemma 17.1,

$$\operatorname{var} \hat{\beta} = \operatorname{var}(a^{-1}XY) = (a^{-1}X)\operatorname{var} Y (a^{-1}X)'$$
$$= (a^{-1}X)(\sigma^2 I)(X'a^{-1}) = a^{-1}\sigma^2.$$

Corollary 2. *The quadratic form*

$$s^2 = \frac{(Y - X'\hat{\beta})'(Y - X'\hat{\beta})}{n - p} \tag{17.13}$$

is an unbiased estimate of σ^2; that is, $E(s^2) = \sigma^2$.

Proof. We can write

$$Y'Y = (Y - X'\hat{\beta})'(Y - X'\hat{\beta}) + \hat{\beta}'a\hat{\beta}.$$

Therefore

$$E[(Y - X'\hat{\beta})'(Y - X'\hat{\beta})] = E(Y'Y) - E(\hat{\beta}'a\hat{\beta}).$$

Using Lemma 17.2,

$$E[(Y - X'\hat{\beta})'(Y - X'\hat{\beta})] = [(X'\hat{\beta})'(X'\hat{\beta}) + n\sigma^2] - (\beta'a\beta + p\sigma^2)$$
$$= (n - p)\sigma^2.$$

Definition 17.7. The quantity $v_\alpha = y_\alpha - \sum_{i=1}^{p} \beta_i X_{i\alpha}$ is defined to be the residual of the αth observation ($\alpha = 1, 2, \ldots, n$). The vector $v = (Y - X'\hat{\beta})$ is termed the residual vector. Since $Xv = X(Y - X'\hat{\beta}) = 0$, there are p linear relations among the n residuals. Hence only $n - p$ of the residuals are independent. Since the quantity s^2 can be written

$$s^2 = \frac{v'v}{n - p}, \tag{17.14}$$

the estimate s^2 is said to have $(n - p)$ degrees of freedom, as it can be written as a sum of squares involving only $(n - p)$ variables.

Remark. An identity which is often used for computing $v'v = (Y - X'\hat{\beta})'(Y - X'\hat{\beta})$ is

$$v'v = Y'Y - \hat{\beta}'XY. \tag{17.15}$$

Proof.

$$v'v = v'(Y - X'\hat{\beta}) = v'Y = (Y - X'\hat{\beta})'Y$$
$$= Y'Y - \hat{\beta}'XY \quad \text{as } v'X' = 0.$$

Corollary 3. *The residuals v are uncorrelated with $\hat{\beta}$; that is, $\text{cov}(v, \hat{\beta}) = 0$; hence s^2 is uncorrelated with $\hat{\beta}$.*

Proof. Note that $E(v) = E(Y - X'\hat{\beta}) = 0$. Therefore $\text{cov}(v, \hat{\beta}) = E[v(\hat{\beta} - \beta)'] = E(v\hat{\beta}')$ as $E(v\beta') = 0$. Since $v = Y - X'\hat{\beta} = (I - X'a^{-1}X)Y$, we have

$$E(v\hat{\beta}') = E[(I - X'a^{-1}X)Y(Y'X'a^{-1})]$$
$$= (I - X'a^{-1}X)(X'\beta\beta'X + \sigma^2 I)(X'a^{-1})$$
$$= (X'\beta\beta'X - X'a^{-1}XX'\beta\beta'X)X'a^{-1}$$
$$+ \sigma^2(X'a^{-1} - X'a^{-1}XX'a^{-1}) = 0.$$

Theorem 17.2. *Let $E(Y) = X'\beta$ and var $Y = V\sigma^2$, where V is positive definite. Then the normal equations for estimating β are $a*\hat{\beta} = XV^{-1}Y$, where $a* = XV^{-1}X'$.*

Proof. Since V is real, symmetric, and positive definite, there exists a matrix Γ such that $V = \Gamma\Gamma'$, where Γ is real and nonsingular. Consider the transformation $Y* = \Gamma^{-1}Y$, $X* = X\Gamma'^{-1}$. Then var $Y* = \Gamma^{-1}(V\sigma^2)\Gamma'^{-1} = I\sigma^2$ and $E(Y*) = \Gamma^{-1}X'\beta = X'*\beta$. Thus the conditions of the Gauss-Markoff theorem are satisfied by $Y*$, and the normal equations are $a*\hat{\beta} = X*Y*$, where $a* = X*X*' = XV^{-1}X'$ and $X*Y* = XV^{-1}Y$.

Corollary 1. *The situation often arises where V can be written as the diagonal matrix*

$$V = \begin{pmatrix} \sigma_1^2 & & & & 0 \\ & \sigma_2^2 & & & \\ & & \cdot & & \\ & & & \cdot & \\ & & & & \cdot \\ 0 & & & & \sigma_n^2 \end{pmatrix} = D(\sigma_1^2, \sigma_2^2, \ldots, \sigma_n^2).$$

Then $\Gamma = D(\sigma_1, \sigma_2, \ldots, \sigma_n)$ and $Y* = D^{-1}(\sigma_1, \sigma_2, \ldots, \sigma_n)Y$, $X* = D^{-1}(\sigma_1, \sigma_2, \ldots, \sigma_n)X$.

Theorem 17.3. *Let $E(Y) = X'\beta$, var $Y = \sigma^2 I$, and let the β satisfy the restrictions $K'\beta = m$, where K' is an $r \times p$ matrix $(r < p)$ of rank r which is known and $m' = (m_1, m_2, \ldots, m_r)$ is a vector of known constants. Then the normal equations for estimating β take the form*

$$\begin{pmatrix} a & K \\ K' & 0 \end{pmatrix} \begin{pmatrix} \beta \\ \lambda \end{pmatrix} = \begin{pmatrix} XY \\ m \end{pmatrix}.$$

Proof. Our problem is to minimize $(Y - X'\beta)'(Y - X'\beta)$ subject to the r linear restrictions $K'\beta = m$. Let $\lambda' = (\lambda_1, \lambda_2, \ldots, \lambda_r)$ be a vector of Lagrange multipliers and form the function $Q = (Y - X'\beta)'(Y - X'\beta) + 2\lambda'(K'\beta - m)$. Differentiating Q with respect to β and setting the derivative equal to zero results in

$$\frac{\partial Q}{\partial \beta} = -2(Y - X'\beta)'X' + 2\lambda'K' = 0,$$

which can be written, after taking the transpose, as

$$a\hat{\beta} + K\lambda = XY. \tag{17.16}$$

Therefore (17.16), together with $K'\beta = m$, is a basis for finding the estimate of β.

Corollary. *Define*

$$\begin{pmatrix} a & K \\ K' & 0 \end{pmatrix}^{-1} = \begin{pmatrix} c_1 & c_2 \\ c_2' & c_3 \end{pmatrix}.$$

Then

(i) $c_1 a c_1 = c_1$

(ii) $\operatorname{var} \hat{\beta} = c_1 \sigma^2$

(iii) $E[(Y - X'\hat{\beta})'(Y - X'\hat{\beta})] = (n - p + r)\sigma^2$

Proof. Multiplying $\begin{pmatrix} a & K \\ K' & 0 \end{pmatrix}$ by its inverse results in the four equations

$$ac_1 + Kc_2' = I, \qquad\qquad (17.17a)$$
$$K'c_1 = 0, \qquad\qquad (17.17b)$$
$$ac_2 + Kc_3 = 0, \qquad\qquad (17.17c)$$
$$K'c_2 = I. \qquad\qquad (17.17d)$$

(i) Premultiplying (17.17a) by c_1 gives

$$c_1 a c_1 + c_1 K c_2' = c_1 a c_1 = c_1,$$

as $c_1 K = 0$ from (17.17b).

(ii) The solutions for $\hat{\beta}$ can be written as

$$\hat{\beta} = c_1 XY + c_2 m.$$

Now, $\operatorname{var} \hat{\beta} = \operatorname{var}(c_1 XY)$, as $c_2 m$ is constant; therefore

$$\operatorname{var}(c_1 XY) = (c_1 X) \operatorname{var} Y (c_1 X)' = (c_1 XX'c_1)\sigma^2 = c_1 \sigma^2.$$

(iii) We can write the residual sum of squares as

$$S = (Y - X'\hat{\beta})'(Y - X'\hat{\beta}) = (Y - X'\hat{\beta}_0)'(Y - X'\hat{\beta}_0) + \lambda' W \lambda$$

where

$$\hat{\beta}_0 = a^{-1} XY,$$
$$W = K' a^{-1} K,$$
$$\lambda = W^{-1}(K'\hat{\beta}_0 - m).$$

Note that $\hat{\beta}_0 = a^{-1} XY$ is the estimate of β ignoring the restraint $K'\beta = m$. Furthermore, the quantity λ is proportional to the deviations of $K'\hat{\beta}_0$ from m. Taking the expectation of λ, we have $E(\lambda) = W^{-1}(K'\beta - m) = 0$, and thus

$$\operatorname{var} \lambda = W^{-1} K' (\operatorname{var} \hat{\beta}_0) K W^{-1} = \sigma^2 W^{-1}(K' a^{-1} K) W^{-1} = \sigma^2 W^{-1}.$$

Since $E\{(Y - X'\hat{\beta}_0)'(Y - X'\hat{\beta}_0)\} = (n - p)\sigma^2$, we find that the expected value of S is

$$E(S) = (n - p)\sigma^2 + \operatorname{tr} W(\operatorname{var} \lambda) = (n - p + r)\sigma^2, \quad (17.18)$$

as $\operatorname{tr} W(\operatorname{var} \lambda) = \sigma^2 \operatorname{tr} WW^{-1} = r\sigma^2$.

Using the relations $(17.17a)$ to $(17.17d)$, it is easy to show that c_1 can be written

$$c_1 = a^{-1}[I - K(K'a^{-1}K)^{-1}K'a^{-1}] \tag{17.19}$$

provided a is not singular. However, if a is singular, we can write a as

$$a = a_0 + DKK', \tag{17.20}$$

where a_0 is nonsingular and D is a nonsingular arbitrary diagonal matrix. Then c_1 can be written as in (17.19), except that a_0^{-1} replaces a^{-1}. From a practical point of view, it is often not convenient to solve for the $\hat{\beta}$ using the $(r + p)$ linear equations of Theorem 17.3. Instead, one can solve the set of p linear equations

$$a_0\hat{\beta} = XY - DKm, \tag{17.21}$$

where the diagonal matrix D is chosen in (17.20), so as to make a_0 a convenient matrix for inversion.

In many applications, the matrix of coefficients $a = XX'$ of the normal equations will be singular and have rank $p - r$. Hence the solutions for the $\hat{\beta}$ will not be unique. This implies that some linear functions of β will not be estimable. It is then convenient to let the $\hat{\beta}$ satisfy r arbitrary linearly independent restraints, chosen such that the restraints are nonestimable functions of β, and use the setup of Theorem 17.3.

REFERENCES

1. A. C. Aitken, On Least Squares and Linear Combination of Observations, *Proc. Roy. Soc. Edinburgh Sect. A*, vol. 55, pp. 42–47, 1934.

2. F. N. David and J. Neyman, Extension of the Markoff Theorem on Least Squares, *Statist. Res. Mem. London*, vol. 2, pp. 105–116, 1938.

3. W. E. Deming, "Statistical Adjustment of Data," John Wiley & Sons, Inc., 1943.

4. C. F. Gauss, "Werke," vol. 4, "Theoria combinationis observationum erroribus minimis obnoxiae," Gottingen, 1873.

5. P. S. Laplace, "Oeuvres," vol. 7, "Théorie analytique des probabilités," 3d ed., Paris, 1886.

6. A. A. Markoff, "Wahrscheinlichkeitsrechnung," H. Liebmann, tr., 2d ed., Leipzig, 1912.

7. R. L. Plackett, A Historical Note on the Method of Least Squares, *Biometrika*, vol. 36, pp. 458–460, 1949.

LIKELIHOOD RATIO TESTS OF LINEAR HYPOTHESIS

17.3   Maximum Likelihood Estimates for Normal Distributions

Definition 17.8.   The (one-dimensional) random variable y is said to have a normal distribution with mean μ and variance σ^2 if its probability density function is of the form

$$f(y;\mu,\sigma^2) = (\sigma^2 2\pi)^{-\frac{1}{2}} \exp\left[-\frac{1}{2\sigma^2} (y - \mu)^2 \right], \qquad -\infty < y < \infty.$$

If $Y' = (y_1, y_2, \ldots, y_n)$ follow a normal distribution with $E(Y) = X'\beta$ and var $(Y) = \sigma^2 I$, then the joint probability density function of Y is

$$f(Y;\beta,\sigma^2) = (\sigma^2 2\pi)^{-n/2} \exp\left[-\frac{(Y - X'\beta)'(Y - X'\beta)}{2\sigma^2} \right]. \quad (17.22)$$

Also any linear function of normally distributed variables will itself follow a normal distribution.

Definition 17.9.   The maximum likelihood estimates of the unknown parameters $\beta' = (\beta_1, \beta_2, \ldots, \beta_p)$ and σ^2 are those estimates which maximize $f(Y;\beta,\sigma^2)$.

Theorem 17.4.   *The maximum likelihood estimates for β and σ^2 are* (i) *the same estimates for β as obtained from the Gauss-Markoff theorem,* (ii) $\hat{\sigma}^2 = (Y - X'\hat{\beta})'(Y - X'\hat{\beta})/n$.

Proof.   Since $L = \ln f(Y;\beta,\sigma^2)$ is a monotonic function of $f(Y;\beta,\sigma^2)$, it is sufficient to maximize L.   Thus

$$L = -\frac{n}{2} \ln 2\pi - \frac{n}{2} \ln \sigma^2 - \frac{1}{2\sigma^2} (Y - X'\beta)'(Y - X'\beta),$$

and

$$\frac{\partial L}{\partial \beta} = -\frac{1}{2\sigma^2}\left[\frac{\partial}{\partial \beta} (Y - X'\beta)'(Y - X'\beta) \right] = 0, \quad (17.23)$$

$$\frac{\partial L}{\partial \sigma^2} = -\frac{n}{2\sigma^2} + \frac{1}{2\sigma^4} (Y - X'\beta)'(Y - X'\beta) = 0. \quad (17.24)$$

It is clear that (17.23) results in the normal equations and that simplifying (17.24) and substituting $\hat{\beta}$ for β give

$$\hat{\sigma}^2 = \frac{(Y - X'\hat{\beta})'(Y - X'\hat{\beta})}{n}.$$

Corollary.   *The value of $f(Y;\beta,\sigma^2)$ obtained by substituting the maximum likelihood estimates for β and σ^2 is*

$$f(Y;\hat{\beta},\hat{\sigma}^2) = [\hat{\sigma}^2(2\pi)]^{-n/2} \exp\left(-\frac{n}{2} \right).$$

17.4   Likelihood-ratio Tests

Let $Y' = (y_1, y_2, \ldots, y_n)$ be a vector of random variables which follow the joint distribution $P(Y;\theta)$, where $\theta' = (\theta_1, \theta_2, \ldots, \theta_k)$ denotes a vector of parameters.* Let Ω be the k-dimensional euclidean space of admissible parameter values for θ and let ω be a subspace of Ω. Often statisticians are interested in testing the hypothesis that the parameters θ lie in the subspace ω. This is often referred to as a null hypothesis and is written H_0: $\theta \in \omega$. The alternative to H_0 is that $\theta \in \Omega - \omega$ and is often written H_1: $\theta \in \Omega - \omega$.

Definition 17.10.   Consider a test of the null hypothesis H_0: $\theta \in \omega$. Define

$$P_0(Y;\hat{\theta}_0) = \max_{\theta \in \omega} P(Y;\theta),$$

$$P_1(Y;\hat{\theta}_1) = \max_{\theta \in \Omega} P(Y;\theta).$$

Thus $P_0(Y;\hat{\theta}_0)$ and $P_1(Y;\hat{\theta}_1)$ are functions only of Y. Also, $\hat{\theta}_0$ is by definition the maximum likelihood estimate for θ allowing θ to take on values within ω, and $\hat{\theta}_1$ is the maximum likelihood estimate of θ allowing θ to take on values over the entire space Ω. Then the likelihood ratio is defined by

$$\lambda = \frac{P_0(Y;\hat{\theta}_0)}{P_1(Y;\hat{\theta}_1)}.$$

Note that $0 \le \lambda \le 1$ because $P_0(Y;\hat{\theta}_0) \le P_1(Y;\hat{\theta}_1)$. Note also that, if H_0 is a correct hypothesis, λ will be near unity, and the closer λ is to unity, the more belief we have in the correctness of H_0.

Since λ depends only on the observations Y, it may be possible to find the distribution of λ and choose a $\lambda = \lambda_\alpha$, say, such that

$$\Pr \{\lambda \le \lambda_\alpha \mid H_0 \text{ is true}\} = \alpha, \qquad (0 < \alpha < 1).$$

Then, to determine whether H_0 or H_1 is supported by Y, we can adopt the rule of accepting H_0 if $\lambda > \lambda_\alpha$ and of accepting H_1 if $\lambda \le \lambda_\alpha$. Adopting such a rule involves the probability α that we shall accept H_1 even though H_0 is the correct hypothesis. The quantity α is termed the level of significance of the statistical test and is often referred to as the type I error. On the other hand, we might accept H_0 when H_1 is correct. The probability of an error of this kind is referred to as the type II error.

---

* $P(Y;\theta)$ denotes a probability density function if the distribution is of the continuous type; if the distribution is of the discrete type, then $P(Y;\theta)$ denotes the discrete probability of Y.

17.5   Likelihood-ratio Tests of General Linear Hypothesis

Let $E(Y) = X'\beta$ and var $y = \sigma^2 I$ and assume that Y follows a normal distribution. Define $\beta' = (\beta_0', \beta_1')$ where β_0 is a $p - r \times 1$ vector and β_1 is an $r \times 1$ vector; $X' = (X_0', X_1')$, where X_0 is $p - r \times n$ and X_1 is $r \times n$. Then $E(Y) = X_0'\beta_0 + X_1'\beta_1$. Let us consider the null hypothesis that

$$H_0: \beta_1 = 0, \qquad -\infty < \beta_0 < +\infty$$

versus the alternative that

$$H_1: \beta_1 \neq 0, \qquad -\infty < \beta_0 < +\infty.$$

By $\beta_1 = 0$ we mean that each element of β_1 is hypothesized to be equal to zero. The expression $-\infty < \beta_0 < \infty$ indicates that the elements of β_0 can take any value on the real line. The likelihood-ratio test will be derived for testing this null hypothesis.

Theorem 17.5.   *The likelihood-ratio test for*

$$H_0: \beta_1 = 0, \qquad -\infty < \beta_0 < \infty$$

is a monotonic function of

$$F = \frac{q_1/r}{q_2/(n-p)}$$

where

$$q_1 = (\hat{\beta}_0 - \tilde{\beta}_0)' X_0 Y + \hat{\beta}_1' X_1 Y,$$
$$q_2 = (Y - X'\hat{\beta})'(Y - X'\hat{\beta}) = Y'Y - \hat{\beta} XY,$$

and where $\tilde{\beta}_0$ and $\hat{\beta}' = (\hat{\beta}_0, \hat{\beta}_1')$ are solutions of

$$(X_0 X_0')\tilde{\beta}_0 = X_0 Y$$

and

$$a\hat{\beta} = XY, \qquad a = XX',$$

respectively.   The quantity F is termed the variance ratio or F statistic.

Proof. The likelihood ratio can be written, by virtue of the corollary to Theorem 17.4, as

$$\lambda = \frac{f(Y; \tilde{\beta}_0, \tilde{\sigma}^2)}{f(Y; \hat{\beta}, \hat{\sigma}^2)} = \left(\frac{\hat{\sigma}^2}{\tilde{\sigma}^2}\right)^{n/2}, \qquad (17.25)$$

where $\tilde{\sigma}^2$ denotes the estimate of σ^2 if H_0 is the true hypothesis and $\hat{\sigma}^2$ denotes the estimate of σ^2 allowing σ^2 and β to take on values over the entire parameter space.

If H_0 is true, $E(Y) = X_0'\beta_0$, and using the Gauss-Markoff theorem results in

$$(X_0 X_0')\tilde{\beta}_0 = X_0 Y.$$

The maximum likelihood estimate for σ^2 is

$$\tilde{\sigma}^2 = \frac{(Y - X_0'\tilde{\beta}_0)'(Y - X_0'\tilde{\beta}_0)}{n}.$$

On the other hand, if H_0 is not a correct hypothesis,

$$E(Y) = X_0'\beta_0 + X_1'\beta_1 = X'\beta$$

and $$a\beta = XY, \qquad a = XX'.$$

Here the estimate is

$$\hat{\sigma}^2 = \frac{(y - X'\hat{\beta})'(y - X'\hat{\beta})}{n}.$$

It suffices, in considering likelihood-ratio tests, to consider any monotonic function of the likelihood ratio as the test criterion. In particular, let us take

$$F = \frac{n - p}{r}(\lambda^{-2/n} - 1) = \frac{(\tilde{\sigma}^2 - \hat{\sigma}^2)/r}{\hat{\sigma}^2/(n - p)} \qquad (17.26)$$

as the test criterion. Substituting the values for $\tilde{\sigma}^2$ and $\hat{\sigma}^2$ in (17.26) gives the desired result.

Corollary. *The quadratic form q_1 appearing in the numerator of F can be written as $q_1 = \hat{\beta}_1'C_{11}^{-1}\hat{\beta}_1$, provided C_{11} is nonsingular.*

Proof. If we define

$$\begin{pmatrix} C_{00} & C_{01} \\ C_{10} & C_{11} \end{pmatrix} = \begin{pmatrix} X_0X_0' & X_0X_1' \\ X_1X_0' & X_1X_1' \end{pmatrix}^{-1}, \qquad C_{01} = C_{10}',$$

then $$\begin{pmatrix} \hat{\beta}_0 \\ \hat{\beta}_1 \end{pmatrix} = \begin{pmatrix} C_{00}X_0Y + C_{01}C_1Y \\ C_{10}X_0Y + C_{11}X_1Y \end{pmatrix}.$$

Therefore $q_1 = (\hat{\beta}_0 - \tilde{\beta}_0)'X_0Y + \hat{\beta}_1'X_1Y$ can be written as

$$q_1 = Y'[X_0'C_{00}X_0 + X_1'C_{10}X_0 + X_0'C_{01}X_1 + X_1'C_{11}X_1 - X_0'(X_0X_0')^{-1}X_0]Y.$$

Now

$$\hat{\beta}_1'C_{11}^{-1}\hat{\beta}_1 = Y'(X_0'C_{10}'C_{11}^{-1}C_{10}X_0 + X_0'C_{10}'X_1 + X_1'C_{10}X_0 + X_1'C_{11}X_1)Y,$$

and thus $q_1 = \hat{\beta}_1'C_{11}^{-1}\hat{\beta}_1$ if

$$X_0'[C_{00} - (X_0X_0')^{-1}]X_0 = X_0'C_{10}'C_{11}^{-1}C_{10}X_0.$$

Since $$(X_0X_0')C_{00} + (X_0X_1')C_{10} = I, \qquad (17.27)$$

$$(X_0X_0')C_{01} + (X_0X_1')C_{11} = 0, \qquad (17.28)$$

we can premultiply (17.27) by $(X_0X_0')^{-1}$ and postmultiply (17.28) by C_{11}^{-1} to obtain

$$C_{00} - (X_0X_0')^{-1} = -(X_0X_0')^{-1}(X_0X_1')C_{10} \qquad (17.29)$$

and
$$C_{01}C_{11}^{-1} = - (X_0X_0')^{-1}(X_0X_1'), \qquad (17.30)$$

respectively.   Substituting (17.30) in (17.29) results in $C_{00} - (X_0X_0')^{-1}$ $= C_{10}'C_{11}^{-1}C_{10}$, which proves the corollary.

Remark 1.   Note that the normal equations $a\hat{\beta} = XY$ can be written

$$\begin{pmatrix} X_0X_0' & X_0X_1' \\ X_1X_0' & X_1X_1' \end{pmatrix}\begin{pmatrix} \hat{\beta}_0 \\ \hat{\beta}_1 \end{pmatrix} = \begin{pmatrix} X_0Y \\ X_1Y \end{pmatrix}$$

and that, if $X_0X_1' = 0$, then $\hat{\beta}_0$ is obtained from the solution of

$$(X_0X_0')\hat{\beta}_0 = X_0Y.$$

Thus $\hat{\beta}_0 = \tilde{\beta}_0$, and q_1 can be written as $q_1 = \hat{\beta}_1'X_1Y$.   In this case, $\hat{\beta}_0$ and $\hat{\beta}_1$ are said to be mutually orthogonal.

Remark 2.   Instead of testing the null hypothesis that a subset of the β's is equal to zero $(\beta_1 = 0)$, we may wish to test whether all β's are equal to zero $(\beta = 0)$.   Then the results of Theorem 17.5 and its corollary immediately follow by setting $r = 0$, modifying the formulas so that terms involving a zero subscript are omitted, and removing the subscript 1 from the remaining terms; for example,

$$q_1 = \hat{\beta}'XY = \hat{\beta}'a\hat{\beta},$$
$$q_2 = (Y - X'\hat{\beta})'(Y - X'\hat{\beta}).$$

Remark 3.   Instead of considering the null hypothesis $H_0: \beta_1 = 0$, we may wish to consider the null hypothesis $H_0: \beta_1 = \beta_1{}^0$, that is, to test the hypothesis that the r parameters β_1 are equal to a vector of given constants $\beta_1{}^0$, where $\beta_1{}^0$ is not necessarily zero for each element.   Since

$$E(Y) = X_0'\beta_0 + X_1'\beta_1 = X_0'\beta_0 + X_1'(\beta_1 - \beta_1{}^0) + X_1'\beta_1{}^0,$$

we can introduce the transformations

$$Y^* = Y - X_1'\beta_1{}^0,$$
$$\beta_0^* = \beta_0,$$
$$\beta_1^* = \beta_1 - \beta_1{}^0$$

and have
$$E(Y^*) = X_0'\beta_0^* + X_1'\beta_1^*.$$

Therefore a test of $H_0: \beta_1 = \beta_1{}^0$ goes over into a test of $H_0: \beta_1^* = 0$, and the results of Theorem 17.5 follow, with $q_1 = (\hat{\beta}_1 - \beta_1{}^0)'C_{11}^{-1}(\hat{\beta}_1 - \beta_1{}^0)$.

Remark 4.   Often we have the setup that $E(Y) = X_0'\beta_0 + X'\beta_1$, such that β_0 and β_1 satisfy the equations

$$K_0'\beta_0 = m_0,$$
$$K_1'\beta_1 = m_1,$$

where K_0', K_1' are matrices of dimension $r_0 \times p - r$ $(r_0 < p - r)$ and $r_1 \times r$ $(r_1 < r)$, respectively, and m_0, m_1 are column vectors of length r_0 and r_1.   We wish to test the null hypothesis H_0: $\beta_1 = \beta_1{}^0$, where m_1 is such that $K_1'\beta_1{}^0 = m_1$.   The variance-ratio criteria will then take the form

$$F = \frac{(\tilde{\sigma}^2 - \hat{\sigma}^2)/(r - r_1)}{\hat{\sigma}^2/(n - p + r_0 + r_1)}.$$

Remark 5.   Sometimes the null hypothesis takes the form of specifying that, say, r linear functions of the β_i are equal to some given constants. Let K' be an $r \times p$ matrix and m an $r \times 1$ vector.   Then the null hypothesis is that $K'\beta = m$.   In this case the variance ratio takes the form

$$F = \frac{(\tilde{\sigma}^2 - \hat{\sigma}^2)/(p - r)}{\hat{\sigma}^2/(n - p)},$$

where $n\tilde{\sigma}^2 = (Y - X'\tilde{\beta})'(Y - X'\tilde{\beta})$ and the $\tilde{\beta}$ are obtained by using Theorem 17.3.

REFERENCES

The method of maximum likelihood was developed by R. A. Fisher [5–9], although Gauss had earlier applied the method to several special cases.   This method of estimation was subsequently investigated by a series of workers, of whom Doob [2, 3], Dugué [4], Hotelling [11], and Wald [20] should be mentioned.   The book by Cramér [1] summarizes this research.   LeCam [14] gives a historical introduction as well as a summary of the more recent work on maximum likelihood.

Likelihood-ratio tests were proposed by Neyman and Pearson [16] in 1928.   In later papers [17, 18], these investigators developed a systematic approach to the problem of testing hypotheses.   It was found in nearly all cases that the likelihood-ratio test turns out to be the "best" test.   Wilks [21] and Wald [19] wrote basic papers on the "optimum" properties of the likelihood-ratio test.

The general linear hypothesis was developed by Kolodziejczyk [13].   Other expositions can be found in Kempthorne [12], Mann [15], and Wilks [22].

1. H. Cramér, "Mathematical Methods of Statistics," Princeton University Press, Princeton, N.J., 1946.

2. J. L. Doob, Probability and Statistics, *Trans. Amer. Math. Soc.*, vol. 36, p. 759, 1934.

3. J. L. Doob, Statistical Estimation, *Trans. Amer. Math. Soc.*, vol. 39, p. 410, 1936.

4. D. Dugué, Application des propriétés de la limite au sens du calcul des probabilités à l'étude des diverses questions d'estimation, *J. École Poly.*, vol. 3, p. 305, 1937.

5. R. A. Fisher, On an Absolute Criterion for Fitting Frequency Curves, *Mess. of Math.*, vol. 41, p. 155, 1912.

6. R. A. Fisher, On the Mathematical Foundations of Theoretical Statistics, *Philos. Trans. Roy. Soc. London. Ser. A*, vol. 222, p. 309, 1921.

7. R. A. Fisher, Theory of Statistical Estimation, *Proc. Cambridge Philos. Soc.*, vol. 22, p. 700, 1925.

8. R. A. Fisher, Two New Properties of Mathematical Likelihood, *Proc. Roy. Soc. London. Ser. A*, vol. 144, p. 285, 1934.

9. R. A. Fisher, The Logic of Inductive Inference, *J. Roy. Statist. Soc.*, vol. 98, p. 39, 1935.

10. R. A. Fisher, "Contributions to Mathematical Statistics," John Wiley & Sons, Inc., New York, 1950.

11. H. Hotelling, The Consistency and Ultimate Distribution of Optimum Statistics, *Trans. Amer. Math. Soc.*, vol. 32, p. 847, 1930.

12. O. Kempthorne, "Design and Analysis of Experiments," John Wiley & Sons, Inc., New York, 1952.

13. S. Kolodziejczyk, On an Important Class of Statistical Hypotheses, *Biometrika*, vol. 27, p. 161, 1935.

14. L. LeCam, On Some Asymptotic Properties of Maximum Likelihood Estimates and Related Bayes' Estimates, *Univ. California Publ. Statist.*, vol. 1, p. 277, 1953.

15. H. B. Mann, "Analysis and Design of Experiments," Dover Publications, New York, 1949.

16. J. Neyman and E. S. Pearson, On the Use and Interpretation of Certain Test Criteria for Purposes of Statistical Inference, *Biometrika*, vol. 20A, pp. 175, 263, 1928.

17. J. Neyman and E. S. Pearson, On the Problem of the Most Efficient Tests of Statistical Hypotheses, *Philos. Trans. Roy. Soc. London. Ser. A*, vol. 231, p. 289, 1933.

18. J. Neyman and E. S. Pearson, On the Testing of Statistical Hypotheses in Relation to Probability a Priori, *Proc. Cambridge Philos. Soc.*, vol. 29, p. 492, 1933.

19. A. Wald, Tests of Statistical Hypotheses Concerning Several Parameters when the Number of Observations Is Large, *Trans. Amer. Math. Soc.*, vol. 54, p. 426, 1934.

20. A. Wald, Note on the Consistency of the Maximum Likelihood Estimate, *Ann. Math. Statist.*, vol. 20, p. 595, 1949.

21. S. S. Wilks, The Large Sample Distribution of the Likelihood Ratio for Testing Composite Hypotheses, *Ann. Math. Statist.*, vol. 9, p. 60, 1938.

22. S. S. Wilks, "Mathematical Statistics," Princeton University Press, Princeton, N.J., 1943.

DISTRIBUTION OF QUADRATIC FORMS AND THE VARIANCE-RATIO TESTS

17.6 Distribution of Quadratic Forms

Let $Y' = (y_1, y_2, \ldots, y_n)$ follow a normal distribution with $E(Y) = \mu$ and var $Y = D(\sigma_1^2, \sigma_2^2, \ldots, \sigma_n^2) = D(\sigma^2)$.

Definition 17.11. The quantity

$$\chi^2 = (Y - \mu)' D^{-1}(\sigma^2)(Y - \mu) = \sum_{i=1}^{n} \frac{(y_i - \mu_i)^2}{\sigma_i^2}$$

is said to follow the chi-square (χ^2) distribution with n degrees of freedom. The probability density function of the χ^2 distribution is

$$g(\chi^2) = \left[2^{n/2} \Gamma\left(\frac{n}{2}\right) \right]^{-1} (\chi^2)^{n/2-1} \exp\left(-\frac{\chi^2}{2}\right), \qquad 0 \leq x^2 < \infty,$$

and the cumulative function is tabulated in many statistical texts.   If $D(\sigma^2) = \sigma^2 I$, the quantity $(Y - \mu)'(Y - \mu)$ is said to follow a $\sigma^2\chi^2$ distribution with n degrees of freedom.

Lemma 17.3.   *Let A be an $n \times n$ symmetric matrix of rank $r \leq n$, such that r of its characteristic roots are unity and the remaining $(n - r)$ roots zero.   Then, if $Y' = (y_1, y_2, \ldots, y_n)$ is normally distributed with $E(Y) = \mu$, var $Y = \sigma^2 I$, the quadratic form $(Y - \mu)'(Y - \mu)$ follows a $\sigma^2\chi^2$ distribution with r degrees of freedom.*

Proof.   There will exist an orthogonal matrix Γ such that

$$\Gamma' A \Gamma = \begin{pmatrix} I_r & 0 \\ 0 & 0 \end{pmatrix}.$$

Hence, if we introduce the transformation

$$Z = \Gamma'(Y - \mu),$$

Z will follow a normal distribution with parameters

$$E(Z) = 0,$$

$$\text{var } Z = E[ZZ'] = \Gamma' E[(Y - \mu)(Y - \mu)']\Gamma = \sigma^2 I.$$

The quadratic form can then be written

$$(Y - \mu)'A(Y - \mu) = Z'\Gamma' A \Gamma Z = \sum_{i=1}^{r} z_i^2.$$

Remark.   A necessary and sufficient condition that the characteristic roots of A be either 0 or 1 is that A be idempotent, that is, $A^2 = A$.

Theorem 17.6.   *Let $Y' = (y_1, y_2, \ldots, y_n)$ be normally distributed with $E(Y) = \mu$ and var $Y = \sigma^2 I$.   Consider*

$$(Y - \mu)'(Y - \mu) = \sum_{i=1}^{k} q_i,$$

where $q_i = (Y - \mu)'A_i(Y - \mu)$ and the A_i are real symmetric matrices. Then any one of the following three properties,

(i) $\sum n_i = n$ $(n_i = rank\ of\ A_i)$,

(ii) $A_i^2 = A_i$ $(i = 1, 2, \ldots, k)$,

(iii) $A_i A_j = 0$ *for all $i \neq j$,*

implies the other two, and these conditions are necessary and sufficient in order that the quadratic forms q_i follow independent $\sigma^2\chi^2$ distributions.

Proof.   Necessity.   If the q_i follow $\sigma^2\chi^2$ distributions, then each A_i has nonzero roots equal to unity.   Since

$$I = \sum_{i=1}^{k} A_i,$$

$$n = \sum_{i=1}^{k} \operatorname{tr} A_i = \sum_{i=1}^{k} n_i.$$

The A_i are idempotent, by the previous remark, and

$$I^2 = \sum_i A_i{}^2 + \sum_{i \neq j}\sum A_i A_j.$$

Taking traces we have

$$n = \sum_i \operatorname{tr} A_i + \sum_{i \neq j}\sum \operatorname{tr} A_i A_j = \sum_i n_i + \sum_{i \neq j}\sum \operatorname{tr} A_i A_j.$$

But $\operatorname{tr} A_i A_j \geq 0$; hence $\operatorname{tr} A^t A_j = 0$, which implies $A_i A_j = 0$, as A_i is idempotent.

Sufficiency.   (i) Assume $\Sigma n_i = n$.   There will exist an orthogonal matrix Γ such that

$$\Gamma' A_1 \Gamma = D_1 = \begin{pmatrix} I_{n_1} & 0 \\ 0 & 0 \end{pmatrix}.$$

Then

$$I = D_1 + \Gamma'\left(\sum_{i=2}^{k} A_i\right)\Gamma$$

and

$$\Gamma'\left(\sum_{2}^{k} A_i\right)\Gamma = \begin{pmatrix} 0 & 0 \\ 0 & I_{n-n_1} \end{pmatrix}.$$

Since $A_1 = \Gamma D_1 \Gamma'$, we have $A_1{}^2 = A_1$, which shows that A_1 is idempotent.   It follows directly that the same transformation reduces each A_i to a diagonal matrix, which implies that all A_i will be idempotent. The proof that $A_i A_j = 0$ follows the same lines as in the necessity part.

  (ii) Assume $A_i{}^2 = A_i$; then, since $I = \Sigma A_i$,

$$n = \sum \operatorname{tr} A_i = \sum n_i.$$

  (iii) Assume $A_i A_j = 0$ for $i \neq j$.   Taking powers of $I = \Sigma A_i$ results in $I = \sum_i A_i{}^s$, and hence $n = \Sigma \operatorname{tr} A_i{}^s$.   This is possible only if every nonzero root of A_i is unity.   Thus the A_i are idempotent, and it follows that $n = \Sigma n_i$.

17.7   Variance-ratio Tests for the General Linear Hypothesis

Definition 17.12.   Let $q_1 = Y'A_1Y$ and $q_2 = Y'A_2Y$ be quadratic forms in Y which follow independent $\sigma^2\chi^2$ distributions with degrees of freedom ν_1 and ν_2, respectively.   Then the ratio

$$F = \frac{q_1/\nu_1}{q_2/\nu_2}$$

is said to follow a variance ratio or F distribution having the probability density function

$$g(F) = \left[B\left(\frac{\nu_1}{2}, \frac{\nu_2}{2}\right)\right]^{-1} F^{\nu_1/2-1}(1 + F)^{-(\nu_1+\nu_2)/2}, \qquad 0 \le F < \infty.$$

The cumulative distribution of the variance ratio is tabulated in almost all statistics texts.

Theorem 17.7.   *The quadratic forms of Theorem 17.5, that is, $q_1 = (\hat{\beta}_0 - \tilde{\beta}_0)'X_0Y + \hat{\beta}_1X_1Y$ and $q_2 = (Y - X'\hat{\beta})'(Y - X'\hat{\beta})$, follow independent chi-square distributions with r and $(n - p)$ degrees of freedom, respectively. Hence $F = (q_1/r)/[q_2/(n - p)]$ follows a variance-ratio distribution and can be used to test the null hypothesis H_0: $\beta_1 = 0$.*

Proof.   Define $C_0 = (X_0X_0')^{-1}$ and $C_{00}, C_{01}, C_{10}, C_{11}$ as in the corollary to Theorem 17.5.   Hence

$$\begin{pmatrix} \hat{\beta}_0 \\ \hat{\beta}_1 \end{pmatrix} = \begin{pmatrix} C_{00}X_0Y + C_{01}X_1Y \\ C_{10}X_0Y + C_{11}X_1Y \end{pmatrix},$$

and q_1 and q_2 can be written as

$$q_1 = Y'(\alpha_1 - \alpha_2)Y = Y'A_1Y,$$
$$q_2 = Y'(I - \alpha_1)Y = Y'A_2Y,$$

where

$$\alpha_1 = (X_0' \quad X_1')\begin{pmatrix} C_{00} & C_{01} \\ C_{10} & C_{11} \end{pmatrix}\begin{pmatrix} X_0 \\ X_1 \end{pmatrix},$$

$$\alpha_2 = X_0'(X_0X_0')^{-1}X_0.$$

Pre- and postmultiplying the identity

$$I = (\alpha_1 - \alpha_2) + (I - \alpha_1) + \alpha_2 = A_1 + A_2 + A_3$$

by $(Y - X'\beta)'$ and $(Y - X'\beta)$, we obtain

$$(Y - X'\beta)'(Y - X'\beta) = q_1^* + q_2^* + q_3^*,$$

where

$$q_i^* = (Y - X'\beta)'A_i(Y - X'\beta) \qquad \text{for } i = 1, 2, 3.$$

We now show that A_1, A_2, and A_3 are idempotent and that hence, by Theorem 17.6, q_1^*, q_2^*, and q_3^* follow independent $\sigma^2\chi^2$ distributions. Multiplying α_1 by α_2 gives

$$
\begin{aligned}
\alpha_1\alpha_2 &= X_0'C_{00}X_0X_0'C_0X_0 + X_1'C_{10}X_0X_0'C_0X_0 + X_0'C_{01}X_1X_0'C_0X_0 \\
&\quad + X_1'C_{11}X_1X_0'C_0X_0 \\
&= X_0'(C_{00}X_0X_0' + C_{01}X_1X_0')C_0X_0 + X_1'(C_{10}X_0X_0' + C_{11}X_1X_0')C_0X_0 \\
&= X_0'C_0X_0 = \alpha_2.
\end{aligned}
$$

We can similarly show that $\alpha_1{}^2 = \alpha_1$, $\alpha_2{}^2 = \alpha_2$; hence

$$
\begin{aligned}
A_1{}^2 &= \alpha_1{}^2 + \alpha_2{}^2 - 2\alpha_1\alpha_2 = \alpha_1 - \alpha_2 = A_1, \\
A_2{}^2 &= (I - \alpha_1)^2 = I - \alpha_1 = A_2, \\
A_3{}^2 &= \alpha_2{}^2 = \alpha_2 = A_3,
\end{aligned}
$$

and all the A_i are idempotent. Therefore q_1^*, q_2^*, and q_3^* follow independent chi-square distributions.

It still remains to show that $q_1 = q_1^*$ and $q_2 = q_2^*$. If H_0 is true, $\beta_1 = 0$, and we can write q_1^* as

$$
\begin{aligned}
q_1^* &= (Y - X_0'\beta_0)'A_1(Y - X_0'\beta_0) \\
&= Y'A_1Y - \beta_0'X_0A_1Y - Y'A_1X_0'\beta_0 + \beta_0'X_0A_1X_0'\beta_0.
\end{aligned}
$$

However, $X_0A_1 = 0$; that is,

$$
\begin{aligned}
X_0A_1 &= (X_0X_0'C_{00} + X_0X_1'C_{10})X_0 + (X_0X_0'C_{01} + X_0X_1'C_{11})X_1 - X_0 \\
&= X_0 - X_0 = 0,
\end{aligned}
$$

and thus $q_1^* = q_1$ only when H_0 is true.

Considering $q_2^* = (Y - X'\beta)'A_2(Y - X'\beta)$, we have

$$
q_2^* = Y'A_2Y - \beta'XA_2Y - Y'A_2X'\beta + \beta'XA_2X'\beta.
$$

We can similarly show that $XA_2 = 0$; therefore, $q_2^* = q_2$. The important point to note is that $q_1^* = q_1$ only if the null hypothesis is true, whereas $q_2^* = q_2$ regardless of the truth of the null hypothesis.

Thus, if H_0 is true, $F = (q_1/r)/[q_2/(n - p)]$ follows a variance-ratio distribution.

REFERENCES

Theorem 17.6, in the form quoted above, was given by Lancaster [4]. It is based on related work by James [5]. The condition $\sum_i n_i = n$ was first proved by Cochran [2], in 1934, and is sometimes referred to as the Fisher-Cochran theorem or as Cochran's theorem. Other discussions can be found in Cramér ([1], pp. 116–118) and Wilks ([6], pp. 105–108).

The distribution of $Z = \frac{1}{2} \ln F$ was first found by Fisher [3]. In practice it is more convenient, for calculation purposes, to use F.

1. H. Cramér, "Mathematical Methods of Statistics," Princeton University Press, Princeton, N.J., 1946.

2. W. G. Cochran, The Distribution of Quadratic Forms in a Normal System with Applications to the Analysis of Covariance, *Proc. Cambridge Philos. Soc.*, vol. 30, p. 178, 1934.

3. R. A. Fisher, On a Distribution Yielding the Error Functions of Several Well-known Statistics, in "Proceedings of the International Mathematics Congress, Toronto," p. 805, 1924.

4. H. O. Lancaster, Traces and Cumulants of Quadratic Forms in Normal Variables, *J. Roy. Statist. Soc. Sec. B*, vol. 16, p. 247, 1954.

5. G. S. James, Notes on a Theorem of Cochran, *Proc. Cambridge Philos. Soc.*, vol. 48, p. 443, 1952.

6. S. S. Wilks, "Mathematical Statistics," Princeton University Press, Princeton, N.J., 1943.

APPLICATIONS

In this part we illustrate the theory of the preceding sections.

17.8 Linear Regression

A frequent problem is that of fitting a straight line to a set of measurements or observations. Given $Y' = (y_1, y_2, \ldots, y_n)$, we desire to fit a straight line, assuming that $E(y_\alpha) = \beta_0 + \beta_1(x_\alpha - \bar{x})$ $(\alpha = 1, 2, \ldots, n)$, where $\bar{x} = (1/n) \sum_\alpha x_\alpha$ and var $Y = \sigma^2 I$. Applying Theorem 17.1 (the Gauss-Markoff theorem), we have

$$X' = \begin{pmatrix} 1 & x_1 - \bar{x} \\ 1 & x_2 - \bar{x} \\ \cdot & \cdot \\ \cdot & \cdot \\ \cdot & \cdot \\ 1 & x_n - \bar{x} \end{pmatrix}.$$

Therefore

$$a = XX' = \begin{pmatrix} n & 0 \\ 0 & \sum_\alpha (x_\alpha - \bar{x})^2 \end{pmatrix}, \qquad XY = \begin{pmatrix} \sum_\alpha y_\alpha \\ \sum_\alpha (x_\alpha - \bar{x}) y_\alpha \end{pmatrix}.$$

The inverse of a is

$$a^{-1} = \begin{pmatrix} \dfrac{1}{n} & 0 \\ 0 & \left[\sum_\alpha (x_\alpha - \bar{x})^2 \right]^{-1} \end{pmatrix}.$$

Hence, since $\hat{\beta} = a^{-1}XY$, we have

$$\hat{\beta}_0 = \frac{1}{n} \sum_\alpha y_\alpha = \bar{y},$$

$$\hat{\beta}_1 = \frac{\sum_\alpha (x_\alpha - \bar{x}) y_\alpha}{\sum_\alpha (x_\alpha - \bar{x})^2}.$$

Using Eq. (17.15),

$$v'v = Y'Y - \hat{\beta}'XY = \sum_\alpha (y_\alpha - \bar{y})^2 - \frac{[\sum_\alpha (x_\alpha - \bar{x}) y_\alpha]^2}{\sum_\alpha (x_\alpha - \bar{x})^2},$$

and thus the estimate of σ^2 is

$$s^2 = \frac{v'v}{n - p} = \frac{v'v}{n - 2}.$$

The estimates for variances and covariances of $\hat{\beta}_0$ and $\hat{\beta}_1$ can be obtained from var $\hat{\beta} = a^{-1}\sigma^2$ by substituting s^2 for σ^2; for example,

$$\text{estimated var } \hat{\beta}_0 = \frac{s^2}{n}, \qquad \text{estimated var } \hat{\beta}_1 = \frac{s^2}{\sum_\alpha (x_\alpha - \bar{x})^2},$$

$$\text{cov } (\hat{\beta}_0, \hat{\beta}_1) = 0.$$

Note that the intercept of the linear equation is a linear function of β_0 and β_1, $\alpha = \beta_0 - \beta_1 \bar{x}$. Hence the best estimate of the intercept is $\hat{\alpha} = \hat{\beta}_0 - \hat{\beta}_1 \bar{x}$, and its variance is

$$\text{var } \hat{\alpha} = \text{var } \hat{\beta}_0 + \bar{x}^2 \text{ var } \hat{\beta}_1 - 2\bar{x} \text{ cov } (\hat{\beta}_0, \hat{\beta}_1)$$

$$= \sigma^2 \left[\frac{1}{n} + \frac{\bar{x}^2}{\sum_\alpha (x_\alpha - \bar{x})^2} \right].$$

A common statistical test is to test whether the slope is equal to a given constant, that is, whether $\beta_1 = \beta_1^0$. This is an application of Theorem 17.5 with $p = 2$, $r = 1$, where

$$X_0' = (1, 1, \ldots, 1), \qquad X_1' = [(x_1 - \bar{x}), \ldots, (x_n - \bar{x})].$$

Remark 3 applies to this problem; therefore

$$q_1 = (\hat{\beta}_1 - \beta_1^0)' C_{11}^{-1} (\hat{\beta}_1 - \beta_1^0).$$

However, since $X_0' X_1 = 0$, $C_{11}^{-1} = \sum_\alpha (x_\alpha - \bar{x})^2$, and thus

$$q_1 = \sum_\alpha (x_\alpha - \bar{x})^2 [(\hat{\beta}_1 - \beta_1^0)'(\hat{\beta}_1 - \beta_1^0)] = \sum_\alpha (x_\alpha - \bar{x})^2 (\hat{\beta}_1 - \beta_1^0)^2.$$

The variance-ratio test is then

$$F = \frac{q_1}{s^2}.$$

17.9 Multiple Regression

A generalization of the preceding example is to fit a function of the form

$$E(y_\alpha) = \beta_0 + \sum_{i=1}^{k} \beta_i x_{i\alpha}.$$

Note that this is a fairly general function, for if $x_{i\alpha} = t_\alpha^i$, we have a polynomial, or $x_{i\alpha}$ can refer to trigonometric terms, etc.   No loss in generality results if we allow $\sum_{\alpha=1}^{n} x_{i\alpha} = 0$ for all i.   Setting

$$X_0 = (1, 1, \ldots, 1), \quad X = (x_{i\alpha}) \quad (i = 1, 2, \ldots, k; \alpha = 1, 2, \ldots, n),$$

$$\beta' = (\beta_1, \beta_2, \ldots, \beta_k),$$

we can write

$$E(Y) = X_0'\beta_0 + X'\beta.$$

Since $X_0 X' = 0$, the normal equations can be written

$$\begin{pmatrix} n & 0 \\ 0 & XX_1' \end{pmatrix}\begin{pmatrix} \hat{\beta}_0 \\ \hat{\beta} \end{pmatrix} = \begin{pmatrix} \sum_\alpha y_\alpha \\ XY \end{pmatrix},$$

and hence

$$\hat{\beta}_0 = \bar{y}, \qquad \hat{\beta} = (XX')^{-1}XY.$$

Often we should like to test the null hypothesis that $\beta_i = \beta_i^0$ for $i = 1, 2, \ldots, k$.   Using Theorem 17.5 we have the variance ratio

$$F = \frac{[(\hat{\beta} - \beta^0)'(XX')(\beta - \beta^0)]/k}{s^2}$$

where

$$s^2 = \frac{1}{n - k - 1}(Y'Y - n\bar{y}^2 - \hat{\beta}'XY).$$

17.10   Testing k-population Means

Let $E(y_{ij}) = \beta_i$ for $j = 1, 2, \ldots, n; i = 1, 2, \ldots, k$.   Let $Y_i' = (y_{i1}, y_{i2}, \ldots, y_{in})$, $Y' - (Y_1', Y_2', \ldots, Y_k')$, $\beta' = (\beta_1, \beta_2, \ldots, \beta_k)$; then $E(Y) = X'\beta$, where

$$X' = \begin{pmatrix} 1 & 0 & \cdots & 0 \\ 0 & 1 & & 0 \\ 0 & 0 & & 0 \\ \cdot & \cdot & \cdot & \cdot \\ \cdot & \cdot & \cdot & \cdot \\ \cdot & \cdot & \cdot\cdot & \cdot \\ 0 & 0 & & 1 \end{pmatrix}$$

and **0, 1** are vectors of n elements consisting entirely of 0s or 1s, respectively. Consider the null hypothesis that all β_i are equal—for example,

$$H_0 \, (\beta_1 = \beta_2 = \cdots = \beta_k).$$

The normal equations over Ω are

$$nI\hat{\beta} = \begin{pmatrix} \mathbf{1}'Y_1 \\ \mathbf{1}'Y_2 \\ \cdot \\ \cdot \\ \cdot \\ \mathbf{1}'Y_k \end{pmatrix}$$

or

$$\hat{\beta}_i = \frac{1}{n} \mathbf{1}'Y_i = \bar{y}_i.$$

Then,

$$\hat{\sigma}^2 = \frac{1}{kn} (Y'Y - \hat{\beta}'XY) = \frac{1}{kn} \sum_i \sum_j (y_{ij} - \bar{y}_i)^2$$

with $k(n - 1)$ degrees of freedom. Similarly, if H_0 is true, $E(Y) = X'\mathbf{1}\beta$. The normal equations are

$$nk\bar{\beta} = \mathbf{1}'Y_1 + \mathbf{1}'Y_2 + \cdots + \mathbf{1}'Y_k$$

or

$$\bar{\beta} = \frac{\sum_i \sum_j y_{ij}}{nk} = \bar{y};$$

and

$$\bar{\sigma}^2 = \frac{1}{kn} (\sum_i \sum_j y_{ij}^2 - kn\bar{y}^2)$$

with $(kn - 1)$ degrees of freedom. Using (17.26), the variance-ratio test is

$$F = \frac{(\bar{\sigma}^2 - \hat{\sigma}^2)/(k - 1)}{\hat{\sigma}^2} = \frac{n \sum_i (\bar{y}_i - \bar{y})^2/(k - 1)}{\sum_i \sum_j (y_{ij} - \bar{y}_i)^2/k(n - 1)}.$$

17.11   Block Designs

A common type of experiment is that in which one is investigating the effects of several treatments on a set of experimental units. The term *treatment* is a generic term which refers to different methods, processes, materials, etc. If the measurements are taken such that they come in relatively homogeneous groups, the group of measurements is termed a *block*. Let there be v treatments and b blocks such that the ith treatment is measured r_i times and there are k experimental units in each block. Let y_{ij} refer to the measurement of the ith treatment in the jth block where y_{ij} is defined only if treatment i is measured on one of the experimental units of the jth block. Further assume that no treatment is measured more than once in the same block. We assume that the mathematical model underlying this experimental situation is

$$E(y_{ij}) = t_i + b_j \qquad (i = 1, 2, \ldots, v; j = 1, 2, \ldots, b),$$

$$\operatorname{var} y_{ij} = \sigma^2, \qquad \operatorname{cov}(y_{ij}, y_{st}) = 0, \qquad i \neq s, j \neq t,$$

where t_i is the effect of the ith treatment and b_j is the effect of the jth block.

Define

$$n_{ij} = \begin{cases} 1 & \text{if treatment } i \text{ is measured in block } j \\ 0 & \text{otherwise.} \end{cases}$$

The $v \times b$ matrix $n = (n_{ij})$ is called the incidence matrix and summarizes the experimental configuration. Thus if $\mathbf{1}$ is a column vector of appropriate dimensions having only unit elements, we have

$$\mathbf{1}'n' = (r_1, r_2, \ldots, r_n) = r'$$
$$n'\mathbf{1} = k\mathbf{1}.$$

Define

$$m_{is}^{(j)} = \begin{cases} 1 & \text{if treatment } i \text{ is measured in the } s\text{th experimental unit} \\ & \text{of block } j \\ 0 & \text{otherwise,} \end{cases}$$

and let $m_j = (m_{is}^{(j)})$, $(i = 1, 2, \ldots, v; s = 1, 2, \ldots, k)$ be a set of $v \times k$ matrices. Also, let y_j denote the $k \times 1$ vector of the measurements in the jth block. Then the experimental setup can be written as

$$E\begin{pmatrix} y_1 \\ y_2 \\ \vdots \\ y_b \end{pmatrix} = \begin{pmatrix} m_1' & \mathbf{1} & \mathbf{0} & \cdots & \mathbf{0} \\ m_2' & \mathbf{0} & \mathbf{1} & \cdots & \mathbf{0} \\ \vdots & & & & \vdots \\ m_b' & \mathbf{0} & & \cdots & \mathbf{1} \end{pmatrix} \begin{pmatrix} t \\ \cdots \\ b \end{pmatrix},$$

where $t' = (t_1, t_2, \ldots, t_v)$ and $b' = (b_1, b_2, \ldots, b_b)$. The normal equations can then be written as

$$\begin{pmatrix} \sum_j m_j m_j' & m_1\mathbf{1} & \cdots & m_b\mathbf{1} \\ \hline \mathbf{1}'m_1' & & & \\ \vdots & & kI & \\ \mathbf{1}'m_b' & & & \end{pmatrix} \begin{pmatrix} \hat{t} \\ \hline \hat{b} \end{pmatrix} = \begin{pmatrix} \sum_j m_j y_j \\ \mathbf{1}'y_1 \\ \vdots \\ \mathbf{1}'y_b \end{pmatrix}.$$

Note that the term $\sum_j m_j m_j'$ can be written as the diagonal matrix,

$$
D(r) = \begin{pmatrix} r_1 & & & & 0 \\ & r_2 & & & \\ & & \cdot & & \\ & & & \cdot & \\ & & & & \cdot \\ 0 & & & & r_v \end{pmatrix}.
$$

Also $\mathbf{1}'m_j$ is simply the jth column of the incidence matrix n. The right-hand side can also be simplified by observing that $m_j y_j$ is the measurement of the ith treatment in the jth block, and thus the ith element of $\sum_j m_j y_j$ is the sum of all measurements having the ith treatment. We denote the ith treatment total by T_i and the jth block total by B_j and set $T' = (T_1, T_2, \ldots, T_v)$, $B' = (B_1, B_2, \ldots, B_b)$. Then the normal equations can be written as

$$
\begin{pmatrix} D(r) & n \\ n' & kI \end{pmatrix} \begin{pmatrix} \hat{t} \\ \hat{b} \end{pmatrix} = \begin{pmatrix} T \\ B \end{pmatrix}.
$$

The matrix of coefficients will always be singular, and it is possible to show that it will have rank $b + v - 1$. To make the solutions unique, we arbitrarily let $\hat{t}$ satisfy $\mathbf{1}'\hat{t} = 0$. (The parameter $\mathbf{1}'t$ is nonestimable.) Therefore, the K' matrix of Theorem 17.3 is the $2 \times b + v$ matrix

$$
K' = \begin{pmatrix} \mathbf{1}' & 0 \\ 0 & 0 \end{pmatrix}.
$$

Using Eq. (17.20) with $D = D(r)$, $J = (\mathbf{11}')$, and

$$
KK' = \begin{pmatrix} J & 0 \\ 0 & 0 \end{pmatrix},
$$

we can write

$$
a_0 = \begin{pmatrix} D(r)(I + J) & n \\ n' & kI \end{pmatrix}.
$$

Hence the inverse of a_0 is

$$
a_0^{-1} = \begin{pmatrix} C_{11} & C_{12} \\ C_{21} & C_{22} \end{pmatrix}
$$

where

$$
C_{11} = [D(r) - \frac{nn'}{k} + D(r)J]^{-1}
$$

$$
C_{12} = -\frac{C_{11}n}{k}, \qquad C_{21} = C_{12}'
$$

$$
C_{22} = \frac{1}{k}\left(I + \frac{n'C_{11}n}{k}\right).
$$

Thus the solutions for $\hat{t}$ and $\hat{b}$ are

$$\hat{t} = C_{11}\left(T - \frac{n}{k}B\right) = C_{11}Q,$$

$$\hat{b} = \frac{1}{k}(B - n't).$$

Formula (iii) of the corollary to Theorem 17.3 enables one to calculate the estimate of σ^2. Thus

$$s^2 = \frac{1}{bk - b - v + 1}\left(\sum_j y_j' y_j - \hat{t}'T - \hat{b}'B\right)$$

$$= \frac{1}{bk - b - v + 1}\left(y'y - \hat{t}'Q - \frac{B'B}{k}\right)$$

with $(bk - b - v + 1)$ degrees of freedom.

Often we are interested in testing the null hypothesis that all treatment effects are zero, that is, $H_0\colon (t_1 = t_2 = \cdots t_v = 0)$ regardless of the values of the b_j. This is an application of Theorem 17.5. Using the corollary to this theorem, the appropriate variance-ratio test is easily seen to be

$$F = \frac{(\hat{t}'C_{11}^{-1}\hat{t})/(v - 1)}{s^2}$$

with degrees of freedom equal to $(v - 1)$ and $(bk - b - v + 1)$. Since $\hat{t} = C_{11}Q$, this variance ratio is usually written in the form

$$F = \frac{\hat{t}'Q/(v - 1)}{s^2}.$$

REFERENCES

Wilks ([3], Chap. IX) is a good reference for illustrating many applications of normal regression theory. The procedures used in testing linear hypothesis, as in Secs. 17.9 to 17.11, are usually known as the analysis of variance. This type of procedure was first introduced by R. A. Fisher and has been generalized by many workers. The reader may refer to Kempthorne [1] for a general exposition of block designs or to the paper by Tocher [2] for a concise, but complete, treatment. The development here follows Tocher. There exists a large literature in this subject which is devoted primarily to the analysis and construction of block designs.

1. O. Kempthorne, "Design and Analysis of Experiments," John Wiley & Sons, Inc., New York, 1952.

2. K. D. Tocher, The Design and Analysis of Block Experiments, *J. Roy. Statist. Soc. Ser. B*, vol. 14, pp. 45–91, 1952.

3. S. S. Wilks, "Mathematical Statistics," Princeton University Press, Princeton, N.J., 1943.

17.12 Some Remarks on Computations with High-speed Computers

Applying the theory of least squares to large sets of data or to models with a large number of parameters has, until the advent of high-speed electronic computers, been restricted because of the large amount of calculations necessary.   However, with the increased use of high-speed computers, these calculations are now beginning to appear routine.

The essential numerical operations in applying the theory of least squares are: (1) a matrix multiplication to obtain the normal equations, (2) the solution of a set of simultaneous linear equations and the inversion of the matrix of normal equations, and (3) some auxiliary computations important to the user, such as the calculation of each residual.   Experience with computers has shown that, with respect to general applications, it is more efficient to program the least-squares computations using an orthonormalizing process.   This will usually result in more accurate calculations and reduce the round-off error. For this purpose the Gram-Schmidt process is particularly attractive as it can be programmed in a recurrence form.   The paper by Davis and Rabinowitz [1] outlines these procedures with reference to electronic computers.   See also Chap. 10.

With more specialized applications such as the analysis of variance, it may be more convenient to use a special analysis of variance program, rather than the more general orthonormalization routine.   Calculating analysis of variance problems on high-speed computers may be particularly appropriate when there is a large amount of data from a single source or when there are many sets of data to be analyzed in the same manner.   The papers by Hartley [2] and Yates, Healy, and Lipton [3] discuss general methods for programming analysis of variance computations on a computer.

REFERENCES

1. P. Davis and P. Rabinowitz, A Multiple Purpose Orthonormalizing Code and Its Uses, *J. Assoc. Comput. Mach.*, vol. 1, pp. 183–191, 1954.

2. H. O. Hartley, A Plan for Programming Analysis of Variance for General Purpose Computers, *Biometrics*, vol. 12, pp. 110–122, 1956.

3. F. Yates, M. J. R. Healy, and S. Lipton, Routine Analysis of Replicated Experiments on an Electronic Computer, *J. Roy. Statist. Soc. Ser. B*, vol. 19, pp. 234–254, 1957.

Index